Register Now f[...]
to You[...]

SPRINGER PUBLISHING COMPANY
CONNECT™

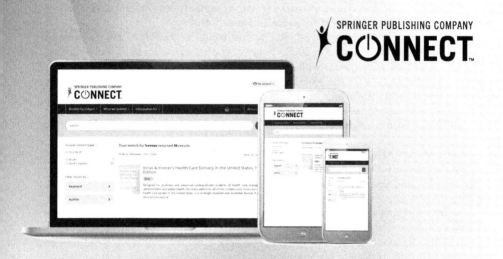

Your print purchase of *Trauma-Informed Approaches to Eating Disorders*, **includes online access to the contents of your book**—increasing accessibility, portability, and searchability!

Access today at:
http://connect.springerpub.com/content/book/978-0-8261-7265-5 or scan the QR code at the right with your smartphone and enter the access code below.

W36PX4WG

Scan here for quick access.

SPC

SPRINGER / PUBLISHING COMPANY
View all our products at springerpub.com

Andrew Seubert, NCC, LMHC, is the cofounder of ClearPath Healing Arts Center in Corning and Burdett, New York. A licensed psychotherapist for 35 years, he has an extensive background in existential-Gestalt Therapy and in music therapy, and provides eye movement desensitization and reprocessing (EMDR) consultation and training for clinicians. Andrew specializes in working with trauma, posttraumatic stress, eating disorders, and the integration of spirituality and psychotherapy.

His first book, *The Courage to Feel: A Practical Guide to the Power and Freedom of Emotional Honesty,* was published in 2008. He has authored a chapter in *EMDR Solutions* on the use of EMDR with clients with intellectual disability and coauthored an article on the same topic in 2011 for the *Journal of EMDR Practice and Research.* He has written two chapters on eating disorders for *EMDR Solutions II* and has completed *How Simon Left His Shell,* a fable and user's guide based on *The Courage to Feel,* to teach emotional honesty to children and adolescents.

Pam Virdi, MEd, RMN, CPN, is an accredited EMDR consultant, integrative psycho-therapist, lecturer, and supervisor who now works full-time in private practice with adults, couples, and young people in Birmingham, UK. She specializes in the treatment of eating disorders, complex trauma, and posttraumatic stress disorder (PTSD). She is an accredited member of The British Association for Counselling and Psychotherapy and EMDR Europe. Originally trained as a psychiatric nurse, Pam has devoted the last 24 years to the National Health Service (UK) as a specialist psychotherapist and trainer in an eating disorder service in Birmingham.

As a lecturer, she has developed, coordinated, and delivered programs of study up to master's level and directed a year-long Eating Disorder Pathway (part of a BSc Mental Health Studies degree) at Birmingham City University for 8 years. She has served as a member on the editorial board of the *European Eating Disorder Review Journal* (1998–2008) and has created and chaired national special interest groups for eating disorders, both generally and EMDR specific.

Trauma-Informed Approaches to Eating Disorders

Andrew Seubert, NCC, LMHC

Pam Virdi, MEd, RMN, CPN

Editors

SPRINGER PUBLISHING COMPANY

Springer Publishing Company, LLC
11 West 42nd Street
New York, NY 10036
www.springerpub.com

Acquisitions Editor: Sheri W. Sussman
Compositor: Graphic World

ISBN: 978-0-8261-7264-8
ebook ISBN: 978-0-8261-7265-5

18 19 20 21 22 / 5 4 3 2 1

The author and the publisher of this Work have made every effort to use sources believed to be reliable to provide information that is accurate and compatible with the standards generally accepted at the time of publication. The author and publisher shall not be liable for any special, consequential, or exemplary damages resulting, in whole or in part, from the readers' use of, or reliance on, the information contained in this book. The publisher has no responsibility for the persistence or accuracy of URLs for external or third-party Internet websites referred to in this publication and does not guarantee that any content on such websites is, or will remain, accurate or appropriate.

Library of Congress Cataloging-in-Publication Data

Names: Seubert, Andrew J., editor. | Virdi, Pam, editor.
Title: Trauma-informed approaches to eating disorders / Andrew Seubert, Pam
  Virdi, editors.
Description: New York, NY : Springer Publishing Company, LLC, [2018] |
  Includes bibliographical references and index.
Identifiers: LCCN 2018012701 (print) | LCCN 2018015895 (ebook) |
  ISBN 9780826172655 | ISBN 9780826172648 (pbk.) | ISBN 9780826172655 (ebook)
Subjects: | MESH: Feeding and Eating Disorders—complications | Feeding and
  Eating Disorders—therapy | Psychological Trauma
Classification: LCC RC552.E18 (ebook) | LCC RC552.E18 (print) | NLM WM 175 |
  DDC 616.85/260651—dc23

LC record available at https://lccn.loc.gov/2018012701

Contact us to receive discount rates on bulk purchases.
We can also customize our books to meet your needs.
For more information please contact: sales@springerpub.com

Printed in the United States of America by Gasch Printing.

Andrew:
For Erin Leah and all of those who suffer from eating disorders, and for the village—the families and clinicians—who walk with them.

Pam:
For my sons, Alex and Jordan.

Contents

Contributors

Madeline Altabe, PhD
Visiting Lecturer of Psychology
Georgia State University
Atlanta, Georgia

Michael E. Berrett, PhD, CEDS
Psychologist
CEO and Cofounder, Center for Change
Orem, Utah

Chiara Callerame, PhD
Psychotherapist and EMDR Practitioner
EMDR Center for Eating Disorders
Milan, Italy

Jeanne Catanzaro, PhD
Center for Self-Leadership
Licensed Clinical Psychologist
Brookline, Massachusetts

Carolyn Hodges Chaffee, MS, RDN, CEDRD
Director, Upstate New York Eating Disorder Services
Elmira, New York

Rayane Chami, MSc
PhD Student
Institute of Psychiatry, Psychology, and Neuroscience
King's College
London, United Kingdom

Cristina Civilotti, PhD
Psychotherapist and EMDR Practitioner
EMDR Center for Eating Disorders
Milan, Italy

Carolyn Costin, MA, Med, MFT, CEDS
Director of the Carolyn Costin Institute
Malibu, California

Sabree A. Crowton
Doctoral Student
Department of Counseling Psychology
Brigham Young University
Provo, Utah

Martina Cussino, PhD, CEDS
Psychotherapist and Accredited EMDR Europe Consultant
EMDR Center for Eating Disorders
Milan, Italy

Marnie Davis, MA, LMHC, CEDS
Certified EMDR Therapist
Founder and Director, A Place for Change
Maitland, Florida

Cynthia "Cyd" Davis-Hubler, MA, LMHC
Counselor and Art Therapist
Eating Disorders Treatment Center
Albuquerque, New Mexico

Elizabeth Doyne, PhD
Private Practice
Licensed Clinical Psychologist and Certified IFS Therapist
Rochester, New York

Holly A. Finlay, MA, LPCC, CEDS, CSP, F. IAEDP
Clinical Director and Cofounder
Eating Disorders Treatment Center
Albuquerque, New Mexico

DaLene Forester, PhD, LMFT, LPCC, CEDS
Psychotherapist, Private Practice
Director and Trainer, Advanced Education Institute (AEI)
Former President and Board Member of EMDR International Association
Redding, California

Deborah A. Good, PhD, ATR-BC, ATCS, LPAT, LPCC
Past President of the American Art Therapy Association
Past President of the Art Therapy Credentials Board
Albuquerque, New Mexico

G. Trevor Hadfield, MBBS, AKC, MRCS, LRCP, DCH, DRCOG, MFFP, RCOG, Adv Dip Clin Hyp
Medical Doctor (retired), Therapist and Lecturer in Clinical Hypnosis
Windmill Health Care and Birmingham City University
Gentleshaw, Rugely, United Kingdom

Susan Kleinman, MA, BC-DMT, NCC, CEDS
Creative Arts Therapies Supervisor and Dance/Movement Therapist
The Renfrew Center
Coconut Creek, Florida

Michael P. Levine, PhD, FABD
Professor Emeritus of Psychology
Kenyon College
Gambier, Ohio

Rachel Lewis-Marlow, MS, EdS, LPC, LMBT
Codirector and Cofounder
Embodied Recovery Institute
Chapel Hill, North Carolina

Kathleen M. Martin, LCSW
EMDRIA Approved Consultant and Trainer
Martin Counseling and Consulting Services
Rochester, New York

Amelia McGinnis, LCSW
Director, McGinnis Counseling and Consulting
Lamont, Pennsylvania

Phil Mollon, PhD
Clinical Psychologist, Psychoanalyst, Energy Psychotherapist
Letchworth Garden City, United Kingdom

Jackie Nicholls, DClinPsy, MSc, BSc (Hons)
Consultant Clinical Psychologist, Systemic Family Therapist, EMDR Europe Accredited
Practitioner
Hereford, United Kingdom

Giovanni Luca Palmisano, PhD
Volunteer Researcher, Department of Psychology
University of Bari
Bari, Italy

Jean Petrucelli, PhD
Clinical Associate Professor at New York University
Faculty at Institute of Contemporary Psychotherapy (ICP)
New York, New York

Natasha C. N. Prenn, LCSW
Senior Faculty
AEDP Institute
New York, New York

P. Scott Richards, PhD
Professor, Department of Counseling Psychology
Brigham Young University
Provo, Utah

Irene Rovira, PhD
Director of Psychology Postdoctoral Program and Psychology Coordinator
Center for Eating Disorders at Sheppard Pratt
Baltimore, Maryland

Paula Scatoloni, LCSW, CEDS, SEP
Private Practice
Cofounder, Embodied Recovery Institute
Chapel Hill, North Carolina

Andrew Seubert, NCC, LMHC
Private Practice
Cofounder and Codirector, ClearPath Healing Arts Center
Corning and Burdett, New York

Robin Shapiro, LICSW
Private Practice
Psychotherapist and Consultant
Seattle, Washington

Jessica K. Slatus, LCSW
Certified Supervisor
AEDP Institute
Boulder, Colorado

Joslyn P. Smith
Director of Policy and Government Affairs
Binge Eating Disorder Association
Severna Park, Maryland

Katie Thompson, LPC, NCC, CEDS
Private Practice
Consano Therapy
Kirkwood, Missouri

Janet Treasure, OBE, PhD, FRCP, FRCPsych
Professor of Psychiatry
Institute of Psychiatry, Psychology, and Neuroscience
King's College
London, United Kingdom

Edward P. Tyson, MD
Adjunct Assistant Professor
Department of Kinesiology and Health Education
University of Texas
Austin, Texas

Johan Vanderlinden, PhD
Department Head, Adult Psychology
Coordinator, Eating Disorder Unit of the University Psychiatric Center
Catholic University of Leuven
Leuven, Belgium

Pam Virdi, MEd, RMN, CPN
Psychotherapist, Private Practice
Birmingham, United KIngdom

Maria Zaccagnino, PhD
Psychotherapist and Accredited EMDR Europe Consultant
EMDR Center for Eating Disorders
Milan, Italy

Foreword

If you are, or are working to become, a clinician who treats eating disorders, you will encounter what are sometimes called "complex presentations." Quite often, the people who are understandably, but inadequately, categorized in this way have some form of anorexia nervosa, bulimia nervosa, or binge eating disorder, compounded by significant levels of anxiety and depression and a history of trauma, which has left in its wake a propensity for dissociation, substance abuse, somatoform (e.g., conversion) symptoms, nonsuicidal self-injury, and/or personality disorder.

The person who "presents" and, typically, suffers in this "complex" manner might well meet the current *Diagnostic and Statistical Manual of Mental Disorders* (5th ed.; *DSM-5;* American Psychiatric Association, 2013) criteria for posttraumatic stress disorder (PTSD). Anyway, the complexity present for treatment providers will almost certainly be extended by body image problems and by intense existential "issues" that eerily reproduce, in the person's life and in the treatment sessions themselves, the crises that constitute Erickson's stages of psychosocial development: trust versus mistrust; autonomy versus shame/doubt; initiative versus guilt; industry versus inferiority; intimacy versus isolation.

I am not a clinician. From 1979 to 2012 I was a professor in the Department of Psychology at an Ohio liberal arts college, where I taught courses in abnormal psychology, clinical psychology, and eating disorders. This position afforded me numerous opportunities to discuss trauma, as well as eating disorders, with scholars in English, Classics, History, Women's and Gender Studies, and Holocaust Studies. Based on my background, I think it important for all of us interested in the overlap between trauma studies, trauma-informed approaches to therapy, and eating disorders to be reminded periodically that the concept of trauma itself is, and has been since at least the time of Homeric tradition before the 7th century BCE, freighted with complexity and controversy (see Jones & Wessely, 2006; Micale & Lerner, 2001; Shay, 1994; Zoellner, Bedard-Gilligan, Jun, Marks, & Garcia, 2013).

This is, in part, because of the fact that the meanings of trauma are inextricably tied to fundamental assumptions about being human, assumptions that shape powerful sociocultural and legal practices. For example, trauma, disorder, and recovery (including posttraumatic growth; Joseph, Murphy, & Regel, 2012) are all linked to one or more of the following: (a) the vagaries of a powerful natural world; (b) power, gender, and the ownership and control of bodies; (c) the meanings of family, self, social class, sexuality, and sexual orientation; (d) the relationship between the limits of the human body, psychological resilience, and vulnerability; (e) what a society calls "progress" (e.g., mines that extract resources from deep in the earth; high-speed trains and airplanes; massive skyscrapers that tower over enormous urban developments); (f) the apparently limitless savagery of war; (g) the potential malevolence of some humans toward others, especially children; and (h) the definition of and responsibility for "real" injury, disorder, and disability.

Although acknowledgment of the complexities, controversies, and sociohistorical twists and turns associated with the meanings of trauma is often missing from the literature on eating disorders, a fair number of articles and individual chapters in edited volumes do emphasize comorbidity between PTSD and eating disorders, as well as the diagnostic, etiological, and therapeutic challenges posed by this combination. This positive state of affairs is attributable in large part to the work of U.S. psychiatrist Timothy Brewerton (see Brewerton, 2015). His presentations on trauma and eating disorders are always packed with clinicians at various stages of their careers, all seeking guidance as to how to help people whose "complex presentations" have perplexed, if not overwhelmed, themselves, their families, and a series of therapists.

Yet, while an online search of *books* in the 136 libraries connected via the OhioLink system revealed approximately 80 *topic areas* associated with "PTSD," not one specifically addressed eating disorders. Expanding the search to "trauma" as a topic yielded approximately 380 areas, with only one focused on eating disorders. Although the links between trauma, PTSD, and eating disorders are of great importance to clinicians and researchers, the only book I could find that is dedicated to this topic was Vanderlinden and Vandereycken's (1997) co-authored volume titled *Trauma, Dissociation, and Impulse Dyscontrol in Eating Disorders*, published more than 20 years ago.

Trauma-Informed Approaches to Eating Disorders is clearly a much needed and long overdue book about treatment, written by a diverse group of clinicians and carefully edited to focus on the needs and strengths of clinicians. But focus and timeliness are only part of the foundation for my appreciation of this collection of chapters by experts from different fields. The complexities and challenges that undergird, surround, and even haunt the nature, diagnosis, treatment, management, and understanding of eating–disorders–in-relation-to-trauma are so great, even for veteran clinicians, that they can leave practitioners at any level of experience feeling helpless and exhausted. This book, in a way that would be appreciated by practitioners of acceptance and commitment therapy (ACT; Hayes, Strosahl, & Wilson, 2012), accepts the reality of those feelings *and* is committed to improving treatment, understanding, and compassion. It delivers hope.

Trauma-Informed Approaches to Eating Disorders is designed to foster respect for complexity and link it to humility in the presence of tragedy, tribulations, and suffering, framed all too often by our own shortcomings as healers. Knowing Andrew, knowing some of the chapter contributors (Carolyn Costin, Michael Berrett, Joslyn Smith), and reading all the chapters, I believe the following is a guiding principle for this book: respect for complexity + humility + hope + courage (defined by the presence of commitment *and* uncertainty/anxiety) + openness = progress in therapy. I would define this progress as more people with trauma-infused eating disorders receiving effective treatment, including earlier and more accurate diagnosis, from more professionals, who can flexibly draw from a wide variety of approaches, depending on the person, the problems, and the circumstances. Moreover, drawing on my experiences as a psychology professor and as a client in psychotherapy for depression and anxiety, I believe that the progress embodied and envisioned in this book moves us in the direction of therapy as a sacred, interpersonal journey toward the forms of integrative healing that have at their core hard-won wisdom through the making of meaning.

The previously described equation does not imply, let alone demand, that all models and treatment approaches are equally valid. We should indeed honor, for example, the contributions of neuroscience and evidence-based treatments grounded in randomized controlled trials AND we should also (with humility) never lose sight of the prejudices and other dangerous forms of arrogance that have been perpetrated and perpetuated for at least 200 years by psychiatry, psychology, and genetics in the name of "science" (Appignanesi, 2008; Gould, 1981; Valenstein, 1986). One of the great strengths of this book, and one of the major needs that it fulfills, is that it encourages us to consider—and keep an open mind about—multiple, sometimes vastly different, approaches to a set of complex, multidimensional, socio-psycho-bio disorders that have baffled healers, artists, and sufferers for thousands of years.

Michael P. Levine, PhD
Samuel B. Cummings Jr. Professor of Psychology, Emeritus
Kenyon College
Gambier, Ohio

■ REFERENCES

American Psychiatric Association. (2013). *Diagnostic and statistical manual of mental disorders* (5th ed.). Arlington, VA: American Psychiatric Publishing.

Appignanesi, L. (2008). *Mad, bad, and sad: A history of women and the mind doctors from 1800 to the present*. London, UK: Virago.

Brewerton, T. D. (2015). Stress, trauma, and adversity as risk factors in the development of eating disorders. In L. Smolak & M. P. Levine (Eds.), *The Wiley handbook of eating disorders (Vol. 1): Basic concepts and foundational research* (pp. 445–460). Sussex, UK: Wiley.

Gould, S. J. (1981). *The mismeasure of man*. New York, NY: W. W. Norton.

Hayes, S. C., Strosahl, K. D., & Wilson, K. G. (2012). *Acceptance and commitment therapy: The process and practice of mindful change*. New York, NY: Guilford Press.

Jones, E., & Wessely, S. (2006). Psychological trauma: A historical perspective. *Psychiatry, 5,* 217–220. doi:10.1053/j.mppsy.2006.04.011

Joseph, S., Murphy, D., & Regel, S. (2012). An affective–cognitive processing model of post-traumatic growth. *Clinical Psychology & Psychotherapy, 19,* 316–325. doi:10.1002/cpp.1798

Micale, M. S., & Lerner, P. (Eds.). (2001). *Traumatic pasts: History, psychiatry, and trauma in the modern age, 1870-1930*. Cambridge, UK: Cambridge University Press.

Shay, J. (1994). *Achilles in Vietnam: Combat trauma and the undoing of character*. New York, NY: Atheneum.

Valenstein, E. S. (1986). *Great and desperate cures: The rise and decline of psychosurgery and other radical treatments for mental illness*. New York, NY: Basic Books.

Vanderlinden, J., & Vandereycken, W. (1997). *Trauma, dissociation, and impulse dyscontrol in eating disorders*. Bristol, PA: Brunner/Mazel.

Zoellner, L. A., Bedard-Gilligan, M. A., Jun, J. J., Marks, L. H., & Garcia, N. M. (2013). The evolving construct of posttraumatic stress disorder (PTSD): *DSM-5* criteria changes and legal implications. *Psychological Injury and Law, 6,* 277–289. doi:10.1007/s12207-013-9175-6

Preface

They call us editors, my associate, Pam Virdi, and myself (Andrew Seubert). However, as a contributing author once described our role, we are the stewards of this book. We have been initiators, organizers, and, of course, editors; yet this amazing project has been personal and communal as well as professional. It has been inspired by a lost daughter, wounded friends, and damaged clients, all to the overwhelming impact of painful life events and to the eating disorders (EDs) employed to tolerate the intolerable. And it has been birthed through the hands and the great hearts of contributing authors, clinicians, and mentors: an entire village.

How This Book Came to Be

EDs are dangerous, ubiquitous, usually chronic in nature, and difficult to treat. Anorexia nervosa (AN) has the highest fatality rate (4%) of any mental illness. Bulimia nervosa reveals a fatality rate of 3.9%. Of all American adults, 2.8% will struggle with binge eating disorder during their lifetime.

It was 18 years ago that we lost our oldest child (my stepdaughter, although more like a daughter), Erin Leah, to AN. She was 23 and had struggled with the disorder since the age of 11. Nothing seemed capable of breaking the stranglehold of the anorexia. Nothing and no one. Seven or more hospitalizations, ongoing therapy, family therapy, medications—all came up short, until it was too late. Erin's passing was, and remains, an inspiration and the motivation for this book.

EDs offer an enormous challenge to therapists because of their complexity, which includes severe medical risk, co-occurring anxiety, depression and personality disorders, an addiction component, and body image distortion—all of this within a media-driven culture of thinness in which starving and purging can for some become lifestyle choices. This complexity is further exacerbated by the presence of painful life experiences or trauma.

The Need for This Book

The only other book to address the presence of trauma in clients with EDs was published in 1997 (Vanderlinden & Vandereycken), and one of its authors, Dr. Johan Vanderlinden, has honored us by contributing to this book with a state-of-the-art literature review. When trauma is understood more broadly, that is, small as well as large events, omission as well as commission, grief and loss as well as attachment injury, it becomes clear that trauma, as well as EDs, is everywhere. Researchers (Brewerton, 2015) have begun to show the relationship between trauma and EDs, but there is very little in the literature to guide the clinician in the nature, role, *and treatment* of trauma in clients with EDs.

EDs, as well as trauma, require a team approach and multifaceted strategies. Much has been contributed by the medical and nutritional fields, as well as by various therapeutic approaches (e.g., cognitive behavioral, acceptance and commitment, dialectical behavioral). Yet, despite the high co-relationship *between* painful life events, painful relationships, attachment injury, *and* the etiology of EDs, very little is offered that presents a *trauma-informed, dissociation-sensitive, and attachment deficit* approach to the treatment of EDs.

The purpose of this edited volume is to begin to fill that gap. *Trauma-Informed Approaches to Eating Disorders* elucidates the connection between trauma and EDs by offering a trauma-informed phase model, as well as chapters describing the ways in which various therapeutic models address each of those phases. It is a book primarily, although not exclusively, for clinicians, one whose purpose is to inspire, educate, and guide the therapist in serving a most complicated and suffering population.

Intended Audience

Above all, *Trauma-Informed Approaches to Eating Disorders* is geared toward clinicians who work with clients suffering from the complexities and dangers of EDs and trauma. In consultations with therapists, many times the clinician, faced with his or her first ED client, calls in a panic: "What do I do? Where do I start? How do I do this?" This book intends to answer many of these questions.

This book will be of interest to treatment facilities, and to clients as well, and readily integrates with both traditional and innovative approaches to EDs. It also provides critical information to therapists, doctors, dietitians, and nutritionists—information necessary for proper assessment and treatment recommendations.

Distinguishing Features

Trauma-Informed Approaches to Eating Disorders offers an in-depth exposition of a four-phase model of trauma treatment. It is inclusive in that it then describes how various therapeutic modalities address these phases, particularly trauma resolution, all within the context of ED exigencies. It is as much a "how to" book as it is a disseminator of information. It is also meant to inspire. Our intention, by way of summary, is to support competence, confidence, and hope to clinicians and to open the door to further research and treatment explorations. A continuously updated online website supports this by offering resources that include scripts, books, articles, recordings, treatment facilities, organizations, and websites.

Our clients have been torn in many directions by their histories and cultures. They have been fractured many times over; but they are not broken. The clinician's challenge is to join the client in a journey to the best in that client. This journey requires a multifaceted and collaborative approach, the very intent and purpose of *Trauma-Informed Approaches to Eating Disorders*. It does, after all, take a village.

■ REFERENCES

Brewerton, T. D. (2015). Stress, trauma and adversity as risk factors in the development of eating disorders. In L. Smolak & M. P. Levine (Eds.), *The Wiley handbook of eating disorders* (pp. 345–360). Hoboken, NJ: John Wiley & Sons.

Vanderlinden, J., & Vandereycken, W. (1997). *Trauma, dissociation, and impulse dyscontrol in eating disorders*. Bristol, PA: Brunner/Mazel.

Acknowledgments

Andrew:
There is gratefulness for many for inspiring and bringing this book to life.

I first thank our children—Zane, Jenna, Ariel, and Jocelyn—for cheering me on, and, above all, my wife, Barbara, for staying the course and helping with the editing, while I spent hours at the computer.

Special thanks go to Sheri W. Sussman, my editor at Springer Publishing Company, for believing in this project, and to Michael P. Levine, whose generous and expert guidance have made him something of a godfather for this book. I am grateful to the generosity of members of the eating disorder community, too many to mention, who provided articles and contacts whenever they could.

This could not have been a solo journey, and with that in mind, I have so appreciated and valued the presence of Pam Virdi, my associate editor. Finally, as always, I am indebted to our clients who, while fighting the good fight and maintaining hope, teach us clinicians how to travel with them.

Pam:
I thank Andrew for inviting me along on what can only be described as a pretty awesome journey. We talked about the need for this book a number of years ago and it has been a huge privilege to join with him and so many others to bring this body of work to publication. Much appreciation to my family and friends who put up with me being absent and who applauded me for having a go at my first venture into the world of book publishing.

A huge thanks to the wonderful library staff at Birmingham and Solihull Mental Health Foundation Trust for going the extra mile in providing me with literature searches and articles. Special mention to Anita who did not sigh once, at least not in my presence, when I booked yet another couple of hours out of her busy day for another "must have" literature search!

Finally, I would like to express heartfelt gratitude to my clients, who have always been my most important teachers.

Introducing Our Terms

■ TRAUMA REDEFINED WITHIN A PHASE MODEL OF TREATMENT

An Expanded Definition of "Trauma"

Trauma, as defined by the *Diagnostic and Statistical Manual of Mental Disorders* (5th ed.; *DSM-5*; American Psychiatric Association, 2013), is, unfortunately, quite limiting when it comes to describing painful life experiences.

The first criterion of posttraumatic stress disorder (PTSD), the symptomatic fallout from trauma as described in the *DSM-5*, is "…exposure to actual or threatened death, serious injury, or sexual violence…" (p. 271). The experience of trauma, however, is much more complicated. There are, for example, "big T" and "little t" events that cause pain and the subsequent, negative story that results from adverse experiences. Trauma is not always of epic proportions, such as abuse, death, or life-threatening experience. It can be a harsh word, continued criticism, being embarrassed in front of a first-grade class, or leaving mom for the first day of school. It can be the result of neglect or an act of omission, rather than commission.

Trauma is complicated by temperament, attachment status, and proximity to the event. It must also include grief and loss, as well as life changes resulting from trauma (Greenwald, 2007). Trauma arises from loss of identity, be it due to a brain injury or the loss of a role in life (parent, caretaker). Trauma is painfully more complicated and entrenched in clients with intellectual disability or with any physical or mental chronic condition. In a word, trauma, or painful life experience, appears in many forms in the life of an individual. There is no "one size fits all" when it comes to trauma.

Of great significance is the negative story that unfolds as a result of any trauma. It is what each of us tells ourself about ourself following painful events, both large and small. The story builds over time: "I'm no good," "There's something wrong with me," "I have no worth," "I'm a loser, hopeless and helpless." And as the story unfolds without awareness, we unconsciously become characters in that story. These are the stories that the authors of this book hope to dismantle, replacing them with stories of possibility, self-acceptance, and dignity.

A Trauma-Informed Phase Model of Psychotherapy

A phase model provides a clinical map, as well as a structure for this book. There have been various forms of phase models, beginning with Pierre Janet (1859–1947) and continuing up to the present time. Judith Herman (1992) wrote: "Recovery unfolds in three stages. The central task of the first stage is the establishment of safety. The central task of the second stage is remembrance and mourning. The central task of the third stage is reconnection with life" (p. 155). A threefold stage of treatment is also described in the work of structural dissociation: stabilization and symptom reduction, treatment of traumatic memories, and personality integration and rehabilitation (van der Hart, Nijenhuis, & Steele, 2006). In the world of eye movement desensitization and reprocessing (EMDR), Francine Shapiro (2018) offers an eight-phase model in which the phase of trauma processing is subdivided into five parts (Shapiro, 2001). Greenwald (2007) uses a four-phase model of history and treatment planning, preparation, trauma resolution, and reevaluation and consolidation of gains.

Although the wording differs among these variations of a phase model, the general intent is similar. First, we have to know the client, assess his or her status, and clarify the goals and treatment plan. Second, the client must be prepared for the work ahead. This includes internal as well as external stabilization and skills. Third, the traumatic experience(s) must be metabolized. Finally, the client must be guided in the integration of the newly freed sense of self with present and future circumstances. This entails not only relapse prevention, but also stepping into a larger and more expansive identity.

For this book, we have chosen a four-phase model. The phases are as follows:

1. **Assessment/evaluation**
2. **Preparation**
3. **Trauma processing**
4. **Reevaluation and integration**

Before giving any content description of the four phases, it is important to remember that any model is a theoretical construct. It is the map, not the territory. The phases of trauma treatment can be understood as treatment components that do not have to be addressed in some rigid order. Probably, the only "must" in this approach is that assessment and preparation are required before processing traumata. That aside, clinical decisions as to what is next and what is needed depend on the client. The model is in the service of the client's dynamic unfolding, not the other way around. Form and structure serve the needs of process and flow.

In speaking with several of our authors, we noticed a concern about rigidity in a phase approach and being forced into a model they might not use. Remember that the phases are guideposts along the ever-changing topography of the client's inner and outer world. Again, the map is not the territory. Those of you who are seasoned trauma therapists may not consciously use a "phase model." We would surmise, however, that you instinctively work in a phase approach without having to name it as such and that you intuitively realize that certain steps must precede others. A trauma-informed phase approach is deeply embedded in client centeredness and embraces any and every therapeutic approach. It enables therapist and client to know at any point where they are in the therapeutic journey and where they need to go next. Also, it generates hope in that the client realizes that there is a beginning, middle, and end to their work. Therapy is not supposed to be forever.

Assessment/Evaluation

This phase is typically composed of history taking, including both an attachment history and a trauma history. A case formulation connects past trauma with presenting symptoms and, from a trauma-informed perspective, makes sense of the symptoms and of the need to metabolize or process the painful roots of those symptoms. The case formulation organically leads to goal selection and treatment planning that now can include trauma processing (see Chapter 7). Regarding eating disorders (EDs), medical and nutritional assessments are absolutely necessary. In addition, screening for dissociation, mood, and personality disorders is requisite.

The assessment phase more often than not requires the teaching of awareness and basic skills for self-regulation before and during history taking. This phase begins with the first client contact and ends with a treatment plan.

Preparation

The preparation phase (see Chapter 8) supports the client in coping with immediate issues of daily life, as well as for the task of traumatic memory reconsolidation. Often this involves stabilization, both at home and in the client's relational life. Stabilization, at times referred to as "case management," also includes medical, nutritional, and psychopharmacological attention.

Preparation also entails developing various skills and resources that enable the client to better deal with everyday life and that strengthen the client for the trauma processing to follow. Personally, we also include short-term successes as part of this phase, a necessity to get clients with EDs onboard with treatment. These goals need to be achievable and of relevance to the client. Maxine, for example, was quite unwilling to address her ED, but quickly engaged in a session that was devoted to helping her set boundaries with her boyfriend. Once we bonded via this collaboration, we were able to slowly approach the ED.

Stabilization, skills, and resource building, as well as short-term successes, are goals in and of themselves and pave the way for successful trauma processing in the third phase. However, they are often required at the very start of the therapeutic journey, even before the assessment/evaluation phase gets underway. As previously mentioned, we will usually introduce skills of awareness, breathwork, and affect management before the tasks of assessment/evaluation are undertaken. "Preparation" skills are taught as needed, not in a rigid order. The client's needs drive the therapeutic bus.

Trauma Processing

This is where various theoretical models of psychotherapy part ways. The reprocessing phase, the "what" of our model, is undertaken via the "how" of different therapeutic traditions. In this phase, memories (both *implicit* and *explicit*) are processed or metabolized and ultimately reconsolidated, so that they no longer disturb the client and no longer color the lens through which the client views himself or herself and the world. For the ED client, this reduces the need for disordered eating patterns that dissociate the client from the traumatic pain and supports change in behaviors that are no longer anchored in unresolved, painful experience.

Reevaluation and Integration

In this final phase, various needs are addressed. Has the trauma processing been completed, or is there still work to be done in that respect? Does the client need to revisit skills to deal with triggers and relapse events? What about future challenges? Body image? And how does the client integrate his or her new story with present relationships? With the rest of his or her life? With the therapist?

■ SUMMARY

For this book to be of service to clinicians around the world, many of whom are reluctant to work with trauma and/or EDs, we believe that the chapters in this volume (particularly the clinically focused ones) need to address the presence of trauma in the ED population, as well as the *phasic components* of a trauma-informed model. The authors of the clinically oriented chapters have not been asked to change the way they work to fit these labels, but they describe how their approaches attend to the elements of the four phases, elements required by any effective approach to trauma and EDs.

■ REFERENCES

American Psychiatric Association. (2013). *Diagnostic and statistical manual of mental disorders manual* (5th ed.). Washington, DC: American Psychiatric Publishing.

Greenwald, R. (2007). *EMDR within a phase model of trauma-informed treatment.* New York, NY: Routledge Press.

Herman, J. L. (1992). *Trauma and recovery.* New York, NY: Basic Books.

Shapiro, F. (2018). *Eye movement desensitization and reprocessing: Basic principles, protocols, and procedures* (3rd ed.). New York, NY: Guilford Press.

van der Hart, O., Nijenhuis, E., & Steele, K. (2006). *The haunted self: Structural dissociation and the treatment of chronic traumatization.* New York, NY: W. W. Norton.

SECTION ONE

Overview and Recognizing the Territory

Every "disorder" has its purpose, the reason(s) why it came into existence. It is typically the default response for a client in dealing with adverse life experiences, often not productive, but the best the client can do. Chapter 1 offers a profile of each of the most common diagnostic categories for eating disorders (Anorexia, Binge Eating Disorder, Bulimia Nervosa) and their commonalities and differences, as well as a description of the "purpose" or "payoff" for each disorder. This chapter does the same for eating disorder variations as found in Other Specified Feeding or Eating Disorder (OSFED), Bulimarexia, and Orthorexia, while describing the presence of eating disorders (EDs) across cultures, genders, and ages.

Chapter 2 reviews current research showing the ED and trauma connection. It highlights the need for treatment of the traumatic roots of EDs (including a cultural body bias), which include small, yet painful events, grief and loss, and attachment injury, all of which are often present in EDs, even when overt and identifiable traumatic events are absent.

CHAPTER 1

The Many Faces of Eating Disorders: Anorexia Nervosa (AN), Bulimia Nervosa (BN), Binge Eating Disorder (BED), Other Specified Feeding or Eating Disorder (OSFED), Bulimarexia, and Orthorexia

Maria Zaccagnino, Martina Cussino, Chiara Callerame, and Cristina Civilotti

▓ INTRODUCTION

Feeding and eating disorders (EDs) are severe mental illnesses. The *Diagnostic and Statistical Manual of Mental Disorders* (5th ed.; *DSM-5*; American Psychiatric Association [APA], 2013) defines them as weight control behaviors, which damage physical health and psychosocial functioning, and they are secondary to no known medical or psychiatric condition.

International epidemiological research in Western countries (e.g., the United States, Hungary, Germany, the United Kingdom, Italy, France, Norway, Canada, Australia, Austria; Hudson, Hiripi, Pope, & Kessler, 2007; Makino, Tsuboi, & Dennerstein, 2004) indicated the prevalence of EDs as follows: anorexia nervosa (AN) at 0.1% to 5.7%; bulimia nervosa (BN) at 0.3% to 7.3%; and Other Specified Feeding or Eating Disorder (OSFED) at between 3.7% and 6.4%. Furthermore, the incidence of new cases per year per 100,000 people is 4 to 8 for AN and 9 to 12 for BN. It has been noted that those with EDs are mostly Western women, but that few cases have appeared in non-Western countries, such as the Middle East and the Republic of China (Makino et al., 2004). Recent studies, in fact, suggest that the prevalence of EDs has been rising in non-Western countries as well (Makino et al., 2004). Indeed, population- and patient-based estimates in 1990 and 2000 for non-Western countries ranged from 0.002% to 0.9% for AN and from 0.46% to 3.2% for BN (Li-Wey Soh & Walter, 2013). Moreover, Pike, Hoek, and Dunne (2014) found that EDs appear to be increasing in Arab and Asian countries in conjunction with increasing industrialization, urbanization, and globalization.

The age of onset is between 10 and 30, with a mean onset at 17, but premenarchal and prepubescent forms, which may have a prolonged course and tend toward chronicity, are not rare (20%–30%; Hudson et al., 2007). Furthermore, there is a female–male ratio of 10:1 for cases of anorexia and for bulimia (Hoek, 2006; Sukkar, Foppiani, & Campostano, 2005). These disorders have a very high mortality rate: AN 5.1% per 1,000 person/year,

BN 1.74 per 1,000 person/year, Eating Disorder Not Otherwise Specified (EDNOS) 3.31% per 1,000 person/year (Smink, van Hoeken, & Hoek, 2012).

In the general category of Feeding and Eating Disorders, the *DSM-5* (APA, 2013) includes Anorexia Nervosa, Bulimia Nervosa, Binge Eating Disorder, Avoidant/ Restrictive Intake Disorder, Rumination Disorder, Pica, Other Specified Feeding or Eating Disorder, and Unspecified Feeding or Eating Disorder. Yet, despite the diagnostic need to categorize the various manifestations of dysfunctional eating behaviors, it is important to underscore that EDs share the same psychopathological nucleus: the tendency to judge personal worth predominantly or exclusively in terms of weight and body form. In addition, in the literature and in clinical practice, it is rare to come across the so-called "pure" forms of EDs because the disorders tend to persist in time and to migrate frequently from one form to another in the same general, diagnostic category (Fairburn, Cooper, & Shafran, 2003).

In the past 30 years, research carried out in the field of EDs has greatly contributed to a better understanding of the relationship between a life story characterized by traumatic events and the development of an ED, putting us face to face with significant empirical evidence. In addition, adverse childhood experiences (ACEs; Felitti & Anda, 2010; Felitti et al., 1998), relational or attachment traumas, and traumatic events are widely recognized as risk factors for the development of this pathology, as has been underlined by the *DSM-5* (APA, 2013; Backholm, Isomaa, & Birgegård, 2013; Felitti & Anda, 2010; Madowitz, Matheson, & Liang, 2015; Monteleone et al., 2015; Murphy et al., 2013; Racine et al., 2015). According to a study by Putnam (2006), the percentage of individuals presenting with such a correlation is, in fact, considerable, namely 30% to 50%.

A meta-analysis conducted by Molendijk, Hoek, Brewerton, and Elzinga (2017) stressed the association between exposure to childhood maltreatment (i.e., emotional, physical, and sexual abuse) on the occurrence of all types of EDs and its defining features. The results show that prevalence was between 21% and 59% in each type of ED. Moreover, another systematic review (Caslini et al., 2016) highlighted the association between different EDs (AN, BN, binge eating disorder [BED]) and distinct types of child abuse (sexual, physical, emotional). The results show that childhood physical abuse was more associated with AN and BN, and childhood emotional abuse more with BN and BED.

Childhood abuse, therefore, may lead to difficulties in emotional regulation that can result in dissociative symptoms and dysfunctional behavior, which may contribute to the onset and maintenance of ED (Trottier & MacDonald, 2017). Recent research has shown a prevalence of dissociative symptoms among ED patients with a history of childhood trauma and binging–purging behaviors, more so when compared to those with restrictive anorexia and without a history of childhood trauma (Caslini et al., 2016).

These data must also be read and understood in the light of theoretical knowledge of attachment theory (Bowlby, 1969, 1988). Being able to create a self-image as someone worthy of love and care is closely connected to having experienced a positive and secure attachment relationship, which makes it possible to develop suitable coping strategies in response to emotionally intense situations. On the contrary, the experience of an insecure or disorganized attachment relationship can lead to the development of a negative self-image, which can result in fewer strategies in dealing with emotional stress (Zaccagnino, Civilotti, Cussino, Callerame, & Fernandez, 2017). Indeed, the development of dysfunctional eating behaviors can be considered an attempt to manage overwhelming emotions and memories connected with traumatic experiences (Jaite, Pfeiffer, Lehmkuhl, & Salbach-Andrae, 2013; Racine & Wildes, 2014).

■ ANOREXIA NERVOSA

AN is characterized by an intense fear of gaining body weight, leading to a persistent restriction of food intake. Consequently, patients developing this pathology tend to have a significantly low body weight (body mass index [BMI]) when taking into account their age, sex, evolutionary trajectory, and state of physical health. BMI is a simple index of weight for height that is commonly used to classify weight in adults. It is defined as a person's weight in kilograms divided by the square of his height in meters. According to this index, a BMI between 18.5 and 24.9 is considered normal weight. An underweight status is a BMI of less than 18.5. This extreme focus on body form and weight greatly interferes with self-esteem (APA, 2013).

It is important to remember that AN may express itself in two different types of behavior aimed at weight control: the restrictive type and the type with bulimic crises/purging behaviors. In addition, the severity of the disorder may be mild (BMI ≥ 17 kg/m), moderate (BMI 16–16.99 kg/m), severe (BMI 15–15.99 kg/m), or extreme (BMI < 15 kg/m).

The prevalence of AN is around 0.9%, with a greater incidence among females than males (the ratio is 10:1). The onset is typically in adolescence or early adulthood and is often associated with a stressful event. From 10% to 20% of those with AN develop a lifelong chronic condition, gravely compromising their interpersonal functioning and their educational or working career. The approximate mortality rate is 5% per decade, loss of life resulting from either suicide or because of medical complications relating to the disorder itself (APA, 2013; Arcelus, Mitchell, Wales, & Nielsen, 2011; Hoek, 2006). Beyond the higher risk of death seen in AN patients, there are also serious consequences from the point of view of both physical (e.g., amenorrhea, hypotension) and psychological (depression and social withdrawal) health.

Recent studies have suggested the importance of transgenerational traumatic dynamics as risk factors for consequent onset of EDs and, in particular, AN (Dalzell, 2000; Luca, Silvia, Giulia, & Renata, 2016). It has been shown that traumatic experiences (e.g., physical or sexual abuse and neglect) are more likely to be present in mothers of daughters with AN. Moreover, Molendijk et al. (2017) have pointed out that only the binge/purge subtype of AN is strictly linked with a history of childhood sexual abuse.

The disorder is characterized by clinical perfectionism; low, nuclear self-esteem; and interpersonal difficulties. Deep dissatisfaction with the body is closely connected to a distortion of the body self-image (Nicholls, Lynn, & Viner, 2011), which provokes feelings of inadequacy, insecurity, and poor self-esteem, all of which lead to the further loss of weight in a dysfunctional circle. Patients with AN typically have no compassion for themselves and are extremely self-critical (Dunkley & Grilo, 2007; Fennig et al., 2008). These characteristics are considered determining factors in the perpetuation of the symptomatology and for the resistance to treatment (Kelly & Tasca, 2016; Sutandar-Pinnock, Blake Woodside, Carter, Olmsted, & Kaplan, 2003). Although the fear of gaining weight is the observable component of the psychopathology, it hides a deeper terror, and the controlling behaviors seem to have a protective role (Zaccagnino, in press). In fact, one of the most important psychological aspects of AN is the concept of control (Surgenor, Horn, Plumridge, & Hudson, 2002), which is linked to the mechanisms of avoidance of negative emotions, failure to handle stressful situations with effective strategies, and use of stereotypes to interpret reality (Zaccagnino, Cussino, Callerame, Civilotti, & Fernandez, 2017). The purpose of the control and the hiding of a more profound fear is self-protection (Zaccagnino, in press).

■ BULIMIA NERVOSA (BN)

BN is characterized by recurrent binge eating, where the person eats a significantly greater amount of food than normal, associated with the feeling of losing control. According to the *DSM-5* (APA, 2013), in addition to recurrent binge eating, persons with BN carry out compensatory behaviors, such as self-induced vomiting or the use of laxatives, with the express purpose of preventing weight gain. For BN to be diagnosed, such behaviors must be present at least once a week for 3 months. The assiduous way in which persons with BN resort to elimination behaviors can have serious medical consequences, such as esophageal lacerations, gastric rupture, and cardiac arrhythmias (APA, 2013). The prevalence of BN in the female population is 1% to 1.5% and is greater among young adults. Similar to AN, the female–male ratio of prevalence is around 10:1 (APA, 2013). The onset is typically in adolescence or early adulthood, and the first episodes of binge eating may start after a period of dieting or stressful events. The course of BN may be chronic or intermittent with periods of remission (Jaffa & McDermott, 2009). Epidemiological studies report a mortality rate that varies from 0% to 3.9% (Crow et al., 2009). Once BN is established, it is rare to evolve into the condition of AN. More likely, there tends to be a migration toward other feeding disorders and EDs or, as in 20% of cases, toward binge ED (APA, 2013).

More than any other traumatic event, a history of sexual abuse is the risk factor that is most involved in the genesis and/or maintenance of this disorder (Brewerton, 2015; Johnson, Cohen, Kasen, & Brook, 2006; Steiger & Zanko, 1990; Vize & Cooper, 1995; Welch & Fairburn, 1994). Moreover, the purging strategies can be significatively and positively associated with a history of victimization and posttraumatic stress disorder (PTSD) symptoms (Dansky, Brewerton, Kilpatrick, & O'Neil, 1997). In this regard, recurrent binge eating and purging behaviors can be seen as an attempt to deal with overwhelming emotions related to negative experiences (Monteleone et al., 2015; Racine et al., 2015).

■ BINGE EATING DISORDER

Only in the most recent edition of the *DSM* is Binge Eating Disorder included in the categories of Feeding and Eating Disorders (APA, 2013). According to the *DSM-5*, to diagnose BED, the individual must manifest the typical behavior of binge eating together with the feeling of losing control during the episode. Unlike BN, however, there is no inappropriate compensatory behavior. Basic characteristics of this disorder are feelings of disgust or depression and anxiety, which accompany the episodes of binge eating.

Epidemiological studies highlight a prevalence of around 2% in adults (APA, 2013; Striegel-Moore & Franko, 2003). A substantial difference with respect to the disorders earlier examined lies in its greater incidence among males (Schneider, 2003). Indeed, compared to AN and BN, the BED ratio with regard to gender is much less asymmetric: the female prevalence is 1.6%, the male, 0.8% (APA, 2013).

According to scientific research, the onset of this disorder is to be found in adolescence or early adulthood (Decaluwé & Braet, 2003). Comparing the data of BN and AN for remission rates with those of BED, it was shown that the latter has higher remission rates (APA, 2013), although the course of BED has similar severity and duration to that of BN. As happens with the other categories of Feeding and Eating Disorders, BED, too, can entail various consequences on a functional level, such as difficulty adapting to a social role or a compromised quality of life, and can be associated with weight gain and obesity (APA, 2013).

A recent study has suggested that there is a great prevalence of traumatic experiences among parents of BED patients, with a prevalence of traumatic experiences occurring in infancy (Cerniglia et al., 2016). Specifically, literature has stressed that BED is associated with child abuse in all its forms (sexual, physical, and emotional abuse; Caslini et al., 2016; Trottier & MacDonald, 2017).

Binge eating behaviors aim to protect the patient through food consumption, regulating their emotional activation and protecting them from a deep sense of vulnerability and shame (Felitti & Anda, 2010; Messman-Moore & Garrigus, 2007; Racine & Wildes, 2014).

■ OTHER DISORDERS

Apart from the disorders described thus far, the *DSM-5* (APA, 2013) includes other symptomatological manifestations in the diagnostic category of feeding and EDs. These are Pica, characterized by a continual ingestion of nonedible substances; Rumination Disorder, in which the person tends to regurgitate and rechew food; and Avoidant/Restrictive Food Intake Disorder (ARFID) that manifests itself via a total disinterest in food or in the careful selection of foods on the basis of their sensorial characteristics. Another diagnostic category is OSFEDs. This exists for all manifestations of EDs that do not fully meet the criteria for one of the diagnostic categories we have listed (e.g., atypical AN or night eating syndrome). Finally, there is the diagnosis of Unspecified Feeding or Eating Disorder (UFED), which is applied to all the cases in which the individual does not meet the criteria for one of the feeding disorders and EDs present in the diagnostic category and the clinician decides not to specify why the criteria are not met. UFED is a category used when the clinician cannot define a type of disorder according to one of the previous diagnostic categories, either with regard to the criteria or to the context. An example of this would occur in an emergency situation, which would prevent the clinician from clearly defining the symptomatology.

Two manifestations of EDs, which are not fully recognized in the *DSM-5*, require their own discussion. They are orthorexia nervosa and bulimarexia, both of which are found more and more frequently in the clinical population.

Orthorexia nervosa, a pathological obsession with healthy eating (Oberle, Samaghabadi, & Hughes, 2017), can be described as "a disease disguised as a virtue." Its literal meaning is "proper appetite" (Koven & Abry, 2015). Orthorexia nervosa often begins with the aim and desire to change some bad habits, like eating food that contains a lot of sugar or chemicals or consuming food that can lead to weight gain. It can also result from developing good eating habits to prevent and treat illnesses such as cancer, diabetes, or heart disease (Oberle et al., 2017). Often prompted by the purpose of achieving a good and healthy lifestyle, this type of pathology may lead to problems such as nutritional anomalies (such as malnourishment) and medical complications (e.g., anemia, osteopenia; Koven & Abry, 2015). Persons with orthorexia nervosa can experience poor quality of life (Koven & Abry, 2015) because this healthy eating can become an unhealthy obsession, and the amount of time they spend planning, preparing, purchasing, and eating their meals can interfere with other aspects of their lives (Donini, Marsili, Graziani, Imbriale, & Cannella, 2004). Even though orthorexia nervosa is not an officially recognized psychiatric disease, it can often be associated with significant impairment.

With these diagnostic criteria in mind, one can notice many similarities between orthorexia, AN, and obsessive-compulsive traits. In particular, orthorexia and anorexia both have aspects of perfectionism and anxiety, a high need for external control, and importance placed on significant weight loss. Anorexia and orthorexia differ in the aims of their symptomatology. Orthorexics want to be healthy and natural and have unrealistic beliefs about certain foods. Anorexics are preoccupied with body image, afraid of being overweight, and want to lose weight. Furthermore, anorexics tend to hide their behaviors, whereas orthorexics are open about their beliefs and habits. Orthorexia is highly prevalent among anorexic and bulimic patients, with orthorexic symptoms increasing after AN or BN treatment (Segura-Garcia et al., 2015).

The combination of the two EDs, AN and BN, is referred to as *bulimarexia*, which is characterized by a mixed pattern of binge eating and then purging by vomiting, fasting, or the overuse of laxatives (Blok, 2002). Boskind-Lodahl was the first to use this term, in 1976, and it is possible to see AN and BN as extremes on a continuum where bulimarexia is in the middle (Cullari & Redmon, 1983). Like anorexics and bulimics, bulimarexics have low self-esteem and a desire for perfection, and, in periods of great stress, the cycle of binge eating and purging becomes a ritual to control uncertainty. Bulimarexia obviously has severe effects on physical health and emotional stability, depression and anxiety being the two symptoms most associated with it (Blok, 2002).

◼ COMORBIDITY

The prevalence of psychiatric comorbidities in patients with EDs is between 20% and 95%. The most common are mood disorders, anxiety disorders (obsessive-compulsive disorders and social phobia being the most common), and substance use disorders (Ulfvebrand, Birgegård, Norring, Högdahl, & von Hausswolff-Juhlin, 2015).

Dellava, Kendler, and Neale (2011) confirmed that an important contributor to the comorbidity between AN and generalized anxiety is that they share genetic and environmental characteristics. Meng and D'Arcy (2015) underline that patients with EDs comorbid with mood and anxiety disorders are younger, stressed, have poorer mental and physical health, are dissatisfied with life, and have weaker ties to the community.

Furthermore, in patients with AN, there is a significant correlation with mood disorders (Miniati et al., 2016). Comorbidity with such pathologies might contribute to ED complications, such as suicide, substance abuse, or chronicity. It is also important to point out the significant presence of personality disorders in ED patients. Among anorexic and bulimic subjects, more than half of them reveal comorbid borderline and avoidant personality disorders (Martinussen et al., 2016). Furthermore, it is not uncommon to observe in AN patients obsessive-compulsive traits, which tend to manifest in their control over food, weight, and body through compulsive and rigid rituals.

With respect to obsessive-compulsive disorder compared to orthorexia, the shared manifestations are recurrent intrusive thoughts about food and health at inappropriate times, a preoccupation with contamination and impurities, and a need to organize food and eat in a ritualized manner. Indeed, the most significant difference between obsessive-compulsive disorder and orthorexia is the ego-syntonic content of the obsession displayed in orthorexics (Koven & Abry, 2015). Bipolar disorder is also prevalent in ED patients, a fact that can be associated with an earlier onset and severity, in particular for BN (Meng & D'Arcy, 2015).

Psychotic disorders and EDs can occur in the same person. This comorbidity is more often seen in treatment centers for psychiatric illnesses, rather than in ED treatment programs. An hypothesis to possibly explain this fact is that psychotic symptoms take precedence and are more flagrant, requiring antipsychotic medication, which contributes to weight gain, hence insidiously worsening the ED. At present, a few studies are investigating these correlations, potentially revealing new information about the comorbidity of these two diagnoses (Altınyazar & Maner, 2014).

Recent studies have also highlighted the comorbidity between attention deficit-hyperactivity disorder (ADHD) and BN, AN, and obesity (Bleck, DeBate, & Olivardia, 2015). Specifically, they stress the fact that persons with ADHD tend to consume unhealthy foods, such as soft drinks, fast food, food additives, or artificial sweeteners, the latter two also affecting levels of hyperactivity (Bleck et al., 2014). Another significant observation emerging from these studies is that obesity is more prevalent in individuals with ADHD than in the general population. One hypothesis for this correlation is that impulsivity can affect the executive function preventing ADHD patients from controlling their eating behavior or losing weight.

Moreover, it seems that there is comorbidity between autism spectrum disorders (ASDs) and AN (Rhind et al., 2014; Westwood, Mandy, & Tchanturia, 2017). In particular, Rhind et al. (2014) highlight that adolescents with AN had elevated traits of ASD, obsessive-compulsive symptoms, and a small proportion fulfill diagnostic criteria for a probable ASD. These two disorders, in fact, seem to share various traits: poor central coherence, meaning the lack of an awareness of context or difficulty in taking a global approach (Frith, 1989; Lang et al., 2014); difficulties with set-shifting (Tchanturia et al., 2012), as in the capacity to shift a course of thought or action according to situational demands (Lezak, 1995); difficulties with emotional processing (Russell et al., 2009); and difficulties in mentalization (Baron-Cohen et al., 1985; Tchanturia et al., 2004).

■ CONCLUSION

Feeding disorders and EDs are considered severe mental illnesses and potentially life-threatening, resulting in death for as many as 5% of those who develop them. They can also cause considerable psychological distress and major physical complications. The purpose of this chapter was to give a concise overview regarding EDs, their diagnostic configuration, and comorbidity with other mental illnesses. Moreover, our focus included vulnerability and psychological aspects of EDs, with particular attention given to the impact of dysfunctional attachment dynamics and relational trauma on the onset of each type of ED. Types of EDs also included those that are not present in *DSM-5*, but are frequently found in clinical practice. Such disorders (e.g., bulimarexia or orthorexia) are symptomatological manifestations that require further investigation to clarify risk factors related to their onset and to shed light on their mechanism of action.

In light of these considerations, treatment should be considered essential for EDs and must be started as early as possible, with the inclusion of stressful and traumatic events as important risk factors in the development of the pathology.

■ REFERENCES

Altınyazar, V., & Maner, F. (2014). Eating disorders and psychosis: Seven hypotheses *Anadolu Psikiyatri Dergisi, 15*(1), 84–88. doi:10.5455/apd.38073

American Psychiatric Association. (2013). *Diagnostic and statistical manual of mental disorders* (5th ed.). Arlington, VA: American Psychiatric Publishing.

Arcelus, J., Mitchell, A. J., Wales, J., & Nielsen, S. (2011). Mortality rates in patients with anorexia nervosa and other eating disorders. A meta-analysis of 36 studies. *Archives of General Psychiatry, 68*(7), 724–731. doi:10.1001/archgenpsychiatry.2011.74

Backholm, K., Isomaa, R., & Birgegård, A. (2013). The prevalence and impact of trauma history in eating disorder patients. *European Journal of Psychotraumatology, 4*. doi:10.3402/ejpt. v4i0.22482

Baron-Cohen, S., Leslie, A. M., & Frith, U. (1985). Does the autistic child have a "theory of mind"? *Cognition, 21*(1), 37–46. doi:10.1016/0010-0277(85)90022-8

Bleck, J. R., DeBate, R. D., & Olivardia, R. (2014). The comorbidity of ADHD and eating disorders in a nationally representative sample. *Journal of Behavioral Health Services and Research, 42*, 437–451. doi:10.1007/s11414-014-9422-y

Blok, S. L. (2002). Eating disordered women's descriptions of issues leading to conflict and the communication strategies used to manage conflict in their family and romantic relationships: A qualitative study. *Dissertation Abstracts International Section A: Humanities and Social Sciences, 63*(3–A), 816.

Boskind-Lodahl, M. (1976). Cinderella's stepsisters: A feminist perspective on anorexia nervosa and bulimia. *Signs, 2*, 342–356. doi:10.1086/493362

Bowlby, J. (1969). *Attachment and loss: Vol 1. Attachment.* New York, NY: Basic Books.

Bowlby, J. (1988). *A secure base. Parent-child attachment and healthy human development.* New York, NY: Basic Books.

Brewerton, T. D. (2015). Stress, trauma, and adversity as risk factors in the development of eating disorders. In L. Smolak & M. P. Levine (Eds.), *The Wiley handbook of eating disorders* (pp. 445–460). New York, NY: Guilford.

Caslini, M., Bartoli, F., Crocamo, C., Dakanalis, A., Clerici, M., & Carrà, G. (2016). Disentangling the association between child abuse and eating disorders: A systematic review and meta-analysis. *Psychosomatic Medicine, 78*(1), 70–90. doi:10.1097/PSY.0000000000000233

Cerniglia, L., Cimino, S., Ballarotto, G., & Tambelli, R. (2016). Do parental traumatic experiences have a role in the psychological functioning of early adolescents with binge eating disorder? *Eating and Weight Disorders-Studies on Anorexia, Bulimia and Obesity, 21*(4), 635–644. doi:10.1007/s40519-016-0303-7

Crow, S. J., Peterson, C. B., Swanson, S. A., Raymond, N. C., Specker, S., Eckert, E. D., & Mitchell, J. E. (2009). Increased mortality in bulimia nervosa and other eating disorders. *American Journal of Psychiatry, 166*(12), 1342–1346. doi:10.1176/appi.ajp.2009.09020247

Cullari, S., & Redmon W. K. (1983). Bulimarexia bulimia, and binge eating: A bibliography. *Professional Psychology: Research and Practice, 14*(3), 400–405. doi:10.1037/0735-7028. 14.3.400

Dalzell, H. J. (2000). Whispers: The role of family secrets in eating disorders. *Eating Disorders, 8*, 43–61. doi:10.1080/10640260008251211

Dansky, B. S., Brewerton, T. D., Kilpatrick, D. G., & O'Neil, P. M. (1997). The National Women's Study: Relationship of victimization and posttraumatic stress disorder to bulimia nervosa. *International Journal of Eating Disorders, 21*(3), 213–228. doi:10.1002/(SICI)1098-108X(199704)21:3<213::AID-EAT2>3.0.CO;2-N

Decaluwé, V., & Braet, C. (2003). Prevalence of binge-eating disorder in obese children and adolescents seeking weight-loss treatment. *International Journal of Obesity and Related Metabolic Disorders, 27*, 404–409. doi:10.1038/sj.ijo.0802233

Dellava, J. E., Kendler, K. S., & Neale, M. C. (2011). Generalized anxiety disorder and anorexia nervosa: Evidence of shared genetic variation. *Depression and Anxiety, 28*(8), 728–733. doi:10.1002/da.20834

Donini, L. M., Marsili, D., Graziani, M. P., Imbriale, M., & Cannella, C. (2004). Orthorexia nervosa: A preliminary study with a proposal for diagnosis and an attempt to measure the dimension of the phenomenon. *Eating and Weight Disorders, 9*(2), 151–157.

Dunkley, D. M., & Grilo, C. M. (2007). Self-criticism, low self-esteem, depressive symptoms, and over-evaluation of shape and weight in binge eating disorder patients. *Behaviour Research and Therapy, 45*(1), 139–149. doi:10.1016/j.brat.2006.01.017

Fairburn, C. G., Cooper, Z., & Shafran, R. (2003). Cognitive behaviour therapy for eating disorders: A "transdiagnostic" theory and treatment. *Behaviour Research and Therapy, 41*(5), 509–528. doi:10.1016/S0005-7967(02)00088-8

Felitti, V. J., & Anda, R. F. (2010). The relationship of adverse childhood experiences to adult medical disease, psychiatric disorders and sexual behavior: Implications for healthcare. In R. A. Lanius, E. Vermetten., & C. Pain (Eds.), *The impact of early life trauma on health and disease: The hidden epidemic* (pp. 77–87). Cambridge, UK: Cambridge University Press.

Felitti, V. J., Anda, R. F., Nordenberg, D., Williamson, D. F., Spitz, A. M., Edwards, V., … Marks, J. S. (1998). Relationship of childhood abuse and household dysfunction to many of the leading causes of death in adults. The Adverse Childhood Experiences (ACE) Study. *American Journal of Preventive Medicine, 14*(4), 245–258. doi:10.1016/S0749-3797(98)00017-8

Fennig, S., Hadas, A., Itzhaky, L., Roe, D., Apter, A., & Shahar, G. (2008). Self-criticism is a key predictor of eating disorder dimensions among inpatient adolescent females. *International Journal of Eating Disorders, 41*(8), 762–765. doi:10.1002/eat.20573

Frith, U. (1989). A new look at language and communication in autism. *British Journal of Disorders of Communication, 24*(2), 123–150. doi:10.3109/13682828909011952

Hoek, H. W. (2006). Incidence, prevalence and mortality of anorexia nervosa and other eating disorders. *Current Opinion Psychiatry, 19*(4), 389–394. doi:10.1097/01.yco.0000228759.95237.78

Hudson, J. I., Hiripi, E., Pope, H. G., Jr., & Kessler, R. C. (2007). The prevalence and correlates of eating disorders in the National Comorbidity Survey Replication. *Biological Psychiatry, 61*(3), 348–358. doi:10.1016/j.biopsych.2006.03.040

Jaffa, T., & McDermott, B. (2009). *I disturbi alimentari nei bambini e negli adolescenti* [Eating disorders in children and adolescents]. Milan, Italy: Raffaello Cortina Editore.

Jaite, C., Pfeiffer, E., Lehmkuhl, U., & Salbach-Andrae, H. (2013). Childhood abuse in adolescents with anorexia nervosa compared to a psychiatric and healthy control group. *Zeitschrift fur Kinder und Jugendpsychiatrie und Psychotherapie, 41*(2), 99–107. doi:10.1024/1422-4917/a000217

Johnson, J. G., Cohen, P., Kasen, S., & Brook, J. S. (2006). Dissociative disorders among adults in the community, impaired functioning, and axis I and II comorbidity. *Journal Psychiatric Research, 40*, 131–140. doi:10.1016/j.jpsychires.2005.03.003

Kelly, A. C., & Tasca, G. A. (2016). Within-persons predictors of change during eating disorders treatment: An examination of self-compassion, self-criticism, shame, and eating disorder symptoms. *International Journal of Eating Disorders, 49*, 716–722. doi:10.1002/eat.22527

Koven, N. S., & Abry, A. W. (2015). The clinical basis of orthorexia nervosa: Emerging perspectives. *Neuropsychiatric Disease and Treatment, 11*, 385–394. doi:10.2147/NDT.S61665

Lang, K., Lopez, C., Stahl, D., Tchanturia, K., & Treasure, J. (2014). Central coherence in eating disorders: An updated systematic review and meta-analysis. *World Journal of Biological Psychiatry, 15*(8), 586–598. doi:10.3109/15622975.2014.909606

Lezak, M. D. (1995). *Neuropsychological assessment* (3rd ed.). New York, NY: Oxford University Press.

Li-Wey Soh, N. L., & Walter, G. (2013). Publications on cross-cultural aspects of eating disorders. *Journal of Eating Disorders.* Retrieved from https://jeatdisord.biomedcentral.com/articles/10.1186/2050-2974-1-4

Madowitz, J., Matheson, B. E., & Liang, J. (2015). The relationship between eating disorders and sexual trauma. *Eating and Weight Disorders-Studies on Anorexia, 20*(3), 281–293. doi:10.1007/s40519-015-0195-y

Makino, M., Tsuboi, K., & Dennerstein, L. (2004). Prevalence of eating disorders: A comparison of Western and non-Western countries. *Medscape General Medicine, 6*(3), 49. Retrieved from https://www.ncbi.nlm.nih.gov/pmc/articles/PMC1435625

Martinussen, M., Friborg, O., Schmierer P., Kaiser, S, Øvergård, K. T., Neunhoeffer, A. L., … Rosenvinge, J. H. (2016). The comorbidity of personality disorders in eating disorders: A meta-analysis. *Eating and Weight Disorders, 22*(2), 201–209. doi:10.1007/s40519-016-0345-x

Meng, X., & D'Arcy, C. (2015). Comorbidity between lifetime eating problems and mood and anxiety disorders: Results from the Canadian Community Health Survey of Mental Health and Well-Being. *European Eating Disorders Review, 23*(2), 156–162. doi:10.1002/erv.2347

Messman-Moore, T. L., & Garrigus, A. S. (2007). The association of child abuse and eating disorder symptomatology: The importance of multiple forms of abuse and revictimization. *Journal of Aggression Maltreatment and Trauma, 14*, 51–72. doi:10.1300/J146v14n03_04

Miniati, M., Benvenuti, A., Bologna, E., Maglio, A., Cotugno, B., Massimetti, G., … Dell'Osso, L. (2016). Mood spectrum comorbidity in patients with anorexia and bulimia nervosa. *Eating and Weight Disorders.* Advance online publication. doi:10.1007/s40519-016-0333-1

Molendijk, M. L., Hoek, H. W., Brewerton, T. D., & Elzinga, B. M. (2017). Childhood maltreatment and eating disorder pathology: A systematic review and dose-response meta-analysis. *Psychological Medicine, 19*, 1–15. doi:10.1017/S0033291716003561

Monteleone, A. M., Monteleone, P., Serino, I., Scognamiglio, P., Di Genio, M., & Maj, M. (2015). Childhood trauma and cortisol awakening response in symptomatic patients with anorexia nervosa and bulimia nervosa. *International Journal of Eating Disorders, 48*(6), 615–621. doi:10.1002/eat.22375

Murphy, J. G., Yurasek, A. M., Dennhardt, A. A., Skidmore, J. R., McDevitt-Murphy, M. E., MacKillopb, J., & Martens, M. P. (2013). Symptoms of depression and PTSD are associated with elevated alcohol demand. *Drug and Alcohol Dependence, 127*, 129–136. doi:10.1016/j.drugalcdep.2012.06.022

Nicholls, D. E., Lynn, R., & Viner, R. M. (2011). Childhood eating disorders: British national surveillance study. *British Journal of Psychiatry, 198*(4), 295–301. doi:10.1192/bjp.bp.110.081356

Oberle, C. D., Samaghabadi, R. O., & Hughes, E. M. (2017). Orthorexia nervosa: Assessment and correlates with gender, BMI, and personality. *Appetite, 108*, 303–310. doi:10.1016/j.appet.2016.10.021

Pike, K. M., Hoek, H. W., & Dunne, P. E. (2014). Cultural trends and eating disorders. *Current Opinion in Psychiatry, 27*(6), 436–442. doi:10.1097/YCO.0000000000000100

Ptacek, R., Stefano, G. B., Weissenberger, S., Akotia, D., Raboch, J., Papezova, H., ... Goetz, M. (2016). Attention deficit hyperactivity disorder and disordered eating behaviors: Links, risks, and challenges faced. *Neuropsychiatric Disease and Treatment, 12*, 571–579. doi:10.2147/NDT.S68763

Putnam, F. W. (2006). The impact of trauma on child development. *Juvenile and Family Court Journal, 57*(1), 1–11. doi:10.1111/j.1755-6988.2006.tb00110.x

Racine, S. E., Burt, S. A., Keel, P. K., Sisk, C. L., Neale, M. C., Boker, S., & Klump, K. L. (2015). Examining associations between negative urgency and key components of objective binge episodes. *International Journal of Eating Disorders, 48*, 527–531. doi:10.1002/eat.22412

Racine, S. E., & Wildes, J. E. (2014). Emotion dysregulation and anorexia nervosa: An exploration of the role of childhood abuse. *International Journal of Eating Disorders. 48*, 55–58. doi:10.1002/eat.22364

Rhind, C., Bonfioli, E., Hibbs, R., Goddard, E., Macdonald, P., Gowers, S., ... Treasure, J. (2014). An examination of autism spectrum traits in adolescents with anorexia nervosa and their parents. *Molecular Autism, 5*(1), 56. doi:10.1186/2040-2392-5-56

Russell, T. A., Schmidt, U., Doherty, L., Young, V., & Tchanturia, K. (2009). Aspects of social cognition in anorexia nervosa: affective and cognitive theory of mind. *Psychiatry Research, 168*(3), 181–185. doi:10.1016/j.psychres.2008.10.028

Schneider, M. (2003). Bulimia nervosa and binge-eating disorder in adolescents. *Adolescent Medicine, 14*, 119–131.

Segura-Garcia, C., Ramacciotti, C., Rania, M., Aloi, M., Caroleo, M., Bruni, A., ... De Fazio, P. (2015). The prevalence of orthorexia nervosa among eating disorder patients after treatment. *Eating and Weight Disorders, 20*(2), 161–166. doi:10.1007/s40519-014-0171-y

Smink, F. R., van Hoeken, D., & Hoek, H. W. (2012). Epidemiology of eating disorders: Incidence, prevalence and mortality rates. *Current Psychiatry Reports, 14*, 406–414. doi:10.1007/s11920-012-0282-y

Steiger, H., & Zanko, M. (1990). Sexual traumata among eating disordered, psychiatric, and normal female groups. *Journal of Interpersonal Violence, 5*, 74–86. doi:10.1177/088626090005001006

Striegel-Moore, R. H., & Franko, D. L. (2003). Epidemiology of binge eating disorder. *International Journal of Eating Disorders, 34*, S19–S29. doi:10.1002/eat.10202

Sukkar, S. G., Foppiani, L., & Campostano, A. (2005). Management and treatment of eating disorders in an Italian region. *Eating Weight Disorders, 10*(3), 204–209. doi:10.1007/BF03327548

Surgenor, L. J., Horn, J., Plumridge, E. W., & Hudson, S. M. (2002). Anorexia nervosa and psychological control: A reexamination of selected theoretical accounts. *European Eating Disorders Review, 10*(2), 85–101. doi:10.1002/erv.457

Sutandar-Pinnock, K., Blake Woodside, D., Carter, J. C., Olmsted, M. P., & Kaplan, A. S. (2003). Perfectionism in anorexia nervosa: A 6–24-month follow-up study. *International Journal of Eating Disorders, 33*(2), 225–229. doi:10.1002/eat.10127

Tchanturia, K., Davies, H., Roberts, M., Harrison, A., Nakazato, M., Schmidt, U., ... Morris, R. (2012). Poor cognitive flexibility in eating disorders: Examining the evidence using the Wisconsin Card Sorting Task. *PLoS One, 7*(1), e28331. doi:10.1371/journal.pone.0028331

Tchanturia, K., Morris, R. G., Anderluh, M. B., Collier, D. A., Nikolaou, V., & Treasure, J. (2004). Set shifting in anorexia nervosa: An examination before and after weight gain, in full recovery and relationship to childhood and adult OCPD traits. *Journal of Psychiatric Research, 38*(5), 545–552. doi:10.1016/j.jpsychires.2004.03.0

Trottier, K., & MacDonald, D. E. (2017). Update on psychological trauma, other severe adverse experiences and eating disorders: State of the research and future research directions. *Current Psychiatry Reports, 19*(8), 45. doi:10.1007/s11920-017-0806-6

Ulfvebrand, S., Birgegård, A., Norring, C., Högdahl, L., & von Hausswolff-Juhlin, Y. (2015). Psychiatric comorbidity in women and men with eating disorders results from a large clinical database. *Psychiatry Research, 230*(2), 294–299. doi:10.1016/j.psychres.2015.09.008

Vize, C. M., & Cooper, P. J. (1995). Sexual abuse in patients with eating disorder, patients with depression, and normal controls: A comparative study. *British Journal of Psychiatry, 167*, 80–85. doi:10.1192/bjp.167.1.80

Welch, S. L., & Fairburn, C. G. (1994). Sexual abuse and bulimia nervosa: Three integrated case control comparisons. *American Journal of Psychiatry, 151*, 402–407. doi:10.1176/ajp.151.3.402

Westwood, H., Mandy, W., & Tchanturia, K. (2017). Clinical evaluation of autistic symptoms in women with anorexia nervosa. *Molecular Autism, 8*(1), 12. doi:10.1186/s13229-017-0128-x

Zaccagnino, M. (in press). The EMDR anorexia nervosa protocol. In M. Luber (Ed.), *Eye movement desensitization and reprocessing (EMDR) scripted protocols and summary sheets: Treating trauma, anxiety, and mood-related conditions.* New York, NY: Springer Publishing.

Zaccagnino, M., Civilotti, C., Cussino, M., Callerame, C., & Fernandez, I. (2017). EMDR in anorexia nervosa: From a theoretical framework to the treatment guidelines. In Lobera, I. J. (Ed.), *Eating disorders. A paradigm of the biopsychosocial model of illness* (pp. 193–213). Rijeka, Croatia: Intech. doi:10.5772/65695

Zaccagnino, M., Cussino, M., Callerame, C., Civilotti, C., & Fernandez, I. (2017). Anorexia nervosa and EMDR: A clinical case. *Journal of EMDR Practice and Research, 11*(1), 43–53.

CHAPTER 2

Trauma and Eating Disorders: The State of the Art

Johan Vanderlinden and Giovanni Luca Palmisano

▓ INTRODUCTION

The *Diagnostic and Statistical Manual of Mental Disorders* (5th ed.; *DSM-5*; American Psychiatric Association [APA], 2013). describes a traumatic event as exposure to actual or threatened death, serious injury, or sexual violence either through directly experiencing or witnessing the event in person, or learning that such an event (i.e., violence, or accidental serious injury or death) has happened to a closer other APA, 2013). This definition of trauma is unfortunately quite limited and does not involve the more "hidden" traumata, such as growing up in invalidating family environments with poor attachment, confrontation with death and loss, emotional abuse and maltreatment, parentification, bullying experiences, leaving home, and frequent critical comments from the parents. These hidden traumata are often not so spectacular, but even more complicated to assess, and have received much too little attention in the literature. In this book, we want to use a broad definition of trauma including also these more hidden traumata.

Overwhelming evidence exists that traumatic experiences leave traces in our minds and bodies. Traumatic experiences such as sexual, physical, and emotional abuse have a negative impact on our capacities to relate to and trust other people, but also on the neurobiological functioning of our brain and thus our mind. They also affect our immune systems (van der Kolk, 2014). Hence, traumatic experiences make dealing with emotions, both positive and negative, quite challenging.

In this chapter, a "state-of-the-art" review reveals the presence of a wide variety of traumatic experiences in eating disorder (ED) patients and its trauma-related consequences. Almost all studies investigated the association of retrospectively reported childhood abuse with current ED symptoms using cross-sectional designs (Trottier & MacDonald, 2017). A special focus is on the presence of dissociation in ED patients, as it is one of the main characteristics in EDs with severe trauma.

EDs are complex psychological–medical conditions characterized by weight and shape concerns and inappropriate eating patterns severe enough to potentially damage health or threaten life (APA, 2013). The etiology of EDs is complex and still unclear, but it likely includes genetic, behavioral, and psychosocial factors. Regarding the latter set of influences, histories of childhood sexual abuse (CSA), childhood physical abuse (CPA), and childhood emotional abuse (CEA) have been studied intensively and are considered to be nonspecific risk factors for the development of EDs (Racine & Wildes, 2015; Sanci et al., 2008). In addition, a large body of literature has strongly been influenced by the assumption that traumatic or adverse experiences occurring in childhood, adolescence, and adulthood are strongly linked with the severity of ED symptoms (Armour et al., 2016; Guillaume et al., 2016; Palmisano, Innamorati, & Vanderlinden, 2016; Vanderlinden, Vandereycken, & Claes, 2007). A very limited number of studies have investigated the role of childhood emotional neglect (CEN) and childhood physical neglect (CPN) in predisposing for EDs (Jaite et al., 2012; Kong & Bernstein, 2009). This type of trauma is often "hidden" and it may include seemingly small, yet painful and cumulative, events such as grief and loss, attachment injury, and/or bullying experiences. In contrast with the many studies on trauma during childhood, fewer studies examined the association between EDs and traumatic experiences in adulthood. Nonetheless, some research suggests that traumatic experiences during adulthood are also linked to the development of EDs (Forman-Hoffman, Mengeling, Booth, Torner, & Sadler, 2012) and may even account for unique variance in ED psychopathology (Collins, Fischer, Stojek, & Becker, 2014).

Despite these data, the understanding of the mechanisms that link both childhood and adulthood trauma and the etiology of EDs remains complex and is not well understood. Consequently, several authors have attempted to reveal possible mechanisms through which traumatic experiences lead to the development of EDs, focusing their interest mainly on dissociative experiences (Pettinati, Horne, & Staats, 1985; Vanderlinden, Vandereycken, van Dyck, & Vertommen, 1993). In this chapter, the complex relationship between trauma and EDs and its mediating factors are outlined with a special focus on dissociation.

■ TRAUMATIC EXPERIENCES AND THEIR CONSEQUENCES IN ANOREXIA NERVOSA

Practically all studies are cross-sectional, and longitudinal studies are lacking. Compared to bulimia nervosa (BN) and binge eating disorder (BED), fewer studies focused on the presence of traumatic experiences in samples of women with anorexia nervosa (AN). Nevertheless, most studies have focused on the prevalence of sexual abuse in AN patients. When comparing the prevalence of trauma in EDs, including AN patients, with normal controls, the data systematically show a higher presence of trauma in every type of ED patient. For instance, Tasca et al. (2013) studied the relationship between childhood trauma and eating psychopathology in a sample of 289 ED patients (21.7% AN, 29.9% BN, 36.2% Eating Disorder Not Otherwise Specified [EDNOS], 12.3% BED) compared with a population-based, nonclinical sample of 897 individuals. The ED sample showed higher levels of CSA, CPA, and neglect compared to the nonclinical sample. Furthermore, the authors found that attachment injury fully mediates between traumatic experiences and the severity of ED psychopathology. Similar results were recently obtained by Monteleone et al. (2015) and Meltzer-Brody et al. (2011).

Some researchers have compared the prevalence of trauma in ED patients to the patients with other psychiatric diagnoses. In one such case–control study (Laporte & Guttman, 2001), data showed that trauma is not a specific factor in AN compared to other psychiatric diagnoses.

One important and consistent finding is the fact that when comparing AN-restrictive type (AN-R) patients with AN-binge/purge type (AN-BP) patients, AN-R patients systematically report fewer traumatic experiences of all kinds compared to AN-BP patients or ED patients with bingeing/purging characteristics (Vanderlinden, 1993). In one of the first studies on this topic, Steiger and Zanko (1990) measured incest and extrafamilial sexual abuse in 73 ED patients compared with 21 psychiatric patients with no ED diagnosis (PC) and with 24 healthy controls (HC). The frequencies of CSA were higher in AN-BP, BN, and PC groups compared with both AN-R and HC groups. These findings were confirmed in another study by Schmidt, Tiller, and Treasure (1993), providing further evidence that BN and AN-BP patients were experiencing more childhood adversity than those with AN-R. van Gerko, Hughes, Hamill, and Waller (2005) evaluated CSA in a sample of 299 ED women and concluded that CSA was more strongly related to binge eating and all forms of purging behaviors rather than to restrictive behaviors (see also Carter, Bewell, Blackmore, & Woodside, 2006; Jaite et al., 2012). In another study, Steiger et al. (2010) evaluated trauma history in a sample of ED clients compared to a normal female sample. Data showed again that ED patients with purging and binge eating revealed a higher likelihood of physical abuse and a combination of either physical or sexual abuse compared to AN-R patients. Only a few studies focused on the presence of other forms of trauma in ED patients including CEA (Pignatelli, Wampers, Loriedo, Biondi, & Vanderlinden, 2017), such as neglect and bullying, as well as CSA and CPA. For instance, Corstorphine, Waller, Lawson, and Ganis (2007) measured childhood traumatic experiences (including neglect and bullying) and comorbid behaviors in 102 individuals who met strict criteria for an ED. Any reported history of childhood trauma was associated with a higher number of impulsive behaviors, such as bingeing and vomiting, and with the presence of multi-impulsivity. CSA was particularly important, and was associated with self-cutting, alcohol abuse, and substance abuse (amphetamines, cocaine, cannabis and "other substances," including ketamine and benzodiazepines). Again, AN-R patients had a lower overall trauma history compared to all other ED subtypes. Similarly, Racine and Wildes (2015), in a cross-sectional study carried out in a sample of 188 AN patients, reported that the rates of CEA and CSA were significantly correlated with both emotional dysregulation and the severity of AN symptoms. Furthermore, emotional dysregulation was found to mediate between CEA and AN symptoms, both in AN-BP and AN-R patients.

A few studies have focused on the prevalence of posttraumatic stress disorder (PTSD) symptoms in AN patients. Reyes-Rodríguez et al. (2011) have rated lifetime traumatic events and PTSD comorbidity in a sample of 753 women with AN diagnosis, including 332 subjects with AN-R, 217 with AN with purging and without binge eating, 115 with AN-BP, and 89 patients with lifetime diagnosis of both AN and BN. The authors found that 39% of the total sample reported one or more traumatic events in their lifetime, and that 13.7% met the criteria for PTSD. In contrast with previous studies (Carter et al., 2006; Jaite et al., 2012), no significant difference was found in the number of traumatic experiences across the AN subgroups. However, the odds of having a PTSD diagnosis were more than twice higher in AN individuals with purging than in individuals with AN-R (8.8% vs. 18.4%).

In an original work carried out by Karwautz et al. (2001), the specific risk factors for AN were examined using a sample of 45 sister-pairs, discordant for an AN diagnosis. The sisters with AN differed from their healthy sisters in terms of personal vulnerability traits and exposure to high parental expectations and sexual abuse. There was evidence of poor feeding in childhood in the AN sisters. In another community-based study, Romans, Gendall, Martin, and Mullen (2001) carried out in a sample of 477 subjects, the data showed a significantly higher frequency of both AN and BN in the CSA group than in the group with no CSA.

However, some contrasting findings with previous research need to be mentioned. In only one study (Wentz, Gillberg, Gillberg, & Råstam, 2005) comparing 51 adolescent-onset AN-R cases with 51 matched HCs, no significant differences were found in sexual abuse rates between the two groups 10 years later after the onset of the ED. Another study by Hepp, Spindler, Schnyder, Kraemer, and Milos (2007) did not find differences in trauma between the different ED samples. However, the data show a more complex psychopathology when trauma is reported. Also, Backholm, Isomaa, and Birgegård (2013) did not report significant differences in trauma history between AN, BN, BED, and EDNOS in a large sample of 4,524 ED patients recruited from 41 ED treatment units across Sweden. However, the trauma group displayed significantly more restraint, eating concern, weight concern, and shape concern compared to the nontrauma group.

In summary: Most studies were cross-sectional. In many studies, attention has been given mostly to CSA, and less to CEA and CFA, and very few studies focused on the hidden trauma. Data show a higher prevalence of trauma in AN compared to normal subjects, but no differences in prevalence of trauma compared to other psychiatric diagnoses such as BPD. AN patients with any form of trauma report more severe AN symptoms, more bulimia, and binge eating and emotional dysregulation. Hence, trauma is much more common in AN patients of the bingeing/purging type compared to AN patients of the restricting type. The quality of attachment seems to mediate between trauma and the ED.

■ PREVALENCE OF TRAUMA AND ITS CONSEQUENCES IN BULIMIA NERVOSA

As with AN, practically all BN studies are cross-sectional, whereas longitudinal studies are lacking. As already mentioned in the previous paragraph, a primary and established finding is the fact that when different types of EDs are compared with each other, data systematically show that the prevalence of trauma histories is significantly higher among patients with disorders involving bulimic symptoms of binge eating and purging than in those patients diagnosed with AN restricting type (Caslini et al., 2016; Grilo & Masheb, 2002; Mitchell, Mazzeo, Schlesinger, Brewerton, & Smith, 2012; Rayworth, Wise, & Harlow, 2004; Striegel-Moore, Dohm, Pike, Wilfley, & Fairburn, 2002; Wonderlich, Brewerton, Jocic, Dansky, & Abbott, 1997). Consistent with these findings, childhood traumatic experiences appear to be related to an increase in binge/purge behaviors (Messman-Moore & Garrigus, 2007; Rhode et al., 2008; Smyth, Heron, Wonderlich, Crosby, & Thompson, 2008).

The presence of traumatic experiences in BN patients has been extensively documented, but the vast majority of these studies have focused only on the relationship between sexual and physical abuse and BN. Few studies have evaluated the more "hidden" traumata, such as emotional abuse and neglect. In one of the first studies on the relationship between traumatic experiences and BN, Root and Fallon (1988) reported that among a total of 172 women with bulimia, 23% were raped, 29% were sexually molested, 29% were physically abused, and 23% were battered. A study by Steiger, Jabalpurwala, and Champagne (1996) reported that 24.6% of 61 bulimic patients had been sexually abused before the age of 13 years, whereas 31.1% reported physical abuse. Other studies reported that, respectively, 61% (Anderson, LaPorte, Brandt, & Crawford, 1997) and 44% (Sullivan, Bulik, Carter, & Joyce, 1995) of BN patients enrolled in their programs reported CSA.

A number of case–control studies corroborate previous findings, showing that, relative to normal eaters and to the general population, bulimic patients reported higher levels of both CSA and CPA (Friedman, Wilfley, Welch, & Kunce, 1997; Léonard, Steiger, & Kao, 2003; Mahon, Bradley, Harvey, Winston, & Palmer, 2001; Miller, McCluskey-Fawcett, & Irving, 1993; Nickel et al., 2006; Schoemaker, Smit, Bijl, & Vollebergh, 2002; Steiger et al., 2008; Welch, Doll, & Fairburn, 1997), CEA (Groleau et al., 2012), CEN (Webster & Palmer, 2000), bullying by peers (Fairburn, Welch, Doll, Davies, & O'Connor, 1997), and multiple forms of abuse (Rorty, Yager, & Rossotto, 1994).

A few studies demonstrated some contrasting findings. Casper and Lyubomirsky (1997) showed that family and individual psychopathology, such as depressive symptoms, suicidality, and impulsive behavior, and not sexual abuse significantly predicted bulimia. The data in a study by Pope, Mangweth, Negrão, Hudson, and Cordás, (1994) did not support the hypothesis that bulimic subjects had endured more severe sexual abuse than other women, nor was there a significant association between history of CSA and severity of bulimic symptoms. Fairburn et al. (1997), in a study comparing 102 BN patients with 204 HC subjects and with 102 people with other psychiatric disorders, reported more exposure to CSA, CPA, and bullying in BN patients than in HC subjects. However, no significant difference was found when compared to patients with a group of mixed psychiatric disorders. Only one study by Vaz Leal et al. (2004) did not find a difference regarding the severity of bulimic symptoms when comparing sexually abused to nonabused BN clients.

Waller (1992), in a clinical sample of 40 women with bulimia, found that a history of unwanted sexual experiences was associated with more frequent binge eating, and, to a lesser extent, vomiting. These symptoms were further marked when the abuse was intra-familial, involved force, or occurred before the victim was 14 years old. More recently, Feldman and Meyer (2007), working with a sample of 193 men, reported that those with a history of CSA are significantly more likely to have subclinical BN compared with men who do not have a history of CSA. Wonderlich et al. (2007), in a study conducted with a sample of 123 BN patients using the Ecological Momentary Assessment, showed that sexual abuse was associated with increased daily purging frequency, rather than with binge eating behaviors. Other researchers (Favaro, Ferrara, & Santonastaso, 2003) have found that a history of physical maltreatment in adulthood significantly increases the risk of reporting lifetime BN, whereas physical or sexual abuse before the age of 18 is significantly associated with both AN and BN.

Several mediating variables in the relationship between traumatic experiences and the development of BN have been documented, such as bodily shame (Andrews, 1997), ineffectiveness, affective instability (Groleau et al., 2012), negative core beliefs, including negative self-image and self-blame (Waller et al., 2001), depression, dissociation, and lack of family support (Vanderlinden, Vandereycken, & Pobst, 1995). Not surprisingly, then, when bulimic patients report a history of abuse, research data show that they are at higher risk of developing more comorbidity including self-injurious behaviors (Claes & Muehlenkamp, 2014), substance abuse, suicide attempts, borderline characteristics, dissociative symptoms, body dissatisfaction, depression, and low self-esteem (Mahon et al. 2001; Matsunaga et al., 1999; Richardson et al., 2008; Utzinger et al., 2016; Vanderlinden et al., 2007).

In addition, several studies on the relationship between trauma and BN have been carried out in nonclinical samples. Garfinkel et al. (1995) in a large cohort study of 8,116 Canadian subjects showed that women with both full and partial bulimic syndrome were significantly more likely to have experienced CSA than a normal female comparison group. Moreover, the association between CSA and a chaotic family environment increases the probability of developing an ED, particularly bulimia (Hastings & Kern, 1994). Sanci et al. (2008), in a longitudinal cohort study of 1,936 adolescents, found that the incidence of BN during adolescence was 2.5 times higher among individuals who reported at least one episode of CSA, and 4.9 times higher among persons who reported two or more episodes of CSA compared with females who did not report any episode of CSA. At the same time, Schoemaker et al. (2002), in a population-based study of 1,987 subjects, found that a history of psychological, physical, and sexual abuse was a specific risk factor for development of BN.

It is worth noting that Kent, Waller, and Dagnan (1999) studied the full range of abusive experiences in a nonclinical sample and found that emotional abuse was the only form of childhood trauma that predicted unhealthy eating attitudes. Other studies in various population samples (urban, rural, and statewide) have shown that sexual victimization places girls at risk for various unhealthy eating behaviors, such as purging and dieting, along with body dissatisfaction (Thompson, Wonderlich, Crosby, & Mitchell, 2001; Wonderlich et al., 2001).

In summary: Practically all studies are cross-sectional, whereas longitudinal studies are missing. Few studies were conducted in male BN patients; however, showed the same findings as in females. Data in both clinical and nonclinical samples show that between 30% and 60% of the subjects with BN report some form of abuse significantly higher compared to NC samples, but not different compared to other psychiatric samples, such as personality disorders. Consistent with the findings in the previous paragraph, childhood traumatic experiences are related to an increase in binge/purge behaviors and more comorbidity, such as self-injury and other impulse dyscontrol behaviors. Different mediating variables between trauma and BN have been identified, such as bodily shame; ineffectiveness; affective instability; negative core beliefs, including negative self-image and self-blame; depression; dissociation; and the quality of family relationships. Some authors suggest that it is not the trauma itself that needs to be treated, but the consequences of the trauma experience.

■ PREVALENCE OF TRAUMA AND ITS CONSEQUENCES IN BINGE EATING DISORDERS

BED is an ED category recently included in the classification of EDs of the *DSM-5* (APA, 2013). BED is characterized by recurrent episodes of binge eating associated with a strong sense of loss of control over the eating during the episodes, which, unlike BN, are not followed by regular use of inappropriate compensatory behaviors. It has been established that approximately 30% of obese subjects meet the criteria for BED diagnosis (de Zwaan, 2001), whereas more or less than 50% of the BED are obese (Hudson, Hiripi, Pope, & Kessler, 2007). Although BED is a recent separate diagnosis, an important number of studies of both its prevalence and the relationship between traumatic experiences and BED have been published. Research data show that childhood abuse is associated with BED, and abuse is roughly two to three times more frequently reported in the BED samples compared to control samples (Becker & Grilo, 2011; Grilo & Masheb, 2001, 2002). For instance, in one of the first case–control studies in this field (Dalle Grave, Oliosi, Todisco, & Vanderlinden, 1997), severe traumatic experiences such as incest, rape, physical abuse, psychological abuse, and neglect were reported by 41% of obese patients with BED, whereas only 14% of subjects in the obese control sample reported trauma experiences. Fairburn et al. (1998) in a study in which they compared 102 women with BN and 40 women with BED to 102 women with other psychiatric disorders, as well as 104 women without an ED, found that BED patients were more likely to report CSA and repeated, severe CPA, and bullying compared to HC subjects.

In addition to CSA and CPA, repeated exposure to negative comments about shape, weight, and eating, must also be considered as risk factors for BED (Pike et al., 2006).

Mitchell et al. (2012), using data from the National Comorbidity Replication Study with both male (n = 2,382) and female (n = 3,310) participants, found that both male and female BED participants (n = 105) showed significantly more exposure to any form of interpersonal trauma compared with the general population, particularly rape, as well as physical abuse by parents and/or partners. Striegel-Moore et al. (2002), in a case–control study involving 162 women with BED, showed that 57% (sexually) and 65% (physically) of BED women were abused in childhood, and 65% had been bullied by peers in childhood or adolescence. Moreover, scores on measures of sexual and physical abuse, as well as bullying by peers, were significantly higher than those reported by a healthy comparison group of 251 women.

Allison, Grilo, Masheb, and Stunkard (2007), in a case–control study in which 176 women with BED were compared to 57 women with night eating syndrome (NES) and to 37 women with obesity, but neither BED nor NES, found that BED individuals reported rates of CEA, CEN, and CPN ranging between 50% and 69%, whereas the percentage of both CSA and CPA was approximately 30%. Reported rates of physical and sexual abuse differed little across groups, whereas reports of neglect and emotional abuse were higher in the BED and NES groups than in the obese comparison group and were associated with elevated depression levels.

Two cross-sectional studies (Grilo & Masheb, 2001, 2002) conducted in samples of 145 and 116 BED patients, respectively, reported rates of CEA, CPN, and CEN similar to those reported by Allison et al. (2007) and two to three times higher than the rates of a normative sample of 1,125 women. However, Grilo and Masheb (2001) showed that none of the five forms of maltreatment were associated with age at the onset of the first binge eating episode, nor with the severity of binge eating behaviors. Another cross-sectional study (Becker & Grilo, 2011) showed that obese women with BED who reported sexual, physical, and emotional abuse had higher body mass index (BMI) and waist circumference compared to nonabused obese women with BED. Expectedly, these forms of childhood abuse in the family of origin were positive predictors of later obesity. On the contrary, Knoph Berg et al. (2011), in a large and representative sample of pregnant women ($N = 45,644$), 931 (2.0%) of whom had a BED diagnosis, found that physical abuse and sexual abuse increased the odds of BED by 1.68 times (physical abuse) and 1.57 times (sexual abuse; see also Gabert et al., 2013).

Finally, Brewerton, Rance, Dansky, O'Neil, and Kilpatrick (2014) in the National Women's Study ($N = 53,006$) found that women with child or adolescent onset of binge eating when compared with women with adult onset of binge eating reported higher rates of molestation (26.4% vs. 18.4%), physical assault (17.5% vs. 11.1%), victimization (68.9% vs. 57.7%), and lifetime PTSD (31% vs. 23%).

In summary: Most of the studies in BED are cross-sectional. High prevalence rates of trauma have been found in BED, roughly two to three times more frequently compared to control samples. Not only CSA, CFA, and emotional abuse but also the minor traumas, such as negative comments about body shape, can increase the risk of developing BED. Studies on mediating factors between trauma and BED are missing. All these findings further support the hypothesis that both childhood and adult maltreatment are associated with a greater risk in developing BED symptomatology (Palmisano et al., 2016).

Trauma and Dissociation in ED Subjects

One of the key concepts in understanding the impact of trauma on mind and body is dissociation. Dissociation is usually defined as a "disruption of and/or discontinuity in the normal integration of consciousness, memory, identity, emotion, perception, body representation, motor control, and behavior, which is normally well integrated in a healthy person" (APA, 2013, p. 291). Dissociation consists of both psychological symptoms (psychoform dissociation), such as identity confusion and fragmentation, and psychogenic amnesia, as well as somatoform symptoms (somatoform dissociation), such as freezing reactions, and experiences of analgesia and anesthesia. Dissociation has been strongly related to childhood trauma (Terock et al., 2016; van IJzendoorn & Schuengel, 1996). Numerous studies have shown that ED clients with a history of trauma report severe dissociative symptoms when compared with HC subjects (Beato, Rodríguez Cano, & Belmonte, 2003; Demitrack, Putnam, Brewerton, Brandt, & Gold, 1990; Vanderlinden, 1993), as well as with other psychiatric samples (Farrington et al., 2002; La Mela, Maglietta, Castellini, Amoroso, & Lucarelli, 2010; Spitzer et al., 2006), with 7% to 20% of ED individuals meeting criteria for a dissociative disorder (Dalle Grave, Rigamonti, Todisco, & Oliosi, 1996; Vanderlinden et al., 1993). On this basis, it has been proposed that dissociative mechanisms may contribute to disordered eating both in clinical (Everill, Waller, & MacDonald, 1995; Fuller-Tyszkiewicz & Mussap, 2008) and in nonclinical samples (Franzoni et al., 2013; Lyubomirsky, Casper, & Sousa, 2001; Rosen & Petty, 1994).

Unfortunately, the nature of this contribution appears complex and difficult to characterize. Dissociation seems not to be a specific characteristic of a particular type of ED, but is transdiagnostic and is rather linked with behaviors such as binge eating and purging, as present in BN, AN-BP, and BED (Koskina, Mountford, & Tchanturia, 2016). In this respect, several studies have found dissociation to be higher in ED patients with a history of childhood trauma and BN and AN-BP diagnosis than in patients with restrictive anorexia and no early history of trauma (Chandarana & Malla, 1989; Everill et al., 1995; Groth-Marnat & Michel, 2000; McManus, 1995; McShane & Zirkel, 2008; Nagata et al., 2001; Oliosi & Dalle Grave, 2003; Richardson et al., 2008; Santonastaso, Favaro, Olivotto, & Friederici, 1997; Vanderlinden et al., 1993; Vanderlinden et al., 1995). Similar results were found with obese patients with BED compared to obese patients without a BED diagnosis (Dalle Grave et al., 1996, 1997). Some authors have also focused on the potential mediating role of dissociation in the relationship between childhood trauma and the development of disordered eating. For instance, Moulton, Newman, Power, Swanson, and Day (2015) found that both emotional dysregulation and dissociation were significant mediators between emotional abuse and eating psychopathology in a sample of 142 female undergraduate students.

It is also noteworthy that dissociation has been found to play an important role as antecedent to both overeating and the severity of binge eating episodes (Engelberg, Steiger, Gauvin, & Wonderlich, 2007; Mason et al., 2017; McShane & Zirkel, 2008; Waller et al., 2001) and may act as both a trigger and maintenance factor for binge eating (McManus & Waller, 1995). In addition, patients often report a state of depersonalization and derealization before and during binge eating episodes (Hallings-Pott, Waller, Watson, & Scragg, 2005; Lyubomirsky et al., 2001), as well as phenomena of postbinge amnesia and timelessness (Abraham & Beumont, 1982). In a study by La Mela et al. (2010), the level of dissociation was the only variable able to predict the number of binge eating episodes. Palmisano et al. (2018) found that ED clients showed both higher levels of childhood trauma and somatoform and psychoform dissociation when compared with a sex- and age-matched control sample. Interestingly, the severity of the binge eating symptoms was best predicted by the severity of both trauma experiences and dissociative symptoms. Data from several other studies collectively corroborate this finding, supporting the notion that dissociation was a significant mediator between childhood trauma and binge eating symptoms (Everill et al., 1995; Kent et al., 1999; Lyubomirsky et al., 2001), but data from other studies have failed to support this hypothesis (Gerke, Mazzeo, & Kliewer, 2006; Rodriguez-Srednicki, 2001).

Although traumatic experiences and dissociation appear to be related to binge eating, the nature of this association remains still unclear. Functional models of binge eating behaviors suggest two ways of understanding this link. In their "escape from self-awareness theory," Heatherton and Baumeister (1991) hypothesized that people with BN may engage in binge eating to avoid confrontation with painful emotions and traumatic memories. According to this model, when negative emotional states are activated, a shift from abstract levels (e.g., self-evaluation) toward lower levels of awareness, cognition, and attention (e.g., physical stimuli, food) is initiated, and this shift involves cognitive processes similar to dissociation (Everill & Waller, 1995; Hallings-Pott et al., 2005; Pallister & Waller, 2008). This mechanism tends to remove the inhibitions and facilitates the start of binge eating without having to face immediately the longer term consequences and guilt associated with loss of control, "being bad," and weight gain (Heatherton & Baumeister, 1991). This conceptualization of bulimic symptomatology suggests that dissociation precedes the initial onset of binge eating, and it is supported by recent evidence both in clinical (Engelberg et al., 2007; Hallings-Pott et al., 2005; Holmes, Fuller-Tyszkiewicz, Skouteris, & Broadbent, 2015) and in nonclinical subjects (Lyubomirsky et al., 2001). Some experiments in which threat cues were introduced to subjects with bulimic symptoms showed that they elicited both dissociation and overeating (Hallings-Pott et al., 2005).

The second hypothesis that attempts to explain the link between childhood trauma, dissociation, and binge eating behaviors is the "blocking model" (Lacey, 1986; Root & Fallon, 1989). According to this theory, binge eating anesthetizes the strong, negative feelings of inferiority and guilt associated with childhood trauma (Vanderlinden et al., 1993). Consistent with this model, dissociation seems to appear more often during binge eating than before bingeing (Groth-Marnat & Michel, 2000; Kennedy, Kennerley, & Pearson, 2013; McShane & Zirkel, 2008; Pallister & Waller, 2008). This model seems to offer an explanation for the maintenance of binge eating, rather than a theory about the origin of this disorder (Kennedy et al., 2013; Lyubomirsky et al., 2001).

Thus, it is possible that both mechanisms, escape from awareness and blocking model, need to be considered for a full understanding of the link between dissociation and binge eating behaviors (Pallister & Waller, 2008). Other authors have also focused on the relationship between dissociation and problems related to body image. Indeed, dissociation, in co-occurrence with childhood trauma and low self-esteem, has been found to predict body shape concerns and body dissatisfaction (Beato et al., 2003; Franzoni et al., 2013). All these findings are consistent with the hypothesis that dissociation might be associated with the degree of dissatisfaction toward one's own body in ED subjects, and it might represent a way of coping or avoiding the confrontation with a negative self-image.

In contrast with the interest in studying the relationship between childhood trauma and dissociation in EDs, very few studies investigated the prevalence of somatic manifestations of dissociation in these types of psychopathology. Somatoform dissociation refers to the physiological components of dissociation, which includes symptoms of anesthesia, analgesia, chronic pain, and freezing, all in response to traumatic events (Nijenhuis, Spinhoven, van Dyck, van der Hart, & Vanderlinden, 1998a; Waller et al., 2000). In this regard, some authors found a greater incidence of both childhood trauma and somatoform dissociation in EDs compared to the general population (Nijenhuis et al, 1999; Nijenhuis, Spinhoven, van Dyck, van der Hart, & Vanderlinden, 1998b; Palmisano et al., 2017). Other authors found that somatoform dissociation is closely related to purging behaviors (Waller et al., 2003) and that body dissatisfaction is the main mediator between somatoform dissociation and the severity of binge eating symptoms (Fuller-Tyszkiewicz & Mussap, 2008). Fuller-Tyszkiewicz and Mussap (2011) have found that somatoform dissociation was associated with bodily related ED symptoms and that these associations were mediated by body image instability.

On the basis of these findings, some authors have postulated that specific ED symptoms, such as body dissatisfaction and binge/purge behaviors, may better reflect trauma-related disruptions of body awareness deriving from the somatic aspect of dissociation (Fuller-Tyszkiewicz & Mussap, 2009; Mussap & Salton, 2006; Treuer, Koperdák, Rózsa, & Füredi, 2005). They consequently stress the need for the assessment of both psychological and somatoform dissociation in ED patients with bulimic symptoms.

In summary: Research data show that both psychological and somatoform dissociative symptoms are more present in ED with childhood trauma and significantly more in EDs with bingeing and purging characteristics. Two hypotheses are formulated suggesting two explanations: One sees dissociation as the initiator of binge eating, whereas the other sees dissociation as maintaining the disorder. More research is needed to further explore these hypotheses.

■ DISCUSSION AND SUGGESTIONS FOR FUTURE RESEARCH

Over the past decades, research data have grown and systematically demonstrated that exposure to traumatic experiences, especially during childhood, can be considered a nonspecific retrospective risk factor in the development of a wide variety of psychiatric and medical conditions, including EDs. This statement has been confirmed by our literature review and a recent meta-analysis about the prevalence of childhood maltreatment in EDs, wherein a total of 13,059 ED clients were included (Molendijk, Hoek, Brewerton, & Elzinga, 2017). Molendijk et al. (2017) reported that the prevalence rates of CSA, CPA, and CEA were, respectively, 31%, 26%, and 45% for all ED categories. Moreover, the prevalence rates of any childhood trauma for each type of ED was higher (21%–59%), statistically speaking, than those reported by healthy (1%–35%) and psychiatric (5%–46%) control groups. ED patients with child molestation (CM) were more likely to be diagnosed with a comorbid psychiatric disorder and to be suicidal relative to ED subjects who were not exposed to CM. ED subjects exposed to CM reported an earlier age of ED onset, a more severe form of their illness, and more frequent binge/purge behaviors compared to ED subjects who did not report CM (Molendijk et al., 2017).

Another recent review and meta-analysis by Caslini et al. (2016) corroborates all these findings, showing a consistent and positive association respectively between CEA and both BN and BED, CSA and BN, and between CPA and all forms of EDs. Only one review and meta-analysis focused on the prevalence of early emotional and physical neglect in the EDs, reporting that the prevalence rates varied, respectively, from 20.7% to 74% for physical neglect and from 33.3% to 69% for emotional neglect (Pignatelli et al., 2017). In line with all these findings, data on the prevalence of abuse in BED clients are impressive, varying between 35% and 82% (Allison et al., 2007; Grilo & Masheb, 2001, 2002), reaching peaks of approximately 100% (Mitchell et al., 2012). A recent review by Palmisano et al. (2016) showed a strong association between childhood trauma and the development of BED in nine of the 10 studies included in the review. This association appears to be particularly strong when the abuse started at an early age and when the abuse was more severe.

Besides the data on trauma in ED subjects, many authors have focused also on the presence of dissociative symptoms. The research is showing that ED subjects who report trauma report higher levels of both psychological and somatoform dissociation. It is hypothesized that the eating symptoms, such as bingeing, purging, and fasting, may serve as survival strategies when no physical escape is possible. Hence, research data demonstrate that dissociative experiences function as a mediating role between the trauma and ED. Other data clearly show that early attachment experiences function as a mediator between the trauma experience and the development of the eating pathology (Pignatelli et al., 2017).

■ CONCLUSION

All these findings, in both clinical and nonclinical studies, strongly support the following hypotheses:

1. Child maltreatment and a wide variety of minor trauma experiences, not just sexual abuse, are associated with various aspects of bulimia-related psychopathology, such as bingeing and purging. Consequently, these adverse events must be considered significant risk factors for the development of BN in EDs (Brewerton & Brady, 2014).
2. Childhood maltreatment increases the risk for the development of more severe and complex psychopathological characteristics, such as emotional dysregulation, dissociative symptoms, and impulse dyscontrol problems, bingeing, purging, automutilation, drug abuse, and suicidality. It is hypothesized that these trauma-related symptoms serve as maintaining factors for the ED and that they are of primary importance to effective treatment (Trottier & MacDonald, 2017)
3. An increase in the number of traumatic events has an additive effect, hence leading to more complex problems.
4. Early attachment experiences (the quality of interpersonal relationships), negative self-referencing beliefs (involving shame and guilt), and dissociation may function as mediating factors between the trauma experience and the development of the EDs.

One important limitation in most studies is that they are cross-sectional in nature. Longitudinal prospective studies are needed to arrive at conclusions about risk factors, causality, and maintenance factors (Trottier & MacDonald, 2017). In many studies, different definitions of trauma are used and different methods are used to retrospectively measure the presence of trauma. Hence, a clear and broad definition of trauma is needed to include the seemingly "minor" traumata. In particular, more attention needs to be given to the study and impact of emotional abuse in EDs (Pignatelli et al., 2017). More research is needed in patients with AN.

Meanwhile, developing more effective treatments for EDs that take into account trauma and dissociation is of primary importance. Hopefully, clinicians are becoming more and more aware of how trauma experiences, especially its consequences, complicate the treatment for many EDs and that novel treatments are needed, integrating evidence from the field of trauma.

■ REFERENCES

Abraham, S. F., & Beumont, P. J. V. (1982). How patients describe bulimia or binge eating. *Psychological Medicine*, 12(3), 625–635. doi:10.1017/S0033291700055732

Allison, K. C., Grilo, C. M., Masheb, R. M., & Stunkard, A. J. (2007). High self-reported rates of neglect and emotional abuse, by persons with binge eating disorder and night eating syndrome. *Behaviour Research and Therapy*, 45, 2874–2883. doi:10.1016/j.brat.2007.05.007

American Psychiatric Association. (2013). *Diagnostic and statistical manual of mental disorders* (5th ed.). Arlington, VA: American Psychiatric Publishing.

Anderson, K. P., LaPorte, D. J., Brandt, H., & Crawford, S. (1997). Sexual abuse and bulimia: Response to inpatient treatment and preliminary outcome. *Journal of Psychiatric Research, 31*(6), 621–633. doi:10.1016/S0022-3956(97)00026-5

Andrews, B. (1997). Bodily shame in relation to abuse in childhood and bulimia: A preliminary investigation. *British Journal of Clinical Psychology, 36*(1), 41–49. doi:10.1111/j.2044-8260.1997 .tb01229.x

Armour , C., Müllerová, J., Fletcher, S., Lagdon, S., Burns, C. R., Robinson, M., & Robinson, J. (2016). Assessing childhood maltreatment and mental health correlates of disordered eating profiles in a nationally representative sample of English females. *Social Psychiatry and Psychiatric Epidemiology, 51*(3), 383–393. doi:10.1007/s00127-015-1154-7

Backholm, K., Isomaa, R., & Birgegård, A. (2013). The prevalence and impact of trauma history in eating disorder patients. *European Journal of Psychotraumatology, 4*(1), 22482. doi:10.3402/ejpt .v4i0.22482

Beato, L., Rodríguez Cano, T., & Belmonte, A. (2003). Relationship of dissociative experiences to body shape concerns in eating disorders. *European Eating Disorders Review, 11*(1), 38–45. doi:10.1002/erv.508

Becker, D. F., & Grilo, C. M. (2011). Childhood maltreatment in women with binge-eating disorder: Associations with psychiatric comorbidity, psychological functioning, and eating pathology. *Eating and Weight Disorders, 16*(2), e113–e120. doi:10.1007/BF03325316

Brewerton, T. D. (2006). Comorbid anxiety and depression and the role of trauma in children and adolescents with eating disorders. In *Eating disorders in children and adolescents* (pp. 158–168).

Brewerton, T. D., & Brady, K. (2014). The role of stress, trauma and PTSD in the etiology and treatment of eating disorders, addictions and substance abuse disorders. In T. D. Brewerton & A. B. Dennis (Eds.), *Eating disorders, addictions and substance use disorders* (pp. 379–404). Heidelberg, Germany: Springer Verlag.

Brewerton, T. D., Rance, S. J., Dansky, B. S., O'Neil, P. M., & Kilpatrick, D. G. (2014). A comparison of women with child-adolescent versus adult onset binge eating: Results from the National Women's Study. *International Journal of Eating Disorders, 47*(7), 836–843. doi:10.1002/eat.22309

Carter, J. C., Bewell, C., Blackmore, E., & Woodside, D. B. (2006). The impact of childhood sexual abuse in anorexia nervosa. *Child Abuse & Neglect, 30*(3), 257–269. doi:10.1016/j.chiabu.2005.09.004

Caslini, M., Bartoli, F., Crocamo, C., Dakanalis, A., Clerici, M., & Carrà, G. (2016). Disentangling the association between child abuse and eating disorders: A systematic review and meta-analysis. *Psychosomatic Medicine, 78*(1), 79–90. doi:10.1097/PSY.0000000000000233

Casper, R. C., & Lyubomirsky, S. (1997). Individual psychopathology relative to reports of unwanted sexual experiences as predictor of a bulimic eating pattern. *International Journal of Eating Disorders, 21*(3), 229–236. doi:10.1002/(SICI)1098-108X(199704)21:3<229::AID-EAT3

Chandarana, P., & Malla, A. (1989). Bulimia and dissociative states: A case report. *Canadian Journal of Psychiatry, 34*(2), 137–139. doi:10.1177/070674378903400214

Claes, L., & Muehlenkamp, J. J. (2014). Non-suicidal self-injury and eating disorders: Dimensions of self-harm. In L. Claes & J. J. Muehlenkamp (Eds), *Non-suicidal self-injury in eating disorders* (pp. 3–18). Heidelberg, Germany: Springer.

Collins, B., Fischer, S., Stojek, M., & Becker, K. (2014). The relationship of thought suppression and recent rape to disordered eating in emerging adulthood. *Journal of Adolescence, 37*, 113–121. doi:10.1016/j.adolescence.2013.11.002

Corstorphine, E., Waller, G., Lawson, R., & Ganis, C. (2007). Trauma and multi-impulsivity in the eating disorders. *Eating Behaviors, 8*(1), 23–30. doi:10.1016/j.eatbeh.2004.08.009

Dalle Grave, R., Oliosi, M., Todisco, P., & Vanderlinden, J. (1997). Self-reported traumatic experiences and dissociative symptoms in obese women with and without binge-eating disorder. *Eating Disorders: The Journal of Treatment and Prevention, 5*(2), 105–109. doi:10.1080/10640269708249213

Dalle Grave, R., Rigamonti, R., Todisco, P., & Oliosi, E. (1996). Dissociation and traumatic experiences in eating disorders. *European Eating Disorders Review, 4*, 232–240.

de Zwaan, M. (2001). Binge eating disorder and obesity. *International Journal of Obesity and Related Metabolic Disorders, 25*(Suppl. 1), S51–S55. doi:10.1038/sj.ijo.0801699

Demitrack, M. A., Putnam, F. W., Brewerton, T. D., Brandt, H. A., & Gold, P. W. (1990). Relation of clinical variables to dissociative phenomena in eating disorders. *American Journal of Psychiatry, 147*, 1184–1188. doi:10.1176/ajp.147.9.1184

Engelberg, M. J., Steiger, H., Gauvin, L., & Wonderlich, S. A. (2007). Binge antecedents in bulimic syndromes: An examination of dissociation and negative affect. *International Journal of Eating Disorders, 40*(6), 531–536. doi:10.1002/eat.20399

Everill, J., Waller, G., & MacDonald, W. (1995). Dissociation in bulimic and non-eating disordered women. *International Journal of Eating Disorders, 17*, 127–134. doi:10.1002/1098-108X(199503)17:2<127::AID-EAT2260170204

Fairburn, C. G., Doll, H. A., Welch, S. L., Hay, P. J., Davies, B. A., & O'Connor, M. E. (1998). Risk factors for binge eating disorder: A community-based, case-control study. *Archives of General Psychiatry, 55*(5), 425–432. doi:10.1001/archpsyc.55.5.425

Fairburn, C. G., Welch, S. L., Doll, H. A., Davies, B. A., & O'Connor, M. E. (1997). Risk factors for bulimia nervosa: A community-based case-control study. *Archives of General Psychiatry, 54*(6), 509–517. doi:10.1001/archpsyc.1997.01830180015003

Farrington, A., Waller, G., Neiderman, M., Sutton, V., Chopping, J., & Lask, B. (2002). Dissociation in adolescent girls with anorexia: Relationship to comorbid psychopathology. *Journal of Nervous and Mental Disease, 190*(11), 746–751. doi:10.1097/01.NMD.0000038169.47040.7C

Favaro, A., Ferrara, S., & Santonastaso, P. (2003). The spectrum of eating disorders in young women: A prevalence study in a general population sample. *Psychosomatic Medicine, 65*(4), 701–708. doi:10.1097/01.PSY.0000073871.67679.D8

Feldman, M. B., & Meyer, I. H. (2007). Childhood abuse and eating disorders in gay and bisexual men. *International Journal of Eating Disorders, 40*(5), 418–423. doi:10.1002/eat.20378

Forman-Hoffman, V. L., Mengeling, M., Booth, B. M., Torner, J., & Sadler, A. G. (2012). Eating disorders, post-traumatic stress, and sexual trauma in women veterans. *Military Medicine, 177*(10), 1161–1168. doi:10.7205/MILMED-D-12-00041

Franzoni, E., Gualandi, S., Caretti, V., Schimmenti, A., Di Pietro, E., Pellegrini, G., … Pellicciari, A. (2013). The relationship between alexithymia, shame, trauma, and body image disorders: Investigation over a large clinical sample. *Neuropsychiatric Disease and Treatment, 9*(1), 185–193. doi:10.2147/NDT.S34822

Friedman, M. A., Wilfley, D. E., Welch, R. R., & Kunce, J. T. (1997). Self-directed hostility and family functioning in normal-weight bulimics and overweight binge eaters. *Addictive Behaviors, 22*(3), 367–375. doi:10.1016/S0306-4603(97)80001-9

Fuller-Tyszkiewicz, M., & Mussap, A. J. (2008). The relationship between dissociation and binge eating. *Journal of Trauma & Dissociation, 9*(4), 445–462. doi:10.1080/15299730802226084

Fuller-Tyszkiewicz, M., & Mussap, A. J. (2009). Short communications on the relationship between dissociation and binge eating. In N. Chambers (Ed.), *Binge eating: Psychological factors, symptoms and treatment* (pp. 1–11). New York, NY: Nova Science.

Fuller-Tyszkiewicz, M., & Mussap, A. J. (2011). Examining the dissociative basis for body image disturbances. *International Journal of Psychological Studies, 3*(2), 3–13. doi:10.5539/ijps.v3n2p3

Gabert, D. L., Majumdar, S. R., Sharma, A. M., Rueda-Clausen, C. F., Klarenbach, S. W., Birch, D. W., … Padwal, R. S. (2013). Prevalence and predictors of self-reported sexual abuse in severely obese patients in a population-based bariatric program. *Journal of Obesity, 2013*, 374050. doi:10.1155/2013/374050

Garfinkel, P. E., Lin, E., Goering, P., Spegg, C., Goldbloom, D. S., Kennedy, S., … Woodside, D. B. (1995). Bulimia nervosa in a Canadian community sample: Prevalence and comparison of subgroups. *American Journal of Psychiatry, 152*(7), 1052–1058. doi:10.1176/ajp.152.7.1052

Gerke, C. K., Mazzeo, S. E., & Kliewer, W. (2006). The role of depression and dissociation in the relationship between childhood trauma and bulimic symptoms among ethnically diverse female undergraduates. *Child Abuse & Neglect, 30*(10), 1161–1172. doi:10.1016/j.chiabu.2006.03.010

Grilo, C. M., & Masheb, R. M. (2001). Childhood psychological, physical and sexual maltreatment in outpatients with binge eating disorder: Frequency and associations with gender, obesity and eating-related psychopathology. *Obesity Research, 9*(5), 320–325. doi:10.1038/oby.2001.40

Grilo, C. M., & Masheb, R. M. (2002). Childhood maltreatment and personality disorders in adult patients with binge eating disorder. *Acta Psychiatrica Scandinavica, 106*, 183–188. doi:10.1002/eat.20796

Groleau, P., Steiger, H., Bruce, K., Israel, M., Sycz, L., Ouellette, A. S., & Badawi, G. (2012). Childhood emotional abuse and eating symptoms in bulimic disorders: An examination of possible mediating variables. *International Journal of Eating Disorders, 45*(3), 326–332. doi:10.1002/eat.20939

Groth-Marnat, G., & Michel, N. (2000). Dissociation, comorbidity of dissociative disorders, and childhood abuse in a community sample of women with current and past bulimia. *Social Behavior and Personality, 28*(3), 279–292. doi:10.2224/sbp.2000.28.3.279

Guillaume, S., Jaussent, I., Maimoun, L., Ryst, A., Seneque, M., Villain, L., … Courtet, P. (2016). Associations between adverse childhood experiences and clinical characteristics of eating disorders. *Scientific Reports, 6*, 35761. doi:10.1038/srep35761

Hallings-Pott, C., Waller, G., Watson, D., & Scragg, P. (2005). State dissociation in bulimic eating disorders: An experimental study. *International Journal of Eating Disorders, 38*, 37–41. doi:10.1002/eat.20146

Hastings, T., & Kern, J. M. (1994). Relationship between bulimia, childhood sexual abuse and family environment. *International Journal of Eating Disorders, 13*, 103–111. doi:10.1002/1098-108X(199403)15:2<103::AID-EAT2260150202>3.0.CO;2-1

Heatherton, T. F., & Baumeister, R. F. (1991). Binge eating as escape from self-awareness. *Psychological Bulletin, 110*, 86–108. doi:10.1037/0033-2909.110.1.86

Hepp, U., Spindler, A., Schnyder, U., Kraemer, B., & Milos, G. (2007). Post-traumatic stress disorder in women with eating disorders. *Eating and Weight Disorders, 12*(1), e24–e27. doi:10.1007/BF03327778

Holmes, M., Fuller-Tyszkiewicz, M., Skouteris, H., & Broadbent, J. (2015). Understanding the link between body image and binge eating: A model comparison approach. *Eating and Weight Disorders, 20*(1), 81–89. doi:10.1007/s40519-014-0141-4

Hudson, J. I., Hiripi, E., Pope, H. G., & Kessler, R. C. (2007). The prevalence and correlates of eating disorders in the National Comorbidity Survey Replication. *Biological Psychiatry, 61*(3), 348–358. doi:10.1016/j.biopsych.2006.03.040

Jaite, C., Schneider, N., Hilbert, A., Pfeiffer, E., Lehmkuhl, U., & Salbach-Andrae, H. (2012). Etiological role of childhood emotional trauma and neglect in adolescent anorexia nervosa: A cross-sectional questionnaire analysis. *Psychopathology, 45*(1), 61–66. doi:10.1159/000328580

Karwautz, A., Rabe-Hesketh, S., Hu, X., Zhao, J., Sham, P., Collier, D. A., & Treasure, J. L. (2001). Individual-specific risk factors for anorexia nervosa: A pilot study using a discordant sister-pair design. *Psychological Medicine, 31*(2), 317–329. doi:10.1017/S0033291701003129

Kennedy, F., Kennerley, H., & Pearson, D. (2013). *Cognitive behavioural approaches to the understanding and treatment of dissociation*. New York, NY: Routledge.

Kent, A., Waller, G., & Dagnan, D. (1999). A greater role of emotional than physical or sexual abuse in predicting disordered eating attitudes: The role of mediating variables. *International Journal of Eating Disorders, 25*(2), 159–167. doi:10.1002/(SICI)1098-108X(199903)25:2<159::AID-EAT5>3.0.CO;2-F

Knoph Berg, C., Torgersen, L., Von Holle, A., Hamer, R. M., Bulik, C. M., & Reichborn-Kjennerud, T. (2011). Factors associated with binge eating disorder in pregnancy. *International Journal of Eating Disorders, 44*(2), 124–133. doi:10.1002/eat.20797

Kong, S., & Bernstein, K. (2009). Childhood trauma as a predictor of eating psychopathology and its mediating variables in patients with eating disorders. *Journal of Clinical Nursing, 18*(13), 1897–1907. doi:10.1111/j.1365-2702.2008.02740.x

Koskina, A., Mountford, V., & Tchanturia, K. (2016). The impact of perceptual, cognitive and behavioural factors on dissociative experiences and body disturbance in eating disorders: An exploratory study. *Advances in Eating Disorders, 4*(1), 59–74. doi:10.1080/21662630.2015.1116016

Lacey, J. H. (1986). Pathogenesis. In L. J. Downey & J. C. Malkin (Eds.), *Current approaches: Bulimia nervosa* (pp. 17–27). Southampton, UK: Duphar.

La Mela, C., Maglietta, M., Castellini, G., Amoroso, L., & Lucarelli, S. (2010). Dissociation in eating disorders: Relationship between dissociative experiences and binge-eating episodes. *Comprehensive Psychiatry, 51*(4), 393–400. doi:10.1016/j.comppsych.2009.09.008

Laporte, L., & Guttman, H. (2001). Abusive relationships in families of women with borderline personality disorder, anorexia nervosa and a control group. *Journal of Nervous and Mental Disease, 189*(8), 522–531. doi:10.1097/00005053-200108000-00005

Lyubomirsky, S., Casper, R. C., & Sousa, L. (2001). What triggers abnormal eating in bulimic and nonbulimic women? The role of dissociative experiences, negative affect, and psychopathology. *Psychology of Women Quarterly, 25*, 223–232. doi:10.1111/1471-6402.00023

Mahon, J., Bradley, S. N., Harvey, P. K., Winston, A. P., & Palmer, R. L. (2001). Childhood trauma has dose-effect relationship with dropping out from psychotherapeutic treatment for bulimia nervosa: A replication. *International Journal of Eating Disorders, 30*(2), 138–148. doi:10.1002/eat.1066

Mason, T. B., Lavender, J. M., Wonderlich, S. A., Steiger, H., Cao, L., Engel, S. G., ... Crosby, R. D. (2017). Comfortably numb: The role of momentary dissociation in the experience of negative affect around binge eating. *Journal of Nervous and Mental Disease, 205*(5), 335–339. doi:10.1097/NMD.0000000000000658

Matsunaga, H., Kaye, W. H., McConaha, C., Plotnicov, K., Pollice, C., Rao, R., & Stein, D. (1999). Psychopathological characteristics of recovered bulimics who have a history of physical or sexual abuse. *Journal of Nervous and Mental Disease, 187*(8), 472–477. doi:10.1097/00005053-199908000-00003

McManus, F. (1995). Dissociation and the severity of bulimic psychopathology among eating disordered and non-eating disordered women. *European Eating Disorders Review, 3*(3), 185–195. doi:10.1002/erv.2400030307

McManus, F., & Waller, G. (1995). A functional analysis of binge-eating. *Clinical Psychology Review, 15*(8), 845–863. doi:10.1016/0272-7358(95)00042-9

McShane, J. M., & Zirkel, S. (2008). Dissociation in the binge-purge cycle of bulimia nervosa. *Journal of Trauma and Dissociation, 9*(4), 463–479. doi:10.1080/15299730802225680

Meltzer-Brody, S., Zerwas, S., Leserman, J., Holle, A. V., Regis, T., & Bulik, C. (2011). Eating disorders and trauma history in women with perinatal depression. *Journal of Women's Health, 20*(6), 863–870. doi:10.1089/jwh.2010.2360

Messman-Moore, T. L., & Garrigus, A. S. (2007). The association of child abuse and eating disorder symptomatology: The importance of multiple forms of abuse and revictimization. *Journal of Aggression, Maltreatment & Trauma, 14*(3), 51–72. doi:10.1300/J146v14n03_04

Miller, D. A., McCluskey-Fawcett, K., & Irving, L. M. (1993). The relationship between childhood sexual abuse and subsequent onset of bulimia nervosa. *Child Abuse & Neglect, 17*(2), 305–314. doi:10.1016/0145-2134(93)90050-F

Mitchell, K. S., Mazzeo, S. E., Schlesinger, M. R., Brewerton, T. D., & Smith, B. N. (2012). Comorbidity of partial and subthreshold PTSD among men and women with eating disorders in the national comorbidity survey-replication study. *International Journal of Eating Disorders, 45*, 307–315. doi:10.1002/eat.20965

Molendijk, M. L., Hoek, H. W., Brewerton, T. D., & Elzinga, B. M. (2017). Childhood maltreatment and eating disorder pathology: A systematic review and dose-response meta-analysis. *Psychological Medicine, 47*(8), 1402–1416. doi:10.1017/S0033291716003561

Monteleone, A. M., Monteleone, P., Serino, I., Scognamiglio, P., Di Genio, M., & Maj, M. (2015). Childhood trauma and cortisol awakening response in symptomatic patients with anorexia nervosa and bulimia nervosa. *International Journal of Eating Disorders, 48*(6), 615–621. doi:10.1002/eat.22375

Moulton, S. J., Newman, E., Power, K., Swanson, V., & Day, K. (2015). Childhood trauma and eating psychopathology: A mediating role for dissociation and emotion dysregulation? *Child Abuse & Neglect, 39*, 167–174. doi:10.1016/j.chiabu.2014.07.003

Mussap, A. J., & Salton, N. (2006). A 'rubber-hand' illusion reveals a relationship between perceptual body image and unhealthy body change. *Journal of Health Psychology, 11*(4), 627–639. doi:10.1177/1359105306065022

Nagata, T., Kaye, W. H., Kiriike, N., Rao, R., McConaha, C., & Plotnicov, K. H. (2001). Physical and sexual abuse histories in patients with eating disorders: A comparison of Japanese and American patients. *Psychiatry and Clinical Neurosciences, 55*(4), 333–340. doi:10.1046/j.1440-1819.2001.00872.x

Nickel, C., Simek, M., Moleda, A., Muehlbacher, M., Buschmann, W., Fartacek, R., ... Nickel, M. K. (2006). Suicide attempts versus suicidal ideation in bulimic female adolescents. *Pediatrics International, 48*(4), 374–381. doi:10.1111/j.1442-200X.2006.02224.x

Nijenhuis, E. R. S., Spinhoven, P., van Dyck, R., van der Hart, O., & Vanderlinden, J. (1998a). Degree of somatoform and psychological dissociation in dissociative disorder is correlated with reported trauma. *Journal of Traumatic Stress, 11*(4), 711–730. doi:10.1023/A:1024493332751

Nijenhuis, E. R. S., Spinhoven, P., van Dyck, R., van der Hart, O., & Vanderlinden, J. (1998b). Psychometric characteristics of the somatoform dissociation questionnaire: A replication study. *Psychotherapy & Psychosomatics, 67*(1), 17–23. doi:10.1159/000012254

Nijenhuis, E. R. S., van Dyck, R., Spinhoven, P., van der Hart, O., Chatrou, M., Vanderlinden, J., & Moene, F. (1999). Somatoform dissociation discriminates among diagnostic categories over and above general psychopathology. *Australian and New Zealand Journal of Psychiatry, 33*(4), 511–520. doi:10.1080/j.1440-1614.1999.00601.x

Oliosi, M., & Dalle Grave, R. (2003). A comparison of clinical and psychological features in subgroups of patients with anorexia nervosa. *European Eating Disorders Review, 11*, 306–314. doi:10.1002/erv.528

Pallister, E., & Waller, G. (2008). Anxiety in the eating disorders: Understanding the overlap. *Clinical Psychology Review, 28*(3), 366–386. doi:10.1016/j.cpr.2007.07.001

Palmisano, G. L., Innamorati, M., Susca, G., Traetta, D., Sarracino, D., & Vanderlinden, J. (2018). Childhood traumatic experiences and dissociative phenomena in eating disorders: Level and association with the severity of binge eating symptoms. *Journal of Trauma & Dissociation, 19*(1), 88–107 doi:10.1080/15299732.2017.1304490

Palmisano, G. L., Innamorati, M., & Vanderlinden, J. (2016). Life adverse experiences in relation with obesity and binge eating disorder: A systematic review. *Journal of Behavioral Addiction, 5*(1), 11–31. doi:10.1556/2006.5.2016.018

Pettinati, H. M., Horne, R. L., & Staats, J. M. (1985). Hypnotizability in patients with anorexia nervosa and bulimia. *Archives of General Psychiatry, 42*(10), 1014–1016. doi:10.1001/archpsyc.1985.01790330094011

Pignatelli, A. M., Wampers, M., Loriedo, C., Biondi, M., & Vanderlinden, J. (2017). Childhood neglect in eating disorders: A systematic review and meta-analysis. *Journal of Trauma and Dissociation, 18*(1), 100–115. doi:10.1080/15299732.2016.1198951

Pike, K. M., Wilfley, D., Hilbert, A., Fairburn, C. G., Dohm, F. A., & Striegel-Moore, R. H. (2006). Antecedent life events of binge eating disorder. *Psychiatry Research, 142*(1), 19–29. doi:10.1016/j.psychres.2005.10.006

Pope, H. G., Jr., Mangweth, B., Negrão, A. B., Hudson, J. I., & Cordás, T. A. (1994). Childhood sexual abuse and bulimia nervosa: A comparison of American, Austrian, and Brazilian women. *American Journal of Psychiatry, 151*(5), 732–737. doi:10.1176/ajp.151.5.732

Racine, S. E., & Wildes, J. E. (2015). Emotion dysregulation and anorexia nervosa: An exploration of the role of childhood abuse. *International Journal of Eating Disorders, 48*(1), 55–58. doi:10.1002/eat.22364

Rayworth, B. B., Wise, L. A., & Harlow, B. L. (2004). Childhood abuse and risk of eating disorders in women. *Epidemiology, 15*(3), 271–278. doi:10.1097/01.ede.0000120047.07140.9d

Reyes-Rodríguez, M. L., Von Holle, A., Ulman, T. F., Thornton, L. M., Klump, K. L., Brandt, H., ... Bulik, C. M. (2011). Posttraumatic stress disorder in anorexia nervosa. *Psychosomatic Medicine, 73*(6), 491–497. doi:10.1097/PSY.0b013e31822232bb

Rhode, P., Ichikawa. L., Simon, G. E., Ludman, E. J., Linde, J. A., Jeffery, R. W., & Operskalski, B. H. (2008). Association of child sexual and physical abuse with obesity and depression in middle aged women. *Child Abuse and Neglect, 32*(9), 878–887. doi:10.1016/j.chiabu.2007.11.004

Richardson, J., Steiger, H., Schmitz, N., Joober, R., Bruce, K. R., Israel, M., ... de Guzman, R. (2008). Relevance of the 5-HTTLPR polymorphism and childhood abuse to increased psychiatric comorbidity in women with bulimia-spectrum disorders. *Journal of Clinical Psychiatry, 69*(6), 981–990. doi:10.4088/JCP.v69n0615

Rodriguez-Srednicki, O. (2001). Childhood sexual abuse, dissociation and adult self-destructive behavior. *Journal of Child Sexual Abuse, 10*(3), 75–90. doi:10.1300/J070v10n03_05

Romans, S. E., Gendall, K. A., Martin, J. L., & Mullen, P. E. (2001). Child sexual abuse and later disordered eating: A New Zealand epidemiological study. *International Journal of Eating Disorders, 29*(4), 380–392. doi:10.1002/eat.1034

Root, M. P. P., & Fallon, P. (1988). The incidence of victimization experiences in a bulimic sample. *Journal of Interpersonal Violence, 3*(2), 161–173. doi:10.1177/088626088003002003

Root, M. P. P., & Fallon, P. (1989). Treating the victimized bulimic: The functions of binge-purge behaviour. *Journal of Interpersonal Violence, 4*, 90–100. doi:10.1177/088626089004001006

Rorty, M., Yager, J., & Rossotto, E. (1994). Childhood sexual, physical, and psychological abuse in bulimia nervosa. *American Journal of Psychiatry, 151*(8), 1122–1126. doi:10.1176/ajp.151.8.1122

Rosen, E. F., & Petty, L. C. (1994). Dissociative states and disordered eating. *American Journal of Clinical Hypnosis, 36*, 266–275. doi:10.1080/00029157.1994.10403086

Sanci, L., Coffey, C., Olsson, C., Reid, S., Carlin, J. B., & Patton, G. (2008). Childhood sexual abuse and eating disorders in females: Findings from the Victorian Adolescent Health Cohort Study. *Archives of Pediatrics & Adolescent Medicine, 162*(3), 261–267. doi:10.1001/archpediatrics.2007.58

Santonastaso, P., Favaro, A., Olivotto, M. C., & Friederici, S. (1997). Dissociative experiences and eating disorders in a female college sample. *Psychopathology, 30*(3), 170–176. doi:10.1159/000285044

Schmidt, U., Tiller, J., & Treasure, J. (1993). Setting the scene for eating disorders: Childhood care, classification and course of illness. *Psychological Medicine, 23*(3), 663–672. doi:10.1017/S0033291700025447

Schoemaker, C., Smit, F., Bijl, R. V., & Vollebergh, W. A. M. (2002). Bulimia nervosa following psychological and multiple child abuse: Support for the self-medication hypothesis in a population-based cohort study. *International Journal of Eating Disorders, 32*(4), 381–388. doi:10.1002/eat.10102

Smyth, J. M., Heron, K. E., Wonderlich, S. A., Crosby, R. D., & Thompson, K. M. (2008). The influence of reported trauma and adverse events on eating disturbance in young adults. *International Journal of Eating Disorders, 41*(3), 195–202. doi:10.1002/eat.20490

Spitzer, C., Barnow, S., Grabe, H. J., Klauer, T., Stieglitz, R. D., Schneider, W., & Freyberger, H. J. (2006). Frequency, clinical and demographic correlates of pathological dissociation in Europe. *Journal of Trauma & Dissociation, 7*(1), 51–62. doi:10.1300/J229v07n01_05

Steiger, H., Jabalpurwala, S., & Champagne, J. (1996). Axis II comorbidity and developmental adversity in bulimia nervosa. *Journal of Nervous and Mental Disease, 184*(9), 555–560. doi:10.1097/00005053-199609000-00007

Steiger, H., Richardson, J., Joober, R., Israel, M., Bruce, K. R., Ng Ying Kin, N. M. K., … Gauvin, L. (2008). Dissocial behavior, the 5HTTLPR polymorphism, and maltreatment in women with bulimic syndromes. *American Journal of Medical Genetics Part B: Neuropsychiatric Genetics, 147B*(1), 128–130. doi:10.1002/ajmg.b.30579

Steiger, H., Richardson, J., Schmitz, N., Israel, M., Bruce, K. R., & Gauvin, L. (2010). Trait-defined eating-disorder subtypes and history of childhood abuse. *International Journal of Eating Disorders, 43*(5), 428–432. doi:10.1002/eat.20711

Steiger, H., & Zanko, M. (1990). Sexual traumata among eating-disordered, psychiatric, and normal female groups: Comparison of prevalences and defense styles. *Journal of Interpersonal Violence, 5*(1), 74–86. doi:10.1177/088626090005001006

Striegel-Moore, R. H., Dohm, F. A., Pike, K. M., Wilfley, D. E., & Fairburn, C. G. (2002). Abuse, bullying and discrimination as risk factors for binge eating disorders. *American Journal of Psychiatry, 159*, 1902–1907. doi:10.1176/appi.ajp.159.11.1902

Sullivan, P. F., Bulik, C. M., Carter, F. A., & Joyce, P. R. (1995). The significance of a history of childhood sexual abuse in bulimia nervosa. *British Journal of Psychiatry, 167*(5), 679–682. doi:10.1192/bjp.167.5.679

Tasca, G. A., Ritchie, K., Zachariades, F., Proulx, G., Trinneer, A., Balfour, L., … Bissada, H. (2013). Attachment insecurity mediates the relationship between childhood trauma and eating disorder psychopathology in a clinical sample: A structural equation model. *Child Abuse & Neglect, 37*(11), 926–933. doi:10.1016/j.chiabu.2013.03.004

Terock, J., Van der Auwera, S., Janowitz, D., Spitzer, C., Barnow, S., Miertsch, M., … Grabe, H. J. (2016). From childhood trauma to adult dissociation: The role of PTSD and Alexithymia. *Psychopathology, 49*(5), 374–382. doi:10.1159/000449004

Thompson, K. M., Wonderlich, S. A., Crosby, R. D., & Mitchell, J. E. (2001). Sexual victimization and adolescent weight regulation practices: A test across three community based samples. *Child Abuse & Neglect, 25*(2), 291–305. doi:10.1016/S0145-2134(00)00243-X

Treuer, T., Koperdák, M., Rózsa, S., & Füredi, J. (2005). The impact of physical and sexual abuse on body image in eating disorders. *European Eating Disorders Review, 13*, 106–111. doi:10.1002/erv.616

Trottier, K., & MacDonald, D. E. (2017). Update on psychological trauma, other severe adverse experiences and eating disorders: State of the research and future research directions. *Current Psychiatry Reports, 19*(8), 45. doi:10.1007/s11920-017-0806-6

Utzinger, L. M., Haukebo, J. E., Simonich, H., Wonderlich, S. A., Cao, L., Lavender, J. M., … Crosby, R. D. (2016). A latent profile analysis of childhood trauma in women with bulimia nervosa: Associations with borderline personality disorder psychopathology. *International Journal of Eating Disorders, 49*(7), 689–694. doi:10.1002/eat.22532

van der Kolk, B. (2014). *The body keeps the score. Mind, brain and body in the transformation of trauma.* London, UK: Penguin Random House.

van Gerko, K., Hughes, M. L., Hamill, M., & Waller, G. (2005). Reported childhood sexual abuse and eating-disordered cognitions and behaviors. *Child Abuse & Neglect, 29*(4), 375–382. doi:10.1016/j.chiabu.2004.11.002

Vanderlinden, J. (1993). *Dissociative experiences, trauma and hypnosis. Research findings and clinical applications in eating disorders.* Delft, Netherlands: Eburon.

Vanderlinden, J., Vandereycken, W., & Claes, L. (2007). Trauma, dissociation, and impulse dyscontrol: Lessons from the eating disorders field. In E. Vermetten, M. J. Dorahy, & D. Spiegel (Eds.), *Traumatic dissociation: Neurobiology and treatment.* Washington, DC: American Psychiatric Publishing.

Vanderlinden, J., Vandereycken, W., & Pobst, M. (1995). Dissociative symptoms in eating disorders: A follow-up study. *European Eating Disorders Review, 3,* 174–184. doi:10.1002/erv.2400030306

Vanderlinden, J., Vandereycken, W., van Dyck, R., & Vertommen, H. (1993). Dissociative experiences and trauma in eating disorders. *International Journal of Eating Disorders, 13*(2), 187–193. doi:10.1002/1098-108X(199303)13:2<187::AID-EAT2260130206>3.0.CO;2-9

Van IJzendoorn, M. H., & Schuengel, C. (1996). The measurement of dissociation in normal and clinical populations: Meta-analytic validation of the Dissociative Experiences Scale (DES). *Clinical Psychology Review, 16*(5), 365–382. doi:10.1016/0272-7358(96)00006-2

Vaz Leal, F. J., Guisado Macías, J. A., García-Herraiz, M. A., López Vinuesa, B., Monge Bautista, M., & Bolívar Perálvarez, M. (2005). History of sexual abuse in patients with bulimia nervosa: Its influence on clinical status. *Actas Españolas de Psiquiatría, 33*(3), 135–140.

Waller, G. (1992). Sexual abuse and the severity of bulimic symptoms. *British Journal of Psychiatry, 161*(1), 90–93. doi:10.1192/bjp.161.1.90

Waller, G., Babbs, M., Wright, F., Potterton, C., Meyer, C., & Leung, N. (2003). Somatoform dissociation in eating-disordered patients. *Behaviour Research and Therapy, 41*(5), 619–627. doi:10.1016/S0005-7967(03)00019-6

Waller, G., Hamilton, K., Elliott, P., Lewendon, J., Stopa, L., Waters, A., … Chalkley, J. (2000). Somatoform dissociation, psychological dissociation, and specific forms of trauma. *Journal of Trauma & Dissociation, 1*(4), 81–98. doi:10.1300/J229v01n04_05

Waller, G., Meyer, C., Ohanian, V., Elliott, P., Dickson, C., & Sellings, J. (2001). The psychopathology of bulimic women who report childhood sexual abuse: The mediating role of core beliefs. *Journal of Nervous and Mental Disease, 189*(10), 700–708. doi:10.1097/00005053-200110000-00007

Webster, J. J., & Palmer, R. L. (2000). The childhood and family background of women with clinical eating disorders: A comparison with women with major depression and women without psychiatric disorder. *Psychological Medicine, 30*(1), 53–60. doi:10.1017/S0033291799001440

Welch, S. L., Doll, H. A., & Fairburn, C. G. (1997). Life events and the onset of bulimia nervosa: A controlled study. *Psychological Medicine, 27*(3), 515–522. doi:10.1017/S0033291796004370

Wentz, E., Gillberg, I. C., Gillberg, C., & Råstam, M. (2005). Fertility and history of sexual abuse at 10-year follow-up of adolescent-onset anorexia nervosa. *International Journal of Eating Disorders, 37*(4), 294–298. doi:10.1002/eat.20093

Wonderlich, S. A., Brewerton, T. D., Jocic, Z., Dansky, B. S., & Abbott, D. W. (1997). Relationship of childhood sexual abuse and eating disorders. *Journal of the American Academy of Child & Adolescent Psychiatry, 36*(8), 1107–1115. doi:10.1097/00004583-199708000-00018

Wonderlich, S., Crosby, R., Mitchell, J., Thompson, K., Redlin, J., Demuth, G., & Smyth, J. (2001). Pathways mediating sexual abuse and eating disturbance in children. *International Journal of Eating Disorders, 29*(3), 270–279. doi:10.1002/eat.1018

Wonderlich, S. A., Rosenfeldt, S., Crosby, R. D., Mitchell, J. E., Engel, S. G., Smyth, J., & Miltenberger, R. (2007). The effects of childhood trauma on daily mood lability and comorbid psychopathology in bulimia nervosa. *Journal of Traumatic Stress, 20*(1), 77–87. doi:10.1002/jts.20184

SECTION TWO

Trauma Treatment in Eating Disorders: A Complex Affair

In and of themselves, eating disorders (EDs) require a coordinated team approach. When complicated by trauma, the therapeutic landscape becomes much more daunting. Chapter 3 emphasizes the need for the clinician to be aware of the presence of attachment injury, developmental trauma, and dissociative states. You cannot heal what you do not know. Chapter 4 focuses on the absolute centrality of the attachment-sensitive, therapeutic relationship necessary for a sense of safety, particularly with clients with ED.

CHAPTER 3

Recognizing the Territory: The Interaction of Trauma, Attachment Injury, and Dissociation in Treating Eating Disorders

Holly A. Finlay

▪ SARAH—A CASE STUDY

Sarah, a 15-year-old with anorexia and exercise addiction, was referred to me by her physician after she had passed out on her exercise bike and was hospitalized. At 5 feet 8 inches in height and weighing 82 pounds, it was recommended that she seek an intensive inpatient program. However, Sarah and her family had no money, and she was not able to afford the treatment. I agreed to see Sarah three times per week, working collaboratively with a dietitian and her primary care physician.

In the initial consultation, it appeared that Sarah had an avoidant style and was hesitant to reveal too much of herself. Although Sarah was reticent to change, it was what her parents wanted, and she did not want to disappoint them, especially her father. Sarah's father had left his first wife. Consequently, her mother, a practicing Catholic and first-time bride, was desperate to make the marriage work. Her mother was a passive, uneducated, and childlike woman, and about 30 years younger than Sarah's father. Her father was patriarchal, emotionally disconnected, rigid, and work-driven. He ran the family with an iron fist, and the two women protected each other from his hot temper by covering up for each other in matters they deemed private.

Sarah's father owned a small business, and Sarah and her mother were expected to be there to help every weekend. Unfortunately, the business was shut down because of mismanagement and the family was being sued. Sarah had very few memories of having any childhood friendships other than her next-door neighbor, Carly, who was of the same age. Sarah and Carly spent all their free time together playing hide and seek and jumping on the trampoline in Carly's backyard. When Sarah was 12 years old, she started her period and her body began to develop curves that drew the attention of Carly's 15-year-old brother, Sam.

Sam began "playing" with the girls and led Sarah into the closet to hide on multiple occasions where he molested her, while his sister took an excessive amount of time *finding* them. Sarah was overwhelmed with shame but could not tell her parents. She attended a private Christian school, and her parents were closed-minded and religious. She could not face the consequences of disappointing her parents with being sullied by what she had "allowed to happen." Sarah was determined to make up for her mistakes and never let it happen again. Even if it meant losing her best friend.

Sarah began focusing on her father's diet. He was an unhealthy 75-year-old diabetes patient, and she was determined to save him from his poor eating habits. Her mother allowed Sarah to do all the food preparation and feed the family as she saw fit. She became obsessed with diet and exercise. At the time of her hospitalization, she was exercising on a stationary bike for 12 hours per day and eating 300 to 400 calories daily. She would pass out on her bike and tumble to the floor. Her parents would pick her up and put her back on the bike, or face the consequences of her irritable and anxious mood. She began ruling the family with her demands for special foods or refusing to eat altogether. She would stop riding at 2 a.m. and eat a small plate of potatoes, ride until 4 a.m., sleep, and repeat this routine the next day.

The therapy focused on nutritional rehabilitation, weight restoration, and improving her depressed, anxious, and irritable moods. Sarah had difficulty identifying and expressing her feelings and frequently became frustrated in treatment. It proved easier for her to speak through the eating disorder (ED) symptoms than to struggle in therapy with stringing together descriptions and expressing emotions. Over time, her ED symptoms began to ameliorate, and she began experiencing body memories from the sexual abuse. Sitting became intolerable. She could feel the area of her body that had been molested against the surface on which she was sitting. This was uncomfortable and triggering to her. She began to discuss the molestation and devastating shame surrounding what she felt she "didn't stop from happening." She described the paralyzing terror she experienced in the closet and her self-hatred for doing nothing to stop it. She loathed herself for no longer being the perfect child her parents knew and labeled herself as "damaged goods." She was determined to fix the painful past, chronic feelings of not measuring up, and to earn feeling worthy by recovering *perfectly*.

However, losing her coping tools (restricting food and exercising) at the time she needed them the most was intolerable. Another memory of an oral rape at the age of 6 began haunting her with flashbacks and body memories. This happened close to home in a neighborhood alley. She ran home and told her mother. However, her simple nonnurturing mother who was terrified of the religious implications and her volatile father told her never to tell anyone. She felt unsafe without the anorexic part of her which "fixed" and erased the womanly body.

During this time, she came up with a project that would distract her and help her channel her energy into something positive. She would make a garden in her backyard and grow healthy food for the family. The only place in the yard for the garden butted up against the wall separating her house from Carly and Sam's house. She began shoveling the "bad dirt" in a trance-like dissociative state from what she perceived as the perpetrator's side of the yard, filling it in with "good dirt" from the opposite neutral side of the yard. The physical activity driven by her anxiety resulted in significant weight loss, which was relieving to her but drove her into a full relapse.

After her second hospitalization, she was granted scholarship into a treatment program and could work on her anorexic symptoms. She was discharged at normal weight and began working on the trauma, which had naturally surfaced. Not unexpectedly, Sarah again threatened her recovery by dabbling in her eating-disordered behavior to cope with her powerful feelings of shame.

■ THE GENESIS OF AN EATING DISORDER

What is it that causes some people to develop an ED, and others to manage eating behaviors in a relatively normal manner? The answer is anything but simple. EDs are a biopsychosocial illness. They are the result of a complex interplay of factors including genes, temperament, social interactions, early attachment, culture, and of course life experiences. These variables come together and affect each other in a *perfect storm* fashion and may result in ED psychopathology.

Genetics and Neurobiological Deficits

"Lots of people diet or want to lose weight, but relatively few of them end up with anorexia nervosa or bulimia nervosa," says Walter Kaye, MD. "Culture plays some role—but maybe less so than we thought in the past" (Weir, 2016, p. 2). Behaviors such as dieting and weight loss seem to expose a genetic vulnerability to an ED. "We think genes load the gun by creating behavioral susceptibility, such as perfectionism or the drive for thinness. Environment then pulls the trigger" (Lamberg, 2003, p. 1437). "Rigorous studies suggest that greater than 50 percent of the variance in liability to eating disorders and disordered eating behaviors can be accounted for by additive genetic effects" (Berrettini, 2004, p. 24).

At present, researchers are beginning to sort out the brain regions and neural circuits that underlie the illnesses to identify those areas of the brain that may be, in part, responsible for the genesis of an ED. Research indicates that when anorexics and bulimics sit down to eat a meal, they became worried (Frank & Kaye, 2012). Another study by Kaye, Wierenga, Bailer, Simmons, and Bischoff-Grethe (2013) revealed that in a betting game the brains of anorexics responded differently to what would be positive in a normal brain. Conclusively, the brains of those with EDs differed from those without EDs, suggesting neurobiological deficits. Among these are deficits in executive functioning.

Executive tasks include (a) working memory, (b) response inhibition, (c) set shifting, and (d) central coherence. *Set shifting* is a major component of executive functioning and involves the ability to move back and forth between multiple tasks, operations, or mental sets. Problems in set shifting may present as cognitive inflexibility or response inflexibility (Miyake et al., 2000).

In addition, *central coherence* is associated with paying attention to details while integrating global concepts into a broader understanding. An individual with anorexia, for example, who focuses intently on the details of exactly what she has eaten and finds it difficult to consider the long-term health consequences of starvation may be viewed as having weak central coherence (Pender, Gilbert, Serpell, & Abelardo, 2014). In summary, weak set-shifting and a weak internal coherence make it difficult for those with EDs to switch gears. Instead, they perseverate on minor details, subsequently losing the forest for the trees.

Temperament and Personality

Temperament and personality studies have shown that those with EDs have traits and characteristics that may function to maintain the ED. According to the Center for Well-Being at Washington University in St. Louis, "Temperament refers to the automatic emotional responses to experience and is moderately heritable (i.e., genetic, biological) and relatively stable throughout life" (Cloninger, 2015, para. 2).

Cloninger's Temperament and Character Inventory (TCI), which is based on a psychobiological model, attempts to explain the underlying causes of individual differences in personality traits and measures four temperament dimensions showing a heritable bias. These are Novelty Seeking, Harm Avoidance, Reward Dependence, and Persistence (Cloninger, Svrakic, & Przybeck, 1993). Studies using the TCI have exposed characteristics that are common to those with EDs.

The metaphor of the *Turtle and the Hare* aptly describes those with anorexia and bulimia, respectively. People with anorexia nervosa display turtle-like behavior, including high levels of harm avoidance and personality traits characterized by worrying, pessimism, and shyness as well as low levels of novelty seeking. Individuals with bulimia nervosa have high levels of harm avoidance, like anorexia sufferers, but the avoidance tendency is paired with high levels of novelty seeking, including impulsivity and preferring new or novel things (Fassino et al., 2002). The *Turtle and Hare* metaphor is congruent with temperament research, which shows that people with binge ED have higher levels of harm avoidance and novelty seeking and lower levels of self-directedness as compared to healthy controls (Grucza, Przybeck, & Cloninger, 2007).

Emotions

People with EDs have difficulty with emotional regulation. Emotional regulation is the ability to recognize and modulate emotions appropriately and in keeping with personal values. The Difficulties in Emotion Regulation Scale (DERS) is used to measure (a) difficulties in awareness, acceptance, and understanding of emotions and (b) strategies to manage emotions and impulse control, and to maintain goal-directed behavior while in distress. Studies using the DERS show that for women with either anorexia nervosa or bulimia nervosa, more ED symptoms were significantly correlated with higher emotional dysregulation (Fiore, Ruggiero, & Sassaroli, 2014; Racine & Wildes, 2013).

Alexithymia, which is the inability to identify and express feelings in words, is common among our clients. Simultaneously, many of our clients describe feeling "too much," or "like I don't have a skin to protect me from feeling everything," and report being shamed for their unique emotional sensitivity. Consequently, they learn to manage this perceived weakness using ED behaviors. The ED obsession, which is all-consuming, provides internal distance from feeling.

Attachment

Bowlby (1969) found that a secure relationship with at least one adult is crucial for the development of adaptive emotional regulation. Early cries of hunger, followed by the caregiver's attunement or misattunement (experienced by the infant as emotional regulation or a lack thereof), formulates the internal working model or template of the early attachment relationship between the infant, caregiver, and significant others. If the attachment is insecure, a basic sense of trust that allows the child to tolerate separations, regulate affect in a mature way, and thrive in other future attachments will be diminished.

In summary, the caregiver's feeding style, whether attuned or misattuned, sets the stage for the child's feelings of either deserving or being unworthy of loving care. Research has shown that insecure attachment has been found to be positively linked to disordered eating (Ward, Ramsay, & Treasure, 2000). Regarding Sarah, the misattuned attachment with her mother greatly affected her sense of worthiness. It seems that the core belief in clients with EDs is a variant of "I don't measure up, I shouldn't exist, I should be invisible, I am undeserving or unworthy."

The Family System

The importance of family systems for those with EDs is well documented. These families are polarized and unbalanced in terms of power. Children need a unified front to feel secure. They need to know that the parents cannot be split and the children do not have more power to make decisions than one or both parents.

One aspect of a relatively functional family is the ability to successfully navigate the waters of change and normal development of the members without breaking apart. The families of those with EDs become rigidly cohesive in the face of change (Stierlin & Weber, 1989). It is no accident that tweens who are entering adolescence, or teenagers leaving home for the first time, develop an ED. When the natural separation process begins, the parents tug tightly on the reigns of the family system, and the teen struggles to find an alternative way to individuate. The teen may use an ED to disconnect within the family system itself. The security and consistency of ED rules serve as a boundary and a safety net which the family cannot provide.

Families of those with EDs are often perfectionistic and secretive. Feelings are not aired in public or within the family system (Stierlin & Weber, 1989). Acting out thoughts and feelings rather than learning to accurately identify and express emotions becomes the language of the child who develops an ED. Sarah's family was patriarchal and unbalanced. Sarah and her mother shielded each other from her father's rigid ideology, criticism, and control. In addition, cohesion and secretiveness was the order of the day. Sarah knew that her mother needed her to remain in this relational triangle, or the family system would splinter: Consequently, Sarah used anorexia nervosa to disconnect while keeping the family system intact. The eating disorder supplanted an age-appropriate separation and individuation.

▓ TRAUMA

A working definition of trauma, recently defined by the Substance Abuse and Mental Health Services Administration (2014), is as follows: "Individual trauma results from an event, series of events, or set of circumstances that is experienced by an individual as physically or emotionally harmful, or threatening and that has lasting adverse effects on the individual's functioning and physical, social, emotional, or spiritual well-being" (p. 7). This definition is all-encompassing as it includes both "big T" and "little t" events. Trauma, therefore, may include events of epic proportions or developmental insults such as public humiliation, verbal abuse, or sleights.

Brewerton (2007) recently synthesized a review of current information describing the role of stress, trauma, and adversity as risk factors in the development of EDs. The scientific literature has shown that trauma may preclude, or increase the risk of occurrence for, EDs not only in adults, but in adolescents and children as well. In fact, some investigation outcomes suggest that those with EDs have a trauma history and it is the posttraumatic stress disorder (PTSD) that predicts the development of an ED (Brewerton, 2004, 2007). In other words, the PTSD response to underlying traumatic events is a possible predictor of the development of an ED.

Sarah presented with PTSD at the age of 19 years when I began seeing her for therapy. As described earlier, she had experienced both "big T" and "little t" traumatic events in childhood. In terms of attachment, mother was only willing to be available to her when Sarah's needs fit in with father's religious schemata of the perfect family. This included no playtime with friends on weekends and only during the week if father was at work. The oral rape she experienced at the age of 6 years was followed by a lack of repair by her mother and hidden from her father. This response taught her that appearance trumped emotions, and that silence and hiding was a preferred approach to coping rather than exposing the ugly realities of her life, even within her own family. Regrettably, both parents' inability to face life's messiness likely set her up to be revictimized. When Sarah endured repeated molestations by her next-door neighbor at 12 years of age, the only skill set she had was to remain speechless and rely on her own limited ability to self-regulate.

■ THE WINDOW OF TOLERANCE

As mentioned earlier, people with EDs have difficulty with emotional dysregulation. "People with PTSD or trauma-related disorders are characteristically predisposed to experience hyper-arousal ('too much' activation) or hypo-arousal ('too little' activation), or they may oscillate between the two states" (Ogden, Minton, & Pain, 2006, p. 26). The window of tolerance (Figure 3.1), or the zone of optimal arousal, depicts the area between hyper- and hypoarousal in which emotional and physiological arousal are managed without disrupting the entire system. "Cortical functioning is maintained, which is critical for integration of information on cognitive, emotional, and sensorimotor levels" (Ogden et al., 2006, p. 27).

The zone of hyperarousal, which sits above the window of tolerance, corresponds to the response of the autonomic nervous system when the person experiences too much activation. At this level, the sympathetic nervous system is preparing for fight, flight, or freeze. Information cannot be processed effectively, and the person may experience flashbacks, body memories, emotional reactivity, or hypervigilance, all of which are PTSD symptoms.

The zone of hypoarousal, which sits below the window of tolerance, corresponds to the autonomic response when the person is overwhelmed to the point of shutting down. In this state, the client may "experience a numbing sense of deadness or emptiness, passivity, and possibly paralysis" (Ogden et al., 2006, p. 26).

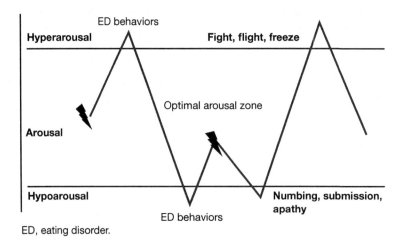

ED, eating disorder.

FIGURE 3.1 The window of tolerance.

Each person has a habitual 'width' of the window of tolerance that influences his or her overall ability to process information. People with a wide window can cope with greater extremes of arousal and can process complex and stimulating information more effectively. "People with a narrow window experience fluctuations as unmanageable and dysregulating. Most traumatized clients have a narrow window and are more susceptible to becoming dysregulated by normal fluctuations in arousal" (Taylor, Koch, & McNally, as cited in Ogden et al., 2006, p. 28). Not surprisingly, our clients with EDs and underlying traumas present with a narrow window of tolerance. To continue functioning optimally, our clients learn to adjust levels of arousal using ED behaviors. Bingeing, purging, and restricting can be used to downregulate, or rev up energetically. The ability to self-modulate difficult emotions gives clients a sense of control and personal effectiveness, which is lacking in people with EDs. Simultaneously, they can escape uncomfortable feelings of dysregulation and operate within predictable parameters with expected outcomes.

The window of tolerance can be used as a cognitive tracking tool for clients to use to monitor emotional intensity. I consistently ask my clients where they are in the window of tolerance to help them learn to identify and regulate themselves outside of the therapy sessions. When our clients become adept at identifying symptoms of dysregulation, they become aware of potential triggers, learn when to self-modulate, and generally feel more in control. Sarah discovered that her anorexic behaviors were in direct response to feeling anxious. Her anxiety was sparked by sensations of heaviness, or in her words "feeling fat," which reminded her of the curvaceous pubescent state her body was in when she was molested by Sam. If Sarah could rid herself of the sensory reminders, she could distance herself from the memories, and the reality of the molestation. Connecting the dots between becoming hyperaroused and being triggered helped her understand the need for distance from her memories. This enabled her to view her anxiety as a red flag, not a true threat to be immediately extinguished. In addition, this knowledge helped her to slow down and work through the anxiety facing her demons using mindfulness and curiosity. Ultimately, Sarah's body dysmorphia decreased and she learned that her body was not the enemy—it was trying to save her from disintegration caused by traumatic events.

■ DISSOCIATION

As described in the previous section, those with EDs have a lower window of tolerance or threshold of response. Consequently, they have heightened vulnerability to traumatic events leading to dissociation and other methods of numbing, including the use of the ED itself.

There has been much discussion in the literature about the most accurate definition of dissociation. Is dissociation an internal event that can only be described subjectively by the client, or is it measured more objectively by symptoms? In other words, is it a *felt* internal state, or an observed external state? For the simplicity of this chapter, "Dissociation in trauma entails a division of an individual's personality, that is, of the dynamic, biopsychosocial system as a whole that determines his or her characteristic mental and behavioral actions" (Nijenhuis & van der Hart, 2011, p. 418).

Sarah modulated her intolerable emotions through food restriction paired with an exercise addiction. This behavior put her into a trance-like dissociative state that helped her to downregulate excessive arousal created by thoughts, intrusive images, or physical sensations. In these extremes, Sarah could disconnect and distance herself from the *sullied self* who was ashamed about freezing in the closet and not stopping the abuse. If she separated herself from the sullied self, she could function. When she did not follow her anorexic rules, however, the sullied self or part threatened to break through the dissociative barrier she had created and overwhelm her with intolerable emotions, memories, and physical sensations.

■ PUTTING ALL THE PIECES TOGETHER

Moulton, Newman, Power, Swanson, and Day (2014) found that both emotional dysregulation and dissociation were significant mediators between childhood trauma and eating psychopathology. In addition, emotional dysregulation has been reported to mediate the relationship between insecure attachment and EDs (Ty & Francis, 2013). Bowlby (1973) considered the idea that when caregiving interactions are insensitively attuned, the infant could develop multiple incompatible internal representations of self and attachment figures, instead of unitary or cohesive attachment. A connection between attachment and dissociation is implied in this language.

Finally, as stated earlier, PTSD has been found to be a predicting factor for the risk of EDs. Exactly what does all this mean? If you boil down this complex soup of variables and mediating factors, it seems that our clients with EDs often begin life with a misattuned caregiver leading to emotional dysregulation and increased emotional vulnerabilities. Subsequently, they are much more likely to experience life as jarring because of the inability to adjust and adapt. As a result, our clients learn to respond in psychopathological ways that serve them by protecting and preserving their abilities to function in the world.

In a nutshell, the ED, which appears to contain elements of dissociation, is a means of adapting to trauma. Is it any wonder that, when our clients' ED symptoms remit, traumatic experiences, whether epic events or with developmental origins, rise to the surface? Sarah could not make lasting progress until the ED was addressed and she was able to resource herself using a skill set that would help her stay physiologically grounded. The trauma could then be attended to, and the family system could be deconstructed and reorganized.

■ THE WHOLE ENCHILADA: TRAUMA, ATTACHMENT INJURY, AND DISSOCIATION

The cycle of being flooded with early, unprocessed trauma upon remittance of ED symptoms, followed by relapse, reduces the foundation of treatment to shifting sand. Unless the trauma and the ED are treated simultaneously, treatment becomes futile at best: fraught with multiple relapses, behavioral substitutions, feelings of hopelessness, and premature termination.

The subsequent chapters of this book offer treatment components and methods to clinicians who need to address this complex and dynamic system, or, put more simply, the *whole enchilada*.

■ REFERENCES

Berrettini, W. (2004). The genetics of eating disorders. *Psychiatry (Edgmont), 1*(3), 18–25. Retrieved from https://www.ncbi.nlm.nih.gov/pmc/articles/PMC3010958

Bowlby, J. (1969). *Attachment and loss: Vol. 1 attachment.* New York, NY: Basic Books.

Bowlby, J. (1973). *Attachment and loss: Vol. 2 separation: Anxiety and anger.* New York, NY: Basic Books.

Brewerton, T. D. (2004). Eating disorders, victimization, and comorbidity: Principles of treatment. In T. D. Brewerton (Ed.), *Clinical handbook of eating disorders: An integrated approach* (pp. 511–548). New York, NY: Routledge.

Brewerton, T. D. (2007). Eating disorders, trauma, and comorbidity: Focus on PTSD. *Eating Disorders, 15,* 285–304. doi:10.1080/10640260701454311

Cloninger, C. R., Svrakic, D. M., & Przybeck, T. R. (1993). A psychobiological model of temperament and character. *Archives of General Psychiatry, 50*(12), 975–990. doi:10.1001/archpsyc.1993.01820240059008

Cloninger, R. (2015). What is the temperament and character inventory [Video]. Retrieved from http://psychobiology.wustl.edu/what-is-the-tci

Fassino, S., Abbate-Daga, G., Amianto, F., Leombruni, P., Boggio, S., & Rovera, G. G. (2002). Temperament and character profile of eating disorders: A controlled study with the Temperament and Character Inventory. *International Journal of Eating Disorders, 32*(4), 412–425. doi:10.1002/eat.10099

Fiore, F., Ruggiero, G. M., & Sassaroli, S. (2014). Emotional dysregulation and anxiety control in the psychopathological mechanism underlying drive for thinness. *Front Psychiatry, 5,* 43. doi:10.3389/fpsyt.2014.00043

Frank, G. K., & Kaye, W. H. (2012). Current status of functional imaging in eating disorders. *International Journal of Eating Disorders, 45,* 723–736. doi:10.1002/eat.22016

Grucza, R. A., Przybeck, T. R., & Cloninger, C. R. (2007). Prevalence and correlates of binge eating disorder in a community sample. *Comprehensive Psychiatry, 48*(2), 124–131. doi:10.1016/j.comppsych.2006.08.002

Kaye, W. H., Wierenga, C. E., Bailer, U. F., Simmons, A. N., & Bischoff-Grethe, A. (2013). Nothing tastes as good as skinny feels: The neurobiology of anorexia nervosa. *Trends in Neuroscience, 36*(2), 110–120. doi:10.1016/j.tins.2013.01.003

Lamberg, L. (2003). Advances in eating disorders offers food for thought. *Journal of the American Medical Association, 290*(11), 1437–1442. doi:10.1001/jama.290.11.1437

Miyake, A., Friedman, N. P., Emerson, M. J., Witzki, A. H., Howerter, A., & Wager, T. D. (2000). The unity and diversity of executive functions and their contributions to complex "Frontal Lobe" tasks: A latent variable analysis. *Cognitive Psychology, 41*(1), 49–100. doi:10.1006/cogp.1999.0734

Moulton, S. J., Newman, E., Power, K., Swanson, V., & Day, K. (2014). Childhood trauma and eating psychopathology: A mediating role for dissociation and emotion dysregulation? *Childhood Abuse & Neglect, 39,* 167–174. doi:10.1016/j.chiabu.2014.07.003

Nijenhuis, E. R., & van der Hart, O. (2011). Dissociation in trauma: A new definition and comparison with previous formulations. *Journal of Trauma & Dissociation, 12*(4), 416–445. doi:10.1080/15299732.2011.570592

Ogden, P., Minton, K., M., & Pain, C. (2006). *Trauma and the body: A sensorimotor approach to psychotherapy.* New York, NY: W. W. Norton.

Pender, S., Gilbert, S. J., Serpell, L., & Abelardo, I. (2014). The neuropsychology of starvation: Set-shifting and central coherence in a fasted nonclinical sample. *PLOS ONE, 9*(10), e110743. Retrieved from http://journals.plos.org/plosone/article?id=10.1371/journal.pone.0110743

Racine, S. E., & Wildes, J. E. (2013). Emotion dysregulation and symptoms of anorexia nervosa: The unique roles of lack of emotional awareness and impulse control difficulties when upset. *International Journal of Eating Disorders, 46*(7), 713–720. doi:10.1002/eat.22145

Substance Abuse and Mental Health Services Administration. (2014). SAMHSA's concept of trauma and guidance for a trauma-informed approach. *Trauma and Justice Strategic Initiative.* Retrieved from https://store.samhsa.gov/shin/content/SMA14-4884/SMA14-4884.pdf

Stierlin, H., & Weber, G. (1989). *Unlocking the family door: A systemic approach to the understanding and treatment of anorexia nervosa* (pp. 19–38). New York, NY: Brunner/Mazel.

Taylor, S., Koch, W. J., & McNally, R. J. (1992). How does anxiety sensitivity vary across the anxiety disorders? *Journal of Anxiety Disorders, 6*, 249–259. doi:10.1016/0887-6185(92)90037-8

Ty, M., & Francis, A. J. (2013). Insecure attachment and disordered eating in women: The mediating processes of social comparison and emotion dysregulation. *Eating Disorders, 21*, 154–174. doi:10.1080/10640266.2013.761089

Ward, A., Ramsay, R., & Treasure, J. (2000). Attachment research in eating disorders. *Psychology and Psychotherapy: Theory, Research and Practice, 73*, 35–51. doi:10.1348/000711200160282

Weir, K. (2016). New insights on eating disorders. *Monitor on Psychology, 47*(4), 36. Retrieved from http://www.apa.org/monitor/2016/04/eating-disorders.aspx

CHAPTER 4

The Centrality of Presence and the Therapeutic Relationship in Eating Disorders

Carolyn Costin

■ THE "HOW" INSTEAD OF THE "WHY"

This chapter offers ways to be an effective therapist for clients who suffer from both an eating disorder and trauma (ED&T). The importance of therapeutic presence and *how* to facilitate safety and healing through the therapeutic relationship are described. The information provided is equally applicable to all phases of treatment.

■ DISSOCIATION AND THE EATING DISORDER SELF

In 1994, while running an eating disorder (ED) unit for a large hospital, I was repeatedly asked to do assessments and consultations on the dissociative identity disorder (DID) unit. Several of the clients, all of whom had trauma histories, also had an ED, or, as I came to discover, at least one of their dissociated parts of self or ego states had an ED. These split-off ego states had many similarities to what I had been calling the "Eating Disorder Self" in my clients. My own ED, and my work with clients, taught me that people with EDs develop a separate ED self that has different core beliefs from those of their healthy self. The ED self directs the person's ED thoughts and behaviors. Treating an ED means strengthening the client's healthy self, so it can take over the job the ED self is doing. This is also how DID clients heal. To learn more about DID treatment, I began attending conferences and learned a great deal about trauma, ego states, dissociation, and integration. I learned several important tenets for treating DID that I was actually using with my ED clients, but until then had no training in, nor language for. These tenets applied to working with fully dissociated parts of self as well as split-off "ego states" or parts that clients are conscious of, but often do not even recognize as split-off from their core self.

Tenets for Working With Dissociated Parts or Ego States:
- Do not make an enemy with any split-off ego states because they will fight back or go into hiding.
- Split-off ego states serve a purpose.

- Do not get too enamored with any ego state because the attention gives it a good reason to stick around.
- Never treat an ego state as overly important, more interesting, or more powerful than the person's core self.
- Do not try to get rid of the split-off ego state; instead, strengthen the client's core self, so it can take over the job.

Integration means the split-off ego state is reunited into the core self, so there is just one, whole person with various personality aspects that can still serve as warning signals if something is wrong or needs to be attended to.

If I replaced the words "eating disorder self" for "ego state," and substituted "healthy self" for "core self," the previous tenets described how I was treating people with EDs. This early trauma training gave what I was doing a system, structure, and language that helped me become a better ED therapist, especially with clients who also suffered from trauma.

■ WORKING WITH EGO STATES AND THE NEED FOR SAFETY AND THERAPEUTIC PRESENCE

Split-off ego states are developed to help people cope and can be useful and/or protective. The fear and resistance involved in letting them go is astounding. For clients to recognize they even have a split-off ego state and that it is destructive, there has to be enormous trust. To heal, they need to trust that their core healthy self can get strong enough to take care of them, so that the functions of the ED self, or other dissociative parts, are no longer needed, because the healthy self takes over their job. Therapists need to know *how* to help clients strengthen their healthy self, and then to contact, transform and integrate the split-off part. Without feeling safe, clients will not take the risks necessary for this to happen. To successfully treat patients with trauma or patients with EDs, and particularly those with ED&T, therapists must create safety, earn trust, and create a positive alliance.

■ THE NEED TO FEEL SAFE

My new patient, Trish, walks into the room looking around at everywhere, but me. She tentatively takes a seat, and I see her wringing her hands and fidgeting. She appears to be disconnected from her body. Her emaciated frame is like a shell moving about without a sense of a self within it, guiding it. I feel and see her scan the room for safety. "Where are the exits? Is this place, this person, safe?" "What is she going to do to me?"

The impressions I get from Trish in a matter of minutes are not unfamiliar. They are the signs I see in someone who has lost a sense of safety, a person who forever scans the environment looking for signs that will alert him or her to danger, a person often with a trauma background. I have no agenda except to help her feel as safe as possible right here, right now. I must be present and stay attuned to myself and to her, including our breathing and body language. I let her sit wherever she wants and slowly move my chair close and then farther from her, asking her what distance feels best to her. I start talking about me, my office, my philosophy, how I work, and how I think therapy works. I make some jokes and all the while check her reaction. Eye contact? Smiling? I invite Trish to ask me questions, so I am not the only one talking and so she can begin to know me.

Overall, I am monitoring Trish's window of tolerance for my questions and comments, and I ease up when I see or sense her getting too uncomfortable. I ask her, "How do you think therapy helps people?" so I can begin to understand what she thinks this process entails. My goal for this first session is to be open, inviting, and interesting, and to create enough safety so that Trish wants to come back for a second session.

Existing in a state where one feels free from impending harm, injury, or loss is a basic need. One's level of safety influences his or her daily functioning, both physically and emotionally. Individuals need to feel safe to grow up physiologically and psychologically healthy or to restore what has been damaged back to health. Thus, an important skill for any therapist is the ability to create and instill safety. For ED&T therapists, it is imperative.

■ ATTACHMENT, TRAUMA, AND LOSS OF SAFETY

A healthy, secure attachment is critical to the functioning of a healthy human being. Through a secure attachment, human beings develop a felt sense of safety that promotes three important functions:

1. The ability to explore themselves and their environment
2. Affect regulation
3. The development of interoceptive awareness, which is the ability to sense, perceive, interpret, and describe stimuli that originate within the body. Attachment research supports that trauma and early lack of attunement results in psychological and biological changes that impair one's ability to appropriately sense danger and safety, disrupting the ability to respond to perceived or actual threats (Schore, 1994, 2003; van der Kolk, 1994, 2011). All three functions of a secure attachment are impaired, such that trauma clients have a hard time exploring and monitoring their environment, overreact to stimuli, respond defensively even when there is no risk, and have a diminished capacity to explain their internal states. Like my client Trish, these clients are on hyper alert with an intense radar system, scanning their environment for any possible sign of threat or danger. Similar to how a dog abused by a previous owner will recoil when a new loving owner reaches out a hand to offer a gentle pat on the head, a traumatized individual will misinterpret many normal human behaviors as a potential threat.

■ EATING DISORDERS AND ATTACHMENT

Similar to those with trauma, people with EDs also have a deficit in the three important attachment functions: They rely on external rather than internal cues to negotiate themselves and their environment, they use ED behaviors to regulate their emotions, and they are deficient in interoceptive awareness (Bizeul, Sadowsky, & Rigaud, 2001; Bruch, 1962; Garner, 2004; Garner, Olmstead, & Polivy, 1983; Smyth et al., 2007). Lack of interoceptive awareness is a trait particularly found in individuals with anxious attachment, along with other traits, such as lacking or misperceiving resources, feeling ineffective or deficient, needing to control, and experiencing inadequacy and insecure neediness. These traits are also present in clients with EDs. Several authors (Armstrong & Roth, 1989; Chassler, 1997) and several studies (Latzer, Hochdorf,

Bachar, & Canetti, 2002; O'Kearney, 1996; Troisi, Massaroni, & Cuzzolaro, 2005; Troisi et al., 2006; Ward, Ramsay, & Treasure, 2000) have found a relationship between attachment disturbances and clients who have EDs. Attachment issues are evident in both ED clients and those with trauma, so attending to attachment issues when working with the ED&T client is an important aspect of healing. Through offering themselves as a secure attachment figure, therapists can help these clients feel safe and internalize important attachment functions.

■ THE IMPORTANCE OF A POSITIVE THERAPEUTIC RELATIONSHIP

Research has demonstrated that a positive outcome in psychotherapy can only minimally be attributed to specific techniques, but that a positive therapeutic relationship is significantly related to successful outcomes (Lambert & Ogles, 2004, Lambert & Simon, 2008; Norcross, 2002, 2011). A positive therapeutic relationship provides a corrective emotional experience, providing healthy attachment, which fosters trust, safety, and the ability to facilitate unmet attachment needs and the internalization of attachment functions. Clients with ED&T use their ED and other symptoms rather than relying on people, so to get their needs met, their strongest relationship becomes the one they have with their ED self. They need to learn to trust someone, become attached to someone, more than they are attached to their ED, and the therapist is the most likely candidate, at least initially. To provide clients this kind of relationship, the therapist needs to offer a safe and secure relationship, but also a dynamic one that is more attractive than the relationship to the ED. This means the therapist has to take an open, active, personal, expert, and nonjudgmental stance:

"I know what I'm doing."
"I do not and will not judge you."
"I'm an expert at eating disorders and trauma, but not an expert on you."
"I know how to navigate life, and I know how to help you do so, too."
"I can't take anything away from you or make you stop anything, but I can help you
    stop if you want to."

Taking a "person first, patient second" approach, therapists need to *not* just pursue data, perform treatment protocols, and function as a blank slate, but, rather, become a real and authentic person. The therapist needs to provide a secure attachment by being present as a human *being*, not just as a human *doing*.

■ BEING VERSUS DOING

Over the years I have asked clients to make a list of *what makes a good therapist*. Though answers vary a bit, they can be summarized as follows:

1. They accept me as I am, while helping me become who I can be.
2. They do not take my behaviors personally.
3. They have wisdom and suggestions, but do not force their ideas on me.
4. They can be with me in pain, not just in trying to fix it.
5. They listen without inserting their own agenda.
6. They pay attention to many aspects, words, body language, silences, and energy.
7. They tell me the truth; hold up a mirror, without judging me.

8. They are role models of responding rather than reacting.
9. They are empathic (or caring, or loving).
10. They are calm, consistent, and comforting even when being strong and setting limits.
11. They admit mistakes.

What clients think makes a good therapist has more to do with the therapist's *"being"* than with his or her "doing." But how does one learn these skills? Through my own study and practice, I discovered that mindfulness and meditation help with this concept of "being" by promoting present moment awareness, acceptance, nonjudgment, and the ability to respond calmly, rather than react emotionally. In a comprehensive review (Geller & Porges, 2014), studies show how mindfulness practices, such as meditation, heighten what is called "therapeutic presence," which deepens the therapeutic relationship and is related to fundamental counseling abilities, such as attention, empathy, nonjudgment, and the feeling of self-efficacy. One study by Grepmair et al. (2007) showed that patients treated by therapists who meditated prior to sessions improved significantly more than patients being treated by nonmeditating therapists. Why would this be so?

Therapeutic presence makes it easier to attune to the client without being biased by preconceived ideas, allowing the therapist and client to resonate with each other and feel mutually understood, connected, and safe (Geller & Greenberg, 2002). Therapeutic presence is a precondition to a positive therapeutic relationship. This does not mean that therapists have to become meditators or meditate prior to sessions to achieve good results, but it does mean that there are ways of "being" a therapist that enhance the therapeutic relationship and contribute to successful therapy.

■ THERAPEUTIC PRESENCE

Therapists in training are not usually taught *how* to facilitate the presence of attunement and resonance, or how to remain open, grounded, and nonjudgmental. These are the qualities that researchers on therapeutic presence, such as Stephen Porges, are trying to assess, understand, and teach. In his polyvagal theory, Porges helps us understand the underlying neural mechanisms that contribute to one's ability to feel safe and spontaneously engage with others, or, on the contrary, to feel threatened and resort to defensive strategies (Porges, 2001). These mechanisms are disrupted in clients who suffer from trauma, and, unless their overactive neurobiological defense strategies (freeze, fright, and flight) are inhibited, they cannot effectively communicate or engage (Geller & Porges, 2014).

Signals of safety or danger are generally communicated interpersonally outside of our awareness by nonverbal cues such as posture and facial expressions. By becoming mindful, therapists can facilitate therapeutic presence through an open posture, soft facial features, soft eye contact, calm breathing, and a receptive and accepting stance (Geller & Porges, 2014). This presence facilitates the downregulation of involuntary defense mechanisms that clients, especially those with trauma histories, have developed (Geller & Porges, 2014). Repeated experiences of this presence regulate the client's nervous system, create new neural pathways, and enhance the client's ability to feel safe, allowing for deep therapeutic work and healing (Geller & Greenberg, 2002; McCollum & Gehart, 2010).

ED&T therapists will benefit from cultivating presence in their own lives and extending this into their sessions with clients. Doing breathing exercises before sessions, paying attention to one's body language, and recognizing and overcoming obstacles to presence that arise can all help. Checking in with clients is critical because it is their experience of therapeutic presence that is important. For information about cultivating presence, readers may want to explore *Therapeutic Presence: A Mindful Approach to Effective Therapy* (Geller & Greenberg, 2012) and the *Therapeutic Presence Inventory* (TPI; see Geller, Greenberg, & Watson, 2010).

■ HOW THERAPEUTIC PRESENCE AND RELATIONSHIP PUT SYMPTOMS OUT OF A JOB

The Present Moment: A Case Example

Our clients' stories can be a bridge to understanding, but, too often, people get stuck on the bridge. Getting too caught up in the story, whether client or clinician, keeps the focus on the past or future. Just knowing our clients' story does not help them learn *how* to deal with their problems in the present. Therapeutic presence helps clinicians pay attention to the present moment, to help clients with their *response-ability* in the here and now. Maintaining therapeutic presence helps clients develop new and better ways of responding to things rather than getting stuck on the *why* or *what* of a specific situation.

Kay, a 20-year-old ED&T client, was sitting in group therapy curled up in a ball, crying silently, rocking and giving no eye contact. This kind of behavior had distanced her from others in the program. When prompted to speak up about what was going on, Kay, almost inaudibly and in broken, stop-and-go phrases, tells a story about talking to her boyfriend on the phone earlier and how he hurt her feelings and is just not there for her... so why should she care? Responding to Kay by asking questions about the boyfriend, about what he said, what she said back, what she could say, does he say these things often, and so on, can get client and clinician stuck in Kay's story, rather than on how Kay can learn to handle issues like this as they arise in her life. Therapeutic presence helps the clinician be in the moment with the client, focusing on how the client reacts to being hurt or afraid, including affect, body language, tone of voice, and other behaviors. This was an opportunity to help Kay see how she reacts to emotions, and help her learn a more useful rewarding response. My questions went something like this: "Kay, do you notice what you are doing with your body?" "How does this posture serve you, does it help?" "Are you aware that you are whispering?" "Can you tell me why you are whispering?" "Do you know how you developed this way of reacting?" "Are you aware of other people's responses to what you are doing right now?" "Would you like to change this?"

I helped Kay explore her physical reactions and, with her permission, helped her begin to change these. I asked her to sit up straight, ground her feet solidly on the floor, take deep breaths, give me and others eye contact, and begin to speak in a more solid, stronger voice.

Like most ED&T clients, Kay needed guidance in *how* to separate herself from her emotions, preventing them from taking control of her body, thus allowing her to more appropriately respond and to become more response-able.

Not Being Attached to the Results

Nonattachment, a stance of openness and acceptance, is one of the main spiritual principles of Buddhism and an aspect of therapeutic presence. Not being attached to the results *does not mean* you do not care, *it means* you accept things that happen, rather than resist them with negativity and judgment.

Nonattachment is essential for a positive therapeutic relationship, which cannot be based on the therapist's agenda or whether or not the client is "doing what the therapist wants." For example, if a young woman comes to therapy for help exploring her gender identity, it would be inappropriate for the therapist to insist she "Work hard to be a female because that is how she was born," or "Have a sex change operation" and then become angry if the client does not follow the advice. However, when treating people with ED&T, therapists and treatment teams often find themselves attached to their agenda with clients, telling them what they have to do, and, at times, even punishing them for lack of compliance.

Being overly invested in, or reactive to, whether clients make changes, follow through with things, or even "want" to get better is counterproductive for the client, the therapist, and the therapy. Not being attached to the results contributes greatly to the success of therapy, because it helps the therapist deal with resistance, limit control battles, and avoid imposing an agenda, which can cause clients to rebel, go underground, or drop out altogether. Furthermore, nonattachment prevents burnout and has allowed me to work consistently with ED&T clients for over 30 years.

Admittedly, not being attached to the results when treating people with ED&T clients is especially difficult because of the damage they so often inflict upon themselves. For example, we cannot sit back and let a client starve to death while under our care. Thus, I actively pursued getting medical conservatorship for the parents of a 21-year-old girl to keep her in the hospital and save her life. All therapists may be called upon to assert their agenda, for example, if a client threatens suicide. But we cannot prevent someone intent on suicide, we can only postpone it, unless the person changes internally and no longer wants to die. In difficult situations, therapeutic presence helps the therapist remain calm, kind, and uncritical, helping clients assess their circumstances, explore their options, understand the consequences of their behaviors, and come up with alternative solutions. Therapeutic presence means remaining neutral while clarifying choices: "You will need to gain weight, or the coach will drop you out of track," or "If you cut that deeply again, I will refer you to a higher level of care." Each client has the ultimate right to decide whether or not to agree to certain recovery goals and whether or not he or she wants to recover at all. Not being attached to the results is like holding up a mirror for clients and asking them if they see what you see, if they want to change it, and, if so, helping them find alternatives, always accepting it as their choice.

Nurturing and Authoritative Therapy

The line between supporting clients where they are and pushing them to grow is a fluid one. In some sessions, the therapist will need to be a passive, reassuring presence, helping clients sit with and feel their feelings. However, no growth will take place unless the therapist also knows when to ask clients to take a risk that unsettles them and challenges them in some way, such as adding calories or journaling before a binge. Unlike the tenets in other therapeutic trainings, direct advice must at times be forthcoming for clients with ED&T. Simply asking them how they feel, allowing long silences, or waiting for them to speak can be frightening to these clients who desperately need to feel that someone is in charge who is transparent, safe, and knows what to do. Therapeutic presence helps therapists pick up on and act according to the client's signals, thus facilitating the art of both nurturing and authoritative therapy, which is necessary for these clients to recover.

Dealing With Resistance

Nonattachment, presence, and a positive therapeutic relationship allow clinicians to successfully deal with ED&T clients' inevitable resistance. A great way to think about dealing with resistance is to follow the principle of an Aikido martial artist. Do not meet force with force; do not resist the "opponent's" energy. Instead, go with it. For example, if a client says, "I don't want to gain weight" or "I don't want to recover," instead of trying to explain the value or importance of weight gain or recovery, it is more effective to ask, "Can you at least tell me why you don't want to?" or "I'd like to learn more about why that is and how you decided that." This nonattached stance maintains the relationship by responding with a curious, open attitude allowing clients to let down their guard. Therapist and client can then explore the pros and cons of weight gain, an emaciated body, and recovery. If, over time, the client remains unable to make any changes, the therapist will have to make a decision whether to hang in there, change tactics, refer to another therapist or, if necessary, facilitate a higher level of care.

Teaching Clients to Reach Out to the Therapist Rather Than Their Disorder

ED&T clients reach out to their ED behaviors and other symptoms rather than people to get comfort, express anger, find solace, or otherwise get their needs met. Therapists need to wean clients off the ED by allowing them to reach out to the therapist instead of their disordered behaviors. Being a trusted figure to whom clients can openly, without fear of judgment, reach out to is the first step. The next is to wean the client off the therapist onto other people. When clients learn to get their needs met from other people, the need to use ED or other symptoms diminishes and eventually disappears.

A positive therapeutic relationship helps clients reach out to the therapist in the session, for example, by enabling clients to become comfortable enough to share secrets, tell the truth, and discuss difficult events. However, ED&T clients need help outside sessions to stop symptomatic behaviors or to accomplish challenging tasks. Therapists can work out specific goals and parameters with each client as to how the client can reach out by texting, emailing, or even calling the therapist when needing support (Costin & Grabb, 2012). Texting, I have found, is one of the most successful of these strategies.

Texting as a Way of Reaching Out

Therapists can use their relationship with the client by asking the client to text before engaging in a behavior. Most clients are quite used to texting and will more readily do it than make a phone call. Email is far less likely to get an immediate response and journaling has to wait until the client brings it in to the session. By letting clients text us when they most need support, we teach them to get familiar and comfortable with reaching out to a person, not a behavior. Once this has been successful, the therapist helps clients move on to texting other people. Texting works best when therapist and client agree to specific texting goals and specific periods of time. For example, an ED&T client might be at a point where he or she is very motivated to stop night binging, but has not been able to do it. The therapist and client can make an agreement that for the upcoming week, the client can text the therapist when the urge to binge at night arises.

Allowing clients access to me at the moment they are actually struggling facilitates progress to such an extent, and has been so successful in my work with ED&T clients, that I cannot imagine not doing it with this population. The therapist does not even have to do that much in response. Instead, just texting back with some comforting, encouraging words, giving the client a vote of confidence, or reminding the client of the reasons he or she has stated for not wanting to binge can help the client abstain from the behavior or meet a challenge.

Therapists need to be clear about their availability, discussing with clients how no one will ever be available to respond at all times. However, sometimes just the act of sending the text is enough to help the client get through the moment without resorting to his or her disordered behaviors. Essentially, when clients text or call, they strengthen their healthy self, because it is the healthy part of them that is reaching out.

Using Transitional Objects

Because attachment figures cannot be around 100% of the time, it helps to have a transitional object as a "stand in." A transitional object is a term from the childhood attachment field that is used to describe an object that functions as a "substitute" for a caregiver's presence to provide comfort or soothing when the person is not around. For example, a pacifier is used as a transitional object to soothe and comfort babies, as a replacement for their mother's breast. Baby blankets and stuffed animals can also be transitional objects. When a positive therapeutic relationship exists, a transitional object can be used to help clients connect with the therapist and the therapeutic work at important times outside of sessions. The therapist can give a client a small item such as a heart made of glass, a beautiful rock, a keychain, a piece of sea glass, or something similar to use as a "transitional object." Clients can carry their transitional object with them and use it as a link or connection to the safety and comfort they feel from the therapist's presence, a reminder of a goal or challenge they are working on, or just to help them get through a difficult situation.

I have found it particularly useful to give transitional objects to ED&T clients. They seem to need them, use them, and appreciate them the most. At a certain point in the therapy, a client will do or say something that indicates that a transitional object might be helpful. For example, "I get really anxious and forget everything I agreed to eat when I get around my father," or "I get flashbacks at night and wake up disoriented and don't know what to do." These statements are what I call "windows" or openings to presenting the idea of a transitional object. As a rock and gem collector, I have always kept a bowl of interesting rocks in my office. When the opportunity presents itself, I explain to the client, who has for sure seen and perhaps even touched these rocks, that I use the rocks as transitional objects. I explain the function of a transitional object. I let them know the rocks in my office were earlier at my house for a long time and have been in the room with us during our sessions. I ask the client to choose a rock that he or she would most like to have. We discuss ways the client might use the transitional object, and I give examples of how other clients have used them.

A client, for example, who was trying to stop purging put the rock on the tank at the back of her toilet so she would see it if she went to the bathroom to purge. As she said, "It helped, because I walked in to purge, and there YOU were." A dissociative client always kept her rock in her pocket and would grab it when she started to dissociate. Looking at it or even feeling it in her pocket could often keep her from going into full dissociation, and sometimes it brought her back. A client with binge ED hung the rock from her car mirror in hopes that it would help her resist buying binge food on her way home from work. Seeing the rock, she thought about me and the work she was doing in therapy and, for the first time, drove home without binging. These stories may be hard to believe, but they are all true. The key is that having a positive therapeutic relationship is what makes the transitional objects effective.

Sand Timers

With certain clients, a sand timer can be effective as a kind of transitional object with an additional function. If clients feel that binging, purging, or cutting is out of their control, sand timers can be used as transitional objects to help the clients healthily self-regain control. When feeling the urge to engage in the behavior, the client is instructed to turn the timer upside down and not act upon the urge until the sand has run out. I start clients with a 3-minute egg timer as there are few who cannot wait for 3 minutes. Irrespective of whether clients engage in the behavior after the 3 minutes are up, they learn that they actually did have control, even if only for a short period of time. Next, I move to a 5-minute or 10-minute timer and work up to an hourglass. Sometimes clients will go ahead with the behavior, sometimes not, but even delaying the behavior shows the client that his or her healthy self can actually get back in control. Once clients can delay binging, purging, or cutting for an hour they are usually able to abstain from it.

■ CONCLUSION

Therapy for ED&T clients involves providing safety, education, insight, and a corrective emotional experience, thereby allowing the client to rectify faulty thought, emotional, and behavioral patterns. Therapists need to use their training *and* the therapeutic relationship for this to happen. Until clients can "do it on their own," the therapist serves as an attachment figure lending his or her support to help clients feel safe and internalize missing psychological functions, such as the ability to express feelings, self-soothe, and internally validate. Using the relationship, therapists can help clients learn to delay gratification, relate to others, regulate tension and moods, and respond, rather than react. Once clients have internalized these abilities into their self-structure, they no longer need to use substitute or self-destructive measures such as ED behaviors to meet their needs or cope with problems.

The presence of the therapist and the relationship between client and therapist cannot be ignored when looking at what contributes to a positive outcome. A variety of approaches and modalities can be used, but it is the alliance between the therapist and client rather than any certain technique that is the most critical factor for success. Most therapists have heard about the importance of the therapeutic relationship but unfortunately do not know exactly what it means or how to learn more about it. Two books that would be of help in this regard are *The Heroic Client* (Duncan, Miller, & Sparks, 2004) and *The Heart and Soul of Change* (Duncan, Miller, Wampold, & Hubble, 2010). My experience treating ED&T clients corroborates the need for therapy training programs to increase their focus on training therapists *how* to achieve therapeutic presence, establish a positive alliance, and use the relationship to put the client's symptoms out of a job.

■ REFERENCES

Armstrong, J. G., & Roth, D. M. (1989). Attachment and separation difficulties in eating disorders: A preliminary investigation. *International Journal of Eating Disorders, 8*(2), 141–155. doi:10.1002/1098-108X(198903)8:2<141::AID-EAT2260080203>3.0.CO;2-E

Bizeul, C., Sadowsky, N., & Rigaud, D. (2001). The prognostic value of initial EDI scores in anorexia nervosa patients: A prospective follow-up study of 5-10 years. *European Psychiatry, 16*(4), 232–238. doi:10.1016/S0924-9338(01)00570-3

Bruch, H. (1962). Perceptual and conceptual disturbances in anorexia nervosa. *Psychosomatic Medicine, 24*(2), 187–194.

Chassler, L. (1997). Understanding anorexia nervosa and bulimia nervosa from an attachment perspective. *Clinical Social Work Journal, 25*(4), 407–423. doi:10.1023/A:1025796416594

Costin, C., & Grabb, G. (2012). *8 keys to recovery from an eating disorder.* New York, NY: W. W. Norton.

Duncan, B., Miller, S. D., & Sparks, J. A. (2004). *The heroic client: A revolutionary way to improve effectiveness through client-directed, outcome-informed therapy.* San Francisco, CA: Jossey-Bass.

Duncan, B., Miller, S. D., Wampold, B. E., & Hubble, M. A. (2010). *The heart and soul of change: Delivering what works in therapy* (2nd ed.). Washington, DC: American Psychological Association.

Garner, D. M. (2004). *The Eating Disorder Inventory-3 (EDI-3). Professional manual.* Odessa, FL: Psychological Assessment Resources.

Garner, D. M., Olmstead, M. P., & Polivy, J. (1983). Development and validation of a multidimensional Eating Disorder Inventory for anorexia nervosa and bulimia nervosa. *International Journal of Eating Disorders, 2*(2), 15–34. doi:10.1002/1098-108X(198321)2:2<15::AID-EAT2260020203>3.0.CO;2-6

Geller, S. M., & Greenberg, L. S. (2002). Therapeutic presence: Therapists' experience of presence in the psychotherapy encounter. *Person-Centered and Experiential Psychotherapies, 1,* 71–86. doi:10.1080/14779757.2002.9688279

Geller, S. M., & Greenberg, L. S. (2012). *Therapeutic presence: A mindful approach to effective therapy.* doi:10.1037/13485-010

Geller, S. M., Greenberg, L. S., & Watson, J. C. (2010). Therapist and client perceptions of therapeutic presence: The development of a measure. *Psychotherapy Research, 20,* 599–610. doi:10.1080/10503307.2010.495957

Geller, S. M., & Porges, S. W. (2014). Therapeutic presence: Neurophysiological mechanisms mediating feeling safe in therapeutic relationships. *Journal of Psychotherapy Integration, 24*(3), 178–192.

Grepmair, L., Mitterlehner, F., Loew, T., Bachler, E., Rother, W., & Nickel, M. (2007). Promoting mindfulness in psychotherapists in training influences the treatment results of their patients: A randomized, double-blind, controlled study. *Psychotherapy and Psychosomatics, 76,* 332–338. doi:10.1159/000107560

Lambert, M., & Ogles, B. (2004). The efficacy and effectiveness of psychotherapy. In M. J. Lambert (Ed.), *Bergin and Garfield's handbook of psychotherapy and behavior change* (5th ed., pp. 139–193). New York, NY: Wiley.

Lambert, M., & Simon, W. (2008). The therapeutic relationship: Central and essential in psychotherapy outcome. In S. F. Hick & T. Bien (Eds.), *Mindfulness and the therapeutic relationship* (pp. 19–33). New York, NY: Guilford Press.

Latzer, Y., Hochdorf, Z., Bachar, E., & Canetti, L. (2002). Attachment style and family functioning as discriminating factors in eating disorders. *Contemporary Family Therapy, 24*(4), 581–599. doi:10.1023/A:1021273129664

McCollum, E. E., & Gehart, D. R. (2010). Using mindfulness meditation to teach beginning therapists therapeutic presence: A qualitative study. *Journal of Marital and Family Therapy, 36,* 347–360. doi:10.1111/j.1752-0606.2010.00214.x

Norcross, J. C. (2002). *Psychotherapy relationships that work: Therapist contributions and responsiveness to patients.* New York, NY: Oxford University Press.

Norcross, J. C. (Ed.). (2011). *Psychotherapy relationships that work: Evidence based responsiveness* (2nd ed.). New York, NY: Oxford University Press.

O'Kearney, R. (1996). Attachment disruption in anorexia nervosa and bulimia nervosa: A review of theory and empirical research. *International Journal of Eating Disorders, 20*(2), 115–127. doi:10.1002/(SICI)1098-108X(199609)20:2<115::AID-EAT1>3.0.CO;2-J

Porges, S. W. (2001). The polyvagal theory: Phylogenetic substrates of a social nervous system. *International Journal of Psychophysiology, 42,* 123–146. doi:10.1016/S0167-8760(01)00162-3

Schore, A. N. (1994). *Affect regulation and the origin of the self: The neurobiology of emotional development.* Hillsdale, NJ: Erlbaum.

Schore, A. N. (2003). *Affect dysregulation and disorders of the self.* New York, NY: W. W. Norton.

Smyth, J. M., Wonderlich, S. A., Heron, K. E., Sliwinski, M. J., Crosby, R. D., Mitchell, J. E., & Engel, S. G. (2007). Daily and momentary mood and stress are associated with binge eating and vomiting in bulimia nervosa patients in the natural environment. *Journal of Consulting and Clinical Psychology, 75*(4), 629–638. doi:10.1037/0022-006X.75.4.629

Troisi, A., Di Lorenzo, G., Alcini, S., Nanni, R. C., Di Pasquale, C., & Siracusano, A. (2006). Body dissatisfaction in women with eating disorders: Relationship to early separation anxiety and insecure attachment. *Psychosomatic Medicine, 68*(3), 449–453. doi:10.1097/01.psy. 0000204923.09390.5b

Troisi, A., Massaroni, P., & Cuzzolaro, M. (2005). Early separation anxiety and adult attachment style in women with eating disorders. *British Journal of Clinical Psychology, 44*(1), 89–97. doi:10.1348/014466504X20053

van der Kolk, B. A. (1994). The body keeps the score: Memory and the evolving psychobiology of posttraumatic stress. *Harvard Review of Psychiatry, 1,* 253–265. doi:10.3109/10673229409017088

van der Kolk, B. A. (2011). Foreword. In S. W. Porges (Eds.), *The polyvagal theory: Neurophysiological foundations of emotions, attachment, communication, self- regulation.* New York, NY: W. W. Norton.

Ward, A., Ramsay, R., & Treasure, J. (2000). Attachment research in eating disorders. *British Journal of Medical Psychology, 73*(1), 35–51. doi:10.1348/000711200160282

SECTION THREE

Brain, Body, and Eating Disorders

Chapter 5 provides a neurobiological explanation of what happens in the brain when trauma is experienced, when eating disorders (EDs) are involved, and when the two intersect. Chapter 6 highlights the multidisciplinary team approach by describing the medical and nutritional needs the clinician should be aware of when referring a client to a physician or a dietician/nutritionist.

CHAPTER 5

The Neurobiology of Trauma and Eating Disorders

Rayane Chami and Janet Treasure

▓ INTRODUCTION

Critical life events and chronic stress have been found to be distal or proximal events that may predispose or precipitate the onset of eating disorders (EDs; Rojo, Conesa, Bermudez, & Livianos, 2006). From conception onwards, individuals with EDs, on average, are more likely to have experienced greater adversity over their life course. Individuals with anorexia nervosa (AN) are two to three times more likely to have experienced premature birth or birth trauma (Cnattingius, Hultman, Dahl, & Sparén, 1999), and their mothers are more likely to have experienced high levels of anxiety during gestation (Taborelli et al., 2013). Moreover, binge eating and purging behaviors are more common among those who have experienced a history of trauma (Ackard, Neumark-Sztainer, Hannan, French, & Story, 2001). Throughout childhood, individuals with EDs are more likely to have experienced weight-related bullying and teasing (Menzel et al., 2010), adverse experiences (e.g., bereavement; Troop & Treasure, 1997), and problematic relationships with their parents (Rorty, Yager, Rossotto, & Buckwalter, 2000).

Undeniably, trauma, in all its forms, can be considered a risk factor for ED development. Research in neuroscience and genetics proposes several potential links between adverse early environments and ED development and maintenance. These include changes in appetite, the experience of reward, and sensitivity to social rejection. Several models have been developed to conceptualize the link between negative experiences and eating behavior; some postulate that food is used as a coping mechanism that provides relief from painful experiences (see Emotional Regulation Model; Gross, 1999), that maladaptive eating is used as a means of escaping or detaching from negative aversive states (see Escape Theory; Heatherton & Baumeister, 1991), or that stress induces functional changes in neurochemical systems (e.g., hypothalamic–pituitary–adrenal [HPA]; described in the following section), increasing the susceptibility to EDs (Micali, Simonoff, & Treasure, 2011). This chapter explores the neurological link between trauma and EDs by first describing one of humans' basic functions: response to stressors.

▓ UNDERSTANDING THE IMPACT OF EARLY LIFE ADVERSITY ON NEURODEVELOPMENT VIA THE "CHRONIC" STRESS RESPONSE

Understanding the sympathetic adrenal medullary (SAM) system and the corticotropin-releasing factor (CRF)/HPA axis system can help conceptualize what happens in the brain during stress. The SAM system is responsible for the "quick" response to stress, whereas the HPA is the "slow"-acting system. As part of the former, the hypothalamus activates the sympathetic system, stimulating the adrenal medulla and leading to the release of epinephrine and norepinephrine (NE). These hormones help one deal with unanticipated stress by increasing heart rate, conserving energy (i.e., glucose) for the organs that need it most, and increasing respiration. Moreover, during the slower response to stress, neurons in the hypothalamus secrete corticotropin-releasing hormone (CRH) and arginine vasopressin (AVP), which stimulate the release of adrenocorticotropic hormone (ACTH) into general circulation (Gunnar & Vazquez, 2015). ACTH then binds to its receptors in the adrenal cortex, leading to glucocorticoid (i.e., cortisol) release. Cortisol also triggers the NE system, via the brainstem locus coeruleus (Melia & Duman, 1991). As NE releases neurotransmitters throughout the brain, it encourages alertness and vigilance, helping one deal with acute threat (Bremner, Krystal, Southwick, & Charney, 1996).

The hippocampus is a limbic structure that plays an inhibitory role on the HPA axis, via projections to the paraventricular nuclei in the hypothalamus (Ulrich-Lai & Herman, 2009). During prolonged stress, cells of the hippocampus are damaged because of extended epinephrine and glucocorticoid release (Sapolsky, Krey, & McEwen, 1985). In addition, the amygdala, a limbic structure that is thought to facilitate fear learning by activating the HPA (Joëls, Fernandez, & Roozendaal, 2011), is also influenced by stress-induced glucocorticoid release in response to early life stress (Malter Cohen et al., 2013).

Frontal cortical regions receive feedback from limbic structures and also play a role in regulating the stress system (Hostinar, Sullivan, & Gunnar, 2014). The orbitofrontal cortex (OFC) and the medial prefrontal cortex (mPFC), both part of the prefrontal cortex (PFC), have two-way connections to limbic structures (Hostinar et al., 2014). Receiving feedback from limbic structures, they slow down the release of glucocorticoids when levels are high and are thought to help individuals regulate emotions (Cone, Low, Elmquist, & Cameron, 2003). Nonetheless, they also receive input from the stress system, and, thus, can be damaged by chronic stress exposure (Arnsten, 2009). See Figure 5.1.

In 2013, Teicher and Samson described a possible developmental phenotype resulting from early stressful environmental experiences—which they named the *ecophenotype*. Compiling 37 papers to explore the neural correlates of childhood maltreatment, Teicher, Samson, Anderson, and Ohashi (2016) found that among adults, a history of maltreatment was associated with smaller hippocampi as compared to nonmaltreated individuals. As the hippocampus plays an inhibitory role on the HPA, its atrophy possibly makes it more challenging to regulate the stress response (Connan, Campbell, Katzman, Lightman, & Treasure, 2003). In line with this, further evidence shows that individuals who experience poor early parental care (Bremner et al., 2003) and insecure attachment (Gunnar & Donzella, 2001) are more likely to show altered cortisol levels. Furthermore, early exposure to maltreatment is associated with an increased volume of the amygdala, whereas later exposure to maltreatment is associated with a decreased size (Whittle et al., 2013), potentially because of early sensitization of the amygdala (Teicher et al., 2016).

Repeated activation of the HPA during chronic stress influences glutamate transporter expression. The "neuroplasticity hypothesis" of chronic stress posits that glutamatergic signaling to the basolateral amygdala is increased during stress, resulting in enhanced expression of brain-deprived neurotropic factor (BDNF) and dendritic outgrowth producing hypertrophy (i.e., growth). In contrast, an increase in glutamatergic signaling in the hippocampus is accompanied by decreased BDNF signaling, inhibiting dendritic growth and leading to atrophy (i.e., breakdown; Boyle, 2013). In other words, the structures of the amygdala and hippocampus are likely to change in response to chronic stress, making it more challenging to regulate the stress response.

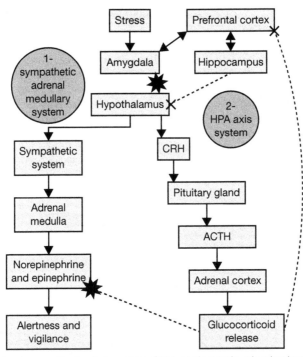

ACTH, adrenocorticotropic hormone; CRH, corticotropin-releasing hormone; HPA, hypothalamic–pituitary–adrenal; SAM, sympathetic adrenal medullary.

FIGURE 5.1 The stress response and feedback frontal loops. As part of the SAM system, on the left, we see the mechanisms that lead to epinephrine and norepinephrine release. As part of the HPA axis system, on the right, we see the pathway to glucocorticoid release, which is also associated with epinephrine and norepinephrine release. The amygdala plays an excitatory role on the hypothalamus, whereas the hippocampus plays an inhibitory role. The prefrontal cortex has two-way connections to these limbic regions, as it slows down glucocorticoid release, but can be damaged by their excessive release during chronic stress.

With regards to frontal cortical regions, the anterior cingulate cortex (ACC) plays an integral role in orchestrating the stress reaction, and is attenuated in individuals with a history of maltreatment (Baker et al., 2013). The attenuation of this frontal cortical region may be associated with deregulation of the stress system, as well as executive functions that are necessary for recovery.

■ EARLY LIFE ADVERSITY AND EATING DISORDER DEVELOPMENT VIA THE STRESS RESPONSE

The influence of chronic stress on neurodevelopment is thought to increase the risk of developing a variety of psychiatric disorders. Connan et al. (2003) developed a multi-factorial threshold explanatory model to conceptualize these findings in EDs. This model postulates that, alongside genetic variability, attachment and early life difficulties interact to influence the development of neurobiological systems, increasing the risk of developing an ED. See Figure 5.2.

Activity of the HPA axis among patients with AN has received mixed findings. Some research shows hyperactivity of the HPA axis and increased cortisol levels among underweight patients with AN (Tolle et al., 2003). This is hypothesized to result from dysregulation of feedback inhibition loops at the level of the hypothalamus (Connan et al., 2003) or dysregulated feedback from prefrontal regions such as the ACC, which is also attenuated among individuals with a history or current episode of AN (McFadden, Tregellas, Shott, & Frank, 2014). Other research shows a blunted cortisol response to interpersonal stress, despite increases in self-reported stress and normal levels at baseline (Het et al., 2015; Zonnevylle-Bender et al., 2005). This blunted cortisol level is not generalized to other experimental tasks, such as a physical exercise condition, in

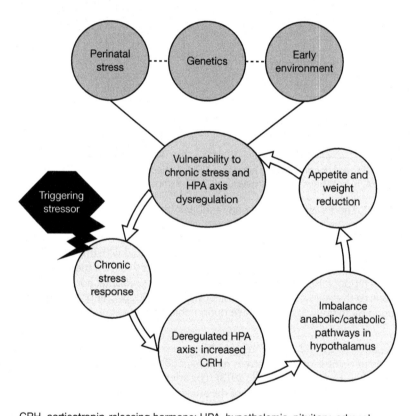

CRH, corticotropin-releasing hormone; HPA, hypothalamic–pituitary–adrenal.

FIGURE 5.2 The multifactorial threshold model, adapted from Connan and colleagues (2003), demonstrates how early attachment and genetic factors can moderate personality features, psychosocial development, and HPA axis sensitivity among individuals with anorexia nervosa. By adolescence, they are increasingly vulnerable to chronic stress, making their HPA axis more susceptible to dysregulation, leading to persistently elevated CRH activity. This results in an imbalance of anabolic and catabolic pathways in the hypothalamus, leading to loss of appetite. Over time, the impact of starvation further impairs psychological and biological systems.

which the HPA was activated equally among individuals with AN and healthy controls (Zonnevylle-Bender et al., 2005).

The cortisol awakening response (CAR) is another marker of HPA axis functioning, indicating the HPA's preparation to deal with anticipated stress. Individuals with AN and bulimia nervosa (BN) who had been exposed to childhood maltreatment showed a lower CAR, indicative of deficiencies in HPA axis functioning, whereas those with AN and BN who had not been exposed to childhood maltreatment showed increases in CAR (Monteleone, Scognamiglio, Monteleone, Perillo, & Maj, 2014). This suggests that there may be a variation in the neurobiology of individuals with AN who were exposed to early adversity, indicating the need to target treatment approaches appropriately.

▓ ENVIRONMENTAL AND GENETIC INTERACTIONS: THE ROLE OF POLYMORPHISMS AND EPIGENETICS

Polymorphisms

Polymorphisms represent genetic variations within a population. Researchers have categorized genetic polymorphisms at behaviorally implicated loci into *orchid* and *dandelion* alleles (i.e., variant forms of a given gene; Mitchell et al., 2010). The orchid and dandelion hypothesis argues that individuals with orchid alleles (i.e., risky, more sensitive alleles) may be more sensitive to their environment and thus, in conditions that are less than ideal (e.g., childhood maltreatment), are more likely to exhibit "worse" outcomes (e.g., problems with prosocial behavior and school engagement; Obradović, Bush, Stamperdahl, Adler, & Boyce, 2010). On the contrary, individuals with the "dandelion" alleles are less sensitive to context and thus have the freedom to grow in different ecosystems.

In 2011, Karwautz and colleagues explored discordant sister pairs with AN and found evidence for the role of nonshared environmental risks (e.g., birth complications; adverse life events) and their interaction with a genetic polymorphism in the serotonin transporter *5-HTT* gene. The interaction between gene and environment was significant in such a way that problematic parenting increased the vulnerability in sister pairs with *LS* and *SS* genotypes, as opposed to those with the *LL* genotype. Akkermann et al. (2012) explain that the *S* allele carriers are biologically more reactive to stressful events. A systematic review by Rozenblat et al. (2016) confirmed that interactions between the *S* allele of *5-HTTLPR* and traumatic life events (such as physical and sexual abuse) increased the likelihood of ED development.

A previous meta-analysis found no association between S allele carriers and binge eating disorder or BN (Calati, De Ronchi, Bellini, & Serretti, 2011). However, Akkermann et al. (2012) found that *5-HTTLPR* might moderate the influence of life events on binge eating. As such, polymorphisms help us understand why individuals can develop different psychopathologies in response to the same environmental trigger.

Epigenetics

Epigenetics refers to the way in which environmental exposures have the capacity to influence the genome in a way that affects later gene expression. DNA methylation has been widely studied as an epigenetic factor. It occurs when methyl groups are added to a DNA molecule, changing the activity of a DNA segment and, hence, gene expression. Evidence suggests that early life experiences of adversity, nurturance, and dietary factors all influence DNA methylation (Crider, Yang, Berry, & Bailey, 2012; Ernst et al., 2008). In addition, research suggests that epigenetics may mediate the impact of the environment on ED development (Campbell, Mill, Uher, & Schmidt, 2011; Strober, Peris, & Steiger, 2014). Project Ice Storm is a prospective study assessing the children carried by women who had been exposed to severe ice storms in southern Quebec. The results suggested that children who were exposed to the ice storm in utero had altered DNA methylation patterns (Dancause et al., 2015) and higher scores on the Eating Attitudes Test (EAT-26) at age 13 (St-Hilaire et al., 2015).

■ MECHANISMS MEDIATING THE RELATIONSHIP BETWEEN EARLY ADVERSITIES AND EATING BEHAVIOR

Appetite

Animal models have been used to assess the influence of aversive environments on eating behavior. A review combining animal studies, to explore the impact of early stressful experiences on eating behavior, has found that short-term stressors, such as cold exposure or social defeat, are associated with a reduction in feeding behavior in animals (Jahng, 2011; Turton, Chami, & Treasure, 2017). However, chronic stress can lead to overeating behaviors (Adam & Epel, 2007). It is hypothesized that the stress response influences appetite because the brain circuitries that both modulate food intake and regulate stress (i.e., HPA axis) converge in the paraventricular nucleus (PVN) of the hypothalamus, whose neurons produce CRH. As starvation progresses, a decrease in insulin stimulates neuropeptide Y (NPY) release, kindling HPA axis activity. However, CRH inhibits NPY, so anabolic pathways are prevented. This is a feed-forward system that requires effective cortisol feedback inhibition. When this system is ineffective during times of stress, increased CRH release persists and inhibits NPY activity (Connan et al., 2003).

In other words, chronic stress is associated with a dysregulated HPA axis, evoking several mechanisms that heighten stress reactivity. When the HPA cannot be regulated, loss of appetite is more likely to take place. Because CRH levels reach great heights, starvation loses its ability to encourage anabolism, thus further dysregulating the HPA. See Figure 5.3.

Ghrelin is a hormone that plays a role in energy homeostasis (Dickson et al., 2011; Skibicka & Dickson, 2011), as it increases during starvation and stimulates appetite (Misra & Klibanski, 2016). The level of ghrelin rises during times of acute psychological stress, and accumulating data suggest that it is involved in stress-induced food consumption by stimulating NPY (Chuang et al., 2011).

ED research shows that ghrelin is often higher among patients with BN and restrained eaters (Hilterscheid & Laessle, 2015) and that it promotes the secretion of ACTH, thus mediating cortisol levels in AN (Misra & Klibanski, 2016). During a stress test, Monteleone et al. (2012) found that ghrelin peaked and remained high for 1 hour after the stress test among those with BN, whereas it peaked and began to reduce at 25 minutes among "healthy" controls. This may explain why individuals with binge-type eating disorders are more likely to overeat in response to stress.

In addition to its effect on appetite, ghrelin has also been examined for its interaction with mesolimbic and cortical circuits, modulating the experience of reward (Schellekens, Finger, Dinan, & Cryan, 2012). Within another study exploring reward among patients with AN and "healthy" controls, plasma levels of ghrelin did not increase after favorite food consumption among those with AN, as it did among "healthy" controls (Monteleone et al., 2016). The section "Reward" further explains the neural basis of reward.

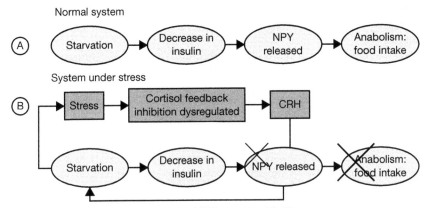

CRH, corticotropin-releasing hormone; NPY, neuropeptide Y.

FIGURE 5.3   The impact of stress on appetite. The subpart (A) shows how, in normal conditions, starvation leads to food consumption. The decrease in insulin in response to starvation stimulates the release of NPY, which encourages food intake. The subpart (B) shows how, under stress, the cortisol feedback loop is in dysregulation, inhibiting NPY release, and, thus, food intake. This is a negative cycle, as it increases the duration of starvation, which further exacerbates the stress response.

Reward

Some researchers theorize that learned responses to adverse early experiences influence the sensitivity to reward and punishment (Gibb, Schofield, & Coles, 2009). The reinforcement sensitivity theory (RST; Gray, 1970) describes how responses to reward and punishment are influenced by particular brain systems: the behavioral activation system, responsive to rewarding stimuli resulting in approach behavior, and the behavioral inhibition system, responsive to aversive stimuli resulting in inhibited behavior (Bijttebier, Beck, Claes, & Vandereycken, 2009; Deary & Johnson, 2009). Individuals with altered sensitivity may be more prone to developing mental illness (Jappe et al., 2011).

Our brains modulate the experience of reward by integrating internal sensations of hunger, satiety, pleasure, and fear with higher order cognitive functions. As depicted in a recent paper (Monteleone et al., 2017), the brain reward system can be split into the bottom-up limbic circuit (i.e., amygdala, anterior insula, anterior ventral striatum, ventral ACC, and OFC), responsible for identifying reward, and the dorsal top-down neural circuit (i.e., caudate and dorsolateral prefrontal cortex [dlPFC]), which is thought to modulate attention, planning, and regulation of affective states (Phillips, Drevets, Rauch, & Lane, 2003). Furthermore, the PFC plays an inhibitory role on motivation and reward-directed behavior (Miller & Cohen, 2001). Along with the ACC, they monitor conflicting situations induced by rewarding stimuli (Vogt, Vogt, Farber, & Bush, 2005; Walton, Bannerman, Alterescu, & Rushworth, 2003).

A systematic review by Harrison, O'Brien, Lopez, and Treasure (2010) showed decreased sensitivity to reward and increased sensitivity to punishment among individuals with EDs. These findings can be supported by neuroimaging research in AN, which shows hypoactivation in brain regions that healthy populations rely on to experience pleasure during food consumption (Holsen et al., 2012). One of these areas is the anterior insula, which drives motivational behavior (Craig, 2009). Individuals with

AN also show inhibited OFC and anterior insula activity when viewing food (Holsen et al., 2012; Uher et al., 2003), suggesting that they may be less prone to responding to its hedonic aspects.

In terms of inhibition during conflict monitoring, Uher et al. (2004) found that women with AN and BN exhibited higher activation of the mPFC in response to food, indicating potentially increased conflict monitoring. Moreover, individuals with BN showed blunted activation in the lateral PFC, paralleling the experience of loss of control over eating in this population.

Reward in overeating behavior has received contradictory findings and is understood as resulting from either hypoactivation of the mesolimbic reward areas (Bohon & Stice, 2011), inclining individuals to seek increased amounts of stimulation to feel pleasure, or hyperactivation of the reward and somatosensory systems, leading to increased pleasure derived from food intake (Schienle, Schäfer, Hermann, & Vaitl, 2009). In favor of the first model, one study found that those with BN showed increased activation of the insula (Schienle et al., 2009), potentially suggesting enhanced reward processing. Moreover, another study finds that women with BN and binge eating disorder show increased activation in the medial OFC when receiving food rewards and that this correlated with the tendency to eat in response to food cues (Simon et al., 2016). Nonetheless, as overeating only temporarily alleviates distress, it is likely to encourage a vicious cycle of overeating (Turton, Nazar, et al., 2017).

In other words, neuroimaging research shows that individuals with AN may be less prone to the hedonic aspects of food, which usually drive individuals to consume. During food consumption, they are also less sensitive to reward. Hence, they may be less likely to approach food and more likely to perceive food consumption as an aversive experience. Among binge-type eating disorders, on the other hand, some researchers hypothesize that these individuals are more likely to approach food, as they are more sensitive to their reward aspects, whereas others explain that they have a decreased sensitivity, inclining them to consume larger amounts of food to obtain the same level of reward.

Rejection Sensitivity

Individuals who have experienced family violence, emotional neglect, or conditional love may become more attentive to social threat cues and have a lower threshold of reaction to these cues (Romero-Canyas, Downey, Berenson, Ayduk, & Kang, 2010). Rejection sensitivity increases the risk of binge eating behavior (Romero-Canyas et al., 2010, p. 127).

Cardi, Matteo, Cornfield, & Treasure (2013) found that, as opposed to "healthy" controls, individuals with EDs exhibited vigilance and failure to disengage from rejecting, critical faces. Moreover, they also demonstrated avoidance of accepting and compassionate faces. This *attentional bias* was associated with anxiety and early aversive experiences (Cardi et al., 2013). Moreover, people with EDs, in comparison to "healthy" controls, were more likely to perceive hostile intent in faces (McFillin et al., 2012). These findings express dual difficulties, as they become not only more attentive to social threat cues but also less sensitive to rewarding ones.

The ventromedial prefrontal cortex (vmPFC) is implicated in many aspects of socioemotional functioning. Among "healthy" controls, researchers find a higher activation of the vmPFC during social rejection. Using a paradigm that induces brain circuitry implicated in social anxiety, research shows that females with body mass indices (BMIs) in the overweight or obese range, who experienced loss of control over eating, exhibited diminished vmPFC activation in response to peer rejection, whereas the opposite result was found for females who did not experience loss of control over eating (Jarcho et al., 2015). Thus, Sabatini et al. (2007) propose that loss of control over eating may be promoted by atypical brain activation patterns during experiences of social stress. As vmPFC activation usually facilitates regulation of negative affect, the inability of some individuals to show increased activation may make them more likely to use disordered eating to cope with socially threatening information (Jarcho et al., 2015).

▓ INTERVENTIONS FROM A NEURAL PERSPECTIVE

Neuroplasticity refers to the brain's ability to create new synaptic connections and reorganize them in response to learning and lifetime experiences (Livingston, 1966); it is a process that can be hindered by chronic stress (Boyle, 2013). Many treatment approaches aim to improve neuroplasticity through a variety of mechanisms.

Neuromodulation

Repetitive transcranial magnetic stimulation (rTMS) is a noninvasive method used to treat psychiatric disorders; it is thought to do so by increasing neuroplasticity. This treatment approach involves holding a stimulating coil close to the head, generating strong magnetic fields, and exciting neurons in a particular area of the brain. The majority of therapeutic rTMS studies have targeted the dlPFC. Some studies have found that it could reduce anxiety, the urge to exercise (Van den Eynde et al., 2013), and core symptoms of AN (McClelland, Kekic, Campbell, & Schmidt, 2016). A novel case series targeting the dorsomedial prefrontal cortex (dmPFC) explored its effectiveness among individuals with comorbid posttraumatic stress disorder and EDs, and found that it may be helpful in reducing posttraumatic symptoms and self-reported emotional regulation (Woodside et al., 2017). Furthermore, among people with BN, it reduced individuals' urge to eat and binge-eating episodes (Van den Eynde et al., 2010). Further research exploring neurocircuitry of EDs is required to better understand the areas to be targeted by TMS.

Deep brain stimulation is a neurosurgical technique that implants a pacemaker into the cortex, creating electrical impulses that aim to target particular dysfunctional brain circuits (Treasure, Cardi, Leppanen, & Turton, 2015). One trial testing its efficacy in treating severe, chronic AN found that it improved physical status (i.e., weight) among more than half of the participants (57%). In addition, it improved mood, anxiety, and affective regulation. Nonetheless, some participants experienced serious adverse side effects, including electrolyte imbalance and pain from the surgical incision (Lipsman et al., 2017).

Neurofeedback

Neurofeedback is a form of biofeedback in which individuals are trained to voluntarily regulate their brain activity in response to real-time feedback from a computer interface (Weiskopf, 2012). As it provides positive reinforcement, it may be used to promote feelings of self-efficacy among individuals with EDs (Etkin, 2012; Fairburn & Harrison, 2003), thus bridging the gap between psychotherapeutic approaches and neuromodulation techniques (Bartholdy, Musiat, Campbell, & Schmidt, 2013). Refer to Chapter 11 for further information about neurofeedback.

Neurocognitive Training

Inhibitory control training (ICT) is a valuable technique that reduces the experience of loss of control over eating (Treasure et al., 2015). Within this technique, patients are trained to inhibit their response to binge foods. One form of ICT, go/no-go training, has shown preliminary efficacy at reducing high-calorie food consumptions among restrained eaters (Adams, Lawrence, Verbruggen, & Chambers, 2017) and individuals with overweight and obese BMIs (Blackburne, Rodriguez, & Johnstone, 2016). A proof of concept study testing its efficacy in increasing inhibitory control among individuals with BN and binge eating disorder found only small nonsignificant reductions in high-calorie food consumption (Turton, Cardi, Treasure, & Hirsch 2017). Given the saliency of inhibitory control deficits in binge-subtype eating disorders (Turton, Cardi, Treasure, & Hirsch., 2017), it may be valuable for future studies to develop the design into more prolonged, multisession training.

Cognitive Bias Modification

Cognitive bias modification is an interventional, computer-based training that targets rejection sensitivity. One type of cognitive bias modification tackling attentional biases is the "attentional probe training task" (MacLeod, Mathews, & Tata, 1986), in which participants are trained and reinforced for attending to positive facial expressions. Another is the "ambiguous scenario training task" (Hirsch, Hayes, & Mathews, 2009), which trains participants to interpret ambiguous scenarios in a benign or neutral way. Using the two training tasks in combination, Cardi et al. (2015) found that patients with AN could be trained to redirect their attention toward accepting faces and to producing fewer negative interpretations of ambiguous scenarios. One session of training a positive response to ambiguous scenarios was associated with a reduction in negative interpretations (Turton, Nazar, et al., 2017).

Oxytocin and Social/Emotional Functioning

Chronic stress is an important moderator in the relationship between early life adversity and eating development (Dölen, Darvishzadeh, Huang, & Malenka, 2013; Hicks et al., 2012). Preclinical studies have found that the neuropeptide oxytocin may be involved in the regulation of social–emotional functioning (Dölen et al., 2013; Hicks et al., 2012). Using oxytocin as a target for treatment, research shows that oxytocin reduced cortisol in conditions of chronic stress (Cardoso, Kingdon, & Ellenbogen, 2014). Moreover, a similar reduction in cortisol was found among individuals with AN, suggesting that it may moderate the threat response (Leppanen et al., 2017; Russell et al., 2017).

■ CONCLUSION

Adverse life events interact with the genome and developmental processes, leading to biological changes that predispose one to a broad range of psychiatric problems, including EDs. The mechanisms involved include abnormalities in the stress response, changes in appetite, altered reward sensitivity, and increased sensitivity to rejection.

Specific genes increase one's susceptibility to stressful experiences, and stressful experiences have the ability to alter one's genes (i.e., epigenetics). Findings from epigenetic research and neural-based interventions offer evidence against the long-standing understanding of genes and neurocircuitry as "rigid" structures. Although these studies remain lacking and disintegrated, exploring specific circuitry and areas associated with these traits is an essential step in confronting different fragments of the illness and understanding the way they frame an individual as a whole.

■ REFERENCES

Ackard, D. M., Neumark-Sztainer, D., Hannan, P. J., French, S., & Story, M. (2001). Binge and purge behavior among adolescents: Associations with sexual and physical abuse in a nationally representative sample: The Commonwealth Fund survey. *Child Abuse & Neglect, 25*(6), 771–785. doi:10.1016/S0145-2134(01)00238-1

Adam, T. C., & Epel, E. S. (2007). Stress, eating and the reward system. *Physiology & Behavior, 91*(4), 449–458. doi:10.1016/j.physbeh.2007.04.011

Adams, R. C., Lawrence, N. S., Verbruggen, F., & Chambers, C. D. (2017). Training response inhibition to reduce food consumption: Mechanisms, stimulus specificity and appropriate training protocols. *Appetite, 109*, 11–23. doi:10.1016/j.appet.2016.11.014

Akkermann, K., Kaasik, K., Kiive, E., Nordquist, N., Oreland, L., & Harro, J. (2012). The impact of adverse life events and the serotonin transporter gene promoter polymorphism on the development of eating disorder symptoms. *Journal of Psychiatric Research, 46*(1), 38–43. doi:10.1016/j.jpsychires.2011.09.013

Arnsten, A. F. (2009). Stress signalling pathways that impair prefrontal cortex structure and function. *Nature Reviews Neuroscience, 10*(6), 410–422. doi:10.1038/nrn2648

Baker, L. M., Williams, L. M., Korgaonkar, M. S., Cohen, R. A., Heaps, J. M., & Paul, R. H. (2013). Impact of early vs. late childhood early life stress on brain morphometrics. *Brain Imaging and Behavior, 7*(2), 196–203. doi:10.1007/s11682-012-9215-y

Bartholdy, S., Musiat, P., Campbell, I. C., & Schmidt, U. (2013). The potential of neurofeedback in the treatment of eating disorders: A review of the literature. *European Eating Disorders Review, 21*(6), 456–463. doi:10.1002/erv.2250

Bijttebier, P., Beck, I., Claes, L., & Vandereycken, W. (2009). Gray's Reinforcement Sensitivity Theory as a framework for research on personality-psychopathology associations. *Clinical Psychology Review, 29*(5), 421–430. doi:10.1016/j.cpr.2009.04.002

Blackburne, T., Rodriguez, A., & Johnstone, S. J. (2016). A serious game to increase healthy food consumption in overweight or obese adults: Randomized controlled trial. *JMIR Serious Games, 4*(2), e10. doi:10.2196/games.5708

Bohon, C., & Stice, E. (2011). Reward abnormalities among women with full and subthreshold bulimia nervosa: A functional magnetic resonance imaging study. *International Journal of Eating Disorders, 44*(7), 585–595. doi:10.1002/eat.20869

Boyle, L. (2013). A neuroplasticity hypothesis of chronic stress in the basolateral amygdala. *Yale Journal of Biology and Medicine, 86*, 117–125. Retrieved from https://www.ncbi.nlm.nih.gov/pmc/articles/PMC3670432

Bremner, J. D., Krystal, J. H., Southwick, S. M., & Charney, D. S. (1996). Noradrenergic mechanisms in stress and anxiety: I. Preclinical studies. *Synapse, 23*(1), 28–38. doi:10.1002/(SICI)1098-2396(199605)23:1SUNIL28::AID-SYN4>3.0.CO;2-J

Bremner, J. D., Vythilingam, M., Anderson, G., Vermetten, E., McGlashan, T., Heninger, G., … Charney, D. S. (2003). Assessment of the hypothalamic-pituitary-adrenal axis over a 24-hour diurnal period and in response to neuroendocrine challenges in women with and without childhood sexual abuse and posttraumatic stress disorder. *Biological Psychiatry, 54*(7), 710–718. doi:10.1016/S0006-3223(02)01912-1

Calati, R., De Ronchi, D., Bellini, M., & Serretti, A. (2011). The 5-HTTLPR polymorphism and eating disorders: A meta-analysis. *International Journal of Eating Disorders, 44*(3), 191–199. doi:10.1002/eat.20811

Campbell, I. C., Mill, J., Uher, R., & Schmidt, U. (2011). Eating disorders, gene-environment interactions and epigenetics. *Neuroscience and Biobehavioral Reviews, 35*(3), 784–793. doi:10.1016/j.neubiorev.2010.09.012

Cardi, V., Esposito, M., Bird, G., Rhind, C., Yiend, J., Schifano, S., … Treasure, J. (2015). A preliminary investigation of a novel training to target cognitive biases towards negative social stimuli in anorexia nervosa. *Journal of Affective Disorders, 188*, 188–193. doi:10.1016/j.jad.2015.08.019

Cardi, V., Matteo, D. M., Cornfield, F., & Treasure, J. (2013). Social reward and rejection sensitivity in eating disorders: An investigation of attentional bias and early experiences. *World Journal of Biological Psychiatry, 14*(8), 622–633. doi:10.3109/15622975.2012.665479

Cardoso, C., Kingdon, D., & Ellenbogen, M. A. (2014). A meta-analytic review of the impact of intranasal oxytocin administration on cortisol concentrations during laboratory tasks: Moderation by method and mental health. *Psychoneuroendocrinology, 49*, 161–170. doi:10.1016/j.psyneuen.2014.07.014

Chuang, J. C., Perello, M., Sakata, I., Osborne-Lawrence, S., Savitt, J. M., Lutter, M., & Zigman, J. M. (2011). Ghrelin mediates stress-induced food-reward behavior in mice. *Journal of Clinical Investigation, 121*(7), 2684–2692. doi:10.1172/JCI57660

Cnattingius, S., Hultman, C. M., Dahl, M., & Sparén, P. (1999). Very preterm birth, birth trauma, and the risk of anorexia nervosa among girls. *Archives of General Psychiatry, 56*, 634–638. doi:10.1001/archpsyc.56.7.634

Cone, R. D., Low, M. J., Elmquist, J. K., & Cameron, J. L. (2003). Neuroendocrinology. In P. R. Larsen, H. M. Kronenberg, S. Melmed, & K. S. Polonsky (Eds.), *Williams textbook of endocrinology* (12th ed., pp. 81–176). Philadelphia, PA: Saunders.

Connan, F., Campbell, I. C., Katzman, M., Lightman, S. L., & Treasure, J. (2003). A neurodevelopmental model for anorexia nervosa. *Physiology & Behavior, 79*, 13–24. doi:10.1016/S0031-9384(03)00101-X

Craig, A. D. (2009). Emotional moments across time: A possible neural basis for time perception in the anterior insula. *Philosophical Transactions of the Royal Society of London. Series B, Biological Sciences, 364*(1525), 1933–1942. doi:10.1098/rstb.2009.0008

Crider, K. S., Yang, T. P., Berry, R. J., & Bailey, L. B. (2012). Folate and DNA methylation: A review of molecular mechanisms and the evidence for folate's role. *Advances in Nutrition, 3*(1), 21–38. doi:10.3945/an.111.000992

Dancause, K. N., Laplante, D. P., Hart, K. J., O'Hara, M. W., Elgbeili, G., Brunet, A., & King, S. (2015). Prenatal stress due to a natural disaster predicts adiposity in childhood: The Iowa Flood Study. *Journal of Obesity, 2015*, 570541. doi:10.1155/2015/570541

Deary, V., & Johnson, W. (2009). Looking for the fundamentals of human nature. *Journal of Mental Health, 18*(6), 459–466. doi:10.3109/09638230902946767

Dickson, S. L., Egecioglu, E., Landgren, S., Skibicka, K. P., Engel, J. A., & Jerlhag, E. (2011). The role of the central ghrelin system in reward from food and chemical drugs. *Molecular and Cellular Endocrinology, 340*(1), 80–87. doi:10.1016/j.mce.2011.02.017

Dölen, G., Darvishzadeh, A., Huang, K. W., & Malenka, R. C. (2013). Social reward requires coordinated activity of nucleus accumbens oxytocin and serotonin. *Nature, 501*(7466), 179–184. doi:10.1038/nature12518

Ernst, C., McGowan, P. O., Deleva, V., Meaney, M. J., Szyf, M., & Turecki, G. (2008). The effects of pH on DNA methylation state: In vitro and post-mortem brain studies. *Journal of Neuroscience Methods, 174*(1), 123–125. doi:10.1016/j.jneumeth.2008.06.027

Etkin, A. (2012). Neurobiology of anxiety: From neural circuits to novel solutions? *Depression and Anxiety, 29*, 355–358. doi:10.1002/da.21957

Fairburn, C. G., & Harrison, P. J. (2003). Eating disorders. *Lancet, 361*, 407–416. doi:10.1016/S0140-6736(03)12378-1

Gibb, B. E., Schofield, C. A., & Coles, M. E. (2009). Reported history of childhood abuse and young adults' information-processing biases for facial displays of emotion. *Child Maltreatment, 14*(2), 148–156. doi:10.1177/1077559508326358

Gray, J. A. (1970). The psychophysiological basis of introversion-extraversion. *Behaviour Research and Therapy, 8*, 249–266. doi:10.1016/0005-7967(70)90069-0

Gross, J. (1999). Emotion regulation: Past, present, future. *Cognition and Emotion, 13*, 551–573. doi:10.1080/026999399379186

Gunnar, M. R., & Donzella, B. (2001). Social regulation of the cortisol levels in early human development. *Psychoneuroendocrinology, 27*(1–2), 199–220. doi:10.1016/S0306-4530(01)00045-2

Gunnar, M. R., & Vazquez, D. (2015). Stress neurobiology and developmental psychopathology. In D. Cicchetti & D. J. Cohen (Eds.), *Developmental psychopathology* (2nd ed., pp. 533–577). Hoboken, NJ: Wiley.

Harrison, A., O'Brien, N., Lopez, C., & Treasure, J. (2010). Sensitivity to reward and punishment in eating disorders. *Psychiatry Research, 177*(1), 1–11. doi:10.1016/j.psychres.2009.06.010

Heatherton, T. F., & Baumeister, R. F. (1991). Binge eating as escape from self-awareness. *Psychological Bulletin, 110*, 86–108. doi:10.1037/0033-2909.110.1.86

Het, S., Vocks, S., Wolf, J. M., Hammelstein, P., Herpertz, S., & Wolf, O. T. (2015). Blunted neuroendocrine stress reactivity in young women with eating disorders. *Journal of Psychosomatic Research, 78*(3), 260–267. doi:10.1016/j.jpsychores.2014.11.001

Hicks, C., Jorgensen, W., Brown, C., Fardell, J., Koehbach, J., Gruber, C. W., ... McGregor, I. S. (2012). The nonpeptide oxytocin receptor agonist WAY 267,464: Receptor-binding profile, prosocial effects and distribution of c-Fos expression in adolescent rats. *Journal of Neuroendocrinology, 24*(7), 1012–1029. doi:10.1111/j.1365-2826.2012.02311.x

Hilterscheid, E., & Laessle, R. (2015). Stress-induced release of GUT peptides in young women classified as restrained or unrestrained eaters. *Eating and Weight Disorders, 20*(4), 435–439. doi:10.1007/s40519-015-0185-0

Hirsch, C. R., Hayes, S., & Mathews, A. (2009). Looking on the bright side: Accessing benign meanings reduces worry. *Journal of Abnormal Psychology, 118*(1), 44–54. doi:10.1037/a0013473

Holsen, L. M., Lawson, E. A., Blum, J., Ko, E., Makris, N., Fazeli, P. K., ... Goldstein, J. M. (2012). Food motivation circuitry hypoactivation related to hedonic and nonhedonic aspects of hunger and satiety in women with active anorexia nervosa and weight-restored women with anorexia nervosa. *Journal of Psychiatry & Neuroscience, 37*(5), 322. doi:10.1503/jpn.110156

Hostinar, C. E., Sullivan, R. M., & Gunnar, M. R. (2014). Psychobiological mechanisms underlying the social buffering of the hypothalamic-pituitary-adrenocortical axis: A review of animal models and human studies across development. *Psychological Bulletin, 140*(1), 256–282. doi:10.1037/a0032671

Jahng, J. W. (2011). An animal model of eating disorders associated with stressful experience in early life. *Hormones and Behavior, 59*(2), 213–220. doi:10.1016/j.yhbeh.2010.11.010

Jappe, L. M., Frank, G. K., Shott, M. E., Rollin, M. D., Pryor, T., Hagman, J. O., ... Davis, E. (2011). Heightened sensitivity to reward and punishment in anorexia nervosa. *International Journal of Eating Disorders, 44*(4), 317–324. doi:10.1002/eat.20815

Jarcho, J. M., Tanofsky-Kraff, M., Nelson, E. E., Engel, S. G., Vannucci, A., Field, S. E., ... Yanovski, J. A. (2015). Neural activation during anticipated peer evaluation and laboratory meal intake in overweight girls with and without loss of control eating. *NeuroImage, 108*, 343–353. doi:10.1016/j.neuroimage.2014.12.054

Joëls, M., Fernandez, G., & Roozendaal, B. (2011). Stress and emotional memory: A matter of timing. *Trends in Cognitive Sciences, 15*, 280–288. doi:10.1016/j.tics.2011.04.004

Karwautz, A. F., Wagner, G., Waldherr, K., Nader, I. W., Fernandez-Aranda, F., Estivill, X., ... Treasure, J. L. (2011). Gene-environment interaction in anorexia nervosa: Relevance of non-shared environment and the serotonin transporter gene. *Molecular Psychiatry, 16*(6), 590. doi:10.1038/mp.2010.125

Leppanen, J., Cardi, V., Ng, K. W., Paloyelis, Y., Stein, D., Tchanturia, K., & Treasure, J. (2017). Effects of intranasal oxytocin on the interpretation and expression of emotions in anorexia nervosa. *Journal of Neuroendocrinology, 29*(3). doi:10.1111/jne.12458.

Lipsman, N., Lam, E., Volpini, M., Sutandar, K., Twose, R., Giacobbe, P., ... Lozano, A. M. (2017). Deep brain stimulation of the subcallosal cingulate for treatment-refractory anorexia nervosa: 1 year follow-up of an open-label trial. *Lancet Psychiatry, 4*(4), 285–294. doi:10.1016/S2215-0366(17)30076-7

Livingston, R. B. (1966). Brain mechanisms in conditioning and learning. *Neurosciences Research Program Bulletin, 4*(3), 349–354.

MacLeod, C., Mathews, A., & Tata, P. (1986). Attentional bias in emotional disorders. *Journal of Abnormal Psychology, 95*(1), 15. doi:10.1037/0021-843X.95.1.15

Malter Cohen, M., Jing, D., Yang, R. R., Tottenham, N., Lee, F. S., & Casey, B. J. (2013). Early-life stress has persistent effects on amygdala function and development in mice and humans. *Proceedings of the National Academy of Sciences of the United States of America, 110*(45), 18274–18278. doi:10.1073/pnas.1310163110

McClelland, J., Kekic, M., Campbell, I. C., & Schmidt, U. (2016). Repetitive transcranial magnetic stimulation (rTMS) treatment in enduring anorexia nervosa: A case series. *European Eating Disorders Review, 24*(2), 157–163. doi:10.1002/erv.2414

McFadden, K. L., Tregellas, J. R., Shott, M. E., & Frank, G. K. (2014). Reduced salience and default mode network activity in women with anorexia nervosa. *Journal of Psychiatry & Neuroscience, 39*(3), 178. doi:10.1503/jpn.130046

McFillin, R. K., Cahn, S. C., Burks, V. S., Levine, M. P., Loney, S. L., & Levine, R. L. (2012). Social information-processing and coping in adolescent females diagnosed with an eating disorder: Toward a greater understanding of control. *Eating Disorders, 20*(1), 42–59. doi:10.1080/10640266.2012.635565

Melia, K. R., & Duman, R. S. (1991). Involvement of corticotropin-releasing factor in chronic stress regulation of the brain noradrenergic system. *Proceedings of the National Academy of Sciences of the United States of America, 88*, 8382–8386. doi:10.1073/pnas.88.19.8382

Menzel, J. E., Schaefer, L. M., Burke, N. L., Mayhew, L. L., Brannick, M. T., & Thompson, J. K. (2010). Appearance-related teasing, body dissatisfaction, and disordered eating: A meta-analysis. *Body Image, 7*, 261–270. doi:10.1016/j.bodyim.2010.05.004

Micali, N., Simonoff, E., & Treasure, J. (2011). Pregnancy and post-partum depression and anxiety in a longitudinal general population cohort: The effect of eating disorders and past depression. *Journal of Affective Disorders, 131*, 150–157. doi:10.1016/j.jad.2010.09.034

Miller, E. K., & Cohen, J. D. (2001). An integrative theory of prefrontal cortex function. *Annual Review of Neuroscience, 24*, 167–202. doi:10.1146/annurev.neuro.24.1.167

Misra, M., & Klibanski, A. (2016). Anorexia nervosa and its associated endocrinopathy in young people. *Hormone Research in Paediatrics, 85*(3), 147–157. doi:10.1159/000443735

Mitchell, C., Notterman, D., Brooks-Gunn, J., Hobcraft, J., Garfinkel, I., Jaeger, K., … McLanahan, S. (2010). *The role of mother's genes and environment in postpartum depression.* Paper presented at Integrating Genetics and the Social Sciences, Boulder, CO.

Monteleone, A. M., Castellini, G., Volpe, U., Ricca, V., Lelli, L., Monteleone, P., & Maj, M. (2017). Neuroendocrinology and brain imaging of reward in eating disorders: A possible key to the treatment of anorexia nervosa and bulimia nervosa. *Progress in Neuro-Psychopharmacology and Biological Psychiatry, 80*(Pt B), 132–142. doi:10.1016/j.pnpbp.2017.02.020

Monteleone, A. M., Monteleone, P., Dalle Grave, R., Nigro, M., El Ghoch, M., Calugi, S., … Maj, M. (2016). Ghrelin response to hedonic eating in underweight and short-term weight restored patients with anorexia nervosa. *Psychiatry Research, 235*, 55–60. doi:10.1016/j.psychres.2015.12.001

Monteleone, P., Scognamiglio, P., Monteleone, A. M., Perillo, D., & Maj, M. (2014). Cortisol awakening response in patients with anorexia nervosa or bulimia nervosa: Relationships to sensitivity to reward and sensitivity to punishment. *Psychological Medicine, 44*(12), 2653–2660. doi:10.1017/S0033291714000270

Monteleone, P., Tortorella, A., Scognamiglio, P., Serino, I., Monteleone, A. M., & Maj, M. (2012). The acute salivary ghrelin response to a psychosocial stress is enhanced in symptomatic patients with bulimia nervosa: A pilot study. *Neuropsychobiology, 66*(4), 230–236. doi:10.1159/000341877

Obradović, J., Bush, N. R., Stamperdahl, J., Adler, N. E., & Boyce, W. T. (2010). Biological sensitivity to context: The interactive effects of stress reactivity and family adversity on socioemotional behavior and school readiness. *Child Development, 81*(1), 270–289. doi:10.1111/j.1467-8624.2009.01394.x

Phillips, M. L., Drevets, W. C., Rauch, S. L., & Lane, R. (2003). Neurobiology of emotion perception I: The neural basis of normal emotion perception. *Biological Psychiatry, 54*, 504–514.

Rojo, L., Conesa, L., Bermudez, O., & Livianos, L. (2006). Influence of stress in the onset of eating disorders: Data from a two-stage epidemiologic controlled study. *Psychosomatic Medicine, 68*, 628–635. doi:10.1097/01.psy.0000227749.58726.41

Romero-Canyas, R., Downey, G., Berenson, K., Ayduk, O., & Kang, N. J. (2010). Rejection sensitivity and the rejection-hostility link in romantic relationships. *Journal of Personality, 78*(1), 119–148. doi:10.1111/j.1467-6494.2009.00611.x

Rorty, M., Yager, J., Rossotto, E., & Buckwalter, G. (2000). Parental intrusiveness in adolescence recalled by women with a history of bulimia nervosa and comparison women. *International*

Journal of Eating Disorders, 28, 202–208. doi:10.1002/1098-108X(200009)28:2<202::AID-EAT9 >3.0.CO;2-G

Rozenblat, V., Ng, D., Fuller-Tyszkiewicz, M., Akkermann, K., Collier, D., Engels, R., … Krug, I. (2016). A meta-analysis of gene (5-HTT) × environment interactions in eating pathology using secondary data analyses. *European Psychiatry, 33,* S83–S84. doi:10.1016/ j.eurpsy.2016.01.035

Russell, J., Maguire, S., Kesby, A., McGregor, I., O'Dell, A., & Treasure, J. (2017). Oxytocin as a treatment enhancer in anorexia nervosa. *European Psychiatry, 41,* S37. doi:10.1016/j .eurpsy.2017.01.171

Sabatini, M. J., Ebert, P., Lewis, D. A., Levitt, P., Cameron, J. L., & Mirnics, K. (2007). Amygdala gene expression correlates of social behavior in monkeys experiencing maternal separation. *Journal of Neuroscience, 27*(12), 3295–3304. doi:10.1523/JNEUROSCI.4765-06.2007

Sapolsky, R. M., Krey, L. C., & McEwen, B. S. (1985). Prolonged glucocorticoid exposure reduces hippocampal neuron number: Implications for aging. *Journal of Neuroscience, 5,* 1222–1227. doi:10.1523/JNEUROSCI.05-05-01222.1985

Schellekens, H., Finger, B. C., Dinan, T. G., & Cryan, J. F. (2012). Ghrelin signalling and obesity: At the interface of stress, mood and food reward. *Pharmacology & Therapeutics, 135*(3), 316–326. doi:10.1016/j.pharmthera.2012.06.004

Schienle, A., Schäfer, A., Hermann, A., & Vaitl, D. (2009). Binge-eating disorder: Reward sensitivity and brain activation to images of food. *Biological Psychiatry, 65*(8), 654–661. doi:10.1016/ j.biopsych.2008.09.028

Simon, J. J., Skunde, M., Walther, S., Bendszus, M., Herzog, W., & Friederich, H. C. (2016). Neural signature of food reward processing in bulimic-type eating disorders. *Social Cognitive and Affective Neuroscience, 11*(9), 1393–1401. doi:10.1093/scan/nsw049

Skibicka, K. P., & Dickson, S. L. (2011). Ghrelin and food reward: The story of potential underlying substrates. *Peptides, 32*(11), 2265–2273. doi:10.1016/j.peptides.2011.05.016

St-Hilaire, A., Steiger, H., Liu, A., Laplante, D. P., Thaler, L., Magill, T., & King, S. (2015). A prospective study of effects of prenatal maternal stress on later eating-disorder manifestations in affected offspring: Preliminary indications based on the Project Ice Storm cohort. *International Journal of Eating Disorders, 48*(5), 512–516. doi:10.1002/eat.22391

Strober, M., Peris, T., & Steiger, H. (2014). The plasticity of development: How knowledge of epigenetics may advance understanding of eating disorders. *International Journal of Eating Disorders, 47*(7), 696–704. doi:10.1002/eat.22322

Taborelli, E., Krug, I., Karwautz, A., Wagner, G., Haidvogl, M., Fernandez-Aranda, F., … Micali, N. (2013). Maternal anxiety, overprotection and anxious personality as risk factors for eating disorder: A sister pair study. *Cognitive Therapy and Research, 37*(4), 820–828. doi:10.1007/ s10608-012-9518-8

Teicher, M. H., & Samson, J. A. (2013). Childhood maltreatment and psychopathology: A case for ecophenotypic variants as clinically and neurobiologically distinct subtypes. *American Journal of Psychiatry, 170*(10), 1114–1133. doi:10.1176/appi.ajp.2013.12070957

Teicher, M. H., Samson, J. A., Anderson, C. M., & Ohashi, K. (2016). The effects of childhood maltreatment on brain structure, function and connectivity. *Nature Reviews Neuroscience, 17*(10), 652–666. doi:10.1038/nrn.2016.111

Tolle, V., Kadem, M., Bluet-Pajot, M. T., Frere, D., Foulon, C., Bossu, C., … Estour, B. (2003). Balance in ghrelin and leptin plasma levels in anorexia nervosa patients and constitutionally thin women. *Journal of Clinical Endocrinology and Metabolism, 88*(1), 109–116. doi:10.1210/jc.2002-020645

Treasure, J., Cardi, V., Leppanen, J., & Turton, R. (2015). New treatment approaches for severe and enduring eating disorders. *Physiology & Behavior, 152,* 456–465. doi:10.1016/j.physbeh.2015.06.007

Troop, N. A., & Treasure, J. L. (1997). Setting the scene for eating disorders, II. Childhood helplessness and mastery. *Psychological Medicine, 27,* 531–538.

Turton, R., Cardi, V., Treasure, J., & Hirsch, C. R. (2017). Modifying a negative interpretation bias for ambiguous social scenarios that depict the risk of rejection in women with anorexia nervosa. *Journal of Affective Disorders, 227,* 705–712. doi:10.1016/j.jad.2017.11.089

Turton, R., Chami, R., & Treasure, J. (2017). Emotional eating, binge eating and animal models of binge-type eating disorders. *Current Obesity Reports, 6*(2), 217–228. doi:10.1007/ s13679-017-0265-8

Turton, R., Nazar, B. P., Burgess, E. E., Lawrence, N. S., Cardi, V., Treasure, J., & Hirsch, C. R. (2017). To go or not to go: A proof of concept study testing food-specific inhibition training for women with eating and weight disorders. *European Eating Disorders Review, 26*(1), 11–21. doi:10.1002/erv.2566

Uher, R., Brammer, M. J., Murphy, T., Campbell, I. C., Ng, V. W., Williams, S. C., & Treasure, J. (2003). Recovery and chronicity in anorexia nervosa: Brain activity associated with differential outcomes. *Biological Psychiatry, 54*(9), 934–942. doi:10.1016/S0006-3223(03)00172-0

Uher, R., Murphy, T., Brammer, M. J., Dalgleish, T., Phillips, M. L., Ng, V. W., ... Treasure, J. (2004). Medial prefrontal cortex activity associated with symptom provocation in eating disorders. *American Journal of Psychiatry, 161*(7), 1238–1246. doi:10.1176/appi.ajp.161.7.1238

Ulrich-Lai, Y. M., & Herman, J. P. (2009). Neural regulation of endocrine and autonomic stress responses. *Nature Reviews Neuroscience, 10*, 397–409. doi:10.1038/nrn2647

Van den Eynde, F., Claudino, A. M., Mogg, A., Horrell, L., Stahl, D., Ribeiro, W., ... Schmidt, U. (2010). Repetitive transcranial magnetic stimulation reduces cue-induced food craving in bulimic disorders. *Biological Psychiatry, 67*(8), 793–795. doi:10.1016/j.biopsych.2009

Van den Eynde, F., & Guillaume, S. (2013). Neuromodulation techniques and eating disorders. *International Journal of Eating Disorders, 46*(5), 447–450. doi:10.1002/eat.22100

Van den Eynde, F., Guillaume, S., Broadbent, H., Campbell, I. C., & Schmidt, U. (2013). Repetitive transcranial magnetic stimulation in anorexia nervosa: A pilot study. *European Psychiatry, 28*(2), 98–101. doi:10.1016/j.eurpsy.2011.06.002

Vogt, B., Vogt, L., Farber, N. B., & Bush, G. (2005). Architecture and neurocytology of monkey cingulate gyrus. *Journal of Comparative Neurology, 485*, 218–239. doi:10.1002/cne.20512

Walton, M. E., Bannerman, D. M., Alterescu, K., & Rushworth, M. F. (2003). Functional specialization within medial frontal cortex of the anterior cingulate for evaluating effort-related decisions. *Journal of Neuroscience, 23*, 6475–6479. doi:10.1523/JNEUROSCI.23-16-06475.2003

Weiskopf, N. (2012). Real-time fMRI and its application to neurofeedback. *Neuroimage, 62*(2), 682–692. doi:10.1016/j.neuroimage.2011.10.009

Whittle, S., Dennison, M., Vijayakumar, N., Simmons, J. G., Yücel, M., Lubman, D. I., ... Allen, N. B. (2013). Childhood maltreatment and psychopathology affect brain development during adolescence. *Journal of the American Academy of Child and Adolescent Psychiatry, 52*(9), 940–952. doi:10.1016/j.jaac.2013.06.007

Woodside, D. B., Colton, P., Lam, E., Dunlop, K., Rzeszutek, J., & Downar, J. (2017). Dorsomedial prefrontal cortex repetitive transcranial magnetic stimulation treatment of posttraumatic stress disorder in eating disorders: An open-label case series. *International Journal of Eating Disorders, 50*(10), 1231–1234. doi:10.1002/eat.22764

Zonnevylle-Bender, M. J., van Goozen, S. H., Cohen-Kettenis, P. T., Jansen, L. M., van Elburg, A., & van Engeland, H. (2005). Adolescent anorexia nervosa patients have a discrepancy between neurophysiological responses and self-reported emotional arousal to psychosocial stress. *Psychiatry Research, 135*(1), 45–52. doi:10.1016/j.psychres.2004.11.006

CHAPTER 6

What Doctors, Dietitians, and Nutritionists Need to Know

Edward P. Tyson and Carolyn Hodges-Chaffee

■ PART 1: WHAT DOCTORS NEED TO KNOW

Overview of Trauma and Eating Disorders

Eating disorders (EDs) are common chronic illnesses that most clinicians, regardless of specialty, will encounter at some point, and trauma is universal in those who have EDs. Trauma from physical and/or psychological injuries overwhelms the mind and body's capacity to adapt, and can set off or perpetuate an already present ED. The primary physical traumas induced by EDs are from malnutrition, which occurs with every ED, and because every organ system requires adequate nutrition, all body systems are impaired. Just as a concussion is a generalized injury to the brain and is miserable to experience, malnutrition is a generalized injury to the entire body, including the brain, and the shock to the body is profound. A myriad of psychological injuries from a variety of sources always occurs in EDs and is both painful and destabilizing. These traumas do not include other painful events that may have preceded the ED, and that may have had a role in its formation or its prolongation. The brain and body respond to these insults by trying to avoid them when possible, or by adapting as quickly as they can, but in trauma, these adaptive strategies are overwhelmed. The clinician should be mindful that trauma can build up over time as one slowly decays from an ED physically and psychologically, or it can occur in a tornadic burst of time.

Brain Changes in Eating Disorders

As in other causes of trauma, anorexia nervosa (AN) has been shown to cause a notable loss of brain mass, especially in the hippocampus and amygdala regions (Giordano et al., 2001). Decreased blood flow to the temporal region and impairment of visual memory and visuospatial capacity have been shown in early onset AN (Lask et al., 2005), as well as in adult women with AN (Key, O'Brien, Gordon, Christie, & Lask, 2006). The latter also had deficits in memory associated with temporal lobe function. In an extensive review of MRIs (10 studies, 236 patients; Van den Eynde et al., 2012) looking at structural changes in EDs, preliminary data indicate that those with AN have decreased gray matter in various regions of the brain, and those with bulimia nervosa (BN) have increased gray matter volume in frontal and striatal areas. Studies also indicated that the previously mentioned changes may reverse with treatment. A review of neuroimaging studies in AN, BN, and binge eating disorder (BED; Frank, Bailer, Henry,

Wagner, & Kaye, 2004) found similar problems with loss of phospholipids and volume of gray and white matter (which appeared to at least partly recover), as well as abnormalities in blood flow, glucose metabolism, and serotonin receptors. This review found that although there were fewer studies done in BN and BED, there may be disturbances of serotonin metabolism in similar brain areas as seen in AN.

A systematic review of functional neuroimaging studies in AN found functional problems in the frontal, parietal, and cingulate areas in both restricting and binge/purge types of AN. Most consistent were the networks involved in attention, arousal and emotional processing, frontal visual, reward processing, and how the body is perceived in space (Van den Eynde et al., 2012). A small study of adolescents tested for working memory by means of functional MRI and psychopathological scales found hyperactivation in the temporal and parietal areas compared with controls; those with lower body mass index (BMI) had higher activation. After 7 months of treatment and weight restoration, these differences from controls disappeared (Frank et al., 2004). By way of summary, it is clear that the brain undergoes significant negative alterations from an ED, and some of them, at least, appear to recover after treatment.

Physical Trauma in Malnutrition and Eating Disorders

Physical trauma, including starvation from any cause, can help trigger dysfunctional eating behaviors and, probably, an actual ED in some cases. In the original study of starvation, conducted by Ancel Keys at the close of WWII (the Minnesota Starvation Experiment), the conscientious objectors who volunteered to "starve so that others be better fed" developed many of the behaviors that are seen in EDs (Kalm & Semba, 2005). Similarly, many who seek care for an ED are athletes who want to be better at their sport or others who want to be "healthier." Both groups typically restrict certain aspects of their intake and get caught up in the vacuum of an ED without having intended to do so.

One common complaint is the cold one experiences as the body temperature can drop several degrees to save energy. The cold can be constant and gnawing and sufferers will try a variety of external ways to get warmer, including using blankets or multiple layers of clothes, when others are comfortable. It is not uncommon for those to use hot baths or showers to feel warm. But that method can result in trauma, as the hot water opens blood vessels in the skin, which can drop the blood pressure, causing one to pass out and fall in the shower, or even drown in the tub. Cognitive slowing is also real and troubling in malnutrition and can have downstream effects on issues such as academic, athletic, and job performance, all of which can be quite traumatic in and of themselves.

EDs can also be triggered by physical trauma, such as illnesses or conditions that focus on or cause a restriction of intake of some food and/or fluids. These can include a variety of illnesses such as diabetes, celiac and Crohn's diseases, AIDS, mononucleosis (where the prolonged sore throat prevents intake of food and fluids), as well as dental, throat, jaw, or abdominal surgery, food poisoning, and such. These situations may trigger an ED, most likely because of unintentionally depleting one or more of the body's key resources, which sets off a downstream set of responses by the brain and body to prevent recurrence. The brain responds paradoxically to keep one uninterested in or resistant to food, and triggers body dysmorphia (a misreading of body cues), and possible bingeing, against all logic, education, and normal physiology. One pharmacist well educated about her celiac disease (an autoimmune disorder where eating gluten causes serious physical injury to the small intestine and other serious reactions, such as intractable vomiting) would appropriately restrict gluten, but then would intention-ally binge on gluten-containing foods in spite of knowing it would also cause her to vomit. Another 13-year-old patient with celiac avoided all gluten, but then that in turn triggered her to restrict other foods until she was dangerously ill from the resulting malnutrition.

Although most unfamiliar with EDs would think that starvation triggers hunger, after a while, starvation can beget more starvation. Another example of this positive feedback loop (which is not very "positive") occurs when the brain increases energy expenditure in the face of starvation. This phenomenon has been seen and studied in rats for decades and has been called activity-based anorexia (Hebebrand et al., 2003). It can lead to death, if not interrupted. Interestingly, adding food to the cage of those rats may not stop the nutritional decline. However, removing the running wheel stopped the hyperactivity. In athletes with EDs, restricting exercise can be completely contrary to their nature, and is often experienced as a serious trauma, with the same kinds of reac-tions seen with other traumas, including a major negative effect on self-worth and, for some, on future economic worth.

Association of Traumatic Events and Food/Eating

The gastrointestinal tract–brain connection has been a focus of intense research in recent years, almost as if none of us ever knew it existed before. But we all have known that upset feelings can affect our gut and vice versa, such as "gut feelings" and "butterflies in my stomach." Most of us have heard or used the expression "That makes me sick to my stomach." Emotional trauma can set off restricted intake of food and/or fluids. Moreover, if food or the sensations around food and eating are associated with seri-ously negative experiences, when the amygdala detects a similar experience, it can trig-ger a traumatic reexperiencing and a hyperreactive response. One young woman had emetophobia, an intense fear of vomiting. However, her fear grew such that almost any food might trigger vomiting, and, as a result, she became severely malnourished, devel-oped refeeding syndrome (RFS; described later in the chapter), and required treatment in an ICU for several weeks to recover. Interestingly, the reality of being so near death and in an ICU eliminated her fear of vomiting, and she soon resumed her normal eating patterns.

Another case of emetophobia occurred in a 14-year-old boy after witnessing a friend vomiting. This patient's reaction was so strong that to avoid any possibility of vomiting, he developed avoidant/restrictive food intake disorder (ARFID) and restricted more and more types and volumes of food until he became seriously malnourished, requir-ing 3 months of intensive treatment to break that fear, although his ED required more outpatient care.

One patient who was sexually abused by both parents would only drink regular Pepsi, even though she restricted everything else. Growing up in her family, the males ate first, then her mother, and what was left, if anything, was for her and her sister. It is no surprise that both she and her sister (as well as her mother and maternal grand-mother) developed EDs. The girls were never allowed soft drinks either, but her parents would drink regular Pepsi in front of them. When my patient finally moved out of the house, she still restricted her food, but in an unrealized and isolated act of defiance (and perhaps some identification with her abusers), she would only drink Pepsi.

Food restriction in victims of oral sodomy can be toward white liquids such as milk, yogurt, and ice cream. As one would expect, eating or considering eating those foods can trigger instant flashbacks and a stream of other traumatic reactions. But a lack of knowledge on the part of the physician of the prior trauma can lead one to have unrealistic expectations in getting such a patient to eat those foods.

Trauma Resulting From Eating Disorder Treatment

Dietitians and physicians focus on the physical aspects of trauma in EDs and how to reverse the destruction, but it is important to remember that often the treatment itself can be traumatic. The first goal is to reverse the nutritional decline. However, this can be one of the most medically precarious times in treatment. RFS is a life-threatening condition in EDs that can even cause sudden death. It occurs during refeeding when the body starts to increase its use of energy stores, but then it runs out of those stores as more of the body increases its metabolism. Cells that use the most energy start to have dysfunction first, including brain, cardiac and skeletal muscle, and red blood cells. Generally, those with chronic or rapidly worsening malnutrition are those most at risk, and may require admission to an ICU as in the case of the young woman discussed earlier. This intervention can be an intimidating and scary place for the patient, with a cost that can put a person in great debt. Tube feedings can be one of the necessary treatments, but even the thought of being "force fed" by a tube is horrifying to almost anyone with an ED. The medical guide from the Academy for Eating Disorders Medical Care Standards Committee (2016) has more details on how to prevent, assess, and manage RFS.

As we saw in the Keys study, it is not unusual for those who have recovered from an ED to state that the treatment was felt to be harder than the starvation. It took some of the men 2 years to recover. It is not uncommon, for example, for patients who have been through some treatment to state they "would never do that again," in spite of it saving their life. When asked why, the expression of their disdain for their experience can be almost palpable. It is often because of how they felt as their body began to adapt, but those adaptations can be uncomfortable, and even painful. This can also occur in those who are in school and who must decrease or stop academic pursuits for a time.

There is also the impact of inpatient treatment. Treatment at a higher level of care at an ED center, as in hospitalization or residential treatment, means the person must be separate from family and friends. The burden of separation from and of the family, especially at a young age or if one has young children, is a heavy strain on everyone, and requires deliberate and careful intervention.

Financial injury and employment futures may be severely impaired by having to be in at a higher level of care. Employers may not have an opening on one's return to work. A patient with AN who was a professional ballerina from another country had to maintain some level of training during treatment or else her entire career was in jeopardy, and she would have to return to her native country starting from scratch to make a living. Without that career, how could she afford the insurance and the medical bills and huge debt that come from adequate treatment? Just the threat of those prospects made her agreeing to treatment much more difficult. Financial trauma from treatment can lead to abandoning a work or college career, or doing without many of the usual comforts or pleasures that require some financial capacity. Treatment can lead to major debt, but without a way to pay off that debt. When faced with these future and additional traumas, it shows great courage to enter treatment.

Medical and nutritional assessment and treatment require physical examination of the sufferer. Getting on a scale without knowing what it says (called a "blind weight") can trigger obsessive rumination over the number on the scale. But knowing the weight can also set off obsession about the number for days, regardless of that number being up, down, or the same. Most persons take a long time before they are comfortable with being weighed, whether it be blind or not.

Other parts of the examination obviously require touching a patient. Any touch on any part of the body may trigger posttraumatic stress disorder (PTSD)-like reactions for some. There are areas of the body where most people are not comfortable being touched, even by a doctor, especially the breast, buttock, and anogenital areas. Someone who was victimized by sexual trauma may experience a revivification during the examination. That can come in the form of withdrawing, freezing, resistance, or dissociating. Even the thought of being examined can trigger those reactions. This can occur in spite of the most careful, empathic, and gentle approach. For example, feeling on the neck and palpating the thyroid or lymph nodes of someone who had a history of being choked or sodomized could suddenly trigger recurrence of the feelings that occurred during the assault. Physicians should show compassion and sensitivity to examine any part of the body of a patient with an ED and only after describing what will be done and why, and after offering an opportunity to ask questions or to refuse the examination.

If someone must have tube feedings (and even if agreed to initially by the patient), the practitioner must anticipate what that person could reexperience when the tube is inserted, and, perhaps worse, when the tube has to remain inserted. If a patient has to have a genital or breast examination, that person might reexperience yet one more act of invasion in a very private part of his or her body. Other somatic triggers from a physical examination that can trigger old trauma include drawing blood for lab, doing an ECG, taking an oral temperature, or even having the patient lie down on the examination table. Inappropriate comments from physicians, such as "You don't look like you have an eating disorder" or "We'll have you fattened up in no time," can confuse, horrify, or cause one to reject any treatment.

If a patient or client has an "excessive" reaction to touching or examining a particular part of the body, the following can help the physician make the person feel safe: stopping what is being done; asking the person whether he or she is okay; seeing whether he or she can explain what he or she is experiencing; reminding him or her that he or she is in complete control, and not one thing will be done to him or her without him or her feeling safe about it and agreeing to it; and certainly seeing whether he or she would prefer someone else be in the room with them. If the person is still in a traumatized state, try interventions such as distraction, talking about a completely different subject, having them state simple truths (such as "I am 23. I live in Texas"), and using benign physical sensations, such as a wet wash cloth, to ground them.

Finally, there is another treatment trauma that physicians and others need to consider when working with EDs. Those who suffered serious trauma and PTSD need to feel safe to recover. But they have a difficult time attaching to those trying to help them, because one of the consequences of trauma is to be guarded and less trusting. Many who need treatment from EDs need to be at higher levels of care, including hospitalization, residential treatment, partial hospitalization, and intensive outpatient care. The significant trend by third-party payers to inappropriately limit stays in the higher levels of care has forced many sufferers to leave a treatment team when they may have just developed enough trust in their team to open up and begin the hard emotional work. If that attachment is suddenly broken off, the patient can experience this as another trauma, a reenactment of prior abandonment. Even though it was directed by an insurance company, patients can generalize the trauma to any treatment. As one would guess, those persons are then much less likely to seek future help for fear of being abandoned yet again.

■ PART 2: NUTRITION AND THE TRAUMA PATIENT

The nutritional support of an individual who struggles with an ED and is a trauma survivor can be one of the most challenging tasks a dietitian encounters. There are many layers that have to be explored and understood before an eating plan can be developed, and, through-out the process, the needs change and require ongoing assessment and modifications. Before assessing the nutritional needs of the trauma patient, most clinicians do not realize that someone does not have to look underfed to be severely malnourished. Malnutrition is difficult to identify in a normal-weight or higher weight individual. One of the most accu-rate ways to assess the nutritional status of the body is to do two types of tests: metabolic testing and body composition analysis (BCA). Both are explained later in the chapter.

The effect that underfeeding the body has on the brain can have lasting consequences and directly affect the body's ability to recover. In addition to being necessary for recovery from an ED, nutritional support is critical to effectively treat PTSD.

The Brain and Malnutrition

The brain's number one fuel is simple sugars and glucose. These are found in grains, fruits, vegetables, refined sugar, and dairy products. Some of these foods are either elimi-nated or severely restricted when an individual is struggling with an ED. The brain has to have energy to function and manage emotions for it to operate optimally. When the brain is not fed, those brain systems that require less energy take over. These are older brain structures that run on threat detection and emotion. These systems are already hypersensitive for individuals struggling with PTSD. Maintaining the body nutritionally helps balance out the body and allows all the systems to run at the same time. When the nutritional intake is restricted, the body does not have the emotional energy to feel and the individual's ability to process emotional feelings is much less. Clients may welcome feeling numb, but this will also stall them in their therapeutic process.

The Gut and Malnutrition

The gut is also greatly affected by the stress of malnutrition. It is often referred to as the second brain and directly affects the brain functioning. Serotonin is a neurotransmitter found in the brain that regulates sleep, mood, and emotions. The majority of serotonin in the body is found in the gut. The body's level of serotonin is directly influenced by how someone eats. Those who restrict their intake will have less carbohydrate and protein available, and the body needs both of these nutrients to manufacture serotonin. There is also decreased nutrient absorption and often an increase in food sensitivities. There is a change in the gut flora populations (microbiome) that can result in a decrease in the production of neurotransmitters needed to help regulate depression and mood. There is also a decreased enzymatic output in the gut, resulting in bloating and constipation that make it much more difficult to consume the food needed to maintain adequate nutri-tional intake. These changes can contribute to a malnourished gut and brain that can impact both neural function and brain chemistry. Multiple functions of the brain can be impaired including concentration, memory, sleep, and mood.

The Nutritional Assessment

A complete history and comprehensive nutritional assessment is key to nutritional support of the individual. Determining the nutritional needs and then creating a food plan that is possible for the patient to achieve is necessary for nutritional support. It is difficult for individuals to understand that the body has caloric demands even when in a vegetative state. Metabolism is the sum of the physical and chemical changes that occur in the body. Our bodies work 24/7 regardless of whether we are awake or asleep. The body is forming new cells, hormones, and enzymes; repairing tissue; growing bone and muscle; and regulating many other processes that are all part of the metabolic function. A minimum of 1,200 to 1,400 calories is needed daily to maintain healthy organs and tissue in adults. Specific needs of the body are as follows: liver, 485 kilocalories; brain, 340 kilocalories; heart, 125 kilocalories; kidneys, 185; and muscle, 325 kilocalories (Food and Agriculture Organization, World Health Organization, & United Nations University, 1985).

When assessing the nutritional status of the body, there are two tests that provide extensive information (Hodges Chaffee & Kahm, 2015). Metabolic testing and BCA can provide data that are not measured by blood work. The metabolic test provides information about the resting energy expenditure of the body (how many calories the body is burning). This is used to determine whether the body is metabolically normal (burning the amount of calories the body should be burning), hypometabolic (burning fewer calories than the body should be), or hypermetabolic (burning more than the estimated amount). We can also determine whether the body is catabolic (breaking down its own protein tissue). When a body is underfed, its natural response is to slow down or become hypometabolic and use its own protein stores to take care of the body's basic needs.

The metabolic rate is assessed by indirect calorimetry (measuring the body's oxygen that is consumed and the carbon dioxide that is produced at rest). The process is called indirect calorimetry. This test can help identify a malnourished state, which is important because the majority of patients have no idea as to what their nutritional status might be. Signs of malnutrition are vague until the individual is severely malnourished, and even then they can be overlooked.

BCA, done by electrical impedance, is a quick and noninvasive test that provides extensive information about the body. Electrodes are placed on the wrist and foot of the individual and a tiny current is passed through the body. The BCA measures the resistance and reactance to the current as it travels through the water and different cells of the body. Lean mass, body fat, lean dry mass (muscle), total body water, intracellular water, extracellular water, and phase angle (a direct measurement of the cell membrane and an indicator of cell integrity) are measured.

Sandy, age 38, grew up never having family meals and had no idea what was normal eating. She had frequent nightmares and realized when she ate very little, she did not think about them. She would not eat during the day and then have a small amount in the evening. She had coffee throughout the day to give her energy to function. She was 5 feet 5 inches and weighed 128 pounds. She never thought she needed more food because she was not losing weight and was worried about gaining weight.

Her metabolic testing showed she was severely hypometabolic, burning only 845 calories a day when she should have been burning 1,750 calories daily. She was also catabolic, using 37% of her body's protein stores, 15% being normal. Her body had slowed down and was burning very little to conserve its energy. The BCA showed she had a very low lean weight and her phase angle measured 4.8, normal being 6.6 to 8.6. This indicated poor cell integrity.

She was severely protein and calorie malnourished, *despite having normal blood work results and being of normal body weight*. She never realized how much her sleep deprivation, exhaustion, mood stability, and memory loss were related to her poor nutritional intake.

The use of these two tests provides a more in-depth assessment of the nutritional status of the body. It is invaluable when educating the patient as to how his or her body is being affected by his or her nutritional intake. The majority of individuals struggling with an ED believe that as long as their blood work is within normal limits, they must be okay. They do not feel "malnourished" and do not recognize vague symptoms, such as fatigue, increased irritability, and poor concentration. Often medical providers indicate patients are healthy if their body weight is a healthy BMI (a measure of body fat on the basis of height and weight of an individual) and blood work is normal. Having the therapist understand the types of tests and data provided helps reinforce the message communicated by the dietitian. These tests can be a game changer in an individual's perception of his or her health. In addition to using the tests for the initial assessment of the body, using them throughout the course of treatment can provide valuable information about the body's response. This helps guide further recommendations and can be a motivator for patients to make changes that are often very difficult. It is not unusual that these are the only tests that show the actual physical consequences of the ED behavior and their actual nutritional state.

The clinician needs to be cautious when sharing information about the body composition, because the fear of weight gain is so prevalent in this patient population. The goal is to help the individual move beyond the numbers and focus on improving the overall health and strength of the body. Information shared that does not typically trigger the individual includes the metabolism measures of the metabolic rate and protein substrate utilization (indicating whether he or she is catabolic) and phase angle obtained by the BCA. Although the BCA is done at each appointment, the only information shared is trends about what is changing in the body, the phase angle, and hydration status. These tests also help individuals move away from using the scale as their indicator of health. Discussion about the natural set point (weight range in which a body is programmed to function optimally) and why diets do not work are also easier concepts to introduce.

Psychological Factors That Influence Eating

In addition to physical reasons for why it is difficult to eat, there are also many psychological factors. The simple act of eating can be very different for those who have experienced trauma associated with it. Other examples include being told to eat all your food by an angry parent, having food withheld as a means of punishment, religious or cultural rituals, sexual abuse when food or the smell of food is present, and sadistic behaviors involving foods.

Many of the ED symptoms become ritualistic to take control of the feelings and body disturbances associated with the trauma. Restricting intake becomes a way to avoid thinking, which may trigger those memories. Purging may be a symbolic way to get rid of any feelings associated with an event. Laxative use allows the individual to feel empty or cleansed. The risk of electrolyte imbalance with these behaviors is very high. Individuals need to be educated about not only the risks but also the signs and symptoms. The binge/purge cycle results in dissociating from the present environment. Binging helps the individual to become numb. Restricting gives a sense of control, and fasting, purging, or laxative abuse allows the individual to feel empty. Food insecurities, as a result of starvation, can also result in ED behaviors. Food hoarding, stealing or hiding food, and consuming large quantities of food to the point of vomiting can be triggered by the lack of food or starvation for any length of time (Karges, 2015).

Body weight is another factor to consider. It becomes much more than just how much an individual weighs for the individual suffering from trauma. Very low body weight may be a way to become invisible. The more asexual one's appearance is, the less attracted the predator will be. Higher body weight individuals may wear excess weight as a shield, creating a barrier to the outside. Excess weight can serve to minimize sexual attraction with the belief that it protects from future abuse. "I never want to be the weight I was when I was being sexually abused." Having the discussion of what body weight means to the individual is critical to the recovery process. A harm reduction approach helps to identify the symptoms that are most harmful to the body with the intention of decreasing these behaviors first. It becomes obvious, then, that the client and clinician need to be on the same page to establish a therapeutic alliance.

The actual act of eating can trigger significant traumatic events. Being judged by parents about what food is being eaten, being ridiculed by peers for eating more than others do, and being judged for eating unhealthy food—these and many other judgments regarding food often lead to anxiety when eating in public. Individuals will avoid eating meals to avoid the fear of being judged. Shame can easily influence the individual's ability to do what is asked.

Many feelings can be attached to the act of eating, body weight, and the foods being eaten that may interfere with the individual's ability to recover. Understanding what traumatic experiences or triggers are connected to the different aspects of the individual's relationship to food and body is imperative when working with an ED patient who is a trauma survivor.

Developing the Eating Plan

There are many things to consider when developing an eating plan. The client needs to understand the difference between a diet and an eating plan. Diet is often perceived as foods being restricted with the intention of weight loss. An eating plan makes recommendations in the service of health and physical well-being. Foods that are difficult for those struggling with an ED to include are usually foods that are high in carbohydrates and fats. Both of these nutrients are feared because the individual links them to weight gain. If the body does not have a balanced intake of carbohydrate, protein, and fat, it does not function optimally. Carbohydrates are the only source of energy for the brain. Fats are needed in the diet for vitamin absorption, hormone production, and normal brain function.

Initially the eating plan should be specific about when meals and snacks should be eaten. Irregular eating patterns can lead to an increase in ED behaviors. Maintaining an adequate fluid intake helps avoid dehydration, constipation, and fluid and electrolyte imbalance.

Food journals can be very helpful and can be modified to avoid triggering the individual. Journals help keep individuals present when eating and can help identify patterns that may contribute to symptom use. Too often, food journals have historically been used in a way that clients feel shamed. Stressing that there is no judgment about what food is eaten is helpful.

It is important to not overwhelm the individual with too much information or too many expectations during the first visit. The language used is also critical. Any comment that can be interpreted as judgmental needs to be avoided. These individuals have difficulty with trust and may feel vulnerable when sharing information about food behaviors. The most important goal of the first appointment is to have the individual feel comfortable and be willing to come in for follow-up appointments. The pace of the process needs to be enough to engage without overwhelming him or her.

As stated earlier, a harm reduction approach initially may be most appropriate. The first step is to increase the calories and protein for those individuals who need nutritional support because of their malnourished state. Liquids are often easier to digest and provide a concentrated calorie source. Explaining symptoms that the client may experience as intake is increased helps the client understand what is going on in the body and helps build trust with the clinician and the process.

The next step is to increase the calorie intake to meet the body's needs to maintain organ function. In adults, this is approximately 1,200 to 1,400 calories initially, and then gradually increasing the overall intake to meet the nutritional needs. Individuals understand that eating is necessary for physical activity, but do not realize that if the body is fed less than 1,200 calories a day, the organs do not have enough energy to perform their functions. Explaining why the body needs the calories is very helpful in decreasing the anxiety about eating. Using the terms "healing" and "repairing the body" keeps the individual focused on the purpose behind the nutritional support. The choice of foods may not look balanced, but the intent is to eventually develop a healthy eating plan. As the body begins to repair, the gut function improves, and it is easier to eat and digest the food. Continued use of the BCA provides guidance for the clinician to make recommendations about changes in nutritional intake and provides information to the client about his or her changing nutritional status. Using the BCA is a way to avoid focusing on body weight, an important consideration, because those struggling with EDs typically focus solely on body weight with no number ever allowing them to feel good about themselves. The measurement of changes in lean muscle mass or improvement in phase angle is information that can be shared with the individual to discuss his or her physical progress without using body weight as an indicator.

Clients should be monitored on a weekly basis. Providing feedback as to how the body is responding gives the individual more control over the process. As much as possible, allow the client choice in the decisions regarding food. Continue to progress with the nutritional support, while asking about and balancing the use of ED symptoms (restricting, purging, laxatives, compulsive exercise, binging, etc.).

Clients may experience a significant increase in symptom use when there is an increase in PTSD symptoms, because ED behaviors are often used to control these symptoms. Weekly monitoring is important because the client will seldom indicate struggles unless specifically asked. Monitoring also helps the client realize how important improvement in nutritional status is to recovery. If symptoms escalate, and the client is physically declining, hospitalization may be needed to stabilize and improve nutritional status to continue to do the trauma work. As discussed earlier, if hospitalization is necessary, provide as much information as possible about the treatment center and why that recommendation is being made.

Strategies for Dealing With Inappropriate Insurance Denials

Inappropriate denial of coverage puts sufferers and their families in a financial paradox—the very thing one expects to help (and has paid dearly to expect that support) becomes the entity that propagates more emotional and financial trauma, as well as less than optimal care. An excellent source for advice on managing conflict with insurance companies is found on the website for Lisa Kantor, an attorney who specializes in insurance and EDs and who is very involved in the ED field (www.kantorlaw.net/Practice-Areas/Eating-Disorders.aspx). This is not to say that one will need an attorney, but the website lists ways in which one can prepare to head off difficulties and know how to respond when they do arise. The website of the National Eating Disorders Association also has some helpful information (www.nationaleatingdisorders.org/learn/general-information/insurance).

■ CONCLUSION

Physicians, dietitians, and nutritionists who treat EDs will, most often, be treating trauma. Physicians, specifically, have a critical role in diagnosing and treating EDs. First, however, they need education about these illnesses, how they develop and present, the role of trauma, and the many ways trauma can occur, even at their own hands if they are not informed and careful. Medical and nutritional personnel need to earn the trust of those affected by being sensitive to how prior trauma may be aggravated, and by being open to learning how to avoid or minimize retraumatization. This patient population struggles with intense shame. Language used can easily be misinterpreted, and clinicians need to be aware of and sensitive to this. Finally, medical caregivers need to let the patients know that they will stay the course and support them for as long as it takes. Physicians, dietitians, and nutritionists then get to see the wonderful birth of a new person.

■ REFERENCES

Academy of Eating Disorders Medical Care Standards Committee (2016). *Eating disorders: A guide to medical care* (3rd ed.). Reston, VA: Academy for Eating Disorders.

Food and Agriculture Organization, World Health Organization., & United Nations University. (1985). *Joint report: Energy and protein requirements.* (Technical Report Series 724). Geneva, Switzerland: World Health Organization.

Frank, G. K., Bailer, U. F., Henry, S., Wagner, A., & Kaye, W. H. (2004). Neuroimaging studies in eating disorders. *CNS Spectrums, 9*(7), 539–549. doi:10.1017/S1092852900009639

Giordano, G. D., Renzetti, P., Parodi, R. C., Foppiani, L., Zandrino, F., Giordano, G., & Sardanelli, F. (2001). Volume measurement with magnetic resonance imaging of hippocampus-amygdala formation in patients with anorexia nervosa. *Journal of Endocrinological Investigation, 24*(7), 510–514. doi:10.1007/BF03343884

Hebebrand, J., Exner, C., Hebebrand, K., Holtkamp, C., Casper, R. C., Remschmidt, H., … Klingenspor, M. (2003). Hyperactivity in patients with anorexia nervosa and in semistarved rats: Evidence for a pivotal role of hypoleptinemia. *Physiology & Behavior, 79*(1), 25–37. doi:10.1016/S0031-9384(03)00102-1

Hodges Chaffee, C., & Kahm, A. (2015). *Measuring health from the inside: Nutrition, metabolism and body composition.* Victoria Canada, BC: Friesen Press.

Kalm, L. M., & Semba, R. D. (2005). They starved so that others be better fed: Remembering Ancel Keys and the Minnesota Experiment. *Journal of Nutrition, 135,* 1347–1352. doi:10.1093/jn/135.6.1347

Karges, C. (2015). Starvation, trauma, and food hoarding. Retrieved from https://www.eatingdisorderhope.com/blog/starvation-trauma-and-food-hoarding

Key, A., O'Brien, A., Gordon, I., Christie, D., & Lask, B. (2006). Assessment of neurobiology in adults with anorexia nervosa. *European Eating Disorders Review, 14,* 308–314. doi:10.1002/erv.696

Lask, B., Gordon, I., Christie, D., Frampton, I., Chowdhury, U., & Watkins, B. (2005). Functional neuroimaging in early-onset anorexia nervosa. *International Journal of Eating Disorders, 37,* S49–S51. doi:10.1002/eat.20117

Van den Eynde, F., Suda, M., Broadbent, H., Guillaume, S., Van den Eynde, M., Steiger, H., … Schmidt, U. (2012). Structural magnetic resonance imaging in eating disorders: A systematic review of voxel-based morphometry studies. *European Eating Disorders Review, 20,* 94–105. doi:10.1002/erv.1163

SECTION FOUR

The Phase Model—Phases I and II

The following sections and chapters are structured per a four-phase model of trauma-informed treatment: (a) Assessment (Evaluation) and Treatment Planning, (b) Preparation, (c) Trauma Processing, and (d) Relapse Prevention, Reevaluation, and Integration. Although not all trauma therapists use a phase model, effective clinicians instinctively do. Various models have contained three, four, and even eight phases, each, in its own way, viewing trauma treatment as consisting of a before, during, and after memory processing. The primary emphasis in a trauma-informed approach is on treating the source of the client's symptomatology, rather than remaining on the symptomatic level.

Chapters 7 and 8 detail aspects of the first two phases, Assessment (Evaluation) and Preparation, which are common to any approach to trauma treatment, as well as those elements in each phase that are specific to clients with eating disorders (EDs). Dialectical behavior therapy (DBT) and acceptance and commitment therapy (ACT), for example, are seen here as part of preparation and are goals in and of themselves, as well as preparing the way for trauma processing.

Fritz Perls famously said, "Leave your mind and come to your senses." Chapter 9 describes how dance/movement therapy (DMT) opens doors for ED clients to reestablish connection with their authentic self by embodying and expressing feelings from within. DMT is considered preparatory, but also achieves its own goals, in that it raises body awareness and acceptance, as well as affects tolerance, in the service of authentic communication and trauma processing.

Chapter 10, The Courage to Feel, spells out the steps in teaching emotional competence, while addressing the phobic attitude toward emotions, particularly anxiety and shame, which is common to all forms of EDs. This approach focuses primarily on tolerating embodied, emotional experience in the moment, while introducing subsequent ways of learning from our feelings. Finally, Chapter 11, Neurofeedback (NFB) and the Eating Disordered Brain, describes how NFB and biofeedback are being used to ameliorate brain conditions, particularly anxiety, compulsivity, and perfectionism, which result from trauma and EDs. NFB, in achieving its own goals of affect regulation, prepares the client for trauma processing simultaneously.

CHAPTER 7

Assessing "Trauma-Driven Eating Disorders": A Road Map Through the Maze

Pam Virdi and Jackie Nicholls

■ INTRODUCTION

This chapter presents a guide for assessing comorbid eating disorders (EDs) and trauma in a way that shapes and directs treatment. We draw together a combination of assessment tools and principles from the fields of EDs, trauma, and generic mental health, as there is limited literature available on this specific area of assessment (see Briere & Scott, 2007). Although both the ED and trauma symptoms require some separate attention during the assessment process, we advocate developing assessment approaches that take into account the interconnectedness of these two diagnoses. When we started to pull together the essential nuts and bolts of this chapter, we quickly realized that the topic had encyclopedic potential! We have therefore summarized various aspects of assessment into distinct sets of guidelines, to help steer the clinician and client through a vast maze of information toward a meaningful formulation and treatment plan.

A trauma-informed conceptualization of EDs underpins our assessment approach. Both authors use the Adaptive Information Processing (AIP) model (Shapiro, 1995), which informs specific sections of our assessment framework. This model views all present disturbing symptoms and negative self-beliefs as having roots in historical, unprocessed experiences (see Chapter 13, Eye Movement Desensitization and Reprocessing [EMDR]). Regardless of one's therapeutic approach, however, we believe that the proposed guidelines can be useful for any clinician undertaking a comprehensive assessment. We have also adopted an expanded definition of trauma as explained in the general introduction.

We conceptualize EDs as affect management strategies for tolerating painful inner and outer experiences that would otherwise overwhelm clients' capacities to cope. EDs involve numbing, distraction, or dissociation, which allows the client to distance himself or herself from painful emotions and experiences that threaten the sense of self. They can also, in part, be a direct manifestation of trauma. They can surface as attempts to control body weight or shape as a means of escaping unwanted predatory sexual attention/ abuse, criticism, or bullying. Purging behaviors can develop to purify or cleanse the body, dieting and exercising can serve as self-perfecting attempts to overcome shame, and starvation can be a form of self-punishment for those who feel unlovable or unworthy.

In our experience, specialist ED services in the United Kingdom have widely different approaches for addressing comorbid trauma and EDs. In some instances, the client's trauma-related difficulties are not systematically addressed in assessment or treatment. In these cases, trauma may be viewed as separate or the business of another generic or specialist mental health service. Various factors influence this state of affairs, including the following: the predominance of medical models of EDs, foregrounding the physical presentation, emphasis on non–trauma-focused models of service delivery (Sweeney, Clement, Filson, & Kennedy, 2016), and the fact that the national UK guidance for ED practice (National Institute for Health and Care Excellence [NICE], 2017) does not sufficiently acknowledge the role of trauma. Furthermore, many clinicians have limited understanding and training regarding psychological trauma (Harris & Fallot, 2001) and are, consequently, often disinclined to work with this comorbidity (Trottier, Monson, Wonderlich, MacDonald, & Olmsted, 2017).

Some clients will of course need lifesaving inpatient interventions when the medical consequences of the ED must be prioritized. However, clients experiencing acute ED medical crises may also be experiencing extreme trauma or posttraumatic stress disorder (PTSD) symptoms, which also require urgent attention. Without attending to acute PTSD symptoms, some clients may be unable to use weight restoration interventions in any sustainable way. In our experience, this can be the beginning of repeated revolving-door inpatient admissions for weight restoration, where short-term gains rarely persist because of unacknowledged PTSD and trauma.

This chapter provides a step-by-step comprehensive assessment guide, which jointly addresses ED and trauma symptoms. We discuss some of the main challenges to clients and clinicians during the assessment phase, including assessment of comorbid mental health conditions (substance misuse, self-harm, suicidality, and multi-impulsive EDs, typically associated with personality disorders) and severe medical risks, all of which necessitate a "safety-first approach" to assessment and treatment.

Consequently, this chapter attends to risk assessment and risk management within the assessment phase and demonstrates how we join with our clients at the beginning of their therapeutic journey in ways that promote safety, trust, compassion, and hope. Assessment is an essential stage of building a collaborative relationship, which in turn promotes insight as to how the ED and trauma symptoms are interconnected and why they need to be addressed conjointly to achieve optimum recovery.

■ INTEGRAL STEPS UNDERPINNING ASSESSMENT OF ED AND TRAUMA

A trauma-informed assessment fundamentally enables the clinician and client to formulate an understanding of why the client is in trouble with his or her eating, identifying the function of his or her ED in relation to the painful experiences it is defending against. Information is woven together to develop a story of why and how the client's ED has reached an unhealthy and problematic level. Although these explorations are also central to therapy, the assessment phase leads to the creation of a road map that directs subsequent therapeutic work. In this sense, assessment is a foot into treatment. It is not an entirely separate phase.

We use a multistep approach to assess for EDs and coexisting trauma, which consists of three parts: an initial assessment and engagement stage (Steps 1–4); followed by a more comprehensive assessment of the ED, trauma, and comorbid difficulties (Steps 5–7); and a formulation and treatment planning stage (Step 8). The first part gathers fundamental information regarding the following: a client's personal and treatment history, an overview of the ED and comorbid mental health difficulties, and pertinent risk factors, alongside barriers to engagement and the client's motivation for recovery. This information is gathered in a collaborative manner, while fostering an orientation to and engagement with a trauma-informed approach to treatment and recovery. The second part assesses trauma and other comorbid difficulties in greater depth. This part aims to establish connections between the ED and significant experiences of trauma, through the creation of timelines. The final part emerges once the relationship between the ED and trauma has been elucidated, and the client's main difficulties, strengths, and goals are mutually understood. The following sections describe each of these steps in more detail.

Significant Personal and Treatment History

Taking a good history involves facilitating the client's telling of her story, while gently guiding the process to keep it focused and on track (we will use the feminine gender in the use of adjectives, as the vast majority of our clients are female). We need to gain a sufficient depth of understanding of the client and her issues within the context of her life to develop a meaningful treatment plan. In this stage, we gather typical demographic information, including the client's developmental, educational, occupational, and forensic histories. From a relational perspective, we enquire about the client's attachment, family relationships, and psychosexual histories, including details of ruptures and relational resources. The importance of identifying an absence of healthy attachments, significant relationships, or developmental opportunities cannot be overemphasized, as this can underpin traumatic loss and shame. A genogram can be a quick way of gathering this information in a succinct way. From a strengths perspective, we dialogue with the client about internal and external resources that have helped her survive and endure her painful history. These conversations help to gauge the client's ability to undertake different aspects of therapeutic work. Throughout this history-taking phase, we note key events that have affected the client's relationship with food, appearance, size, or body shape.

We emphasize enquiring about the client's general physical health and medical history, along with contact details of her general medical practitioner (GP) and other relevant physicians/clinicians. We explain that continuous medical assessment and liaison with GPs is a necessary and nonnegotiable aspect of treatment, to ensure her safety and well-being. We enquire about the client's previous treatment history and ask what has been helpful/unhelpful in the past. It is useful to ask more broadly about any other kinds of nonprofessional help (including family and friends) that has helped her to manage or overcome aspects of her ED.

Promoting Engagement and Overcoming Challenges to Assessment

There are a multitude of challenges to fully engaging clients within the assessment process. The challenges are often characterized by relational tussles on the basis of distrust and fear about losing control, choice, and autonomy. Clients with anorexia nervosa (AN) typically fear that clinicians are going to make them eat more than they are comfortable with, anticipating terrifying increases in weight and size. We anticipate these dilemmas and conflicts and reassure clients from the outset that we will work at a pace that is manageable for them.

REASONS FOR SEEKING PROFESSIONAL HELP

People with AN rarely show up for treatment under their own volition. There will usually be a worried other desperately, sometimes even frantically, pushing them through your door. What must that feel like for the client? What challenges does that bring to the therapist? What does it take to build a solid, trusting therapeutic relationship with the client under these circumstances? How do you approach this task with a client who is a reluctant participator? The person with AN usually wants help to get others off her back. The arguments over not eating have by now depleted even the most positive of relationships and are causing a lot of distress to all concerned. Clients usually want relief from exhaustion, sleeplessness, and constantly feeling cold, anxious, and depressed. However, they usually do not want their low body weight to be challenged and strongly resist eating and weight-related aspects of treatment. They want to feel better, but without necessarily making any changes to their eating-related behaviors. We join the clients in their predicament and empathically help them to understand how they have found themselves in this complicated and confusing mess.

Clients with bulimia nervosa may seek professional help when their secret has been exposed, when the bingeing and purging are no longer controllable to circumscribed times, or when there are serious medical effects that can no longer be denied. They may experience confusion about why their attempts to lose weight through purging are persistently failing. In fact, their weight might be increasing despite regular purging. In this situation, clients often seek help because they want their bingeing to stop. However, they wish to maintain their restrictive and purging behaviors in constant pursuit of thinness. They may view the problems purely on a behavioral level and may be in denial about any psychological factors. Clients with a binge ED typically seek help when their attempts to lose weight repeatedly fail. They hope that professionals will help them to achieve their weight loss goals. This client group can often experience strong self-disgust and shame when their eating feels completely out of control. Given the nature of dissociation, they can also be unaware of the psychological issues driving their ED.

SHAME-BASED BARRIERS TO ASSESSMENT

Clients often experience shame in relation to extreme body dissatisfaction and may experience strong fear about being judged, especially in relation to binge-eating and purging behaviors. They often report concerns regarding confidentiality because of their shame-inducing symptoms. Shame poses significant barriers to assessment, as clients are understandably reluctant to disclose symptoms that they fear will be viewed with disgust, criticism, or rejection. To be asked to put your most despised and loathsome behaviors into words for someone you barely know is a challenging task for anyone. Equally challenging is being questioned about your most prized achievement, that is, finally being a "size zero." Why should clients reveal their secrets, especially when they believe that professionals will try to strip them of their most cherished achievements and aspirations? It is understandable then that we are initially told only the parts of the story that are safe and palatable for the client to disclose (see Chapter 4). Strengthening the therapeutic relationship and revisiting questions over time is often necessary to enable ongoing disclosure.

THE INTERNAL CIVIL WAR: PARTS OF SELF IN CONFLICT

A state of two-mindedness or ambivalence is the norm for someone with an ED. Part of the self sees that the ED behaviors are hijacking important wants and goals in life. Another part, however, is firmly clinging to the behaviors for much needed safety and emotional regulation regardless of any negative consequences. We can conceptualize this duality through a lens of ego state or "parts" theory, as two parts of the internal self-system that conflict with each other (see Chapters 4, 15, and 16). One method for starting to delineate these ego states is to invite the client to write two letters to their ED, one to "anorexia—their friend" and the other to "anorexia—their enemy" (Serpell, Treasure, Teasdale, & Sullivan, 1999). We usually introduce this exercise after obtaining information about key aspects of the ED history and presentation. We find this exercise helps pave the way toward discussions about dissociation and ego states and how different parts can hold conflicting needs and drives. The following clinical example illustrates that this therapeutic letter writing can uncover the ways in which the ED serves the client and reveals clues about why it came into existence in the first place.

Sarah is 15 years old and is rapidly losing weight to the point at which she may soon require an inpatient admission. She is invited to have a go at this letter-writing exercise. Her letters are reproduced with her permission.

Case Illustration

To Anorexia My Friend,

Firstly, I must thank you for all that you've done for me. You've stuck by me and encouraged me and you helped me achieve my goal. I wanted to lose weight and I did. I couldn't have done it without you. You gave me the strength and determination I needed.

You've been my friend when everyone else was angry or disappointed in me. You've become part of me and I can't and don't want to let you go.

You've given me an excuse to be less energetic and achieving. You've gotten rid of all the pressures of life, school, friends and sport. I can just sit back and let life pass me by. Easy. All I need is you. You've helped me to open up to people and show them my weaker side. Now they know I needed help with life and that I couldn't get through it alone. I wasn't as strong as they thought. But now I have you instead to help me.

To Anorexia My Enemy,

I hate you. You're always telling me what to do and what not to do. You're so controlling. You've made me so deceitful through your deceit. I hate what you've turned me into. I no longer see the enjoyment in life. It just passes me by, wasting away. My friends must think that I'm no fun. My family don't like you and what I become around you. And it is you, NOT me.

I didn't ask for your help, so will you please just leave me alone? You're destroying me and my family. I just can't cope any more. I want it just to be over. You make me feel like giving up on everything.

Why should I be your friend when all you do is deprive me of food and make me cold, thin, pale with thinning hair and brittle bones and weak?

Just leave me alone and let me be me again—if I can remember who that is.

The letter to "Anorexia My Friend" illustrates the helpful functions of the ED ego state. These letters often have the following themes: experiencing anorexia as consistent and dependable; providing a sense of safety and protection; creating direction and structure; enabling the avoidance of negative feelings; and increasing confidence through a sense of being different, superior, and special, because of successfully achieving weight loss (Serpell et al., 1999). This inappropriate positive affect, associated with feeling special or superior, needs to be targeted in treatment, as it can lead clients to relapse after weight restoration. A typical scene at that point might involve a weight-restored client being around others engaging in "diet talk." Hearing others talking about their desire to lose weight stokes up urges in the client to reexperience the "high" of losing weight herself. In our experience, the addiction protocols used in EMDR therapy (Miller, 2012; Popky, 2005) can be helpful in neutralizing the urges to return to weight loss as a means of experiencing strong (but inappropriate) positive feeling states. In our clinical experience, recovery is not on solid ground until this aspect of treatment has been completed.

The findings of a further study by Serpell and Treasure (2002) indicate that letters written to bulimia nervosa (BN) reveal similar themes to those associated with AN. Additional negative themes include shame and low self-esteem stemming from bingeing and purging. This usually means that clients with BN are more motivated to make changes and embark on recovery-related work. Two additional positive functions of BN were identified: bingeing and purging were viewed as a way of eating and not becoming fat, and as a way of dealing with boredom. It is therefore important to assess the meanings and functions of each client's symptoms, rather than assessing symptoms in isolation.

SAFEGUARDING THE CLIENT FROM POTENTIAL IATROGENIC INJURY

Clients can become emotionally overwhelmed, triggered, or retraumatized when asked about aspects of their trauma histories. For this reason, it is advisable to equip clients with grounding and emotional regulation techniques before undertaking an assessment of their trauma history. A client's ability to regulate her emotions can be assessed using the "Difficulties in Emotion Regulation Scale" (DERS; Gratz & Roemer, 2004). The "window of tolerance" (Ogden, Minton, & Pain, 2006; Siegel, 1999) is a useful concept for helping clients understand the importance of emotional regulation. It can be used to help the client recognize triggers to her own hyper- and hypoaroused states. It is useful to have a visual representation of the "window of tolerance" for checking the client's level of emotional regulation during the assessment process.

PROMOTING HOPE REGARDING CHANGE AND RECOVERY

We ask our clients about their hopes and goals regarding change and recovery and discuss which aspects of their ED and trauma symptoms they would like to change. Clients usually report that their sense of hope increases as a direct result of acquiring a trauma-informed understanding of their ED. The aim of assessment is to design a realistic treatment plan, which incorporates the client's current needs, values, and life goals.

Assessment of Current ED Presentation

We use a semistructured interview to obtain the following information about different aspects of the client's ED symptoms:

- Current nature of eating and weight-related problems
- Frequency, quantity, and types of food eaten or avoided
- Rituals around eating and underlying beliefs about these behaviors
- Fluid intake (assessing for risks of dehydration or water intoxication)
- The nutritional value of food consumed, by establishing which food groups are included and which have become eliminated or "forbidden"
- Body mass index (BMI) = weight (kilograms) divided by height (in square meters)
- Current weight trend to assess rapidity of weight loss
- Frequency of purging behaviors (e.g., vomiting and use of laxatives)
- Use of dieting products
- Activity levels (e.g., compulsive exercising)
- Body image concerns
- The relationship between the client's ED and her emotions
- Cultural and social variables influencing the ED

A sample of the questions we use to elicit this information can be found on the web (see www.clearpathtrainingcenter.com/eating-disorders.html). Food diaries can be used to assess the client's current and ongoing eating patterns (Waller et al., 2007). It is not unusual for clients to have misconceptions about nutrition and weight regulation. These gaps in knowledge and erroneous beliefs tend to perpetuate the ED behaviors and therefore need to be assessed and corrected. We find the Eating Attitudes Awareness Test useful in this regard (Schmidt, Ali, Slone, Tiller, & Treasure, 1995).

Sometimes our clients feel reassured when they see their symptoms written down. Helping clients to view their difficulties in understandable terms can reduce shame and alienation. However, this process can sometimes be a double-edged sword for some clients with AN, who feel upset that their specialness is reduced to universal principles or words on a piece of paper. It is very easy for the client to become alienated and objectified during the assessment process if too many forms are used or psychometric measures are introduced too early in the process. The advantage of a clinical interview is that it allows the client space to construct her own narrative, which makes for richer discussion about pertinent aspects of her experience.

In some instances, we use the Eating Disorder Examination (Fairburn, Cooper, & O'Connor, 2014), which is viewed as the "gold standard" measure of EDs and is widely used by specialist ED services in the United Kingdom. It provides a measure of the range and severity of ED symptoms and generates operational *Diagnostic and Statistical Manual of Mental Disorders* (5th ed.; *DSM-5*; Amercan Psychiatric Association, 2013) ED diagnoses. The measure is available in two forms: an interview format (Fairburn et al., 2014) and a self-report questionnaire (Fairburn & Beglin, 2008). These measures are commonly used in outcome research studies and are a useful way of evaluating the relative effectiveness of therapeutic interventions.

ED Risk Assessment

Safety is paramount and needs to be addressed in various ways depending on the clinical setting. Working in an ED multidisciplinary team allows all aspects of medical and psychological risk to be easily coordinated and managed in-house.

However, in the United Kingdom, the constitution of ED services can vary from locality to locality, and some services do not employ medical staff or dietitians. These teams usually consist of a team manager and a group of nurses or psychotherapists trained in a range of therapeutic modalities. In such cases, the team will need to actively link in with the GP for medical assessment and input. It will also be necessary to link in with a generic psychiatrist for support with the management of complex comorbid conditions.

Medical staff need to be made aware of the recommended guidance for medical monitoring. Some medical colleagues may not have specific training or experience of monitoring the health of patients with EDs and will need advice from the ED practitioner or ED service. In the United Kingdom, GPs or hospital physicians are advised to follow *A Guide to the Medical Risk Assessment for Eating Disorders* (Treasure, 2009). The core components of this assessment involve the following: a full medical examination, regular monitoring of biochemistry, an ECG test to assess cardiovascular health, a DEXA scan to determine bone density and assess for signs of osteoporosis, and a "squat test" to determine muscle strength and physical conditioning. Chaffee and Kahm (2015) recommend that metabolic rates and body composition are also included in the medical monitoring of EDs.

Given the complexity and medical risks of EDs, we do not advise clinicians to work in isolation. Regular communication with the client's GP is essential for safe practice. There may be many reasons why the client may be reluctant to consult with her GP. Clients are reluctant to be weighed and often deny health consequences of their ED (see Chapter 6). The following clinical examples demonstrate the extent to which clients can deny the risks of severe purging behaviors.

WEIGHT: IS IT NECESSARY TO WEIGH THE CLIENT?

If the client is low weight, then the answer is a resounding YES. Why? Because the degree of weight loss and how quickly weight is lost is indicative of the extent of medical risk.

Case Examples of Particular Risks Associated With Purging

Jodie locks herself away in the house every weekend and immerses herself in bingeing and purging. She takes 30 Senokot laxative tablets per day and makes herself vomit after binge eating vast quantities of food. She is severely dehydrated and her electrolytes are dangerously depleted. One weekend during a purging episode, she has a seizure on the bathroom floor. Another time, she becomes dizzy while crossing the landing to reach the bedroom and loses her balance. She falls head first down a flight of stairs and is very lucky to only break an arm.

Heather has a 20-year history of severe and enduring anorexia. She has the most severe case of laxative misuse that one of the authors has ever seen. Prior to admission to an inpatient service, Heather reports she is taking 60 Senokot tablets, 1 packet of Epson salts, and 2 tablespoons of Lactulose per day. Her compulsion to purge is unremitting, despite losing one kidney because of this extreme level of laxative misuse.

Weight calculations are made using BMI calculations and the following are useful rules of thumb for intensification of treatment:

BMI 17.5: Diagnostic threshold for anorexia nervosa
BMI 15: Day treatment indicated/cognitive impairment likely to be present
BMI 13.5: Inpatient admission indicated
BMI 10: Usually incompatible with life

It is important to note that risk is not a singular concept. A picture of risk needs to be based on a number of factors, which are outlined in *A Guide to the Medical Risk Assessment for Eating Disorders* (Treasure, 2009).

Weight monitoring can be a tricky negotiation process, and clients with AN are usually resistant to this. We approach this issue by explaining to our clients that it is of utmost importance that we support them to maintain adequate safety and that we cannot know how safe they are if we do not know their weight. We convey empathy regarding their fear of discovering that their weight has increased and acknowledging certain numbers on the weighing scales. Clients are given a choice as to whether they wish to be told their weight or undertake weight monitoring without knowing their current weight. Addressing the psychological aspects of weight-related issues becomes a further focus within the treatment phase.

INTRODUCING THE CLIENT TO NONNEGOTIABLES

Regular weight monitoring has to be introduced to the client as a nonnegotiable aspect of treatment (Geller & Srikameswaran, 2006). This needs to be presented in a compassionate, yet honest, way that minimizes control battles. In our experience, this is not usually a problematic negotiation once the client is given a clear and sound rationale for why this is necessary. If the client feels respected and heard, it is rare for a client to outright refuse to cooperate. A client refusing to be weighed usually isn't feeling safe in the therapeutic relationship. Listening empathically to the client's concerns and gently bringing her back to the nonnegotiable need for safety typically resolves the issues quickly.

Assessment of Trauma and Comorbid Mental Health Problems

Comorbid mental health problems complicate the ED and need to be included in the assessment and treatment plan. Anxiety, depression, and obsessive-compulsive disorder (OCD) commonly exist within an ED presentation. It can be difficult to establish whether these symptoms in part or totality are a consequence of semistarvation, which in and of itself is known to create this symptom constellation (Keys, Brožek, Henschel, Mickelsen, & Taylor, 1950). We explore how anxiety and depression may be responses to the physiology of trauma, fears about eating, and terror about weight gain. Taking a thorough history of when these symptoms first started will help to work out the most appropriate treatment response. Many clients find that their mood-related symptoms recede as nutrition and hydration are adequately improved.

Next, we undertake a detailed assessment of the client's trauma-related difficulties. We are interested in discovering whether the ED is a direct manifestation of trauma and whether it is acting as an affect management strategy. The first step in conducting a trauma assessment is to determine the client's current psychological stability and capacity to undertake the assessment itself. As mentioned earlier, clinicians should avoid placing further strain on an already challenged client and take precautions to prevent retraumatization.

As mentioned from the outset, it is important to assess trauma cautiously at the client's pace and within her "window of tolerance." We assess the client's present and historical trauma-related difficulties through the construction of a timeline, to determine whether the client's experiences of trauma have any direct relevance to the client's ED (see the following section for details). Psychometric measures should be used only with clients who are sufficiently resourced to cope with brief recall of their trauma experiences. The Trauma Symptom Checklist (Briere & Runtz, 1989) and the Traumatic Experiences Checklist (TEC; Nijenhuis, Van der Hart, & Kruger, 2002) are useful measures for establishing the nature, range, and severity of the client's trauma symptoms and experiences. These checklists are particularly useful when clients are struggling to verbalize their experiences, because of either feelings of shame or the need to avoid recall of painful memories.

We assess the severity of psychological disturbance to determine whether the client's symptoms meet the full or partial criteria for diagnoses of PTSD or complex PTSD (C-PTSD). A PTSD diagnosis includes four symptom clusters: reexperiencing (e.g., flashbacks), avoidance of stimuli associated with the trauma, negative cognitions and mood (e.g., persistent negative emotional states and inability to experience positive emotions), and arousal (e.g., hypervigilance, concentration problems, and sleep disturbance [APA, 2013]).

The diagnosis of PTSD can be made using the Posttraumatic Diagnostic Scale for *DSM-5* (PDS-5; Foa et al., 2016), which is a 24-item questionnaire. We refer the reader to an article by Lancaster, Teeters, Gros, and Back, (2016) for a detailed overview of the assessment of PTSD. The Impact of Event Scale (Weiss, 2007) is useful for measuring the severity and impact of single-event traumas and for tracking symptom reduction during therapeutic work. It is important to consider the accuracy of self-report, given the amnesic and dissociative features of severe trauma. We therefore advise directly assessing the level and severity of the client's dissociation, which can be done via the Dissociative Experiences Scale (DES-11; Carlson & Putnam, 1993) and Multidimensional Inventory of Dissociation, version 6.0 (MID; Dell, 2006).

Clients who have experienced repetitive emotional, sexual, or physical abuse or neglect in childhood are likely to meet the diagnosis for C-PTSD. This diagnosis includes the core symptoms of PTSD in conjunction with profoundly negative alterations in identity and sense of self, including extreme feelings of helplessness, worthlessness, and persistent feelings of fear and terror (Courtois & Ford, 2009). Using an AIP conceptualization of trauma and PTSD diagnoses can help the client to make better sense of her symptoms and inform the case formulation and treatment planning discussions.

A thorough assessment is required for clients with personality disorder diagnoses. This typically reviews the client's ability to tolerate distress and regulate emotions, assessed through the DERS (Gratz & Roemer, 2004). We also recommend assessing the following: interpersonal functioning and attachment styles via the Adult Attachment Interview (George, Kaplan, & Main, 1985); identity issues and negative core self-beliefs, via the Young Schema Questionnaire (Young, 2005); and an assessment of any impulsive, self-harming, and suicidal behavior.

Clients who have an extensive history of trauma may also present with alcohol or drug addictions (Driessen et al., 2008). A thorough assessment should establish the pattern of substance usage (alcohol or drugs of any variety) and the day-to-day problems created for the client and significant others. Various measures and best-practice recommendations can be found in the United Kingdom's National Institute for Health and

Care Excellence (NICE) guidance for the following: alcohol-use disorders (2011) and drug-use disorders in adults (2012). The Severity of Alcohol Dependence Questionnaire (SADQ) is useful for determining whether the client needs assisted alcohol withdrawal. Assessment of drug and alcohol use needs to weigh up whether specialist addiction services are also required.

Risks Associated With Comorbid Presentation

The most serious risk commonly associated with clients with personality disorders is that the clients' extreme emotional dysregulation will cause them to harm themselves or others. A relatively large proportion of people with a diagnosis of borderline personality disorder complete suicide, with some estimates as high as 10% (Paris, 2004).

The safety of the client and others needs to be thoroughly assessed and any resulting concerns attended to throughout the development of a workable and client-agreed safety plan. The risk of suicide, however, is not solely associated with clients receiving personality disorder diagnoses. Suffering a life burdened with the effects of trauma and an ED can become unbearable for many of our clients, and the risk of suicide escalates when the client is weight restored and not yet free of her emotional pain.

There are a variety of measures available to assess suicidal ideation and risk. We recommend Marsha Linehan's self-report, The Reasons for Living Inventory (RFL; Linehan, Goodstein, Nielsen, & Chiles, 1983), which identifies adaptive attitudes and beliefs that mitigate suicidal impulses. Inventories are available for various age groups and can be downloaded from the Internet (http://depts.washington.edu/uwbrtc/resources/assessment-instruments).

We take care to sensitively enquire about the possibility of current or ongoing abuse or traumatization for all of our clients, which would require safeguarding measures to be taken.

Establishing Connections Between the ED and Trauma

We use timelines to explore the interconnections between the client's ED and experiences of trauma. This typically involves exploring relationships between the following timelines: (a) eating difficulties, (b) body image, and (c) trauma (small t and big T). We also create a timeline of the client's relational and emotional resources to establish the client's history of coping abilities in the face of adversity and trauma. This information allows us to determine what level of preparation clients require for trauma-focused therapeutic work. We orient the client to a trauma-informed approach to assessment/treatment before constructing a trauma timeline and check their emotional regulation and grounding abilities, to ensure that they can manage trauma symptoms during this assessment process.

SOCIALIZING THE CLIENT INTO A TRAUMA-INFORMED APPROACH
TO ASSESSMENT/TREATMENT

As mentioned earlier, we help our clients understand the connection between their ED and experiences of trauma during this part of the assessment phase. This requires an educative process that aims to help the client understand the nature of trauma. Clients often do not recognize that some of their symptoms, which can present in fragmented ways, are related to the effects of trauma or PTSD. One example would be intense emotional reactions disproportionate to the circumstances in which they occur. Other clients may have unprocessed body memories that appear as medical conditions (e.g., vulvodynia or sexual dysfunction linked to previous sexual abuse or bodily pain associated with a physical assault).

Psychoeducation is provided to help clients understand the difference between trauma memories and ordinary memories. Ordinary memories are stored in explicit memory, as stories about specific experiences that can be verbalized. Trauma memories, on the other hand, are stored largely in implicit memory, in their original, raw, state-specific form. These memories typically contain intense feelings, negative self-beliefs, sounds, smells, images, and body sensations that were experienced at the time of the actual traumatic event (Shapiro, 1995). The part of the brain that holds implicit memory does not have capacity for using language or the concept of time. Any reminders of the painful experience, such as smells, people, places, or dates, transport the client back in time to reexperience the original feelings, body sensations, negative self-perceptions, and thought processes as if they were occurring in present time. In this triggered state, the client will turn to whatever means she has to try to numb out this pain. Starving, bingeing, purging, compulsive exercising, and other behaviors serve to create distance from the agony that has been unleashed. Unprocessed trauma memories, containing negative beliefs about the self, build up over time to create a negative story about the self. EDs can often be understood as clients' attempts to improve or perfect themselves as a way of compensating for an impoverished self-identity. Similarly, EDs can be a means of eliciting care to bolster a sense of self-worth.

MAPPING CONNECTIONS BETWEEN ED, BODY IMAGE, AND TRAUMA TIMELINES

We ask the client to place only a representative word or two on the timeline of traumatic events, and rate how distressing it feels to her at the present time on a subjective level of distress (SUD) rating scale, from numbers 0 to 10, to avoid opening up distressing memories, which risk flooding the client with negative effect. Clients can just use a mark/symbol to denote something of significance, if labeling these events with words is problematic. In other words, we do NOT ask for any details. We construct the trauma timeline with the client to ensure that this is done safely, in a way that doesn't overwhelm the client. This may be the first time for many clients that their trauma history has been laid out before them as a whole story, which is likely to be very distressing. This is an important reason for constructing the timeline in short manageable chunks and to be guided by the capacities of the client.

Weight History and ED Symptoms Timeline

We identify the development of episodes of starving, bingeing, and purging. It can sometimes be difficult for clients to remember aspects of their weight history, given that they are viewing their past through the lens of body image distortion. This may color their perceptions and skew their narrative. A more objective picture of weight changes can be established by inviting the client to bring in photographs of herself from birth onwards to support the construction of this timeline.

Body-Image Timeline

Negative and positive experiences that have influenced the client's body image over time are identified. These are then plotted on a body-image timeline. We are particularly interested in identifying shaming experiences, which are often key to the onset and maintenance of the ED. We explore how the client manages and reacts to her body. Sometimes clients may have extreme reactions to parts of the body they loathe the most, such as attempting to cut off or beat parts of their body.

Further details of body image concerns can be uncovered with the help of the Body Dysmorphic Disorder Examination (BDDE; Rosen, Reiter, & Orosan, 1995).

Trauma Timeline

We begin by plotting general unprocessed traumatic experiences and adverse life events, including secondary trauma that may have arisen because of the ED itself. The client, for example, may have developed a fear of sudden death because of electrolyte imbalances, experiences of seizures, medical emergencies, overdoses, and choking on food.

Once completed, the weight, body image, and ED timelines can be mapped onto the trauma timeline to explore patterns and connections between past and current ED symptoms and underlying emotional distress. By way of illustration, it may become evident that a client has been restricting and losing weight whenever there have been episodes of interpersonal difficulties or incidents of domestic violence.

Resources Timeline

The aim of taking this timeline is to establish how resourced the client is in her inner and outer world. We take a strength-based approach to this part of the assessment, exploring the client's capacities, strengths, abilities, and external resources. This includes identifying the people and supports available to the client, and how willing and able they are to use those supports.

Trauma-Informed Formulation and Treatment Planning

Finally, information gathered during each assessment stage is brought together to create a trauma-informed formulation of the client's ED difficulties. We privilege the language and values of the client and refrain from using unnecessary professional jargon, such as the word "formulation." The formulation is a story that connects the client's personal and trauma histories to her current ED behaviors and broader difficulties. It draws on earlier psychoeducational conversations that explain how unprocessed trauma memories create distress in the here-and-now and generate debilitating negative self-beliefs. Developing a multifaceted story that makes sense of the client's difficulties helps her to feel understood and motivated to invest hope and trust in the therapeutic relationship. Creating a "trauma-informed" account with the client can offer new insights, which can have liberating and hope-instilling effects.

The treatment plan, which is on the basis of the client's difficulties, needs, and goals, naturally flows out from the formulation. Our approach to formulation and treatment planning is depicted in Figure 7.1. We co-construct suitable goals for treatment, which take account of the client's life skills, relational resources, and support networks. The identification of realistic and meaningful goals is likely to generate or further reinforce hope regarding change. We recommend working on small, achievable goals at first to create experiences of mastery and success.

When the client begins to entertain the possibility of change and understands the premise of a trauma-informed approach to recovery, it is often easier to agree to the nonnegotiable aspects of the therapy contract. Nonnegotiables include the following: regular weight monitoring for clients with low or highly fluctuating weight, physical health monitoring (Treasure, 2009), developing and implementing a regular pattern of eating, developing alternative ways of tolerating distressing emotions, refraining from suicidal behaviors, and attending to any safety concerns.

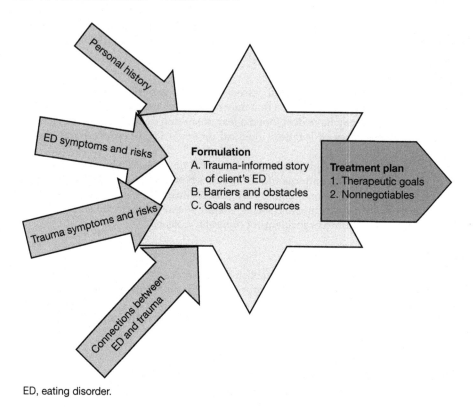

ED, eating disorder.

FIGURE 7.1 Assessment, formulation, and treatment planning process.

It is important to assess the client's willingness to engage with all the essential aspects of treatment before proceeding with trauma processing work. Barriers to safe and effective treatment need to be addressed from the outset. Uncertainty, ambivalence, and internal conflict about change and recovery will need to be resolved through ego state/parts work. Specific maintaining factors, such as engagement with pro-Ana websites (websites actively promoting anorexic practices and lifestyles through extreme ideologies and imagery), self-harm, or drug and alcohol addiction, will need to be addressed early on in treatment.

Assessment also helps to determine whether other treatment services (e.g., community mental health services, drug and alcohol services, and specialist personality disorder services) are required. Appropriate medication to alleviate distressing symptoms of clinical depression, extreme anxiety, and obsessive-compulsive symptomatology is, of course, an important consideration.

The treatment plan identifies short-term goals for stabilizing and preparing the client for the processing of specific trauma memories. Consideration is given to the order in which specific memories are processed. Priority should be given to memories that generate the most current risk, memories that are directly driving the ED behaviors, and memories linked to negative core beliefs that evoke the most emotional distress. We aim to reduce PTSD symptoms as soon as possible, because of the debilitating effects on the client's ability to sleep and function in everyday life. Reduction of these symptoms early on in treatment can significantly improve the client's functioning and further motivate her to engage with ongoing treatment.

We hope that our guidelines will enable clinicians to implement trauma-informed assessments routinely within their ED practice. This chapter has provided a road map to facilitate comprehensive assessments that lead to the construction of insightful formulations and the delivery of engaging treatment plans. We believe that trauma-informed ED assessment guides safe and effective treatment, shining a beacon of light on the road toward transformation and healing.

■ REFERENCES

American Psychiatric Association. (2013). *Diagnostic and statistical manual of mental disorders* (5th ed.). Arlington, VA: American Psychiatric Publishing.

Briere, J., & Runtz, M. (1989). The trauma symptom checklist (TSC-33) early data on a new scale. *Journal of Interpersonal Violence, 4*(2), 151–163. doi:10.1177/088626089004002002

Briere, J., & Scott, C. (2007). Assessment of trauma symptoms in eating-disordered populations. *Eating Disorders, 15*(4), 347–358. doi:10.1080/10640260701454360

Carlson, E. B., & Putnam, F. W. (1993). An update on the dissociative experiences scale. *Dissociation: Progress in the Dissociative Disorders, 6*(1), 16–27.

Chaffee, C. H., & Kahm, A. (2015). *Measuring health from the inside: Nutrition, metabolism & body composition*. Victoria, BC, Canada: FriesenPress.

Courtois, C. A., & Ford, J. D. (Eds.). (2009). *Treating complex traumatic stress disorders: An evidence-based guide*. New York, NY: Guilford Press.

Dell, P. F. (2006). The multidimensional inventory of dissociation (MID): A comprehensive measure of pathological dissociation. *Journal of Trauma & Dissociation, 7*(2), 77–106. doi:10.1300/J229v07n02_06

Driessen, M., Schulte, S., Luedecke, C., Schaefer, I., Sutmann, F., Ohlmeier, M., … Broese, T. (2008). Trauma and PTSD in patients with alcohol, drug, or dual dependence: A multi-center study. *Alcoholism Clinical and Experimental Research, 32*(3), 481–488. doi:10.1111/j.1530-0277.2007.00591.x

Fairburn, C. G., & Beglin, S. (2008). Eating disorder examination questionnaire (EDE-Q 6.0). In C. G. Fairburn (Ed.), *Cognitive behaviour therapy and eating disorders* (pp. 309–313). New York, NY: Guilford Press.

Fairburn, C. G., Cooper, Z., & O'Connor, M. (2014). Eating disorder examination (17.0D). Retrieved from http://credo-oxford.com/pdfs/EDE_17.0D.pdf

Foa, E. B., McLean, C. P., Zang, Y., Zhong, J., Powers, M. B., Kauffman, B. Y., … Knowles, K. (2016). Psychometric properties of the posttraumatic diagnostic scale for *DSM-5* (PDS-5). *Psychological Assessment, 28*(10), 1166–1171. doi:10.1037/pas0000258

Geller, J., & Srikameswaran, S. (2006). Treatment non-negotiables: Why we need them and how to make them work. *European Eating Disorders Review, 14*(4), 212–217. doi:10.1002/erv.716

George, C., Kaplan, N., & Main, M. (1985). *Attachment interview for adults*. Unpublished manuscript, University of California, Berkeley.

Gratz, K. L., & Roemer, L.(2004). Multidimensional assessment of emotion regulation and dysregulation: Development, factor structure, and initial validation of the difficulties in emotion regulation scale. *Journal of Psychopathology and Behavioral Assessment, 26*(1), 41–54. Retrieved from http://journals.sagepub.com/doi/pdf/10.1177/0145445514566504

Harris, M., & Fallot, R. D. (2001). *Using trauma theory to design service systems: vol. 89, New directions for mental health services*. San Francisco, CA: Jossey Bass.

Keys, A., Brožek, J., Henschel, A., Mickelsen, O., & Taylor, H. L. (1950). *The biology of human starvation* (Vols. 1–2). Minneapolis: University of Minnesota Press.

Lancaster, C. L., Teeters, J. B., Gros, D. F., & Back, S. E. (2016). Posttraumatic stress disorder: Overview of evidence-based assessment and treatment. *Journal of Clinical Medicine, 5*(11), E105. doi:10.3390/jcm5110105

Linehan, M. M., Goodstein, J. L., Nielsen, S. L., & Chiles, J. A. (1983). Reasons for staying alive when you are thinking of killing yourself: The reasons for living inventory. *Journal of Consulting and Clinical Psychology, 51*(2), 276–286. doi:10.1037/0022-006X.51.2.276

Miller, R. (2012). Treatment of behavioral addictions utilizing the feeling-state addiction protocol: A multiple baseline study. *Journal of EMDR Practice and Research, 6*(4), 159–169.

National Institute for Health and Care Excellence. (2011). Alcohol-use disorders: Diagnosis, assessment and management of harmful drinking and alcohol dependence (NICE Clinical Guideline No. 115). Retrieved from https://www.nice.org.uk/guidance/cg115.

National Institute for Health and Care Excellence. (2012). Drug use disorders in adults (NICE Quality Standard 23). Retrieved from https://www.nice.org.uk/guidance/qs23.

National Institute for Health and Care Excellence. (2017). Eating disorders: Recognition and treatment (NICE Guideline 69). Retrieved from https://www.nice.org.uk/guidance/ng69.

Nijenhuis, E. R., Van der Hart, O., & Kruger, K. (2002). The psychometric characteristics of the traumatic experiences checklist (TEC): First findings among psychiatric outpatients. *Clinical Psychology & Psychotherapy, 9*(3), 200–210. doi:10.1002/cpp.332

Ogden, P., Minton, K., & Pain, C. (2006). *Trauma and the body: A sensorimotor approach to psychotherapy.* New York, NY: W. W. Norton.

Paris, J. (2004). Is hospitalization useful for suicidal patients with borderline personality disorder? *Journal of Personality Disorders, 18*(3), 240–247. doi:10.1521/pedi.18.3.240.35443

Popky, A. J. (2005). DeTUR, an urge reduction protocol for addictions and dysfunctional behaviors. In R. Shapiro (Ed.), *EMDR solutions: Pathways to healing* (pp. 167–188). New York, NY: W. W. Norton.

Rosen, J. C., Reiter, J., & Orosan, P. (1995). Assessment of body image in eating disorders with the body dysmorphic disorder examination. *Behaviour Research and Therapy, 33*(1), 77–84. doi:10.1016/0005-7967(94)E0030-M

Schmidt, U., Ali, S., Slone, G., Tiller, J., & Treasure, J. (1995). The eating disorders awareness test: A new instrument for the assessment of the effectiveness of psychoeducational approaches to the treatment of eating disorders. *European Eating Disorders Review, 3*(2), 103–110. doi:10.1002/erv.2400030206

Serpell, L., & Treasure, J. (2002). Bulimia nervosa: Friend or foe? The pros and cons of bulimia nervosa. *International Journal of Eating Disorders, 32*(2), 164–170. doi:10.1002/eat.10076

Serpell, L., Treasure, J., Teasdale, J., & Sullivan, V. (1999). Anorexia nervosa: Friend or foe? *International Journal of Eating Disorders, 25*(2), 177–186. doi:10.1002/(SICI)1098-108X (199903)25:2<177::AID-EAT7>3.0.CO;2-D

Shapiro, F. (1995). *Eye movement desensitization and reprocessing: Basic principles, protocols and procedures* (1st ed.). New York, NY: Guilford Press.

Siegel, D. J. (1999). *The developing mind: How relationships and the brain interact to shape who we are.* New York, NY: Guilford Press.

Sweeney, A., Clement, S., Filson, B., & Kennedy, A. (2016). Trauma-informed mental healthcare in the UK: What is it and how can we further its development? *Mental Health Review Journal, 21*(3), 174–192. doi:10.1108/MHRJ-01-2015-0006

Treasure, J. (2009). *A guide to the medical risk assessment of eating disorders.* London, UK: Kings College. Retrieved from https://www.kcl.ac.uk/ioppn/depts/.../GUIDETOMEDICALRISKASSESSMENT.pdf

Trottier, K., Monson, C. M., Wonderlich, S. A., MacDonald, D. E., & Olmsted, M. P. (2017). Frontline clinicians' perspectives on and utilization of trauma-focused therapy with individuals with eating disorders. *Eating Disorders, 25*(1), 22–36. doi:10.1080/10640266.2016.1207456

Waller, G., Cordery, H., Corstorphine, E., Hinrichsen, H., Lawson, R., Mountford, V., & Russell, K. (2007). *Cognitive behavioral therapy for eating disorders: A comprehensive treatment guide.* Cambridge, UK: Cambridge University Press.

Weiss, D. S. (2007). The impact of event scale: Revised. In J. P. Wilson & C. S.-K. Tang (Eds.), *Cross-cultural assessment of psychological trauma and PTSD* (pp. 219–238). New York, NY: Springer US.

Young, J. E. (2005). *Young Schema Questionnaire–Short Form 3 (YSQ-S3).* New York, NY: Cognitive Therapy Center.

CHAPTER 8

The Preparation Phase

Andrew Seubert

■ INTRODUCTION

The preparation phase of our four-phase model is not a one-and-done event. It is visited and revisited often during the therapeutic journey. At the start, a certain amount of preparation is usually required to support the client while establishing the therapeutic relationship and in gathering client history throughout the assessment/evaluation phase. The need for preparation for the third phase of processing traumata is self-evident. After the processing phase, specific preparation for the final phase of integration—new identities, attitudes, and challenges—is not uncommon. Preparation work is ubiquitous and continuous!

■ A TRIPARTITE PREPARATION PHASE

I conceptualize the preparation phase in three parts for teaching and learning purposes. Remember, however, that preparation is an ongoing event, returned to from time to time throughout the course of treatment.

Stabilization

The first part of preparation is *stabilization*, sometimes referred to as case management. It is the sine qua non for the remaining parts. The goal here is to make sure that the client is externally safe, as well as internally stable. External safety requires above all else physical safety. You do not process a person's physical abuse while he or she is still living with the abuser or medically compromised because of an eating disorder (ED). First, you make the person factually safe. Safety and stability also mean strengthening the client to deal with emotional storms generated from mental and emotional onslaughts from people and events, as well as those emotional waves that arise from within the client's internal instability, often in the form of anxiety and/or shame.

Beth was 48 years old when we first met. She was emaciated, displaying extremely low energy levels, making it difficult for her to focus and stay awake. In addition, she was in a marriage with a bully who controlled every aspect of her life. Beth had learned never to reveal anger as a child. Daddy would have punished her for that. Beth consequently controlled her anger and unhappiness by not eating and obsessively cleaning her house. The angrier she became, the less she ate, and the cleaner the house got.

Her history of painful events (aka trauma history) could not be approached without a great deal of stabilization. She was not able to increase her food intake on an outpatient basis, and so required an inpatient hospitalization for her ED. Possessing a very wry sense of humor, she arrived at the hospital around noon and announced, "I don't do lunches!" She improved enough to allow her medications to become more effective (a starving brain inhibits effectiveness of pharmaceuticals), and returned home, unfortunately, to the same marriage.

We then worked on skills that helped her cope with both the fear and the shame surrounding eating, as well as her husband's bullying, until the day arrived when she was strong enough to divorce him. Until that point, Beth had to learn to quiet her fight-or-flight sympathetic system via mindfulness, breathwork, and emotional regulation. As she developed her capacity to self-soothe and stabilize her internal world, she grew stronger, found her voice slowly, and became strong enough to leave her marriage. When her life, both internal and external, stabilized, we began to explore the roots of her disorder. Particularly during this time, psychoeducation regarding trauma, bodily health, and EDs was a constant requirement. The client requires *trauma psychoeducation* to dismantle the power of perceptions and thoughts that are driven by anxiety, shame, posttraumatic stress disorder (PTSD), and the obsessive thinking of EDs (see Chapters 3 and 7). It is also required for the client's caregiving system to strengthen support from family, friends, and, for children and clients with intellectual disabilities, the larger caregiving network. Without an understanding of what the client is going through because of trauma treatment, family and friends may often come up short on compassion, which first requires an understanding of the client's process.

Psychoeducation applies to EDs (see Chapter 7) as well. When treating a client with an ED, his or her behaviors will often make no sense to family and friends. If there is no understanding, there is no compassion. Education about the purpose or payoff of an ED, as well as the physical dangers, particularly of anorexia nervosa (AN) and bulimia nervosa (BN), needs to be delivered systemically and continuously. Seventeen-year-old Marisa was caught between a rock and a hard place. She had been given up for adoption at birth, and was raised by a severely critical and prudish adoptive father and a passive adoptive mother. She was placed on medications for anxiety and depression at the age of 10. She began an early sexual development 1 year later, much to the difficulty and chagrin of the father.

Her adoptive parents divorced, and her mother married a state penal system lawyer who exuded criticism. Her critical adoptive father married a critical and jealous woman. Regardless of which household she was at, Marisa was constantly criticized and berated for her anorectic and her self-injurious (cutting and drinking) behaviors. They just could not understand why she would do such things!

I brought the two sets of parents into a session and told them Marisa's "story" from a therapeutic (and human) perspective. It was the story of how someone given up at birth, criticized constantly, and shamed at her development as a young woman might not think too highly of herself, might carry tremendous anger, shame, lack of control, and grief. Also, when you do not know what to do with such pain, you will find ways, albeit unhealthy, of releasing and compensating for them.

The four adults fell silent. Marisa and her behaviors began to make sense to them. At this point, with less adversity at home, Marisa and I could begin the work she came to do. Not only the delivery of psychoeducation but also collaboration among the various required helping professionals is part and parcel of stabilization. Awareness of the impact of trauma and dissociation in ED clients is often lacking among medical and mental health professionals. This requires diplomatic education. No therapist, nor any doctor or nutritionist, can afford to navigate independently in the complex waters of ED treatment. Establishing channels of communication with psychiatrists, medical doctors, and nutritionists, among others, as well as inpatient facilities is critical. With EDs, it does take a village.

Internal safety or equilibrium includes attention to physical stability typically compromised by the ED. This is something that many medical professionals are not able to assess, given their inability to measure metabolic rate or body composition (see Chapter 6). Stephanie was referred to me by an excellent, local physician. The physician stated that she gave Stephanie a complete physical, and that Stephanie was in very good health. But the good doctor suspected the presence of an ED.

Even with the clean bill of health from a physician, I still will not work with a potential ED client unless he or she has been seen at our local Nutrition Clinic (Upstate New York Eating Disorder Services), because most medical practices are not able to test for metabolic rate or body composition. I received a phone call from the Clinic's director a day after Stephanie was seen there.

"If Stephanie is not eating better in two weeks, I'll have to inpatient her!" the director told me.

The huge difference between a "clean bill of health" and "inpatient" is blurred when the required medical tests are not available. Stephanie looked fine on the outside, but on the inside her body was beginning to feed on itself.

Common among clients with EDs are mood disorders, led by anxiety, and perfectionistic and obsessive-compulsive tendencies. Medications have traditionally been prescribed to reduce mood imbalances and are often needed. It is important to remember, however, that if the client is malnourished, his or her brain is starving, which means that neurotransmitters are not functioning, which in turn dilutes the effectiveness of the medications.

Complements to psychotropic medications, often reducing the need for pharmaceuticals, are Neurofeedback (see Chapter 11) and HeartMath (Heartmath.com). These systems work directly on regulating brain balance (Neurofeedback) and heart rate variability (HeartMath), respectively, addressing the neurobiological source of stress or mood disturbances, particularly anxiety and obsessive-compulsive behaviors, hallmarks of EDs (see Chapters 10 and 12).

By way of summary, the first segment of the preparation phase addresses internal and external stability. Like any other aspect of this phase model, it is not written in stone. This means we might need to continue attending to stabilization issues throughout treatment (particularly medical well-being) or return to stabilization at different points during the overall treatment plan. There needs to be, however, a sense of flexible flow within the structure of the phases. Without a sense of "phases," it is easy to become lost in the complexity of the client's journey. Yet, without the attunement to the client's organic process, we enter the world of the cookie cutter. Structure exists for the sake of process, not the other way around.

Skills and Resources

A second part of the preparation phase is *developing skills and resources*. Among these are skills that involve changing internal states (self-soothing) and containment of disturbing affect. I teach some of these skills early on at the start of the assessment phase of treatment to facilitate successful and safe information gathering. It is also the phase of treatment when dissociative parts or ego states need to be acknowledged, understood, and worked with.

Working with parts or ego states is addressed in greater depth in Chapters 3, 4, 8, and 16 to 18. For now, suffice it to say that EDs inevitably involve dissociation at various degrees of intensity, which is why EDs are often so difficult to treat. You cannot change what you do not know, so contacting and collaborating with dissociated parts of Self becomes a necessity in treating EDs.

Before any other preparation work, even before the history taking, I teach the basics of **awareness**, these days commonly referred to as mindfulness, **and breathwork**. Without an awareness of what is taking place internally, in the body itself, and in one's surroundings, very little can change. Growth requires noticing things as they are, or *awaring* (Packer, 1995), and then assuming the response-ability and courage to change, be it a thought, a feeling, an image, or a body sensation. Unless a client *notices, observes,* or *is aware,* he or she lives an unconscious life in which required changes are outside of awareness and, consequently, out of reach.

An awareness script** can be of help to both therapist and client (*I have inserted** whenever a script is available at* www.clearpathtrainingcenter.com/eating-disorders.html). Awareness of body and body sensations (particularly hunger and satiety) can feel dangerous and threatening for the ED client, hence the common presence of avoidance and dissociation of somatic awareness. As we shall see, exercises that raise body acceptance (awareness without judgment) must begin with body awareness. These skills are part of preparation for trauma treatment *and are goals unto themselves.* Mindfulness alone can ameliorate ED symptoms and behaviors. Judy Lightstone describes the use of a mindful application to binge eating disorders (BEDs; Lightstone, 2004). In bringing awareness to the emotions that precede the urge to eat, the client can step back from the moment, observe, and make a different choice. Kristeller, Wolever, and Sheets (2014) conducted a randomized trial to explore the efficacy of a Mindfulness-Based Eating Awareness Training (MB-EAT). "At 4 months postintervention, 95% of those individuals with BED (binge-eating disorder) in MB-EAT no longer met the BED criteria versus 76% receiving PECB (psychoeducation/cognitive-behavioral)." I encourage my own clients to "be with" (see Chapter 11) the anxiety that often precedes eating and the shame that follows. Awareness and acceptance (observation without judgment) of the momentary feeling typically reduces its intensity. Breathwork, particularly knowing how to breathe diaphragmatically and how to control the speed of the inbreath and outbreath, is critical for learning how to regulate the fight/flight response of the sympathetic nervous system (Neurofeedback and HeartMath are helpful in this regard). This is of importance in dealing with anxiety and compulsive behaviors, and when needing to ground dissociated clients in the present time. From a brain perspective, Paulsen and Lanius (2009) write, "Breathing, as used in Taoist and Buddhist practice, as part of relaxation training, and as an essential part of somatic interventions, appears to have a profound effect on amygdalar hippocampal functioning" (p. 352). The therapist can easily introduce the client to diaphragmatic breathing by emphasizing a prolonged exhale, directing the client to raise both arms above the shoulders, and then "breathe into the belly, releasing the breath through the mouth as if through a thin straw." Raising the arms lifts the rib cage and frees the diaphragm from the weight of the upper torso. A similar effect can be achieved by lying on one's back, feet flat on the floor, knees in a "tent" position. Again, without gravity pushing the torso down and against the diaphragm, the breath goes immediately to the area of the stomach, a good way to begin the day before getting out of bed and to end the day just before sleep.

A caveat regarding breathing. As I often say to clients, "Breathing is a good thing!" Yet deep breathing can feel invasive to some. Breath can enter places in the body that store traumatic material, as well as places in the body that trigger shame. As breath enters these areas, it can activate past traumata stored there, along with accompanying anxiety and panic. In such cases, returning the breath rate to normal via breath control with eyes open (grounding), possibly changing posture and moving about the room, and an occasional glass of cold water can remedy the reaction, opening the door to reflective understanding and normalizing of what just happened.

Specific to ED treatment are skills that develop a sense of ownership of and connection to one's body, precisely because much of body awareness has been dissociated. Cognitive distortions and restructuring play an important role in the ongoing treatment plan, but, as Cook-Cottone (2016) writes, "Our relationship with our bodies is multifaceted and can't be fully captured by a set of ideas or concepts (e.g., body dissatisfaction). Connection to the body is emotional, physical, and relational. Phenomenologically, we are our bodies" (p. 99).

More is said about a trauma-focused cognitive behavioral approach in Chapter 14, whereas Chapters 9 (dance and movement therapy), 21 (somatic experiencing), and 22 (sensorimotor psychotherapy) address **embodied approaches** more specifically. In support of embodied practices of mindful self-care and yoga in the prevention of EDs, Cook-Cottone (2016) writes further:

> The neurological experience of the human being is more than a set of risky or healthy conceptualizations. It is embodied. What we do and embody co-creates our knowing and sense of self. Prevention of eating disorders should be a top-down, bottom up, and integrative process. Along with the tried and tested tools of combating media and cultural pressures to judge and objectify the body, effective prevention should include positive mind/body practices such as yoga within the larger context of self-care. Deep, authentic, and resilient love and appreciation of our bodies is most likely associated with being in our bodies in a mindful and caring way. (p. 102)

Reawakening the body's signals of satiety and hunger and retraining them is yet another aspect of body attention that is challenging for ED clients. All of these skills— both cognitive and embodied—will continue to require attention throughout the entire course of treatment.

Emotional regulation is typically problematic for clients with EDs, particularly anxiety and shame. Also, *beyond regulating and managing feelings is the task of emotional competence*, the task of learning from our emotions and using the energy they possess. Mindful attention to the body as the "home" of emotions also makes body awareness threatening. If I do not know *where* I feel an emotion, then I do not really feel it. But if the body is dissociated from one's awareness, then emotional experience is truncated. Chapter 10 explores this dilemma.

Dialectical behavior therapy (DBT) was developed by Linehan (2015) to, among other things, affect regulation. Taught in a structured group setting, this approach provides skills required for daily living, as well as for future trauma processing. Acceptance and commitment therapy (ACT) is yet another approach that focuses on the use of mindful awareness of experience, inclusive of emotions, followed by a commitment to take action to bring about changes that support one's values (Sandoz, Wilson, & DuFrene, 2010). Both approaches can be extremely helpful in achieving short-term emotional skills and successes, as well as in preparing for Phase III of trauma processing. Before mentioning a few other **imagery-based skills** that are particularly helpful with ED clients, I would first stress the importance of imagery and its development. Often in trauma trainings, participants are taught a "safe place" procedure, as well as a containment skill, without an understanding as to why they are learning these skills to begin with and the role that imagery plays.

Think of an image as a communicative bridge between unconscious material, potential capacities, and the conscious mind. Another metaphor is to consider the image as a key that unlocks doors to both dissociated parts of Self, as well as to potential, positive skills and states. The image of a lake in summer might evoke the *experience* of calm and peace. An image of Mother Teresa might *actualize* one's potential for kindness and forgiveness. The purpose of the image is to open the person to *an experience of an internal state change* or *the actualizing of a potential capacity*. The goal of imagery is direct experience of, rather than thinking about, the desired outcome.

In developing an image for these purposes, it is important to elicit as many details of the image as possible, because the greater the detail, the less the brain recognizes the difference between the image and the real thing. Once this has occurred, there needs to be time for the image to *activate* the desired state or capacity, allowing the client to *experience* the state both *emotionally and somatically* (see end of the chapter for a procedure for developing imagery).

When we allow our minds to wander into unsavory territories, it is negative images that often cause us distress. We are using the same power of imagery when we elicit positive state changes and affect management. State change is the goal of such procedures as the "safe place" or "calm place." I prefer to call this a resource place (or person, or activity, such as cycling) so the client can fill in the blank and choose the desired state, because it is not always about safety.

Another aspect of safety is what O'Shea (2009) refers to as "safe state." It is not the image (as mentioned earlier), but the state that is important. The lake or the beach doesn't contain the state. The state is internal to the client. It is the client's capacity that is awakened, not bequeathed by the image. Also, with respect to safety, it is important for the client to learn to feel safe when he or she is actually safe.

The "light stream" (Shapiro, 2018) is another such state changing image from the Tibetan tradition that invites a healing light to touch places of emotional disturbance in the body. A "container" (**) is an image developed to contain or put away disturbing material at the end of or in between sessions.

Resource development and installation (RDI; Korn & Leeds, 2002) uses imagery to either create a state change or elicit potential capacities, such as courage and patience. An image is chosen that represents the desired state or capacity, and then detailed to access the changes themselves. Finally, the resource is inserted into a "movie," either a remake of a previous, negative experience (corrective movies) or a movie of how the client (with the help of the resource) wishes to handle the situation in the future.

An example of such a resource that I often use is what I call the circle of support, adapted from the "circle of excellence" used in neurolinguistic programming (NLP). The client is asked to bring up images of (or a sense of) people living or dead, pets, spiritual beings, or imagined figures in whose presence the client feels supported and positive about himself or herself. The client is then asked to (a) approach the circle and feel the support and, (b) if able, enter the circle, stand in the middle, and receive the support from the circle with each inhalation. The client is finally asked to anchor the image of the circle somewhere in his or her body.

Short-Term Successes: A Case Illustration

The third aspect of the preparation phase focuses on short-term successes in which the client gains mastery and confidence in dealing with *changeable life circumstances*, something of a personal trainer approach (Greenwald, 2007). By applying newly acquired skills and resources to doable, changeable patterns of thinking, feeling, and behaving, the client achieves successes that are more immediately relevant, usually learning to do more of something, to do less of something, or to do something differently.

Veronica, an attractive and lively 17-year-old high school student, was referred for her struggles with restrictive eating and distorted body image. And she was not shy.

"First of all," she announced to me, "you're a man, and there's no way I'm going to talk about food and my body to a *man!*"

I thanked her for sharing (I really did) and proceeded to ask what she would be open to working on as long as she was having sessions with me.

"So what would you like to be different in your life? You're the boss!" She was interested.

"Well, there was this guy in my class who was supposed to be my good friend, and he starts to grope me on a class bus trip. You see, we were in the same seats, being friends and all. I did report it, but some of my friends tell me it's no big deal, that he's a good guy, blah, blah, blah. So I don't know what to do when I run into him or what to do with the bitches who tell me to get over it. What would you do?"

We spent the next two sessions processing the fondling, as well as the blame coming from her classmates, with eye movement desensitization and reprocessing (EMDR) (see Chapter 13). At the end of that piece of work, she had come to trust me and knew that I was on her side. Our relationship was becoming as important to her as her relationship to her ED. It was not long before we were exploring the payoffs of her ED and why it had become her primary relationship.

Given the need for hope and relevance at the start of ED treatment, short-term, relevant goals encourage and strengthen the client and the therapeutic bond. Goals that are often years away can seem daunting, particularly if the client is attached to the ED (which is usually the case) and is not about to make the ED the enemy, but sees it as a best friend (Schaefer, 2004).

By way of summary, the preparation phase establishes stability, and develops skills and resources, which lead to short-term successes. The various aspects of this phase can be ubiquitous and continuous, depending, as always, on the client's needs. All of this stabilizing and strengthening, however, must first and foremost be held within the safe, consistent, and caring embrace of the therapeutic relationship.

▣ TEMPLATE FOR CREATING IMAGES (**)

Images provide a way to access and actualize latent qualities and internal states. When the image is detailed and brought to life, the brain is unable to differentiate between the image and the real life. We consequently are able to *experience* these states and qualities. The image is what we call a **resource** in that it helps us access the needed experience. Whether we are developing the image of a "safe place" or a "container" or an image representing any internal quality or state, the image acts as something of a key to the experience of potential, desirable states. It's all about state change.

Various qualities and state changes go by different names (calm, safe, strong, etc.), but these are all abstractions. It is necessary to move from abstract, left-brain functioning to the more experiential and holistic language of the right side of the brain to access and activate these states. This is where imagery is invaluable. It is the language of the unconscious.

The *procedure for developing images* for various states and qualities is pretty much the same.

1. Determine the **internal state or quality** you need to handle a situation more positively or to process a memory successfully. *Example*: strength (an abstraction).
2. Pick an **image that would represent that quality**. The image (or resource) can be found in **m**emories, **m**odels, **m**irrors, or **i**maginings **. *Example*: a memory of when I acted with strength, or the lion in Wizard of Oz. Remember that the

resource can be an activity (biking, running, quilting, etc.) as well as a place, pet, person, or object.

3. Get a "sense" (does not have to be visual, as in "visualize") of the image, noticing all of the **details**: place, time, activity, and all of the sensory details, that is, visual, auditory, tactile, and olfactory—as many senses as possible, so as to allow the image to appear more real to the brain.

4. Pause to **experience** the feelings and body sensations connected to the desired feeling or state.

5. **Breathe** into the place in the body where you notice these feelings.

6. Add a **cue word or short phrase** that represents the desired feeling or state. *Example*: "strong" or "lion."

7. Create a **physical anchor** (this could be the breathing or pressing two fingers together, among other possibilities).

8. **Practice accessing the desired feeling/state** on awakening and before sleeping by bringing to mind the image, the feelings/sensations, and cue word/phrase and anchor together, effectively "wiring" them together.

The purpose of all of this is to access the desired feeling/state when you need it. Recall any of the elements of this procedure (image, body location, cue word, anchor), and, if it has been practiced, any element should activate the feeling/state. Example: The word "strong," or breathing into the body where you have felt the feeling, the image itself, or the cue word/phrase should bring up the feeling/state needed in the moment. What is wired together, fires together.

A way of recalling where we might find resource imagery is to use the letter "M" as a mnemonic. (a) **M**emories—actual experience of the feeling or desired state; (b) **M**odels—any person (living or dead), spiritual being, pet, or object that represents the quality/feeling; (c) **M**irrors—others who have told us that they see this quality/state in us; (d) i**M**aginings—any fictitious character from books or movies (Princess Leia, Superman, etc.) or simply imagined (a fairy godmother, personal superhero, etc.; Seubert, 2005, pp. 300–301).

■ SCRIPT: DEVELOPING A RESOURCE VIA IMAGERY (**)

(What the therapist says is in **bold italics**)

1. Ask for the target memory or situation.

2. *What quality, internal state, or resource would help you successfully process this memory/situation?*

3. If the client gives an abstraction (courage, kindness, safety), ask: *Is there an image* (memory, model, mirror, imagining/magic) *that would represent that quality for you?*

4. *Bring up that image and notice as many details as possible* (ask for details in various modalities: visual, auditory, etc.).

5. *Stay with that image and notice any positive feelings and/or body sensations.*

6. *Is there a cue word or short phrase that would remind you of this resource?*

7. OPTION (Circle of Excellence—NLP): *Join the resource image inside a circle.*

8. *I'd like you to concentrate on that image, the feelings and sensations, and the cue word/phrase. Breathe into the place in your body where you* <u>experience</u> *the resource.*

9. *Repeat twice or as long as the positive feelings/sensations increase.*

■ SCRIPT: CREATING A MOVIE (**)

(Script adapted from Greenwald, R. [2007]. *EMDR within a phase model of trauma-informed treatment.* New York, NY: Haworth Press.)

1. *I want you to recall the problem you're working on and the last (or next) time this happened (you think this will happen) ....*
2. *Bring up the details of the situation ....*
3. *You're going to run a movie in your mind, which begins with the situation, particularly the moment of decision. At that point, recall the thoughts, feelings, and body sensations at that moment.*
4. *They (thoughts, feelings, and body sensations) will be signals for you to bring up your resource/skills to help you make the better choice.*
5. *Then proceed with the situation, step by step, handling it the way you want to, bringing you to a final scene or image of the outcome you would like. Note the details of that final image and how you would feel in it.*
6. After you have created the movie, ask the client to run the movie from beginning to end. *Start at the beginning and let me know when the movie is at the end.*
7. Teach the client how to do this on his or her own in between sessions.

■ REFERENCES

Cook-Cottone, C. (2016). Embodied self-regulation and mindful self-care in the prevention of eating disorders. *Eating Disorders, 24*(1), 98–105, doi:10.1080/10640266.2015.1118954

Greenwald, R. (2007). *EMDR within a phase model of trauma-informed treatment.* New York, NY: Haworth Press.

Korn, D. L., & Leeds, A. M. (2002). Preliminary evidence of efficacy for EMDR resource development and installation in the stabilization phase of treatment of complex posttraumatic stress disorder. *Journal of Clinical Psychology, 58*(12), 1465–1487. doi:10.1002/jclp.10099

Kristeller, J., Wolever, R., & Sheets, V. (2014). Mindfulness-based eating awareness training (MB-EAT) for binge eating: A randomized clinical trial. *Mindfulness, 5*, 282–297. doi:10.1007/s12671-012-0179-1

Lightstone, J. (2004). Dissociation and compulsive eating. *Journal of Trauma & Dissociation, 5*(4), 17–32. doi:10.1300/J229v05n04_02

Linehan, M. M. (2015). *DBT skills training manual* (2nd ed.). New York, NY: Guilford Press.

O'Shea, K. (2009). EMDR friendly preparation methods for adults and children. In R. Shapiro (Ed.), *EMDR Solutions II: For depression, eating disorders, performance, and more* (pp. 289–312). New York, NY: W. W. Norton.

Packer, T. (1995). *The work of this moment.* Rutland, VT: Charles E. Tuttle.

Paulsen, S. L., & Lanius, U. (2009). Toward an embodied self: Integrating EMDR with somatic and ego state interventions. In R. Shapiro (Ed.), *EMDR Solutions II: For depression, eating disorders, performance, and more* (pp. 335–388). New York, NY: W. W. Norton.

Sandoz, E. K., Wilson, K. G., & DuFrene, T. (2010). *Acceptance and commitment therapy for eating disorders: A process-focused guide to treating anorexia and bulimia.* Oakland, CA: New Harbinger.

Schaefer, J. (2004). *Life without Ed.* New York, NY: McGraw-Hill.

Seubert, A. (2005). EMDR with clients with mental disability. In R. Shapiro (Ed.), *EMDR solutions: Pathways to healing* (pp. 293–311). New York, NY: W. W. Norton.

Shapiro, F. (2018). *Eye movement desensitization and reprocessing: Basic principles, protocols, and procedures* (3rd ed.). New York, NY: Guilford Press.

CHAPTER 9

Discovering the Power of Movement: Dance/Movement Therapy in the Treatment of Eating Disorders and Trauma

Susan Kleinman

■ INTRODUCTION

One may wonder what comes first—the chicken or the egg—as in the case of the large number of individuals with eating disorders (EDs) who also suffer from a history of trauma. Dance/movement therapist and psychologist Ann Krantz believes that "the symptoms of EDs serve to disconnect affect from the body, particularly as sexuality, trauma, and cultural influences contribute to conflicts in the woman's [individual's] developmental struggle toward self-identity" (1999, p. 81). Individuals with both conditions are known for ignoring the experience of living in their body. By ignoring their inner feelings and sensations (interoceptive experiences), they bury their emotions, and the burial ground is the body itself (Kleinman & Hall, 2006). "In all their forms, eating disorders offer a creative form of adaptive disassociation" (Shure & Weinstock, 2009, p. 167). According to van der Kolk, "The more people try to push away and ignore internal warning signs, the more likely they are to take over ..." (2014, p. 97).

Our Bodies, Our Selves

Our bodies house our feelings, sensations, and our native language, movement. From the first kick in our mothers' womb till our dying breath, we participate in a dance of life (Kleinman, 1994). Individuals suffering from both trauma and EDs have difficulty making their "house" a "home." They often run away from "home" in an attempt to feel safer, centering their lives on using emotionally driven behaviors as a way of attempting to alleviate the often horrific anxiety they might otherwise experience. Ressler explains, "As obsessed as clients with eating disorders are about their bodies, they are not really 'living in' or 'grounded in' their bodies. The body is not used as a place to live or experience, but as an object needing to be controlled" (2009, p. 145).

Erin (not her real name), a 45-year-old trauma survivor, suffered from chronic, severe anorexia nervosa. I watched as she curled up in a chair, absorbed in her usual dance of anxiety: leg shaking frantically, hands strumming together, chewing gum as if in a panic. Then, hands climbing toward her neck, she began pinching herself to keep from "giving in" to experiencing feelings. I knew that if I could not get her attention, I would not be able to engage and help her move from a frozen place to one where she could take charge of her past and eventually move forward into the present. She was now under the spell of *the voice*, listening to the negative messages she had been hearing all her life from her perpetrators and other like-minded people. She had taken what we had come to refer to as a "detour." It was always the same. When faced with overwhelming feelings, often triggered by words, sounds, smells, or actions reminiscent of her trauma, she would retreat into isolative states in which she was unable to take charge and function. Survival was her unconscious goal.

Living With Trauma and an Eating Disorder

Erin's philosophy of living was on the basis of fears resulting from sexual and emotional trauma that began early in her life. Because of these life-shaping experiences, she unconsciously created an ED to feel more "in control." By restricting food, she was attempting to meet her emotional need to restrict feelings and thoughts; by trying to be invisible and disappear, she was attempting to find a way to feel safe. The process of helping patients like Erin feel secure enough, over time, to shift from their survival mode to a mode in which they can reclaim a connection to living in their bodies is essential to recovery. Erin's journal entry explains her beliefs, on the basis of rules she created to deal with her ED and trauma issues. She wrote:

> I notice a feeling start to come. I question what could be causing that feeling. If the feeling isn't appropriate to the situation, I try to stop it. If the feeling is appropriate to the situation, but happens at a time when I shouldn't be expressing feelings, I try to stop it. If the feeling is appropriate, and it is appropriate for me to feel the feeling, then I have the feeling, but I try not to allow it to linger. Unfortunately, there are times when feelings do linger. That is when I become afraid of the feelings.

Erin shared this material to allow me to better understand her inner dialogue, and she agreed to let me help her shape this "mantra" to embrace more realistic and humane goals:

> My body is my home. I contain feelings in my body. It is the only place I have to feel and to live. My head helps me understand and determine my actions based on my feelings … when I can express fully, when I need to hold back, when it is safe to let go.

Inherent in the challenge of embracing this mantra is making it safe enough for Erin to begin to experience, express, and understand the connection between what she experiences inwardly and how it connects to the bigger picture of her life. Taking this a step further, incorporating these skills leads to "embodying an essence of the self as a whole being—emotions, thoughts and actions in harmonious synchrony" (S. Kleinman & A. Ressler, personal communication, February 18, 2017). Likewise, trusting oneself to quiet the mind and lead with the body can assist in embodying what Winnicott refers to as the "true self." "Only the true self can be creative and only the true self can feel real" (1965, p. 147). As Marks-Tarlow states, "We process clinical information from the bottom-up, moving from lower level, body-based sensory and emotional origins towards higher-level cortical processing" (2014, p. xvii). The concepts, process, and frame of dance/movement therapy (DMT) follow Marks-Tarlow's premise and combine with the belief in the importance of creating a pathway for authenticity to surface and be expressed.

Embracing the Concepts: Use of Self

Dance/movement therapists strive to center their own feelings and thoughts in a way that allows them to balance therapeutically as a type of empathic receptor, grasping the mindset of others kinesthetically. This process is not scripted, thus allowing for the organic unfolding of actions and interactions with spontaneous responses. Kleinman shares:

> As a dance/movement therapist, I use the cues and signals from my own body to respond to what the patients present through their own expression. Achieving and sustaining this level of authenticity requires balancing the knowledge from my personal and professional senses with my cognitive and clinical knowledge that emerges simultaneously in the moment. (2017, p. 7)

We can all transform our own intuitive senses into extraordinary therapeutic skills through use of the DMT concepts that follow. The three interrelated concepts that embrace these cues and signals are called *rhythmic synchrony, kinesthetic awareness*, and *kinesthetic empathy*.

Rhythmic synchrony represents the ability to be in tune with ourselves and our patients. This includes modifying our own way of being in our body including tone of voice, speed of movement, and way of moving to attune to our patients. In everyday language, we might refer to this as getting on the same page with our patients. Consciously attuning to the patient's core elements that he or she presents in this way can lead to sharing emotions later in the process.

The second concept, *kinesthetic awareness*, refers to the ability to maintain conscious awareness of our "self" physically, emotionally, and cognitively, while facilitating experiences that help patients experience their own feelings. These two concepts blend together to create a rapport that flows between patient and therapist as well as patients with their own inner feeling states. Pallaro (2007) writes that "this process indicates the ability to respond to another's feelings and states and understanding them is, in fact, a result of bodily based kinesthetic empathy" (p. 183). *Kinesthetic empathy*, coined by Berger in 1956, manifests in our ability to foster shared expression by tapping into the patient's issues in an embodied fashion and even sharing feeling states with them (1989). Understanding and practicing use of these concepts can help clinicians discover and trust their innate ability to "attend" empathically, respond authentically, and translate nonverbal experiences into cognitive insights (Kleinman, 2016, pp. 139–157; Ressler, Kleinman, & Mott, 2010, pp. 404–425).

Dance/Movement Therapy—The Process

Dance/movement therapists weave together nonverbal dialogues that transform everyday movements into expressive communication (Kleinman, 2014). The process facilitated by the therapist opens a pathway designed to help patients explore and reestablish connection with their body. As patients experience and express feelings, they increase the ability to identify how emerging awareness parallels and reflects their unique behavioral patterns. These patterns are explored through both nonverbal and verbal reflections (Kleinman, 2016, pp. 139–157). Metaphors emerging from the expressive movements serve as "a barometer telling the state of the soul's weather to all who can read it" (Graham, 1991, p. 4). Patients are encouraged to be "detectives," viewing their embodied experiences and cognitive reflections as clues to help them recognize and decode their own emotional issues. As this occurs, disconnected experiences ignite into meaningful expression and understanding of their experiences that can contribute to lasting change. This example from Erin's treatment demonstrates the power of the DMT process.

"The more I try to control this anxiety, the more I lose control of it," Erin said. "Trying to make a decision when I don't know what to expect, causes it to increase even more.

The doctor I saw this week asked why I was a bundle of nerves. I didn't know it showed. I think I am disconnected." Erin understood this in her head, but continued to fight her inability to connect her unconscious experiences with conscious awareness and thoughts. She agreed to let me help her lean into sensations to embody and understand. This fit with the tenets of the mantra we had developed earlier regarding accepting her true self.

We began by moving in circles that seemed never ending. "I don't know how to stop," she said, "and if I did, I wouldn't know what to do!" Using my own *kinesthetic empathy*, I moved with Erin to understand what she was experiencing. As we shared our experiences, we expressed what it felt like to move in repetitive circles, not knowing when or how to stop. I became dizzy and nauseated; she remained unaware of what she felt. We created a goal to stop going in circles and move toward the other side of the room to symbolize Erin's fear of facing the unknown. She protested, "How will I know when to stop?" "Listen to your body," I responded. Eventually she stopped circling, put all of her weight on one leg, began shaking the free leg, and then brought it over on top of the standing leg that was trying to control everything. I tried to do this also to discover what I felt in my body. I recognized I felt a lot of tension from trying to maintain this position. Although Erin's body shook from the stress of the position she attempted to hold, she repeated that she did not know what she felt. Again, we touched base cognitively to identify and connect what she was or was not feeling or thinking.

Every step of the way became a battle as the inner voice of her perpetrator cautioned her to not believe in herself. Erin was able to recognize that the "inner child" she called *Trouble* was scared and wanted to connect with her. Because she could not allow herself to connect with her fears, she rejected her vulnerability whenever it emerged as *Trouble*, which, in turn, increased her anxiety. The vicious cycle kept her locked in her rising anxiety.

In spite of this, I encouraged her to risk exploring what needed to happen next in her movement sequence. She knelt to the ground facing what was before her, thus putting it on the same level with her instead of having it hovering over her. It was safer that way, she said, but again the perpetrator voice intervened and caused her to stop herself from trusting her actions. As she described it: "I was afraid to move further away from what I knew. I became stuck, almost frozen in this newer space. Then I became emotional. The loud, critical, mean, intimidating voice took over. Any trust I may have had within myself was taken away." We ended by reviewing the process of how we had worked on these issues.

I asked Erin to practice noticing when this pattern occurred during the week and to try to modify her usual ways of coping by using her new insights. Following our session she wrote, "I am trying hard to just let myself be and trust that what happened in our session was supposed to happen rather than to engage in my usual over thinking that causes me to continue to move and think in circles."

Erin established a growing connection between her movement discoveries and her cognitive thoughts. Anchoring in this way also provided her with a new reference to cope with the fears related to her past by making the unknown known, and the unconscious conscious.

Articulating the Therapeutic Frame: The Cognitive Markers (CMs)

The *CMs* represent five stages of the DMT therapeutic process: exploration, discovery, acknowledgment, connection, and integration. These markers provide a guide to:

- Explore an experience.
- Make discoveries regarding what has been explored.
- Acknowledge that the discoveries are important.

- Connect the meaning of a discovery with a familiar pattern or experience.
- Integrate the meaning of the connection in their lives so that insights can be explored over time.

(Stark & Lohn, 1993, pp. 130-131; Kleinman & Hall, 2006, pp. 14–15; Kleinman, 2016, pp. 151-155)

The CMs can be used by therapists and patients alike to decode, track, and understand the experiences that fit into the bigger picture of their lives. Erin's next DMT session explains this further.

Erin reported that she had been feeling sad all week. I knew she had a lot to feel sad about, but the fact that she had been experiencing these feelings without disassociating represented progress. It was new for her to connect to her feelings, so, as a result, she questioned the notion that feelings could actually precede thoughts. As we explored her thoughts and feelings, Erin acknowledged what she had been wondering about. "Tears come to the eyes (body) before the mind recognizes you are sad. Is this right?" she asked. We explored the validity of Erin's carryover from our last session, as she became more anchored in this new understanding.

I reinforced with her that by connecting the meaning of her movement experience with her fear of the unknown, she had been very insightful. My response to her was, of course, the opposite of the inner voice representing her perpetrators to which she had been listening. Now, feeling my support, she shifted gears, and responded by acknowledging that the pillow she was clutching was there to help her "cover up." We discussed her perceptions/discoveries regarding her body and how, throughout her life, she survived by disconnecting from her feelings. We also explored how this "disconnect" was the way in which she coped with life and how it had been expressed in our sessions through her movement experiences (Kleinman, 2017, p. 70). I validated her discoveries and asked her to explore a movement experience with the pillow. My hope was that she would be able to understand this experience more fully, as she reviewed it through the voice of her body. Sharing her discoveries and connections following her movement experience, she said:

> As I sat down to write about what had happened, I noticed that I had wanted to cover-up desperately—to be unseen. I felt exposed. In order to move on, I had to throw down the one thing that allowed me to hide (the pillow). I discovered I was feeling emotional—I was sad, and I questioned why, because I had nothing to be sad about. My mind and my body moved in circles as I tried to get unstuck. I finally stopped myself by putting my weight on one side of my body to get myself balanced and then I took a few steps forward, kneeling down, I assessed the situation from a different perspective as I had done last week. Again I was stuck. I wasn't able to go further, but today I understood the connection in my life. It was because the beliefs of my past were in my way. I have held onto these beliefs my whole life. If I give them up, then what! What beliefs can I hold onto? We processed this together, and I knew that the beliefs I formed in my past were in my way. I was reminded of these beliefs by the voices that reared up inside of me whenever I tried to make a change. We placed bunches of pillows by my side to represent these beliefs, and then we moved them aside to explore and discover what it felt like once the "past" was moved out of my way. I was now free to move on, but discovered the only way I could was to crawl forward because I was unready to walk.

We crawled together, and Erin moved beyond the symbolic perpetrators, leaving the pillows (the perpetrators) behind. The anxiety diminished, but she felt alone and acknowledged that her risk was to be able to see herself in a new way and to build perceptions that were hidden in conflict. She said: "Once I crawled forward enough, I left the 'past' behind, but immediately felt alone, as if I had nothing to hold onto. I think I have 'become' these beliefs, and now I am truly stuck. I feel as if I am stranded on an island with no life support, and I don't know how to swim to safety."

In discussing what had occurred, we identified the crutches she had used throughout her life to "survive." She explained that she did not want to stay the way she was, she wanted to change, but was very scared. She acknowledged that the pillow she had used as a cover-up represented a kind of protective shield:

> I use it to cover the parts of my body I feel the most shame about (my stomach, breasts and private parts). When I am holding onto it, it feels like a security blanket. I think that I use my eating disorder the same way. I use it to hide—isolation has become a cover. I wanted to carry the pillow/cover-up with me as I tried to move forward, but knew I couldn't take it with me anymore, so I threw it down.

Erin's ability to decode her experience created new understanding of how avoidance in addressing what she fears escalates her anxiety and causes her to detour away from her present reality. She noticed that as she moved her expression outward, feelings underlying her anxiety emerged and signs of stressful symptoms visibly diminished. They had been replaced with the pain of her sadness. She was leaning into her feelings, and it scared her. But she agreed to continue working on facing her losses and strengthening her ability to face change. Her awareness, I believed, was a sign of newly formed insights that could help her sustain and integrate change. The most telling sign of movement toward recovery was that Erin was truly in motion.

Final Thoughts: The Challenge of Change

Regarding the importance of connecting with internal states, psychotherapist Laura Weisberg writes:

> As therapists, we need to create a safe place where our clients can begin to connect to and explore their own internal experiences. We utilize our intuitive capacities to sense when to support and when to challenge, when to lean in and when to allow space, when to increase the level of activation in the room and when to help soothe and calm things down. (2015, pp. 11–12)

Erin's experiences demonstrate the stunning power of DMT as a treatment method to bring the true self forward into the present, so as to create and facilitate sustained movement toward wholeness. Erin says of these experiences:

> I have been in awe with how DMT allows me to express so much inner turmoil without having to speak using words. My body, which has always been a stranger, spoke for me and it didn't lie. Living with the voice of my perpetrator my whole life has caused me to be afraid to believe in myself. In experiencing this work, I now know what is true. While I still have obstacles to face, I am ready to live an authentic life, to be true to myself.

■ REFERENCES

Berger, M. R. (1989). Bodily expression of experience and emotion. In J. Fried, S. Katz, S. Kleinman & J. Naess (Eds.), *A collection of early writings: Towards a body of knowledge* (Vol. 1). Columbia, MD: American Dance Therapy Association. (Original work published 1956)

Graham, M. (1991). *Blood memory*. New York, NY: Doubleday.

Kleinman, S. (1994, February). *Submission for the Record, Statement of the American Dance Therapy Association to the Sub-committee on Ways and Means, House of Representatives Hearing on The Congressional Budget Office's Analysis of the President's Health Care Reform Proposal, Volume XII, President's Health Care Reform Proposals: Impact on Providers and Consumers, Part 3 of 3* (pp. 70–74). Serial 103–91, Washington, DC: U.S. Government Printing Office.

Kleinman, S. (2014). Eating disorder hope. Dance and movement therapy in the treatment of eating disorders: Re-claiming authentic connection with the self. Retrieved from http://www.eatingdisorderhope.com/recovery/self-help-tools-skills-tips/dancemovement-therapy-in-the-treatment-of-eating-disorders-re-claiming-authentic-connection-with-the-self

Kleinman, S. (2016). Becoming whole again: Dance and movement therapy for individuals with eating disorders. In S. Chaiklin & H. Wengrower (Eds.), *The art and science of dance and movement therapy: Life is dance* (2nd ed., pp. 139–157). New York, NY: Routledge.

Kleinman, S. (2017). Learning to trust my true self: A work in progress. *Perspectives*, 7–8. Retrieved from http://renfrewcenter.com/sites/default/files/WINTER%202017%20PERSPECTIVES_web_1.pdf

Kleinman, S., & Hall, T. (2006). Dance and movement therapy: A method for embodying emotions. In W. Davis & S. Kleinman (Eds.), *The Renfrew Center Foundation healing through relationship series: Contributions to eating disorder theory and treatment (Vol 1): Fostering body-mind integration* (pp. 2–19). Philadelphia, PA: Renfrew Center Foundation.

Krantz, A. (1999). Growing into her body: Dance/movement therapy for women with eating disorders. *American Journal of Dance Therapy*, 21(2), 81–101. doi:10.1023/A:1022104603189

Marks-Tarlow, T. (2014). Introduction. In *Awakening clinical intuition: An experiential workbook for psychotherapists* (pp. xvii–xxxvi). New York, NY: W. W. Norton.

Pallaro, P. (2007). Somatic countertransference: The therapist in relationship. In P. Pallaro (Ed.), *Authentic movement: Vol. 2. Moving the body, moving the self, being moved: A collection of essays* (pp. 176–193). London, UK: Jessica Kingsley.

Ressler, A. (2009). Body mind treatment: Connecting to imprinted emotions and experiences. In M. Maine, W. N. Davis, & D. J. Shure (Eds.), *Effective clinical practice in the treatment of eating disorders: The heart of the matter* (pp. 145–163). New York, NY: Routledge.

Ressler, A., Kleinman, S., & Mott, E. (2010). The use of holistic methods to integrate the shattered self. In M. Maine, B. H. McGilley, & D. W. Bunnell (Eds.), *Treatment of eating disorders: Bridging the research-practice gap* (pp. 404–425). London, UK: Academic Press.

Shure, J., & Weinstock, B. (2009). Shame, compassion, and the journey toward health. In M. Maine, W. N. Davis, & D. J. Shure (Eds.), *Effective clinical practice in the treatment of eating disorders: The heart of the matter* (pp. 163–179). New York, NY: Routledge.

Stark, A., & Lohn, A. (1993). The use of verbalization in dance/movement therapy. In S. Sandel, S. Chaiklin, & A. Lohn (Eds.), *Foundations of dance/movement therapy: The Life and work of Marian Chace* (pp. 130–131). Columbia, MD: American Dance Therapy Association.

van der Kolk, B (2014). *The body keeps the score: Brain, mind, and body in the healing of trauma* (p. 97). New York, NY: Viking.

Weisberg, L. J. (2015). Intuition in psychotherapy. *Perspectives*, Winter, 11–12.

Winnicott, D. W. (1965). *The maturational processes and the facilitating environment: Studies in the theory of emotional development* (International Psycho-Analytical Library, No. 64). London, UK: Hogarth Press and the Institute of Psycho-Analysis.

CHAPTER 10

The Courage to Feel: Eating Disorders and the Case for Emotions

Andrew Seubert

In our sleep, pain which cannot forget falls drop by drop upon the heart, until, in our own despair, against our will, comes wisdom through the awful grace of God. —*Aeschylus*

▓ INTRODUCTION

Please do not skip this chapter.

Clinicians often assume they know what emotions are about: What they are, and how to regulate them and stay within that "window of tolerance" (Siegel, 1999). All well and good. I have heard, described, and experienced in clients the understandable danger of emotions that flood, overwhelm, break us down, and lead to destructive behaviors (Goleman, 1995). In other words, the messiness and the pain of it all. Yet, little is said of the brilliance of our most exquisite emotional radar, the felt system of knowing that lets us know when things are alright or not, the energies that motivate and mobilize us, and the experiences that, when honest and transparent, connect us one to the other, guiding the emotional journey that brings us home—back to who we most truly are.

Leaving home is hard. It is hard to leave high school friends for college. It is hard to leave a family home for our own apartment on the other side of town. It is hard to choose a career that takes us far from our neighborhood. Many of us do these things anyway, believing we have made the break. We have grown up, so we are convinced. Yet no one told us that we might be 30-, 40-, or 50-something, still unable to leave home.

No one told us that we could achieve work skills and academic degrees, marry, and bring children into the world while suffering a handicap that could ruin it all. No one taught us that as long as we responded and reacted emotionally to the world around us as we had as children, leaving home would never happen.

Even after our physical separation has been achieved, we often continue to struggle with feelings just as we had in our early years. In those younger days, rare was the adult or mentor who had developed emotional wings of his or her own, thereby making it impossible for us to take flight. They could not show us *how* to listen to our feelings, and very few could model the *courage* to feel. Most of them had not left home either.

It took me many years to appreciate the power and freedom of emotional honesty. I had been a graduate student at New York University, taking a course in group therapy. The small class became the group, and we learned by being and doing with each other. One evening, chaos descended on us. The group was scrambling to find its usual and predictable balance, when one young man erupted with emotion about several members of the group. He had been silent for too long. The group mind attempted to shut him down, to regulate him, to make him safe. And something in me broke open.

I was overcome with a protective mission, driven by an anger that had no intention of giving an inch. They were not going to shut this fellow down. I stood with him; the others backed off and gave him the emotional space he needed. My body shook, and I experienced a bittersweet mix of relief and sadness. The room became quiet, and the professor turned to me and said, "You've become the guardian of the emotions."

I have carried that moment with me ever since. Why the relief? The sadness? That is the stuff of this chapter.

■ TEACHING CLIENTS WHY WE HAVE FEELINGS

Throughout this chapter, I have used the terms "emotion" and "feeling" interchangeably, although neurologically they can be understood as different stages of the emotional experience (Damasio, 2003). But whether we refer to emotions or to feelings, clients often dread them, because they regard them primarily as sources of pain. And this is, to a good extent, true. Much of this chapter is how I teach clients emotional courage and competence, but it has also helped many clinicians in their own journeys.

Feelings: Our Emotional Global Positioning System (GPS)

Pain is not necessarily a bad thing. It is a signal letting us know that something is amiss. There is actually no such thing as a "bad" feeling. Feelings are either well-being or warning events, and both enter the home of our awareness with a message. Feelings are quite purposeful, as Rumi describes in *The Guest House* (Rumi & Barks, 1996):

This being human is a guest house.
Every morning a new arrival.

A joy, a depression, a meanness,
Some momentary awareness comes
As an unexpected visitor.

Welcome and entertain them all!
Even if they are a crowd of sorrows,
Who violently sweep your house
Empty of its furniture,
Still treat each guest honorably.
He may be clearing you out
For some new delight ...

Our clients need to be educated as to the "why" of emotions and convinced that it is worthwhile to not only deal with them but also be guided by them. Feelings are, above all, radar signals that carry a message. Is the message always accurate, reality based? Of course not, but the feeling is always doing its job. It is responding not so much to reality, but to internal (thoughts, beliefs) and external (perceptions) input. A feeling, functionally speaking, is an emotional response to a thought, belief, or perception, raising our awareness and asking us to pay attention to a danger (fear), a loss (sadness), a transgression (anger), and so forth. The feeling is an emotional GPS. It is embodied, emotional

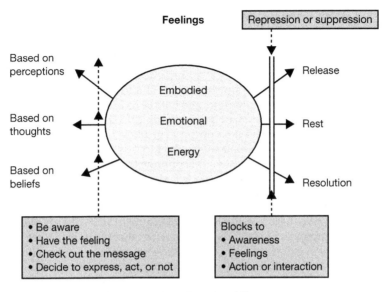

FIGURE 10.1 Emotional Process

energy that is signaling us to check things out. However, to do this, we must be able to first regulate the emotion, thereby allowing the thinking brain to do its reality checking.

Feelings, however, can be rendered ineffective: blocked or dissociated from awareness, robbed of expression, or not allowed to evolve into action and interaction. As seen in Figure 10.1, feelings can be used as our radar system in life or can be cut off and buried. But buried alive. Our clients need to understand that painful emotions have a purpose, but emotional energy that is blocked no longer fulfills its mission. It is pain repeated, pain without a purpose, which is one definition of suffering.

Stephanie had been gang raped as a teenager, and became pregnant, which led to an abortion. Her guilt, shame, and grief were intolerable. With nowhere to turn to, no one to help her deal with the feelings and the trauma itself, she simply stopped eating. She began to receive compliments as to how good she looked, so she continued to starve herself. Years later, as she sat in front of me in my office, I asked her what happened to the shame and guilt while she was starving herself, even during a time in which she was also being abused by the single father of a child she was babysitting. "It just went away," she replied. "It wasn't there. As long as I stayed thin, I felt great."

The shame, I believe, was always there, but embedded somehow in her body, which she was causing to disappear. And she wondered why she was so triggered and filled with shame in the present when engaging sexually with her boyfriend.

As I explain to my clients, when emotional energy is blocked, it stockpiles and creates a "sore spot" (Greenwald, 2007). I continue to describe how this stockpiling can make us sick, both physically and emotionally, and how the sore spot is precisely what is hit (triggered) by present events, causing us to react in the present as if it were the past.

I once heard emotions described as land mines, ready to go off when triggered. I find that description too narrow and too militaristic. I would suggest the notion of radar or a GPS. Feelings are essentially reactors, as shown in Figure 10.1. They do not react, however, in some pure and uninfluenced manner, but through a lens, a lens that is colored by how we perceive and think about whatever is being experienced, internally or externally. And that coloring is the result, not only of our present experience and state of consciousness but also of what we have experienced in the past, particularly painful events.

I am standing on a street corner. Someone accidentally bumps into me. My radar system kicks in, registering some shock or surprise, alerting me to pay attention. As soon as I am able to check out the situation and find it to be a harmless one, the alarm subsides, returns to a state of equilibrium, and both of us can go our merry way.

However, if I am having a bad hair day, someone accidentally bumps into me, and I begin to think: "That S.O.B. did it on purpose, grumble, grumble!" Then a different signal kicks in. Instead of surprise or shock, the radar system sets off the anger alert because of a sense of possible violation. If I continue to think and assume negatively, the anger will remain. If I do a reality check and realize that it was just an accident, my new thought and perception will hopefully override the unfounded assumptions and the anger will subside.

Then again, if I have been conditioned to believe that I must always please others, must always get approval, must always take care of others first, then I get a different signal and different outcome. As soon as the accidental bumping occurs, and given the presence of a self-sacrificing belief, my radar system can react only with a guilty signal. I now respond with, "Oh, oh, my fault! My fault! Sorry, sorry." Once again, a reality check of the situation might lead to a perception that would override the guilt and let it simply be experienced as an accident. Or not.

The point is that the situation is exactly the same. However, depending on the perception, thought, or belief that is operating, the lens through which we have the experience, our emotional system will react differently. This is the point where many would say, "You see! You just can't trust your feelings! They're so illogical; you can't rely on the buggers!" Feelings, I would claim to the contrary, are always doing their job. It is the way we perceive, think/assume, or believe that is often the root of the problem, but it is the emotional radar that signals us to check things out and, possibly, to take action or find expression.

Problems occur, however, either when we ignore the emotional signals by avoiding or numbing them or when we are overwhelmed by a flood of them. In the first case, access to the emotions is prevented, and one has retreated to a state of hypoarousal, as described in Siegel's "window of tolerance" (Siegel, 1999). In this state, feelings cannot be released and healed, nor can they teach us. In the latter case, an emotional tsunami results in a state of hyperarousal, which also makes it impossible to work with, heal, and learn from the feelings. In this state, the thinking and analyzing part of our brain has been taken offline, past becomes present, and the fight, flight, or freeze functions of our survival system are engaged.

There must be a mind, body, and heart marriage for healing to occur. In the service of this union, our clients need to become experts about their emotional GPS. They must, of course, be able to regulate the power of their emotions, but must also learn to appreciate emotional wisdom, motivation, and connection.

Feelings: Emotional Motivators and Connectors

When our feelings are properly regulated, they can not only guide us but also motivate us and connect us one to the other. Our clients, I believe, need to hear this, as well as the need for "affect management" to prevent an "amygdala highjacking" (Goleman, 1995). Thoughts require an emotional valence to have meaning and to create incentive. A thought about an oncoming truck *without the feeling of fear* might not, unfortunately, motivate us sufficiently to get out of the way. Knowledge that I did something harmful to another must be accompanied by an appropriate feeling of guilt to motivate me to make amends and not repeat the behavior. The belief that my partner is manipulating or abusing me requires righteous anger to do something about it. Without anger, despite what we cognitively know, we are in danger of becoming someone's doormat.

The need for emotional energy also applies to the well-being feelings of joy, happiness, excitement, and peacefulness. Depression, of course, is a classic example of what happens to a person when these feelings are muted. Mary, a former client, taught me a great deal about the power of depression and what life is like without joy or excitement. She became angry with me one day (a good sign) as I tried to motivate her to take action (physical exercise) to decrease the power of the depression. "You don't get it!" she exclaimed. "If there was a magic wand that would make the depression disappear, and it sat on top of your desk across this room, and if the depression was as strong as it usually is, I wouldn't be able to walk across the room to pick it up!" I finally got it. No emotional energy, no life to speak of.

Equally problematic is the *fear* of positive feelings. Various reasons lie at the base of this form of avoidance. Examples sound like the following: "If I feel good, the other shoe will drop, and the crash will be all the more painful"; "If I feel anything at all, the floodgates will open"; "If I feel happy, something bad always happens"; "I don't deserve (or am not allowed) to feel good"; "Feeling happy just seems weird and uncomfortable!" As one client unforgettably proclaimed, "If I feel happy, that will make me fat!"

The courage to feel requires the ability to feel all our emotions with full awareness. The very desire to live, to look forward, to have hope, and to have a vision requires positive or well-being feelings to motivate us toward those ends.

Finally, at the very heart of authentic and vital relationship is emotional connection. We can do things together, share our thoughts and our dreams, but the relationship immediately moves to a more intimate level when we become emotionally transparent and honest with each other. Even when the emotions shared are uncomfortable, such as anger or sorrow, we step into honest connectedness. Withholding difficult emotional truth from my partner only widens the gap between us. Emotional honesty and courage bridges that gap. Kornfield (1993) credits one of his teachers with the following: The mind creates the abyss; the heart must cross it.

■ SOMEONE ASKED FOR STEPS

In the often-complicated landscape of emotional experience, my encouragement is often to "follow what is given." Several years ago, I was teaching this principle of being aware of and following emotional experience to a group of scientists and engineers at a Fortune 500 company. I had spent the better part of the hour emphasizing the importance of *being with* the feeling, rather than *thinking about* it, when one gentleman raised his hand and asked, "Could you give us some steps?"

"Steps?!" I growled to myself. "It's a *process*! It doesn't have neat, little steps (still silently)." I regulated my assumed sense of violation (anger), took a few deep breaths to downregulate my fight system and any homicidal impulses, and could consider his request more rationally as I drove home from the class. It was then that I realized how important his request was.

The complex terrain of emotions is, for many clients, like being a stranger in a strange land. Without guidance and guideposts, feelings can readily become land mines to be avoided at all costs. The question arose: Are there steps or guideposts? Does one thing come before another when learning emotional competence? And so was born something of a flexible map of guideposts, always reminding myself that the map is never the territory.

■ THE A–B–C–D GUIDEPOSTS FOR EMOTIONAL COMPETENCE

In a territory that is so foreign to many of our clients, particularly those suffering with eating disorders (EDs), it helps for there to be some kind of "how to" user's guide to serve as a compass, especially for first-time emotional users. These guideposts are not always sequential, but usually can be followed in the following order:

A: Be **aware** of the emotion.
B: **Be** with and **breathe** into the feeling.
C: **Check** the message of the feeling.
D: **Decide** to act, express, or not.

Step A: Awareness of the Emotion

Buddhist tradition refers to this as *mindfulness*: mindful of each moment, each action, each sensation both internally and externally generated. Noticing, paying attention, and observing are all synonymous with the notion of awareness or mindfulness. We exist quite often in the very limited darkness of automatic living. Awareness is the light out of that pattern of living.

Also, it is a *way of being in the world*. It is not something to be turned on and off occasionally, but requires daily practice, as well as courage. It is the first of the four steps and possibly the single most important living skill any client can learn, but only if he or she practices. Remember, the client is in training, training to take back and unfold a life. There is so much more to life than we think, stuck as we often are in our boxes of limited awareness. Emotions will lead us to the larger picture, and awareness is the first step to be taken.

We begin with the practice of awareness of what is around us, what our senses are telling us, what gestalt therapy describes as the "outer zone." This is succeeded by noticing what we can notice in the "middle zone," or the body and its sensations. Finally, there is the "inner zone," the interoceptive world, of thoughts and feelings. A short article, "The Power and Peace of Awareness" (**), summarizing this practice can be found at www.clearpathtrainingcenter.com/eating-disorders.html (** when inserted refers the reader to this link where downloadable copies of articles and scripts can be found).

It takes courage to be aware. It requires that we make the commitment to step outside our autopilot way of living. Autopilot living is like falling into a turbulent river, caught up in the white rapids, crashing into rocks, and being tossed around with all kinds of debris. As the river carries you downstream, you notice the branch of a large tree that extends from the river's edge across several feet of the rushing waters. As you pass under the branch, you grab onto it, pull yourself out, and sit down on the bank. Catching your breath, you look out onto the river, noticing, observing, glad that you are no longer caught up in the stuff that whirls by.

This is what awareness does for us. It gets us out of the rapids and onto a solid bank. It lets us *observe*, rather than being swept into the torrents of daily busyness. It enables us to step back, creating separation between "I" and the turbulence. A great deal of life's debris is input from the inside, as well as from the outside. Sometimes the input is toxic, sometimes it is just too much, and it begins to overwhelm us. And if we are not paying attention, we get caught in the landslide.

Awareness opens the front door, enabling us to greet and work with the emotional visitors that Rumi speaks of. For ED clients, emotional numbing and avoidance is achieved through the disorder, making emotional awareness alone an act of courage.

Step B: Being With the Feeling

This step or guidepost is at the heart of the preparation phase of trauma treatment (see Chapter 8). Its goal is to render the emotional reaction manageable, to keep it within that window of tolerance. To "be with" is synonymous with "being present to." It requires separation or space (achieved somewhat through awareness), as well as contact. The hypo- and hyperstates of arousal prevent this space/contact experience from occurring. When a feeling is avoided or dissociated (hypoarousal), there is all space, but no contact. When a feeling overwhelms (hyperarousal), there is an enmeshment, so to speak, meaning too much contact and no space.

Beth grew up with a younger sister with cerebral palsy. Her parents, particularly her father, were very demanding of their oldest daughter, giving much of their time and attention to the disabled child. Above all, she was not allowed to show a hint of anger or unhappiness. Beth eventually married a man who replicated the demanding and bullying behaviors of her father.

Her anger was often outside of her awareness in session. It was so dissociated that, even when I drew her awareness to her body language (tight jaw, clenched fists), she could not recognize the experience as anger. When at home, and the anger arose and broke into her awareness, she would avoid it by furiously cleaning the house and restricting her food intake. She had the cleanest home in town, but weighed only 80 pounds at 5 feet 7 inches, and had to be admitted to inpatient treatment.

In the absence of awareness (Step A) or the willingness to be with the feeling (Step B), Beth's anorexia nervosa (AN) distracted her from forbidden feelings and gave her one place in her life where she believed she had control. Unfortunately, the inability to contact and manage her feelings placed the control in the hands of the ED.

Another client, on the contrary, becomes overwhelmed by emotions and resorts to her EDs to handle the feelings. Sally, a 53-year-old Caucasian woman, married and without children, suffers from dissociative identity disorder (DID) and experiences a shift from one ED to another. When one part of her begins to experience a tidal wave of grief and sadness, instead of riding the emotional wave, she buries the feeling with food. At this point, another part becomes overwhelmingly anxious at the thought of becoming a "fat, ugly pig," a name she had been called as a teenager in a foster home. The anxiety is ferocious, and the anxious part handles the feeling of anxiety and shame by purging and then entering a restrictive phase. In the absence of emotional competence and courage, both parts use EDs as a way of tolerating the intolerable.

There are several chapters in this book that describe ways in which our clients can learn to be with their feelings, keeping them within the window of tolerance, and strengthening them for trauma processing (see Chapters 8, 18, 21, and 22). Rather than asking "What are you feeling?" which sends the attention to the cognitive brain in search of a feeling word, I focus attention on the physical expression, the *experience*, of the feeling, teaching the client to use breath work to downregulate (diaphragmatic breath) or activate (rapid, short breathing) the autonomic nervous system. I bring attention to body sensations, body tensions, posture, as well as space/time orientation. Drinking cold water and adding movement (stretching, shaking, pushing, pulling) both release excessive energy, while aiding in grounding the client in the here-and-now.

I also use the acronym **L.I.D.S.** to teach elements of managing, as well as releasing, affect (Seubert, 2008). Poet Robert Bly describes the "long bag we drag behind us." It is the sack we carry over our shoulder, filled with more emotional baggage every time we ignore an emotional event. It is like holding a 1-pound bag of sugar in your hand. Not a problem immediately, but over the course of a few hours it becomes unbearably heavy. This emotional weight inevitably takes a toll on us physically.

The first part of L.I.D.S. is to **locate** the feeling. We typically experience the emotion as a physical event because the feeling takes place in the body. Where is it in your body? In your face? Jaw? Chest? Belly? Neck? Shoulders? Arms? Legs? Buttocks? Genitals? Hands? Feet? Just notice that.

The second part of L.I.D.S. is to determine the **intensity** of the feeling in the moment and how intense one wants it to be to manage and work with the emotion. "On a scale of 0–10, with zero representing no feeling at all and ten representing the strongest you've ever felt this feeling, how strong is it now?" I will then ask clients to what level they want the feeling reduced. At this point, one knows where one is in terms of emotional intensity and where one wants to go.

These two phases have already created the experience of separating oneself from the feeling. This is not denial, but the ability to observe the feeling, allowing it to move through.

The "D" in L.I.D.S. asks the client to **describe** the emotion as experienced in the body. How big is it? Does it have a shape? A color? A temperature? Does it move? The benefit of this is that it keeps us in touch with the *experience of the feeling*, while reinforcing the position of observer.

Finally, the fourth letter instructs us to **send** the emotion forth from the body. Recall the image of emotional waves, now moving through, rather than being stuck, in the body. We need a vehicle to move the emotional energy and a destination to do this.

The vehicle is actually your *intention* to honor the feeling, allowing it to move through, learning what you can from it, leaving you at peace, or at least ready to express or act. A physical form of this intention is the use of *breath* to move the emotional energy outward, for example:

> *Breathe into wherever your feeling is and, on the exhale, send out a stream of it into the universe (or to whatever destination/container you have chosen).*

Step C: Checking the Message of the Feeling

Feelings contain messages, but to be able to discern whether the message applies accurately to the present reality or not requires the previous two steps that provide the banks for our emotional rivers. Once the banks are in place and the emotional waters under control, we can examine the messages.

Generally speaking, a feeling (sadness, for example) is an emotional response to the perception, thought, or belief that I *may* be experiencing loss. Guilt is an emotional response to the perception, thought, or belief that I *may* have violated someone or some code of ethics or morals. In both examples, the operative word is *may*. The feeling is not the judge, jury, and executioner. The feeling is a *signal*, advising us to check out the reality of the situation.

To *feel* guilty does not mean that I *am* guilty. The feeling is telling us to check things out and to ask questions, such as (guilt), "Have I really violated someone (or some code of ethics)?" Anger's message is that someone else *may* have violated me. When checking out the reality, I then need to ask, "Is (or has) someone violating (violated) me in some way? What was his or her intention?"

Every feeling has a constructive reason for existence, and every feeling has its toxic version. Two of the most frequently experienced emotions in ED clients are anxiety and shame. Anxiety is frequently triggered by the belief or "story" that something catastrophic is about to occur, or that other intolerable, overwhelming feelings are about to surface. If I eat that slice of pizza, I will become a fat pig; if I do not stuff more food down my throat, I'll drown in uncontainable sadness; if I do not purge what I just ate, I will turn into a shameful blimp. In such situations, the first task is to step back from and become aware of the feeling. The next task of being with and managing/tolerating the feeling follows, hopefully leading to the "presence of mind" to examine the reality of the emotional response.

Toxic shame, rather than reminding us that we must live from the best values in us, is triggered by the story that who I *am* is defective, not good enough, damaged, unimportant. Again, the feeling is doing its job. It is the story that triggers the feeling that must be questioned and challenged, but we cannot reality check these stories as long as the anxiety or shame is in full activation. Hence, the need for the first two steps.

Here are a few feelings with the messages they bear:

ANGER is the response to a perception, thought, or belief that I *may* have been violated.

GUILT is the response to a perception that I *may* have violated someone or some code of ethics or morals.

FEAR is the response to a perception that someone or something *might* be about to harm me.

SADNESS is the response to a perception that I *may* have lost someone or something.

SHAME is the response to a perception that I *may* have been untrue to my core values and lessened myself.

HAPPINESS/JOY is the response to a perception that things *may be* well with myself, the world, and others.

EXCITEMENT is the response to a perception that something good *might* be coming my way.

BOREDOM is the response to a perception that I *may* not be getting the stimulation I require.

JEALOUSY is the response to a perception that I *may* not be getting the response and connection I expect from a significant other.

LONELINESS is the response to a perception that I do not have enough interpersonal connection.

Once the message is understood, our task is to check out the reliability of the response by asking creative questions, such as the following:

Anger: Have I really been violated?
Guilt: Have I really violated someone or some code of ethics/morals?
Sadness: What have I really lost?

Fear: Is something really about to harm me? What's the worst that could happen?

Shame: Have I betrayed my own core values, my Real Self? Am I really less, really damaged, really inadequate?

Step D: Deciding to Express, Act, or Not

The last of the four steps in emotional mastery is often optional. It is the decision to act or not, to express or not. It is also the step that is commonly feared the most, because it invites us to interact with the world and with others. It is the arena in which we just might get hurt.

Recall the different reasons why we have feelings to begin with. They are our radar, and they connect us to others. They are also energizers and motivators, mobilizing us to do what must be done and to express what must be expressed. They let us know what is okay or not okay; they motivate us to make things right when they're not.

It is important to recall that Steps A (awareness of the feeling) and B (having/being with the feeling) are often sufficient for the return to internal equilibrium. The opposite of emotional repression or suppression, as mentioned earlier, is *not* expression. It is awareness. Regardless of how many of the four steps or guideposts we use, the return to an inner peace and balance, as well as to a healthy connection with our interpersonal world, is the goal of emotional mastery.

It is necessary to listen to and, eventually, trust our emotional guidance system to let us know whether emotional awareness and presence is enough, or whether action/expression is being called for. Only the individual can tell, moment to moment, event by event.

This is what our feelings are there to help us do: to move more and more fully into aliveness, into active living in accordance with the best in each of us. Nothing less.

Step D, as mentioned earlier, is a choice point. To do, or not to do. To express, or not to express. To intend and to act—or not act—in accordance with the best in us is, in fact, to act out of love rather than fear. A feeling is *emotion*, needing to move through and out. When it is in need of expression and the expression occurs, there is typically an experience of relief, lightness, and *increased positive energy*. This is your system's signal that you did what was needed. You acted out of love, not fear—whether fear of hurting the other, fear of reactions, or fear of loss of love or approval.

When our system calls for action or expression, it is leading us to *greater contact and connection with the other*. Even in disagreement and anger, we can still connect to each other if we are truthful and responsible (i.e., not blaming, attacking, or defending) in how we express our feelings.

Radical honesty is not always easy, but this is not about feeling "good" or "comfortable." It is about being real. It is about the increase of positive energy inside and a felt sense of connection. At times, we have to go through unpleasant confrontation and conflict to get there, but the price is so well worth it. Beth, as you may recall, was taught never to express her anger, regardless of how appropriate it might be. She used the first three steps with her husband, but could never express it to him or to anyone. The result was a 15-year marriage that was more like being held hostage by him and by her inability to voice her anger. She rerouted the anger into cleaning and her anorexia.

It is time to express or act:

- After making sure that action/expression is not dangerous (and it usually is not)
- When feeling the weight of inaction or withholding feelings and in need of more positive energy

- When feeling powerless, weak, or voiceless
- When feeling the disconnect from another because of inaction or withheld feelings and in need of renewed contact or connection
- When you are in the blame game and are holding someone else responsible for your own misery or happiness

■ UNFINISHED BUSINESS: TRAUMA, FEELINGS, AND EDS

When feelings arise and are attended to with the help of these four guideposts, they fulfill their purpose and pass on. When trauma occurs and is experienced as intolerable, the attendant feelings must be avoided, numbed, and frozen. EDs are one of the strategies through which this is accomplished.

As mentioned earlier, one of Sally's "parts" had been viciously teased, as well as beaten and then sexually abused by three older brothers in a foster home. Just the thought of eating and gaining weight triggered a panic state. She would be severely punished for every pound gained. Restricting was the way for her to survive when there was no way out. Physically she was trapped, and emotionally she had nowhere to go. The ED kept her alive, which is why it became such a powerful ally. Until now.

Now this part is slowly learning to manage the anxiety when food is taken into the body. She is learning to self-soothe and to ground herself in the present space and time. Eventually, with the help of other parts of Sally's internal system, she will be able to tolerate the processing of her past trauma. She will metabolize and digest them, learn from them, and, as Ernest Hemingway described it, become stronger in those broken places. The past will no longer be the present for Sally, and her feelings, once feared, will be her armor and her sword.

As mentioned earlier, there are times when pure awareness is sufficient to strengthen emotional tolerance. JB would panic during her menstrual cycle, because it left her feeling "bloated," which was translated as "fat." All she could think to do was to starve herself further. During one session, she was experiencing the bloated/fat feeling, and agreed to work on reducing her reactivity. All I asked her to do was to observe the sensation in her body, be with it, breathe, and let the content of her awareness pass through, "just like passing clouds." As she did this, I applied the bilateral stimulation of EMDR therapy (see Chapter 13).

Andrew: *And what do you notice?*

JB: *"Fat" thoughts. Anxious in my chest. More racing thoughts, like I have to do something* (restrict) *to stop it all.*

Andrew: *Keep watching, breathing, letting go....*

We continued this process, watching, observing, noticing, until at one point JB exclaimed:

JB: *It's weird! I don't know how to describe this, but it's like I'm watching me being bloated, and the "me" that is watching is okay.*

Andrew: *And how strong is your anxiety now?*

JB: *Oh, maybe a 1 ....*

And the agent of change was primarily her awareness, which decreased the anxiety and eliminated the need for compensatory restriction.

■ CONCLUSION

DuBos (1922) wrote that, "The important thing is this: To be able at any moment to sacrifice what you are for what you could become." Change is what we most often fear, even if it means shaking off toxic residue and stepping into the unknown of a different and healthier identity. So-called "good" feelings often end up scaring us as much as the "bad" ones, because they, too, invite change. Feeling requires courage.

Feelings are the movement of the life inside of us. The emotion knocking on your door is letting you know that you have reason to be excited or fearful and that your aliveness is calling you to a larger version of yourself. Consequently, we avoid not only the "negative" emotions (warning signals) but the "positive" ones (well-being or growth signals) as well, because both can be unnerving invitations to get real. They ask us to attend to what we want or do not want in our lives, to what is good or not good for us. They ask us to hold onto ourselves.

Our feelings, used competently, guide us home. As clinicians, part of our task is not only to teach emotional regulation but also to inspire the valuing of feelings: their energy, connectivity, and wisdom. We must also bring meaning to painful experiences of emotions, reminding clients that if pain has a purpose, it may be "… clearing you out for some new delight." As Markova (2000) writes, "The deeper the channel that pain carves into our souls, the greater the capacity we have to allow the river of joy to run through us" (p. 81).

Teaching and modeling this journey is the challenge and the privilege of our profession.

■ REFERENCES

Damasio, A. (2003). *Looking for Spinoza*. New York, NY: Harcourt Books.

DuBos, C. (1922). *Approximations* [première série]. Paris, France: Plon-Nourrit

Goleman, D. (1995). *Emotional intelligence*. New York, NY: Bantam Books.

Greenwald, R. (2007). *EMDR within a phase model of trauma-informed treatment*. New York, NY: Haworth Press.

Kornfield, J. (1993). *A path with heart*. New York, NY: Bantam Books.

Markova, D. (2000). *I will not die an unlived life: Reclaiming purpose and passion*. Berkeley, CA: Conari Press.

Rumi, J., & Barks, C. (1996). *The essential Rumi*. New York, NY: HarperCollins.

Siegel, D. J. (1999). *The developing mind*. New York, NY: Guilford Press.

Seubert, A. (2008). *The courage to feel: A practical guide to the power and freedom of emotional honesty*. Conshocken, PA: Infinity.

CHAPTER 11

Neurofeedback and the Eating Disordered Brain

Amelia McGinnis

■ INTRODUCTION

My office looks like most private practices, with one difference: my neurofeedback equipment. As a client sits on my couch, he or she sees on the wall ahead of him or her a computer with two monitors (Figure 11.1), a bunch of wires, and a white Styrofoam head with 19 labeled red stickers all over it (Figure 11.2). New clients usually ask about the head first, "What is that used for?" I explain that it shows the different spots on the scalp where I can place a sensor to do neurofeedback. Then the follow-up question is "What's neurofeedback?"

Neurofeedback therapy is a modality that can help a stuck brain get unstuck and learn new and better ways to fire and function. In this chapter, I describe what neurofeedback therapy is, how it works, and how it can be a valuable part of treatment for eating disorders (EDs).

FIGURE 11.1 Neurofeedback equipment.

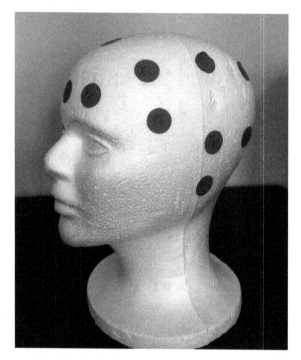

FIGURE 11.2 Styrofoam head.

■ WHAT IS NEUROFEEDBACK?

Neurofeedback therapy, also called EEG biofeedback or neurotherapy, makes use of the brain's capacity for change to reshape brain networks. Neurofeedback is a training tool that helps clients to regulate their brain through operant conditioning and biofeedback. It is not a new modality. In the late 1960s and through the 1970s, there were breakthroughs that confirmed that one could use feedback to change brainwaves (Kamiya, 1968) and that those changes have an effect on how we tolerate certain pathological conditions (Sterman, Macdonald, & Stone, 1974). In the decades since then, neurofeedback has grown in breadth and depth, being used for many different disorders, including attention, anxiety, and depression, as well as conditions such as learning disabilities and Parkinson's disease. Neurofeedback has been heavily researched since the mid-1960s and further studied in recent years, evidenced by Myers and Young (2012) who conducted a review that showed 250 published neurofeedback studies between 2005 and 2012.

Neurofeedback can change the state in which the brain is firing, essentially adjusting the brain's arousal and, ultimately, the client's ability to manage affect as well as help regulate other brain-based conditions. Neurofeedback works because of the brain's ability to change. This change is called neuroplasticity. Neuroplasticity allows the brain to compensate and adjust its neural activity when presented with a new situation, whether an injury or a reaction to the environment. Neurofeedback allows us to directly provide information, so a client has direct access to this neuroplasticity. It does this through the use of EEG and specific frequency domains in that EEG that correspond to different states of arousal.

■ EEG AND BRAINWAVES

Neurofeedback uses EEG information to provide feedback to the trainee. The EEG, or electroencephalogram, shows the wavelength activity for a part of the brain. It consists of frequency bandwidths that make up the entire raw EEG. These bandwidths are often categorized by their frequency, the number of times a waveform rises and falls in 1 second, and can be measured by their amplitude, or power, measured in voltage, specifically microvolts. Different frequencies are often associated with different states of arousal, as seen in Table 11.1.

On the most basic level, neurofeedback focuses on arousal. The therapist accesses EEG data via sensors placed on the scalp and then sets training parameters, or protocols, that encourage the brain to fire at a different level of arousal, while providing positive reinforcement when the client's brain responds appropriately. Figure 11.3 is a screenshot of what a neurofeedback therapist sees using an EEGer system.

It is important, however, to remember that our brain is producing all of these frequencies at once and a brain is best regulated when it is flexible (Demos, 2005). Think about someone who is participating in a classroom or work discussion. Beta is needed to be able to focus and attend to the conversations. A shift from beta to alpha may be necessary to be able to reflect inwardly, and theta may be engaged during problem solving and brainstorming (Demos, 2005). But what if the EEG is not normative? As mentioned earlier, a brain can become stuck in a state of arousal and then cannot shift easily. In these cases of dysregulation, there is often a bandwidth that may be too dominant that then inhibits the brain's ability to be flexible. Often, with clients who have trauma in their background, neurofeedback therapists train to increase lower frequency bandwidths,

TABLE 11.1 Brainwave Frequency Ranges

	CPS[a]	Wavelength	Associated Activity
Delta	<4		Sleep
Theta	4–8		Drowsy
Alpha	8–12		Relaxed focus
Sensorimotor rhythm	12–15		Relaxed thought
Beta	15–18		Active thinking
High beta	>19		Excited

[a]Cycles per second or hertz.

Source: Based on Demos, J. N. (2005). *Getting started with neurofeedback* (pp. 112–122). New York, NY: W. W. Norton.

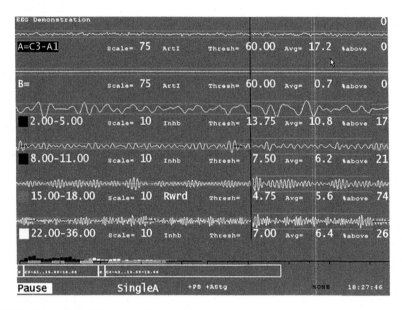

FIGURE 11.3 EEGer™ system therapist screen.
Source: EEG Education and Research Inc., 2017.

alpha and theta, while reducing the firing of high beta waves to get the brain "unstuck" and move toward regulation.

Recently, there have been more studies aimed at understanding the EEG abnormalities in ED individuals. Studies suggest central nervous system dysfunction (Jáuregui-Lobera, 2012), as well as reduced relative alpha power in frontal, central, and temporal regions, while simultaneously showing increased relative beta power in frontal lobes (Hatch et al., 2011). This low alpha/beta ratio could be interpreted as hyperarousal of the nervous system. This information helps us to develop possible protocols for neurofeedback to specifically address EDs, as evidenced in a 2016 study (Lackner et al., 2016).

■ NEUROFEEDBACK FOR EATING DISORDERS

As the research continues to emerge regarding the use of neurofeedback specifically for ED, findings suggest that neurofeedback can support ED treatment by addressing the symptoms related to anxiety and posttraumatic stress disorder (PTSD; Ackerman & Greenland, 2002; Hammond, 2003, 2005; Peniston, Marrinan, Deming, & Kulkosky, 1993). Lackner et al. (2016) published one of the first articles that looks specifically at using neurofeedback for adolescent patients suffering from anorexia nervosa (AN). Although there were a relatively small number of participants (*n* = 22) for their study, they did record significant results with relatively little intervention. This study provided only 10 neurofeedback sessions over a 5-week period, which is only one-third of a typical neurofeedback treatment schedule. Despite the limited neurofeedback intervention, the changes that were seen were quite notable and significant. The group that received neurofeedback in addition to traditional treatment showed improvement in eating behavior and the ability to recognize their own emotions when compared with those who did not receive neurofeedback training.

Despite positive outcomes in the domains of eating behavior and recognition of one's own emotions, there was no significant weight increase in the participants who received neurofeedback, and there were no notable changes in clinical ratings. This is an indicator of the complexity of AN, and thus informs practitioner decisions about treatment options. Future studies containing an increase in the number of neurofeedback sessions are needed to clarify the amount of impact neurofeedback can have on an AN patient. For now, all we know is that it does have a positive influence as part of a treatment regimen.

From the treatment perspective, Lackner's findings reinforce the complexity of AN and compel practitioners to explore blended treatment options beyond traditional approaches. In particular, this study acknowledges the importance of clients' increased emotional awareness in relation to AN (Lackner et al., 2016). This increased awareness over the long term opens the door to developing new coping skills and a higher level of self-awareness to cope with overwhelming emotional stress. Avoiding system overload helps to lessen the opportunities of backslide, whereby clients come to rely on old habits of AN.

It is yet unclear whether EEG abnormalities are predetermining factors of AN or changes that are seen after a brain is starved. Specifically, elevated theta power in the parietal–occipital lobe of underweight clients with AN has been shown to not return to normal after refeeding (Hatch et al., 2011). This leads one to question whether elevated theta is a premarker of AN or an effect of starvation on the brain (Lackner et al., 2016). Greater understanding of these abnormalities can help us to refine our use of neurofeedback specifically with regard for patients with an AN diagnosis.

■ COMORBIDITY OF EATING DISORDERS AND ANXIETY DISORDERS

Recent studies have found that underlying issues, such as trauma and PTSD symptoms, must be addressed for successful recovery from ED to occur. It has been suggested that to successfully recover from ED, trauma and PTSD symptoms must be addressed and that preexisting anxiety disorders, as well as PTSD, can lead to ED clients being more vulnerable to stress (Brewerton, 2015). Studies have also shown that women with any form of ED have higher rates of PTSD symptoms than those without ED (Dansky, Brewerton, O'Neil, & Kilpatrick, 1997). Neurofeedback has been used to help address PTSD and anxiety symptoms successfully (Passini, Watson, Dehnel, Herder, & Watkins, 1977; Peniston et al., 1993) and, therefore, supports ED treatment by reducing client anxiety.

In addition to these studies showing significant improvement with anxiety symptoms after the initial alpha/theta neurofeedback treatment, it is also notable that the improvements were reported to continue for weeks after the treatment was complete. Some of the subjects were able to report that they no longer had any PTSD symptoms, whereas those who still had symptoms reported significant reductions (Peniston et al., 1993).

Hammond (2005) concluded that according to the biofeedback efficacy criteria, neurofeedback treatment of PTSD qualifies for the status of "probably efficacious." These studies, along with others that continue to emerge, support neurofeedback as a complementary and, at times, alternative treatment to traditional modalities. Thus far, neurofeedback has been shown to help with eating behaviors, emotional awareness, and reduction of anxiety and PTSD symptoms. Neurofeedback can also address issues of developmental trauma and attachment (Fisher, 2014), another more complicated factor that affects many ED clients.

■ EATING DISORDERS AS AN AFFECT REGULATION PROBLEM

EDs are described, in part, as an affect regulation problem that is often rooted in early attachment experiences. If a child is not given the opportunity to learn how to regulate his or her own emotions with the help of a caregiver, he or she often will turn to extreme and harmful coping mechanisms. Scholom (2009), in her chapter of *EMDR Solutions II,* wrote the following:

> ED symptoms are major defenses erected to keep people from experiencing and examining certain feelings .... Anorexics restrict food to feel in control ... bulimics turn to food as their primary source of comfort, coping, and emotional fulfillment. Thus, affect regulation is expressed via the eating disorder. (p. 115)

The quality of early attachment determines the ability to regulate emotions or not. Early developmental trauma, or lack of attunement from caregivers, can lead to a hyper-aroused limbic system. Effective affect regulation comes from "good enough" parenting and coregulation from caregiver to infant (Schore, 2003). Infants need their caregiver to be "in tune" with them and use their own ability to regulate affect to help the infant find his or her own way. This hyperarousal can continue into adulthood, affecting how the brain fires and its ability to be flexible. Not only is attachment important to how our brain develops but developmental trauma is also a strong precursor to one's ability to regulate emotions and, when that ability is diminished, can heighten our brain's response to perceived threatening stimuli.

■ AROUSAL AND AFFECT

We know that in trauma, specifically childhood trauma, fear structures, such as the amygdala, are in overdrive (Fisher, 2014). They have been habituated to respond at the slightest possible threat, create "false alarms," and do not have any checks and balances, because the inhibitory structures are underactivated and unable to do their job. This kind of brain is constantly on high alert (Fisher, 2014).

A client that I have worked with for some time has just this kind of brain. Sarah (a pseudonym) suffers from severe anxiety, depression, obsessive-compulsive disorder (OCD), and PTSD because of childhood abuse from her father. There are many stories from our sessions that remind me of this kind of existence, but one in particular has always stayed with me.

Sarah is an avid reader. She uses reading as a means to escape, but is very careful about her book choices, so as not to set her system into overdrive because of a disturbing plot line. Knowing this, I was surprised when she shared that one of her favorite series was *The Hunger Games.* In this series, games are held every year, and each district in Panem must offer up one boy and girl to participate in a televised game to the death. There is only one victor. The victor will bring home food and much needed supplies to his or her district for the following year. This dystopian novel deals with the struggle for self-preservation that the people of Panem face and *The Hunger Games* in which they must participate. The citizens' starvation and their need for resources, both in and outside of the arena, create an atmosphere of helplessness that the main characters try to overcome in their fight for survival.

Sarah shared that the central character, Katniss, provided comfort to her. In the novel, Katniss sacrifices herself to participate in *The Hunger Games* instead of her younger sister. Sarah could identify with Katniss through their shared experience: living with constant fear, yet possessing the strength to survive.

My personal experience with this book was juxtaposed to Sarah's experience. I was left unsettled and upset most of the time. This story was filled with death, constant fear, impossible choices, helplessness, and was told through Katniss, who suffers several mental breakdowns throughout the series. *The Hunger Games* takes readers on an emotionally intense roller coaster, and yet Sarah found comfort in this. A world that is war-filled and poverty stricken, full of death and pain, is where her brain feels at home. It enabled me to recognize on a deeper level what a fear-driven brain feels like and how far my client had to go to feel some sort of brain normalcy.

Sarah's experience with *The Hunger Games* exemplifies what Sebern Fisher states in her book about neurofeedback and developmental trauma (2014):

> These inflexible and unstable nervous systems are routinely overtaken by subcortical neuronal storms that give rise to affect dysregulation. When arousal becomes emotion, it becomes a quality of the mind and it is felt. Arousal becomes affect. (p. 121)

When a brain is highly aroused, it correlates to dysregulated and intense emotional states. Sarah's brain personifies this dysregulated state. Her brain was in a constant state of high arousal, which she experienced as anxiety, fear, shame, and OCD. These intense emotions, or affects, determine a person's state, self-experience, and perception of the world (Fisher, 2014). Sarah was determined to believe that the world was not safe, that she was to blame for most of her experiences, and that fear was the only way to protect herself. She had not only accepted these states as a given but also created a narrative that supported and provided meaning to these states. To her, they were true.

This is what happens with most people. We create narratives around the states we experience in our brains (Fisher, 2014). Neurofeedback can help clients shift this arousal, hence shifting their internal state and, ultimately, the narrative they tell themselves about the world and how they fit into that world. This shift can have an amazing impact on a client's state, as well as the coping mechanisms he or she has learned to deal with hyperarousal. This is exemplified in another client whom I saw in my office many years ago while she was struggling with OCD, another common diagnosis that is present with EDs.

Tammy (pseudonym) came to my office for neurofeedback to address her OCD. Neurofeedback can be used to reduce anxiety as part of a treatment regimen for OCD (Passini et al., 1977). She was seeing another therapist for talk therapy, so I was offering only neurofeedback therapy. After a few months of training, she came into session with a new haircut. I commented on it, as I would with anyone, and was surprised by what she shared regarding the choice to cut her hair. She stated that she always styled her hair exactly the way she had in high school, at least 15 years prior. That week she woke up and looked in the mirror and said, "What if I don't have to do my hair this way anymore?" This thought led her to make an appointment to change her hairstyle. She shared that making this new choice was a little disorienting and was glad she had her therapist to help her work through the changes. However, she was excited about the choice and the thought that things did not always have to be done the same way.

After completing her course of treatment, Tammy decided to add another beautiful child to her family. She felt much more in control of any OCD thoughts that came up and felt that things that used to be overwhelming just weren't as important anymore.

Tammy felt empowered to change her narrative and think positively about the flexibility required and unpredictability associated with parenting an infant.

ED clients have more than their fair share of obsessive-compulsive thoughts and behaviors. Just as neurofeedback freed Tammy from her rigid thinking and reduced the importance of those thoughts, I propose that it can have an impact on the obsessive-compulsive behaviors and thoughts for ED clients as well.

Hammond (2003, 2005) has published multiple case studies showing the efficacy of neurofeedback training for OCD. He noted that scores on the Yale-Brown Obsessive Compulsive Scale and the Padua Inventory normalized in two clients after treatment. He has also had success treating someone who struggled with a type of OCD that was resistant to traditional therapy and medications. As seen in other studies, these improvements were maintained at 10 months after treatment was complete (Hammond, 2005).

Neurofeedback can be an important adjunct to traditional ED treatment, as measured through outcomes and supported by the benefits of the training process itself. Although the effects of neurofeedback training on anxiety and trauma are evident, the process of neurofeedback training is notably helpful as well. The way in which neurofeedback provides positive reinforcement through an operant reward framework and is client driven may be helpful for ED clients who struggle with issues of control and motivation (Lackner et al., 2016). Let us delve into what a typical session looks like to demonstrate how the process of neurofeedback training supports better outcomes in traditional ED treatment.

■ WHAT DOES A SESSION LOOK LIKE?

When a client comes in for a typical neurofeedback session, sensors are placed on the scalp to obtain the EEG information and begin training. The client then looks at a screen that has feedback provided through games like the ones in Figure 11.4. The client is told that he or she needs to keep the Pac-Man moving or keep the spaceship in the middle of the screen winning the race. When his or her brain is firing in the way that aligns with the therapist's protocol, the client gets rewarded on his or her game. During the session, the client's job is to watch the screen and try to figure out how to keep the positive feedback (beeps, motion, etc.) coming consistently. The training session lasts about

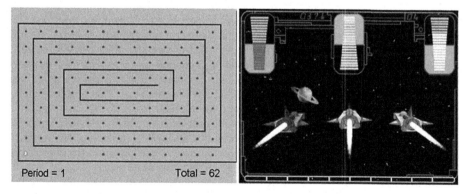

FIGURE 11.4 EEGer™ system client screens.
Source: EEGer™ Neurofeedback Software, 2017.

30 minutes, on average. Clients often want to know how to make this happen. Depending on the protocol that we are training, they will achieve it differently. The therapist will often coach the client to stay calm or try to be present in the room, but it is really a process that we trust the brain will figure out as long as the client is engaged in using the feedback to get the beeps. It is not mind control. As stated earlier, we are attempting a state shift for the brain; if the clients are using the feedback to increase the reward, their brain will shift state.

◾ INTRODUCING A CLIENT TO NEUROFEEDBACK

In my office, I have learned how important it is to educate my clients about what neurofeedback is and what it is not. Neurofeedback is a *course of treatment*. I say it that way, because, although we hope that clients will begin to feel some relief from symptoms or shifts of state within the first couple of sessions, neurofeedback is a cumulative process. Once the brain learns how to be better regulated, it does like to stay there. It is the repetitive nature of the training that allows the brain to create new ways of firing. I often relate it to physical therapy. Neurofeedback is physical therapy for the brain. It takes time and commitment to access the full benefits of this modality. It is important that the client understands the process and commitment to treatment.

By going to the gym only every couple of weeks, one sees little change over time without the commitment and discipline of regular training. Neurofeedback sessions are typically done twice a week for 30 minutes each time. When possible, it can be done more frequently, but, at the very least, once a week. The amount of time that it takes for a course of treatment can vary. In the field, we often say about 30 sessions, but it is extremely variable depending on the client and how much change is needed in the brain. Traumatized brains often take much longer to realize the full effects of the training.

Neurofeedback is not dangerous, because anything we do in one session is not permanent. It is the cumulative process that makes it a powerful treatment tool. The neurofeedback system does not transmit electricity of any kind into the brain. The sensors are like a stethoscope. Just as a stethoscope allows us to hear the heartbeat, the sensors allow us to see the electrical frequencies of the brain. It is the therapist who decides what part of the brain to exercise by establishing a treatment protocol. Going back to my white Styrofoam head, there are many sites on which we can place the sensors. This allows for a lot of flexibility in training protocols and offers the ability for the therapist to create protocols specific for each client.

Neurofeedback should never be added to treatment without a thorough assessment and without assessing needs continuously throughout training. This is especially important when a client is concurrently prescribed a medication to manage symptoms. As a brain responds to neurofeedback, the client may require only a lower dose of medication, so involving his or her psychiatrist in the treatment is crucial.

◾ CONCLUSION

Neurofeedback is a powerful training tool that can be used within a comprehensive treatment plan to assist clients to begin to have more control over how their brain fires. Licensed therapists trained in the neurofeedback modality can help their clients to rewire overly aroused brains, allowing them to become better regulated.

Neurofeedback therapy shifts arousal in the brain, which helps clients to alter the state they experience and to create a new narrative about themselves and the world around them.

Research specifically focusing on neurofeedback and ED is just now emerging and is yielding promising results. These results are supported by prior findings that show neurofeedback's efficacy for affect regulation, OCD, and many other comorbid conditions that surface in ED clients, particularly those with trauma histories. From my personal experience, neurofeedback has been a powerful addition to my practice, enabling me to help clients in a way that offers hope and measurable possibilities for change.

Please refer to the following list for more information about adding neurofeedback to your practice or locating a licensed neurofeedback therapist in your area:

International Society for Neurofeedback & Research: www.isnr.org/resources
The Association for Applied Psychophysiology and Biofeedback, Inc.: www.aapb.org
EEG Education and Research: www.eegspectrum.com
www.eeginfo.com
www.aboutneurofeedback.com

■ REFERENCES

Ackerman, D. L., & Greenland, S. (2002). Multivariate meta-analysis of controlled drug studies for obsessive-compulsive disorder. *Journal of Clinical Psychopharmacology*, 22(3), 309–317. doi:10.1097/00004714-200206000-00012

Brewerton, T. D. (2015). Stress, trauma, and adversity as risk factors in the development of eating disorders. In L. Smolak & M. P. Levine (Eds.), *The Wiley handbook of eating disorders*. Chichester, UK: Wiley. doi:10.1002/9781118574089.ch34

Dansky, B. S., Brewerton, T. D., O'Neil, P. M., & Kilpatrick, D. G. (1997). The National Women's Study: Relationship of victimization and posttraumatic stress disorder to bulimia nervosa. *International Journal of Eating Disorders*, 21, 213–228. doi:1002/(SICI)1098-108X(199704)21:3<213::AID-EAT2>3.0.CO;2-N

Demos, J. N. (2005). *Getting started with neurofeedback*. New York, NY: W. W. Norton.

Fisher, S. F. (2014). *Neurofeedback in the treatment of developmental trauma: Calming the fear-driven brain*. New York, NY: W. W. Norton.

Hammond, D. C. (2003). QEEG-guided neurofeedback in the treatment of obsessive compulsive disorder. *Journal of Neurotherapy*, 7(2), 25–52. doi:10.1300/J184v07n02_03

Hammond, D. C. (2005). Neurofeedback with anxiety and affective disorders. *Child and Adolescent Psychiatric Clinics of North America*, 14(1), 105–123. doi:10.1016/j.chc.2004.07.008

Hatch, A., Madden, S., Kohn, M. R., Clarke, S., Touyz, S., Gordon, E., & Williams, L. M. (2011). EEG in adolescent anorexia nervosa: Impact of refeeding and weight gain. *International Journal of Eating Disorders*, 44(1), 65–75. doi:10.1002/eat.20777

Jáuregui-Lobera, I. (2012). Electroencephalography in eating disorders. *Neuropsychiatric Disease and Treatment*, 8, 1–11. doi:10.2147/NDT.S27302

Kamiya, J. (1968). Conscious control of brain waves. *Psychology Today*, 1, 56–60.

Lackner, N., Unterrainer, H. F., Skliris, D., Shaheen, S., Dunitz-Scheer, M., Wood, G., … Neuper, C. (2016). EEG neurofeedback effects in the treatment of adolescent anorexia nervosa. *Eating Disorders*, 24(4), 354–374. doi:10.1080/10640266.2016.1160705

Myers, J. E., & Young, J. S. (2012). Brain wave biofeedback: Benefits of integrating neurofeedback in counseling. *Journal of Counseling & Development*, 90(1), 20–28. doi:10.1111/j.1556-6676.2012.00003.x

Passini, F. T., Watson, C. G., Dehnel, L., Herder, J., & Watkins, B. (1977). Alpha wave biofeedback training therapy in alcoholics. *Journal of Clinical Psychology*, 33(1), 292–299. doi:10.1002/1097-4679(197701)33:1+<292::AID-JCLP2270330166>3.0.CO;2-L

Peniston, E. G., Marrinan, D. A., Deming, W. A., & Kulkosky, P. J. (1993). EEG alpha-theta synchronization in Vietnam theater veterans with combat-related posttraumatic stress disorder and alcohol abuse. *Medical Psychotherapy: An International Journal, 6*, 37–50.

Scholom, J. (2009). Integrating eating disorders treatment into the early phases of the EMDR protocol. In R. Shapiro (Ed.), *EMDR solutions II*. New York, NY: W. W. Norton.

Schore, A. (2003). *Affect dysregulation and disorders of the self*. New York, NY: W. W. Norton.

Sterman, M. B., Macdonald, L. R., & Stone, R. K. (1974). Biofeedback training of the sensorimotor electroencephalogram rhythm in man: Effects on epilepsy. *Epilepsia, 15*(3), 395–416. doi:10.1111/j.1528-1157.1974.tb04016.x

SECTION FIVE

Approaches to Trauma Processing and Eating Disorders—Phase III

The intent of Trauma-Informed Approaches to Eating Disorders *is to encourage the clinician, regardless of his or her orientation, to include a phase model and trauma-informed approach in treating clients with eating disorders (EDs). How one specifically undertakes the four phases (assessment/evaluation, preparation, trauma processing, and integration), however, depends on the theoretical model that guides the clinician.*

Section five provides an overview of various models that address trauma treatment and EDs. In each chapter, the author is asked to address the following:

1. *From your theoretical perspective, how do you assess or evaluate your clients?*
2. *What do you stress when preparing your client for trauma processing?*
3. *Specifically, how do you process traumatic events?*
4. *What does "reevaluation/reintegration" mean in your theoretical model (this should include attention to the addictive aspects of EDs, body image distortion, and relapse prevention)? This question involves the integration of change into the present/future.*

CHAPTER 12

Interpersonal/Relational Psychodynamic Treatment of Eating Disorders

Jean Petrucelli

■ INTRODUCTION

British analyst and essayist Adam Phillips has said, "Everybody is dealing with how much of their own aliveness they can bear and how much they need to anesthetize themselves." Woody Allen has said, "I'm not afraid of death; I just don't want to be there when it happens." From London to the upper Westside, what both of them are referring to is the difficulty people have in struggling with the fear of being consumed by terrible feelings, leading them to believe that "not feeling" is the only answer. We see this in all our patients in different ways, but when you are working with patients with eating disorders (EDs) or disordered eating, you live, breathe, digest, and metabolize this with them.

It is a chilling experience to live in the emotional abyss of an ED. Past, present, and future collapse. The insidious negative self-talk is loud, the aftermath of trauma pervasive, the effects overwhelming. What might have been a full life can be reduced to the myopic world of a donut. Culture, with its many offerings of visual objectification, provides patients with EDs much opportunity to feel scrutinized, objectified, and cut off from their bodies. When bodies are experienced as aesthetic wrappers of the self (Baker-Pitts, 2014) while simultaneously being thought of as central signifiers of identity, one is more vulnerable to expressing pain via an ED. Yet cultural influences on the development of EDs are only one part of a much larger story.

Patients with EDs live under the assumption that if they feel their sensations and feelings, these will overwhelm them "forever."

When they grow accustomed to relying on eating-disordered behaviors, which are often part of a dissociated state invoked to make the sensations and feelings go away, they also lose confidence in learning to tolerate feelings without engaging in these maladaptive behaviors. However, an ED symptom is not just something to simply get rid of, but rather something to profoundly understand as it holds dissociated parts of oneself and one's relational history. It reflects aspects of one's history that cannot be tolerated as part of the self, and thus part of embodied experience. Understanding the function of EDs in creating dissociative body-states and the function of dissociation in creating ED symptoms is then vital to treatment. Being able to tolerate one's subjective, affective experience is part of being able to internally represent one's states of being. This includes one's body-states, which has to do with embodiment, how one lives in one's body, at a given moment, relative to the felt experience. This can be internally accepted as a part of oneself and lead to developing a body that is stable—or not. This chapter focuses on an interpersonal/relational psychodynamic approach to working with EDs, which illuminates the links between symptom and meaning, action and words, isolation and relatedness.

Novelist Alice Munro has said, "To be made of flesh is humiliation." My patient, Willa, has said: "Give me a really good reason I shouldn't get out of bed right now and go out to get food ... thinking a pizza or five of them ... to binge on. I FEEL FAT, so what does it matter ..., but I'm trying, trying to convince myself, NO!"

When one is in the throes of an ED, one is trapped in the prison of one's own body-mind. One cannot imagine freedom, because one cannot imagine what it is like to change. Finding freedom is not effortless, and only those deprived of it have the barest inkling of what it is. Interpersonal and relational psychodynamic treatment provides eating-disordered patients with an opportunity to find, in the words of Sullivan (1953), one of the founders of interpersonal psychoanalysis, solutions to eating problems, body image, and problems in living.

Willa uses food to drown out the noise in her head. Her early memories of "noise" involved vitriolic screaming fights between her parents, but the later adult noise is a perseverative angst and constant worry from the mundane to the multifaceted. The intensity of the whirring noise in her head is profound and never matches the force of the problem at hand. It is a constant internal prison of sorts. Willa binges and purges six to seven times a day, clenches her jaw, grinds her teeth causing numerous root canals, snores when she sleeps, and hunches her shoulders when she sits. She has extreme allergic reactions to most medications and comes to my office with a swollen face on many occasions. Willa wears a baseball cap to hide her face and walks with her eyes always averted from the gaze of others.

The disconnect she feels in her body experience is tortuous. It fills her with pain, tormenting her every step. Her bodily based behaviors take place without an intellectual understanding of what she feels or a concerned curiosity about how her body holds her angst. Yet, Willa is a beautiful young woman with an athletic body, and if one were to see her on the street, one would have no clue as to how riddled with self-conscious loathing and shame her inner world keeps her. Willa's only source of freedom from this pain has been to manage one pain with another—by bingeing and purging, she dissociates to quiet her mind (Petrucelli, 2016).

Willa does not dare to see what is there to be seen. On a gut level, she does not feel that others can imagine what she feels on the inside. Therefore, part of our work is helping her make the connection between "not-body" as a temporary body-state and something that is "not-me" as a self-state. Body-states are nonverbal experiences and may not be known through the mind with words. The body "articulates" the unspoken. Therefore, we look for the blind spots, the gaps in the continuity and coherence of her life's story, looking for what is not being said with words. These are the moments when the symptoms take over. My inquiry with Willa puts its *"foot into the holes of this veritable Swiss cheese of avoidances"* (Evans, 1996; Levenson, 1982, 1987, 1988) that we then try to fill and expand; and when we are able to do that, the ED symptom becomes a self-state located in the body—not just a behavior that has to be dissociated. In a manner of speaking, the process of treatment involves creating a new template by filling in the dissociative "holes."

For example, a 19-year-old female patient with anorexia identified her "thighs" as the "culprit" for all that ailed her as she hated this body part that filled her with feelings of disgust and rage. On exploration in treatment, she remembered and revealed a memory that demonstrated how bodies concretize internal and historical experience. One day she commented how she felt about how my thighs looked good in pants. An in-depth exploration of her feelings about my thighs and her thighs and a discussion of the function and many shapes of thighs in general uncovered in her a memory of being 9 years old and being held over her grandfather's head to see above a crowd. She remembers feeling his fingers creep around her thighs, into her genital region. She remembers feeling physically unable to move and emotionally frozen. She remembers how he thrust his fingers into her. She said she had never spoken these words out loud (Petrucelli, 2008). My patient's body-state is an affective state, like all self-states are. In this example, her body-state involving the hatred of her thighs exists on the dissociative continuum as a nonverbal and unconscious "articulation" of what her body was expressing.

EDs are about the understanding of various body-states and their relational meanings, creating and "allowing" these states existence. The split of mindbody or bodymind (meaning top-down organization—mind to body; or bottom-up organization—body to mind) functioning is always being enacted in many arenas in the eating-disordered patient's life. Concretely, a patient believes that disciplining or controlling his or her body is a means to psychic equilibrium and interpersonal effectiveness. One might then conceive of an ED as an attempt at self-cure, which ultimately fails and leads to further isolation, chaos, and helplessness. Within the context of the therapy relationship, it is through the linking of symptoms with their emotional and interpersonal meanings that patients with EDs can find their way out. The work in treatment allows them to identify and understand the sequestered body-states that they inhabit in their attempts to survive the unbearable (Petrucelli, 2015).

EDs are complex illnesses that are multidetermined and require a multidisciplinary approach. They must be thought about and treated in a sociocultural context, while taking into account the individual's biology, genetic predisposition, vulnerability, and psychological determinants. A person's underlying genetic structure shapes his or her vulnerability and resilience, affecting how he or she perceives, organizes, and responds to experiences. Nature and nurture go hand in hand (Maine & Bunnell, 2010). Symptoms hold complex, personal stories of the individual's relationship to food and his or her body, as well as to the caretakers who fed and/or did not feed him or her. They hold the relational context in which needs were met or dismissed, and in which life came to feel as if it could or could not hold the potential for satisfaction, possibilities, and meaning. At their core, EDs are disorders of desire, in which wanting, longing, hunger, and the vulnerability of reaching with one's appetite toward the world of others have been subverted. Patients with EDs remain mythically haunted and psychically alone. They live between two worlds: the world of food and the world of people.

EDs interfere with the normal ability to hold the conflicting tensions of hunger and satiety. When thinking about these patients, we must also take into account the effects of early developmental feeding and issues of attachment, as well as the extent to which self and affect regulation difficulties play a role in how eating is felt and symbolized. Symptoms truncate emotional experience for an eating-disordered patient, serving both expressive and defensive functions. Behavioral enactments often demonstrate an aspect of the patient's subjective state that is not yet articulated, in which the body is used in the service of the mind (Stolorow & Atwood, 1991). Eating-disordered patients struggle with their underlying terror of interpersonal relatedness, which is often obscured by their symptoms. When patients' affects are split off by an unconscious fear that their experience will be unbearable, they end up living a marginal existence.

■ PRINCIPLES OF AN INTERPERSONAL/RELATIONAL PSYCHODYNAMIC APPROACH

An interpersonal/relational psychodynamic perspective values the unique fit between patient and therapist and the opportunity it offers of a mutually regulating system. We must take into account both our successes and failures, while recognizing that treatment often requires creativity to step outside of the proverbial box. For example, there is a link between a patient's self-regulation with food and the way in which he or she regulates relatedness with the therapist. The relational dyad between patient and choice of food (as part of the symptom) is highly textured. Why do some patients binge on sugar, some on salt or a combination of both, and others only on healthy foods? Does it have to do with the capacity to recognize the aftereffects of ingesting salt versus sugar, for example, as they affect the individual differently? Thinking clinically, to what "flavor" in our personality is our patient intuitively responding that allows him or her to feel comfortable enough to begin this work? What makes a good enough "fit"? How do we, as therapists, stay empathetic to a human condition that at times seems alien, destructive, and unbearable? How do we begin to discern the interpersonal meanings embedded in the unique ways our patients choose to take us in or spit us out?

An interpersonal/relational approach takes as a starting point the idea that an ED symptom is not simply to be gotten rid of, but rather holds dissociated parts of the patient's self and relational history. An eating-disordered patient may feel like the symptoms have minds of their own as they find voice through the body. Our work requires helping these patients learn how to have a different relationship to their self-states, body-states (which hold the symptoms), and physical bodies, a relationship that allows them to "feel generative and animated as well as alive to ordinary discontents and longings" (Orbach, 2009, p. 76). This is a tall order, because as we discover the disowned or dissociated parts of a person, we experience and witness firsthand his or her various self-states and body-states.

Symptoms as Adaptive Functions to Maintain Self-Continuity

We observe the adaptive function of dissociative processes as patients attempt to maintain "self-continuity and self-organization" (Bromberg, 1998, p. 206) with the use of symptoms, such as starving, bingeing, and purging. Eating-disordered patients communicate through these dramatic bodily actions, comprising a population where alexithymia (Barth, 2001; Krueger, 2001) and unformulated experience (Stern, 1997) rule. Not only do these patients have difficulty identifying their emotions but also they often have difficulty distinguishing and appreciating the emotions of others. Not knowing what one feels can be unbearable in and of itself but for those who do have a sense of what they feel, spoken words are often inadequate to express their experience. The shame they bear, as well as the fear of not being understood, dampens the curiosity required for self-exploration. EDs speak to a loss of faith in the reliability of human relatedness. For example, an orthodox mother of four who chain smokes three packs of cigarettes a day stops smoking cold turkey each week on Shabbat for 24 hours. She routinely experienced nicotine withdrawal weekly that exhibited itself in rage-filled bursts of unfiltered anger toward her young daughter at the dinner table. Unable to understand her mother's familiar, yet inconsistent and intermittent rage, the daughter retreated into her inner world and starved herself to feel "whole" and "untouchable."

Symptoms are often "used" to compensate for a lack of capacity to deal with a conflict or to counteract difficulty in mentalizing. Unable to reflectively experience dissociated parts of himself or herself, the patient has difficulty experiencing having a mind of his or her own. Meanwhile, self-development is sadly derailed. On a gut level, eating-disordered patients do not feel that others can imagine what they feel on the inside. They never feel like they are "good enough." Self-states and body-states—ways of being and bodily expression—allow a certain representation or part of the self to emerge for these patients.

Sometimes the patients need to know that we can feel their experience viscerally in our bodies (Sands, 1997), creating an uncanny, shared body-state. Patients may relate to the analyst as another body in the room by projecting their disowned parts onto the analyst and relating to the analyst as an embodied other. Processing this mutual experience allows the patient to experience body-states relationally and to reflect upon this experience. Interpersonal/relational perspectives recognize that the therapist, engaging with the patient's disowned/dissociated self- and body-states, will inevitably be pulled into the relational dynamics implicated in the patient's symptoms. One cannot treat this group from the "outside," meaning treating the patient in a one-person—doctor/patient—interpretation "delivered" model. A two-person model of co-construction of meaning between the patient and the therapist is necessary.

The Meaning of Food

How may we understand a patient's relationship to food in relational terms? Food is often the single most significant relationship in an eating-disordered patient's life. The symptoms have lost connection to the problems and vulnerabilities that stimulated their onset and have taken on a life of their own. They are now ingrained habits, with their own rhythms and expressions. For example, food may begin as a "valued friend/secret companion that helps" lessen anxiety or soothe unbearable feelings. Over time, however, it may become a "strict taskmaster or abusive tyrant that harshly punishes transgressions" (Davis, 2009, p. 37). The therapist is often pulled into this relational configuration, first idealized and valued, and then feared as the rule maker.

With the eating-disordered patient, the analyst lives in the interplay between attending directly to the food and disengaging from the pull to do so. These are compulsive patterns that have roots in relational interactions. When we feel the tug to attend or disengage, we are simultaneously sensing patients shifting from one part of themselves to another—in other words, shifting in self- or body-states. Let us say you are talking with an actively symptomatic patient and you realize you have spent an entire session without discussing the patient's relationship to food and eating. Most likely, you have been pulled into a dissociative process, alerting you that the eating-disordered part of the patient is no longer in the room.

A central feature of working interpersonally or relationally involves focusing on the uniqueness of each patient, each analyst, and each analytic dyad. If a crucial ingredient in therapeutic action involves being known by one's analyst, then the question becomes the following: How is the patient's uniqueness best revealed or uncovered (Glennon, 2012)? How do we obtain a historical narrative and enter into an eating-disordered patient's ritual-obsessed private world of food? We must try to understand the reasons that food and body image issues were important in the family of origin for starters. Food is a central issue in most people's lives. We all have memories of and feelings about family mealtime, family food behaviors, and cultural and family messages around image, appearance, and success. Food is also, of course, a particularly compelling substitute for what Kohut (1972) calls an internalized "self-object function"—the aspect of a parent/child relationship that provides the first medium for the transmission of soothing and comfort. By turning to food, the person attempts to circumvent the need for human self-object responsiveness to avoid further disappointment and shame. Food is trustworthy. How do we, as therapists, become trustworthy and help legitimize our patients' needs and yearnings, sometimes giving these feelings words before the patient can?

Although the eating-disordered population wants immediate results, recovery involves a long-term therapeutic process. Therapists who work with multiple eating-disordered patients often report an accumulation of tension in themselves. Some of this tension arises from their patients' urgent need to gain immediate control over their lives. Thus, the delayed gratification of a psychoanalytically oriented psychotherapy poses a particular challenge for the therapist who may countertransferentially feel a patient's sense of urgency. In addition, and to further complicate matters, social trends are at odds with participating in meaning-centered long-term treatment. Through texting, tweeting, twittering, swiping, and Skyping, the concepts and experiences of sitting with feelings, holding thoughts, and delaying gratification are challenged as obsolete modes of being, doing, or operating in the world. The irony is that these patients urgently wish to control their lives, and, paradoxically, to fully be in control, one must learn to relinquish control and find a way to tolerate life's ambiguities.

EDs are disorders of desire; for desire to stay on the agenda, it must stay on the analytic menu. A patient with anorexia refuses food to keep her desire alive. By refusing food, she privileges desire and holds a space for her desire to live. If she says she eats nothing, then nothing is the object that holds her desire and keeps her feeling something (Fink, 2004, p. 60). Being mindful of the textured and problematic influences that culture and technology add to issues around desire, we struggle to find the key—a way to come between our patients and their relationship with food. For patients to explore the significance of pleasure, desire, emotional intimacy, and safety, they must ultimately talk about things other than eating, weight, shape, and food. Why is it that "not wanting to want" gives you comfort? Is there a feeling of "too much-ness" to your desire so you would rather not choose? What would feel so scary about going to the party that you would prefer to stay home engaging in food rituals that give you the illusion of safety? What would be on your mind if you were not worried about your weight? What do you like about bingeing? What keeps getting in the way of your resolve to stop bingeing and purging?

Inviting the Symptom In

By safely exploring these questions, we will get nowhere unless we begin with symptom-focused approaches around the food and food behaviors and feelings to establish the physiological, medical, and psychological stability that will allow for the normalization of eating. It is essential to respect and invite the symptoms into the treatment, while recognizing them as vehicles for understanding that which cannot be communicated directly with words. Symptom relief is, in a sense, the easiest part of this work. The more challenging aspect is the long-term structural, behavioral, and personality change that requires creating new neural templates. Bromberg (2011) refers to this as a more flexible community of neural networks in the brain that will support the mind's ability to allow greater interconnection between self-states and more flexible self-state networks.

Patients do not care how much you know until they know how much you care. Treatment must convey empathic acceptance, while simultaneously pushing for things to be different. Integration requires a collaborative alliance and an explicit push for change (Maine & Bunnell, 2010). Bromberg (2011) writes, "what most nourishes the soil of therapeutic growth—is a patient's capacity to change while remaining the same—it is the foundation of development because it is the foundation of hope" (p. 93). When our patients can feel that being with them as they are brings us genuine pleasure in spite of their struggles and symptoms, they can see glimmers of hope even if we must hold their hope until they can. Holding the hope often necessitates another kind of integration, one requiring the use of adjunct resources in a team approach.

In interpersonal/relationally oriented clinical work, we learn to speak the patient's language. With eating-disordered patients, we must learn to speak their language of food and bodily concerns (Brisman, 1994). At the same time, we must introduce a language of mindfulness, self-care, groundedness, and the possibilities for human contact and a life. Our first job is to discover all the patient's body-selves and form relationships with each of them. For example, when a patient with bulimia has her head in the toilet purging her guts out, I want to understand the part of her that was in such unbearable pain that whatever she felt inside of her could not be tolerated or contained. Each holds its own truth, its own reality, and its own agenda, and all must be taken seriously. In attempting to understand unformulated experience, sometimes it requires "having to find what you don't know how to look for" (Stern, 2008, p. 398).

The Initial Phase

Working psychoanalytically in the treatment of eating-disordered individuals requires the necessary integration of behavioral techniques as well as behavioral change. Harry Stack Sullivan had a behavioral sensibility. Sullivan was interested in what people actually do with one another in the real world (Mitchell, 1999). With an eating-disordered patient, food often takes the place of an "other." Knowing about a patient's relationships to food and others, as well as to his or her day-to-day lived experience, is as important as what we wish to understand about his or her inner fantasy life. Working with these patients involves actively intervening with direct, concrete engagement with eating-disordered behaviors to elaborate the personal and interpersonal meanings trapped in these actions.

In the initial phase of treatment, we must gather data. The techniques we use to understand this analytically may include playing with food metaphors, a detailed inquiry (Sullivan, 1953, 1954), contracting, and food journaling, all of which help us understand how, when, and what went wrong, and what worked. An interpersonal approach to treatment is clinically more oriented to acts and experiences than to theories and interpretations. We try to get facts—or at least get patients to talk about what they subjectively experience as facts—so that we can have something concrete to work with. In Sullivan's view, such immediacy and direct connection to the patient's real-life situations were highly informative. He paid careful attention to specifics. Sullivan's willingness to use language that sounded acceptable to the patient was an example of his eagerness to learn from the patient. Obtaining specifics about a patient's ED involves using techniques that link words and actions. Doing so, we discover the patient's capacity to self-soothe, self-regulate, tolerate emotional experience, and manage appetite and desire. These techniques help us to *name* the emotions the patient is experiencing, rather than leaving the patient to be overwhelmed by them. It is not the specific techniques, but rather the relational interactions around them that create meaning. For example, how the patient thought about why she decided to NOT call the therapist in a moment of need—how she imagined the therapist would or would not respond—becomes an important ingredient in the mix to better understand her process, rather than focusing on the act of not reaching for help itself. These interactions become part of the attachment and affect regulation process. Often the worsening of symptoms is the patient's way of upping the ante, a kind of "speaking louder" so the therapist can hear the patient's unformulated communication. By using action-oriented tools, patients begin to differentiate between, and move from, the self-limiting statements of "I am ..." to "I feel ...." The "I feel" statements begin the process of recognition, identification, and acknowledgment of a feeling without being consumed by it (Kuriloff, 2004). "I am fat," for example, may reflect deeper feelings, such as "I feel alienated and alone."

The co-construction of meaning allows us as therapists to help patients reshape and redirect their inner experiences so they may have more freedom of choice and a greater sense of agency to become the author of their own story. How they tell their story is through the use of actual food as metaphor, the use of food metaphors, and food as a concretized sense of identity. The notion of "you-are-what-you-eat" becomes a reality for some patients. What remains undifferentiated is the distinction between the patient as a person and food, in and of itself. Eating changes the patient's need for relationships, as food becomes the substitute for this need.

Speaking the Same Language

Using food metaphors is one way of speaking an eating-disordered patient's language. As we shift the focus from food and weight toward an interpersonal exchange, talking about the therapeutic relationship via food metaphors is an effective way to build a symbolic bridge, enabling an eating-disordered patient to link various aspects of his or her self-experience. For example, consider the regulation of relatedness between patient and analyst. There is the analyst's potential of listening, waiting, and reverie, and there is the patient's potential of digesting how much of the analyst's words can be taken in before the patient feels overwhelmed, "too full," or "stuffed," resulting in a dissociation or "purging" of the other. There is a kind of unknowing that is necessary for analytic work, but we also have to help patients "savor" new ideas by letting them "percolate" or "brew," analogous to tolerating ambiguity or holding conflicted thoughts. We sometimes experience the impulsive expulsion—the metaphorical spitting out—of words and feelings as a "purge," or their punishing silence as a way to "starve" them of an "other." We take small bites, chew each morsel, mix foods on a plate, and allow for the taste of a new food. We help our patients articulate experience with words; identify the nameless, but powerful, emotions that are unattended to; and together decide how we might tolerate the ambiguity of a moment. If you ask patients, *"What are you really hungry for?"* they might answer that, lurking in the dark and ebony of night, they wish to sneak a morsel or maybe just a bite. It might not be a binge, as they are not hungry for food, but looking for something that will fill them, heal them from being broken and bruised. They are hungry for compassion, protection, faith, love, and family, and, in a sense, they are starving for recovery, to break free of these chains that bind them.

Nonetheless, linking behaviors to specific feelings can feel like a familiar menu of criticism, engendering feelings of shame that may be more than a patient can digest. It is helpful to use straightforward direct questions, but in tiny morsels, offered in "espresso spoons." These may help the patient identify and manage feelings without our necessarily expecting symptoms to disappear or diminish.

The Detailed Inquiry

The detailed inquiry (Sullivan, 1953, 1954, 1956) can promote a sense of safety that enables the patient to reveal information, including the disclosure of an ED, sometimes for the first time. As you explore the patient's food and bodily obsessions, you may help the patient build skills that regulate affect (see Barth, 2001, 2008; Brisman, 1995, 1998; Davis, 1991; Kuriloff, 2004; Petrucelli, 2004, 2010, 2015). Using the detailed inquiry and pursuit of the particular (Levenson, 1988), I try to be curious, searching for meaning in interactions or behaviors, while keeping an eye on shifts in feeling states. I start by asking directly, but sometimes data are obtained from unexpected clinical moments.

In the beginning phase of treatment, taking a detailed history involves an intricate description of specific moments around eating; the symptomatic behaviors of starving, bingeing, purging, or bodily obsession; and the affective states that accompany these behaviors. The history includes tiny details of a patient's daily life that account for significant parts of his or her experience. It is in these details that we may discover perplexing gaps in the patient's understanding of emotions and behavioral patterns, which might otherwise have been overlooked. Sometimes therapists have difficulty asking questions such as, *"Exactly how many chocolate cakes did you have?" "Which garbage can did you pull the food out of?" "How do you get yourself to purge—fingers or forks?"* or *"Do you brush your teeth after a purge?"* With these questions, we, as analysts, are trying to determine whether dissociation is at play or whether the patient lacks the capacity for mindfulness. Perhaps it has never occurred to this patient that the disordered behavior leaves a trail of crumbs as clues. Perhaps this is the relational point. The goal is to join our patients in an exploration of what, when, and where, so we can begin to understand how to help them develop the capacity to process, modulate, and manage overwhelming affects that have never been verbalized.

A detailed inquiry is a valuable tool for inquiring about the self-care necessary for being centered and grounded in one's life. This involves understanding patterns and behaviors regarding food, sleep, and what one does for fun. These questions may seem insignificant or unanalytic, but they are indicative of the ways patients can and cannot soothe themselves as they touch on their dreams, desire, yearnings, or lack thereof. When a behavioral suggestion is offered, it is done without the expectation that the suggestion will necessarily be followed. What does it mean to a patient if you provide a behavioral suggestion? What does it mean as an analyst if you give patients a specific suggestion about something they actually do differently? The analytic focus lies in what happens between patient and therapist in these exchanges. Does the patient feel heard, judged, accepted, or criticized as he or she describes a "bizarre" food ritual? If the therapist asks a question, does it feel like a demand? As if the therapist always knows better, like mother always knew best, which, as Bruch (1973) noted, is often not the case and represents a repetition of the child not being recognized as having his or her own voice?

Ultimately, what becomes most important in these interactions are the thoughts, fantasies, and discussion that arise from asking questions, working on alternative behaviors, and the obstacles that present themselves when behavioral suggestions are made. These dialogues are opportunities for the patient and therapist to play with a new assortment of ideas and possibilities.

In these interpersonal exchanges, the patient and the analyst live out the "Levensonian" question: "What is going on around here?" (Levenson, 1983). The therapist learns what happens in this relational dyad and sees the patient's maladaptive attempts to solve problems and conflicts. How does "eating food on a plate, counterclockwise, taking one bite from each food group, with food never mixing or touching, and with only even bites," help manage the volcanic anger and feelings of betrayal that lie dormant in her body? Does she feel like "an orange that is peeled and thrown away because there is a peach around the corner?" What parts is she hiding from me so that she can remain "the good girl," showing me what she now thinks is the only part of her I care about? To not ask a question is to ignore the parts of her that are dissociated—the parts for which she feels the most disgust, repulsion, and hatred.

Dissociation

Dissociation, that is, the numbness or psychic closing off that so often accompanies trauma and follows in its wake, facilitates and contributes to a patient's silence. In the face of trauma, keeping a secret is often not a conscious decision. Powerful internal and external forces are at play and prevent information from surfacing. The defense that helps people to cope at one point ultimately complicates their lives at another. Dissociation involves not knowing there is a secret you are keeping. This secret is an attempt to protect an aspect of self and, sometimes, also to protect others (Petrucelli, 2010). Relating in new ways to eating-disordered patients facilitates the uncovering of secrets so that the patient can move from "*being* the secret" to "*knowing* the secret" (Bromberg, 2011, p. 42). Bromberg (2007) emphasizes the importance of recognizing the split-off dissociated aspects of self—the various self-states—that enter the room by paying attention to clinical moments, slips of the tongue, or uncanny felt experiences that represent another voice that the patient, and sometimes the analyst, has not revealed or had access to. Speaking about the unspeakable allows us, as patient and therapist, to authentically connect to the parts of a patient that feel destabilized. Putting words to the unspoken, talking about food and rituals, and considering alternative behaviors give us access into a patient's system, his or her organizing principles, and where he or she might find hope and the promise of a better life.

Especially in the early stages, a patient may not be able to provide specific information about his or her eating behavior, because the person who engaged in the behavior is rarely the person whom you are asking to describe it in detail. Instead, the therapist is confronted by a patient's self-state that knows *about* the behavior, but does not have the experience of it being personal (Bromberg, 2011). This is true for all patients with seriously dissociative mental structures, but is particularly relevant with eating-disordered patients, as the nature of their symptoms—such as bingeing or purging—enhances dissociative tendencies.

Dual Attention

As Wachtel (1993) and others (Frank, 1990; Mitchell, 1988) have noted, deepening the process of exploration and promoting greater access to warded off parts of the self, that is, transitioning between the intrapsychic and the interpersonal, between psychodynamics and behavior, can be viewed as analytic explorations. Active interventions or suggestions provide more grist for the mill. Sometimes concrete, self-soothing behavioral suggestions are appropriate. Among these are activities to increase mindfulness, such as turning off the TV while eating; activities that occupy one's hands, such as knitting; or activities that shift a mood until the uncomfortable moment passes. However, for this to be truly beneficial, the analyst must work in the here-and-now, with the patient's absence of mindfulness as it is manifested, even while these suggestions are being made. It is not uncommon for a patient to have a dissociative response while we are making recommendations, even when they are fairly benign, such as suggesting playing a game, making a cup of tea, taking a walk, practicing yoga, calling a friend, taking a bath with candles, dancing to a favorite song, or using music in novel ways.

However, it is not just about real-life interventions to promote mindfulness or about helping patients look at what goes on between them and others. It is also important, if not more so, to keep the patient's mind, not just his or her life and eating habits, as a primary focus in the here-and-now. A patient who night binges rigged his refrigerator door to play music when he opened it, hoping a favorite song would wake him sufficiently and prevent him from his nightly eating ritual. The music also woke up other people in the house who entered the kitchen, preventing him from eating. This led to our discussion of how unconsciously creative this patient was to finally "demand" the help and recognition he needed from his family and from the treatment as well.

What is said and not said, or what is seen and not seen, often creates a challenge for the therapist as to when to focus on the eating-disordered behaviors/symptoms or on underlying emotions and relational dynamics. Moving back and forth in this terrain is often intuitively felt—if the therapist stays mindful. It is often the unspoken agenda that is most important.

Attending to what is *not* said magnifies the possibility of revealing the unspoken agendas—what is being selectively unattended to—that interfere with a patient's attempts to self-regulate eating. For example, one patient who was very obsessive about her food plan spent 2 to 3 hours per day writing down her meals for that day. Not only did she count calories but also she thought at length about her afternoon classes and what she should wear to them, given what she was going to eat. She also thought about whom she was likely to see during the day and how she should adjust her food plans, depending on whom she might run into. But her struggles with time management were uncovered only when I discovered why she *needed* to change her appointment time: It took her 2 hours to walk to her session, no matter what her body was experiencing. It had never occurred to me that she would walk to the Upper West Side of Manhattan from Brooklyn! She revealed that she never took subways or buses; she *had to* walk. Such information, as in this example, unfolds when you do a detailed inquiry, but to be clear, it unfolds only when the patient is not dissociating during the process. Dissociation is not amnesia for events in and of themselves. Rather, it is an ability to "sort-of-know," which means "knowing about," but not knowing "it."

Contracting

A verbal contract is an agreement made between patient and therapist regarding substituting alternative behaviors for disordered eating behaviors or thinking. The alternative behaviors are those that the patient is willing to engage in instead of, or before, turning to food. They may include self-soothing, communication, self-exploration, use of food in a structured manner, and sometimes pure distraction. But most important, they begin to create the idea that there can be a relationship to others—and that relationship can start with you, the therapist—standing in the space where disordered food behaviors have been. The goal of the contract is not merely the abatement of eating behavior, but also understanding what making the contract means to the patient, as the patient trusts you with more of his or her life (Brisman, 1998; Petrucelli, 2004, 2015).

Contracting is a way of beginning to mentalize or hold the other in mind. Patients have to hold you holding them in mind. Adhering to or breaking the contract is an equally important factor in understanding who the patient is and how he or she functions in a relationship—in this case, the relationship with the therapist. I have done all kinds of contracting with patients. With each patient I keep a book, in which I take notes. This activity is in itself an interpersonal dynamic. Some patients love it when I write, some patients want to read their book, and some ask, "Is that book all me?" Some patients see it as a barrier between us and become too focused on me writing, so I stop taking notes. All of these interactions have a dynamic meaning in our relationship and become ways in which our relationship inches its way into the patient's once covert and closed relationship with food—and then, transferentially, to other relationships in his or her life.

Over the years, contracting tools, as well as the process, have changed along with advances in technology. Beepers, phone machines, and voicemail have given way to emailing and texting, which sometimes enable patients to reach me more quickly. What has not changed is the underlying point of the contracting: to build mentalization through the medium of a strengthened relationship with the analyst. Another purpose of contracting, also unchanged, is that the patient first begins to entertain the idea of an alternative behavior and, second, learns to delay, when only impulse existed before.

Contracting does not work for all patients, some of whom experience it as "forced feeding." Others, hungry for symptom relief and symptom substitution, are hungry—that is, they are hungry for relatedness with another person. In other words, with contracting, the patient begins the process of taking me in, digesting my words, holding feelings, and using me as an alternative to using food.

What does it mean to a patient to hold the idea of an agreement in one's head? When a patient chooses to call, either when about to break our contract or when the contract is already broken, we discuss what it feels like to be attuned to our agreement, even though he or she feels that calling me is the last thing in the world he or she wants to do. When a patient does not call, and then tells me about it in the next session, we talk about why he or she did not call. This conversation includes exploring the feelings before the binge, the planning and timing, how he or she binged or purged, whom he or she told, if anyone, and what he or she imagined would happen if he or she had called me. By understanding what the patient does in keeping or breaking a contract, the analyst begins to see the relational components of the ED; in other words, the patient's capacity to self-soothe and regulate internal experience.

Food Journaling and Texting

Another way to invite the symptom in the room is to ask eating-disordered patients to keep a journal in which they record their weekly food intake as well as other ingested substances (alcohol, laxatives, diuretics, drugs, etc.). Texting has infiltrated this arena, as I receive picture texts of plates of food as well.

Food charts involve recording the time, place, food, levels of hunger and satiety, substance use, feelings, and ED symptomatic behaviors. Often patients are recording this with a nutritionist, but I sometimes start the process to get a baseline and ascertain the extent to which a patient can use this effectively. Some patients prefer to write just for themselves, whereas others use writing as a tool of interpersonal exchange. They can "bookmark" their thoughts via email without me being expected to reply. One patient will say that writing is calming and centering; another will report that it makes him or her tense and anxious for he or she can never find the "right" words. Some patients initiate a break from writing and return to it when they feel that they are becoming more symptomatic. The relational exchange of decision making and implementation is important information as patients gravitate toward, or away from, a tool—such as journaling, emailing, or texting.

Writing may be used as a vehicle to connect to one's internal process. It facilitates knowing and trusting one's self. Writing can be excruciatingly painful for a patient with an ED as one goes through the process of recording the time one eats, what one eats, how much one eats, bingeing and purging behavior, and what one is feeling around food. However, it begins the process of naming the affective experience, formulating for patients what they are experiencing, and facilitating interpersonal trust as they share it with another. On the contrary, revealing one's secret world to the therapist may also elicit myriad feelings of being judged, of shame, disgust, self-loathing, and even relief. Food journaling may also serve as a container for the out-of-control feelings related to food.

Likewise, journaling helps patients gain access to a place untraveled within them. Putting something on paper requires the person to develop the ability to stand back and observe. When all goes well, the process of journaling food and behaviors teaches self-monitoring, while serving as a transitional object that often provides the patient with a sense of safety.

Journal writing, as well as the anticipated reading and sharing of one's thoughts and feelings concerning food with the therapist, may facilitate the patient's "ability to be alone in the anticipated presence of another" (Winnicott, 1965, 1971). Journal writing also facilitates "potential space," a place from which to become aware (Rabinor, 1991). The writing provides an opportunity to access cutoff aspects of one's own self-experience. The hope is that a patient may initially open up to himself or herself and then may later share this awareness with his or her therapist.

■ CONCLUSION

The work of any treatment of EDs is an ongoing, complicated mixture of direct intervention with the symptom and exploration of what the intervention means to the patient, including the role the symptom plays in the patient's intrapsychic and interpersonal world. Understanding this as it unfolds relationally allows the inter-subjective experience of both patient and therapist to collide, mingle, and ultimately coexist. As clinicians, we are fortunate to have the opportunity to share in a patient's journey toward health and recovery. We come face to face with our patients' courage, strength, limitations, and perseverance, which often fly in the face of severe medical and psychosocial stressors. It is a humbling and inspiring experience, one that keeps us striving to make fresh assessments of what really works, what is helpful, and what is not in making those shifts (Zerbe, 1993).

Cultivating our curiosity and the curiosity of the patient means finding and recon-necting the parts of the patient that have been disconnected for so long. It means allow-ing the frightened shadows of self to ally with a new sense of being that moves toward acceptance of health, in mind and body. Our hope is to inspire patients to tell their story, as well as to accept our willingness to hear their pain without judgment, to hold their disgust, their skeletal pieces, their fat, and their hurts. Curiosity converts strangers into people with whom we can empathize. Our goal is to help our patients, through a process of reflection, exploration, and self-discovery, increase their capacity for more fulfilling relationships, experience less guilt and shame, tolerate a wider range of affects, and face their challenges with greater flexibility and less fear of the unknown. We help them learn to live in the "gray," to endure imperfection by accepting their bodies with the idea of a body being "good enough," and probably, above all, to help them establish a sense of self that is not on the basis of their ED. This means making peace with both whom one is and whom one is not, respecting personal histories and limits without letting these define the individual.

Thinking about working with patients with EDs from this vantage point means that the experience of conflict is a therapeutic gain, not obstacle. Multiplicity and the capacity for dissociation are seen as part of the manifestations of what happens with patients with EDs. When the dialogue between their self-states or body-states is shut down because of defenses, extreme dissociation, and trauma, symptoms increase. Therapeutic action inevitably entails enactments with the patient and therapist as cocreators and coactors in the drama of what has been dissociated. When the patients experience the therapist's empathy for all the different self-states and body-states, and "*their*" needs, they can begin to experience increased empathy among their parts. This includes the nonnegation of their often-contradictory needs and accompanying affects and therefore the links and sharing between parts can ulti-mately diminish their separateness, working through their experiences of conflict and choices together.

■ REFERENCES

Baker-Pitts, C. (2014). "Look at me—What am I supposed to be?": Women, culture, and cosmetic splitting. In J. Petrucelli (Ed.), *Body-states: Interpersonal and relational perspectives on the treatment of eating disorders* (pp. 104–119). London, UK: Routledge.

Barth, D. (2001). Thinking, talking and feeling in psychotherapy. In J. Petrucelli & C. Stuart (Eds.), *Hungers and compulsions: The psychodynamic treatment of eating disorders & addictions* (pp. 41–52). Northvale, NJ: Jason Aronson.

Barth, D. (2008). Hidden eating disorders: Attachment and affect regulation in the therapeutic relationship. *Clinical Social Work Journal, 36*, 355–365. doi:10.1007/s10615-008-0164-2

Brisman, J. (1994). Learning to listen: Therapeutic encounters and negotiations in the early stage of treatment. *Eating Disorders, 2*(1), 68–73. doi:10.1080/10640269408249102

Brisman, J. (1995). Psychodynamic psychotherapy and action-oriented technique: An integrated approach. In I. Yalom & J. Werne (Eds.), *Treating eating disorders* (pp. 311–370), San Francisco, CA: Jossey-Bass.

Brisman, J. (1998). When actions speak louder than words: Verbal and non-verbal wrangling in the therapeutic arena commentary on paper by F. Diane Barth. *Psychoanalytic Dialogues, 8*(5), 707–714. doi:10.1080/10481889809539284

Bromberg, P. M. (1998). *Standing in the spaces: Essays on clinical process, trauma, and dissociation* (p. 206). Hillsdale, NJ: Analytic Press.

Bromberg, P. M. (2007). *Awakening the dreamer: Clinical journeys.* Hillsdale, NJ: Analytic Press.

Bromberg, P. M. (2011). *The shadow of the tsunami and the growth of the relational mind.* New York, NY: Routledge.

Bruch, H. (1973). *Eating disorders, obesity, anorexia and the person within.* New York, NY: Basic Books.

Davis, W. (1991). Reflections on boundaries in the psychotherapeutic relationship. In C. Johnson, (Ed.), *Psychodynamic treatment of anorexia and bulimia* (pp. 68–85). New York, NY: Guilford Press.

Davis, W. (2009). Individual psychotherapy for anorexia nervosa and bulimia: Making a difference. In M. Maine, W. David, & J. Shure (Eds.), *Effective clinical practice in the treatment of eating disorders* (pp. 35–48). New York, NY: Routledge.

Evans, F. B. (1996). *Harry Stack Sullivan: Interpersonal theory and psychotherapy.* New York, NY: Routledge.

Fink, B. (2004). *Lacan to the letter: Reading Écrits closely.* Minneapolis: University of Minnesota Press.

Frank, K. A. (1990). Action techniques in psychoanalysis: Background and introduction. *Contemporary Psychoanalysis, 26*, 732–756. doi:10.1080/00107530.1990.10746688

Glennon, S. S. (2012, June). *Therapeutic action from a relational perspective.* Paper presented at a meeting of the Comparative Psychoanalysis Group, NYU Postdoc, New York, NY.

Kohut, H. (1972). Thoughts on narcissism and narcissistic rage. *Psychoanalytic Study of the Child, 27*, 360–400. doi:10.1080/00797308.1972.11822721

Krueger, D. W. (2001). Body self. Development, psychopathologies, and psychoanalytic significance. *Psychoanalytic Study of the Child, 56*, 238–259. doi:10.1080/00797308.2001.11800675

Kuriloff, E. (2004). When words fail: Psychosomatic illness and the talking cure. *Psychoanalytic Quarterly, LXXIII*, 1023–1040. doi:10.1002/j.2167-4086.2004.tb00191.x

Levenson, E. A. (1982). Follow the fox: An inquiry into the vicissitudes of psychoanalytic supervision. *Contemporary Psychoanalysis, 18*, 1–15. doi:10.1080/00107530.1982.10745675

Levenson, E. A. (1983). *The ambiguity of change.* New York, NY: Basic Books.

Levenson, E. A. (1987). The purloined self. *Journal of the American Academy of Psychoanalysis, 15*, 481–490. doi: 10.1521/jaap.1.1987.15.4.481

Levenson, E. A. (1988). The pursuit of the particular: On the psychoanalytic inquiry. *Contemporary Psychoanalysis, 24*, 1–16. doi:10.1080/00107530.1988.10746216

Maine, M., & Bunnell, D. (2010). A perfect biopsychosocial storm: Gender, culture, and eating disorders. In M. Maine, B. H. McGilley, & D. Bunnell (Eds.), *Treatment of eating disorders* (pp. 3–16). Burlington, MA: Academic Press.

Mitchell, S. A. (1988). *Relational concepts in psychoanalysis: An integration.* Cambridge, MA: Harvard University Press.

Mitchell, S. A. (1999). Attachment theory and the psychoanalytic tradition: Reflections on human relationality. *Psychoanalytic Dialogues, 9*, 85–107. doi:10.1080/10481889909539308

Orbach, S. (2009). *Bodies.* New York, NY: Picador.

Petrucelli, J. (2004). Treating eating disorders. In R. H. Coombs (Ed.), *Handbook of addictive disorders: A practical guide to diagnosis and treatment* (pp. 312–352). Hoboken, NJ: Wiley.

Petrucelli, J. (2008). When a body meets a body: The impact of the therapist's body on eating-disordered patients. In F. Anderson (Ed), *Bodies in treatment: The unspoken dimension* (pp. 237–254). New York, NY: Analytic Press.

Petrucelli, J. (2010). Things that go bump in the night: Secrets after dark. In J. Petrucelli (Ed.), *Knowing, not-knowing & sort-of-knowing: Psychoanalysis and the experience of uncertainty* (pp. 135–150). London, UK: Karnac Books.

Petrucelli, J. (2015). Mermaids, mistresses and Medusa: Getting "inside out and outside in" the relational montage of an eating disorder. In J. Petrucelli (Ed.), *Body-states: Interpersonal and relational perspectives on the treatment of eating disorders* (pp. 13–34). London, UK: Routledge.

Petrucelli, J. (2016). Who moved my "Swiss" cheese? Eating disorders and the use of dissociation as an attempt to fill in the "whole." In E. Howell & S. Itzkowitz (Eds.), *The dissociative mind in psychoanalysis* (pp. 163–174). London, UK: Routledge.

Rabinor, J. (1991). The process of recovery from an eating disorder: The use of journal writing in the initial phase of treatment. *Psychotherapy in Private Practice, 9*(1), 93–106.

Sands, S. H. (1997). Protein or foreign body? Reply to commentaries. *Psychoanalytic Dialogues, 7*, 691–706. doi:10.1080/10481889709539213

Stern, D. B. (1997). *Unformulated experience: From dissociation to imagination in psychoanalysis.* Hillsdale, NJ: Analytic Press.

Stern, D. B. (2008). On having to find what you don't know how to look for: Two perspectives on reflection. In E. Jurist, A. Slade., & S. Bergner (Eds.), *Mind to mind: Infant research, neuroscience and psychoanalysis* (pp. 398–413). New York, NY: Other Press.

Stolorow, R. D., & Atwood, G. E. (1991). The mind and the body. *Psychoanalytic Dialogues, 1*(2), 181–195. doi:10.1080/10481889109538892

Sullivan, H. S. (1953). *The interpersonal theory of psychiatry.* New York, NY: W. W. Norton.

Sullivan, H. S. (1954). *The psychiatric interview.* New York, NY: W. W. Norton.

Sullivan, H. S. (1956). *Clinical studies in psychiatry.* H. S. Perry, M. L. Gawel, & M. Gibbon (Eds.). New York, NY: W. W. Norton.

Wachtel, P. L. (1993). Active intervention, psychic structure, and the analysis of transference: Commentary on Frank's "action, insight, and working through." *Psychoanalytic Dialogues, 3*, 589–603. doi:10.1080/10481889309538995

Winnicott, D. W. (1965). The capacity to be alone. In M. Masud & R. Khan (Eds.) *The maturational processes and the facilitating environment* (pp. 29–36). London, UK: Hogarth Press and the Institute of Psycho-Analysis, (Original publication 1958).

Winnicott, D. W. (1971). *Playing and reality.* New York, NY: Basic Books.

Zerbe, K. (1993). Treatment: The body reclaimed. In K. Zerbe (Ed.), *The body betrayed: A deeper understanding of women, eating disorders, and treatment* (pp. 347–374). Carlsbad, CA: Gürze Books.

CHAPTER 13

Eye Movement Desensitization and Reprocessing (EMDR)

DaLene Forester

■ WHAT IS EMDR?

Eye movement desensitization and reprocessing (EMDR) is an integrative, client-centered psychotherapy developed by Francine Shapiro, PhD, in 1987 (Shapiro, 2001). EMDR engages the natural information processing systems in the brain to process disturbing life experiences that are, according to Shapiro, the bases of pathological behaviors.

Sometime in the early to mid-1980s, Dr. Shapiro was walking and processing some of her own disturbing life experiences when she realized the thoughts she was having shifted in a way that she knew was not typical for those kinds of thoughts. Being an astute self-observer, she noticed that although she was engaging these kinds of thoughts, her eyes were moving rapidly back and forth in a diagonal pattern. She reports that initially she thought she had stumbled on to a natural type of processing and began asking others if they noticed their eyes moving while processing disturbing thoughts.

What Dr. Shapiro found was that people did not notice eye movements when engaging in their own disturbing life experiences. When she asked them to mimic what she described, they often did not have the eye muscle strength to move their eyes bilaterally for a sustained period of time. Dr. Shapiro began using her hand to guide their eyes back and forth, which was the beginning of the development of her eight-phase model of psychotherapy, now known as EMDR therapy.

The current industry standard of training for learning EMDR is extensive and conducted over the course of a minimum of 20 didactic hours, 20 hours of practicum, with an additional 10 hours of case consultation with an EMDR International Association (EMDRIA) accredited training provider. EMDR therapy trainings approved by the EMDRIA (www.emdria.org) are the only trainings endorsed by Dr. Shapiro.

The AIP Model

The Adaptive Information Processing (AIP) model was developed by Francine Shapiro to explain the effects of EMDR therapy; guide case conceptualization, treatment planning, and interventions; and predict treatment outcomes. The AIP model assumes that both pathology and health are the development of early life experiences that are stored in neurobiological memory networks. Early life experiences, therefore, are the building blocks of perception, attitudes, and behaviors. Neurobiologically speaking, our life experiences get translated into physically stored memories on which we rely to guide us in life choices and interpretations.

The AIP model postulates that our brain, like our bodies, has a natural healing and learning mechanism. Living organisms seek homeostasis. We seek balance as we adapt to new information, and we incorporate new or novel information in a way that makes sense. Sometimes this adaptation is healthier than others. We have all known clients who, as a protection from the belief that loved ones are capable of harming them, take on the belief that they were responsible for the harm they suffered.

According to this model, there are two ways in which individuals can begin to function pathologically. First, there is the natural learning of unhealthy belief systems, such as growing up in an alcoholic family and learning it is "normal" for children to make sure that mommy or daddy wakes up in time for work or that food can become a substitute for feelings of emotional emptiness. Second, there are traumatic life experiences that cause a disruption of the normal AIP. This would be something more like a car accident in which a parent is killed in front of a child, causing a disruption in the ability to process the experience. In the eating disorder (ED) world, we often see this when a client has experienced a sexual assault. The incident is so shocking that the individual is unable to process the information in an effective way. As clinicians, we work to help the victims of sexual assault to see and know they clearly did not plan or participate in the occurrence of the assault. That the assault is not their fault. That the perpetrator is fully responsible for the abusive act. It is not unusual for the victim of a sexual assault to go into a shock state, a psychological numbness that interferes with the processing of the experience. The experience then gets trapped in memory networks and the nervous system. This exposure to a traumatic life experience causes unprocessed information to be dysfunctionally held in memory networks in the brain. In other words, rather than moving trauma information from the mute or nonverbal, limbic part of the brain to the adaptive prefrontal cortex, the information remains stuck in a state-specific form in a part of the brain that words cannot reach.

The AIP model views patterns of dysfunctionally stored emotions, physical sensations, and perceptions as symptoms to be addressed, not the cause of psychopathology. It requires the processing of earlier life experiences to achieve healing (for a comprehensive explanation of the AIP model, go to www.emdria.org, the Francine Shapiro library, or YouTube).

The AIP Model Applied to Eating Disorders and Disorders of Eating

The AIP model views an ED as a pattern of maladaptive behaviors, dysfunctionally stored emotions, physical sensations, and perceptions that need to be processed to healthy resolution. A simple example might be that of an individual who learns to overeat to regulate feelings of fear and abandonment following an experience of being left home alone at a young age or abandoned by an unavailable parent due to his or her own depression or substance abuse. Feelings and sensations associated with relief following a binge–purge cycle, as in bulimia nervosa (BN), can become a pattern that both is a coping mechanism and reflects an underlying belief that there is something wrong with "me," otherwise I would not be left or abandoned. This pattern of dysfunctionally stored information results in overeating, or binging, to calm fears, followed by purging to produce the experience of relief.

Many clinicians and researchers have noted the connection between trauma and the development of EDs. EDs can develop as a coping mechanism to help an individual deal with not only feelings such as shame and fear resulting from earlier life experiences but also experiences of being out of control, overwhelmed, unlovable, or not good enough. Most individuals can relate to turning to food at one time or another to soothe emotions; why else would references to turning to ice cream or alcohol following an emotional breakup be so common with comedians, movies, and television shows? In the beginning, the ED is a very helpful coping strategy, bringing immediate relief to uncomfortable feelings. EDs come into someone's life to help, but in the long run they wreak havoc. I often tell my clients that at first the individual uses the ED to help control feelings of being out of control, only to lose control completely.

Case Example of Binge Eating Disorder: Belinda

"Belinda," age 41, came into therapy to get help with "food issues." A professional woman, she was very articulate and stated that she was prepared to do whatever it took to stop binging. She reported she engaged in binge eating nearly every night when she came home from work starting approximately a year earlier. She described no history of weight issues as a child or young adult. She stated that she had always been very goal oriented and believed she had high expectations of herself. She described herself as a type "A" personality.

In gathering information about precipitating events to the binge eating, she shared that, just prior to when the binge behavior occurred, she had volunteered to lead a particularly difficult team project at work. She stated that when she took on the project, she had a "gut feeling" that she was getting in over her head. To complicate matters, others who had offered to provide support for the project were unreliable and failed to complete portions of the project for which they had taken responsibility. As the deadline approached, she found herself working many extra hours to compensate for what others had failed to do. On the day the project was due, she attempted to open the file on her computer to discover the file was corrupt and would not open. She reported having an "anxiety attack" at that moment. She stated she was ultimately able to recover an earlier saved version of the file and the project was completed on time. She reported going home that night and binging. She stated that after that she would periodically binge on highly stressful days and feel better at the time. However, these episodes would be followed by feelings of guilt and shame for losing control.

Negative beliefs associated with maladaptive emotional regulation support the development of an ED as a resolution to emotional pain, so the AIP model can predict successful resolution of the ED once the maladaptive information is processed to a healthy resolution. An individual may learn, for example, that being left alone as a child resulted in an ongoing fear, but that overeating helped to calm those fears and that purging brought feelings of relief. This behavior became a way to cope whenever feelings of fear arose. When EMDR therapy accesses the memory network that stored binging and purging as a way to bring emotional relief, the maladaptive belief system, with the concomitant behaviors, feelings, and body sensations, is neutralized or, in EMDR language, desensitized. The brain spontaneously allows more adaptive information to be associated with the earlier experience, supporting the client in learning that fear is a normal reaction to being left alone as a young child, that he or she is no longer that alone child, and that, as an adult, he or she can now deal with present fears more adaptively. We can further backtrack, using the AIP model, and look for underlying root causes of the fear of abandonment in the first place. With EMDR, we can help the individual go back to the very earliest memories of these emotional states and the culminating negative beliefs assigned. EMDR moves the negative beliefs to a healthier, adaptive resolution.

The individual learns that although fear is a normal reaction, binging to calm fear is not, and that, although purging brings an associated feeling of relief, it does not solve underlying problems. Once the individual fully metabolizes the unprocessed fear associated with the experience of being left alone, new information is allowed to come forward and new learning can occur. EMDR therapy allows the dysfunctionally stored experience to be accessed, so that the innate processing systems in the brain can connect maladaptive information with more adaptive information and skills. In effect, EMDR therapy can be understood as an information processing model.

Phases 1 and 2: Preparing for Treatment and Trauma Processing

EMDR therapy targets the "root" of an issue regardless of the pathology the individual is experiencing. As postulated in the AIP model, all pathologies not organically based are derived from adverse or difficult life experiences. Take, for example, an individual whose parents divorced when he or she was 7 or 8 years old. That person may have had a perfectly loving family experience until the parents began arguing after the child went to bed. The child heard angry voices and connected the angry voices with events earlier in the day when one of the parents became short with the child about chores not being done. The child thinks, "They are arguing, because I did not clean my room," and the negative cognition (NC), "it's my fault," begins. The next day the parents sit the child down and share that they are planning to get a divorce. The parents are clear it has nothing to do with the child, but the child who was already feeling responsible for the argument walks away with the underlying belief that he or she caused his or her parent's divorce. This belief and the accompanying feelings of guilt and shame now resurface in the client's adult life whenever anything goes awry, be it during daily events or in relationships.

PHASE 1: HISTORY TAKING AND TREATMENT PLANNING

In preparing an ED client for treatment and trauma processing, we first want to determine what the overall therapeutic goal is. In EMDR therapy, we are seeking a comprehensive treatment plan that provides the best therapeutic outcome, while maintaining client stability as much as possible. Therefore, it is important to get a full history of the client, including the particulars of the development of the specific ED (anorexia nervosa [AN], BN, binge eating disorder [BED], etc.).

Although EMDR therapy is an appropriate therapeutic model for addressing the underlying issues of an ED as well as the issues that support an ED's continuance, it must be clear that, of all the EDs, anorexia is the most difficult one to treat. Furthermore, anorexia is the most life-threatening. Therefore, at the very start of treatment, the AN client needs to be medically stabilized and well on the way to weight restoration prior to beginning EMDR therapy. Malnutrition plays a strong interrupting factor in an individual's ability to process memories and information.

The history-gathering phase is the first phase of the eight-phase model of EMDR therapy and helps to identify appropriate targets for processing. Many clinicians use what is known as a "trauma timeline" or list of the major events in a person's life. Other clinicians are more adept and comfortable using a genogram. The clinician must also prioritize the symptoms to be addressed, some immediately (especially related to physical health), others later. Symptoms can range from restrictive behaviors to managing emotions with food. The history taking phase begins with the first client contact and ends with goals and a treatment plan.

In seeking a history of the ED, I find it helpful to ask some or all of the following questions:

How long have you had an issue with food/restricting/exercising/binging/purging?
When was the first time you remember engaging in ED behaviors?

How old were you with this first occurred?

How did the idea come to you to restrict/binge/purge/exercise?

What else was going on in your life when this first happened?

Has there ever been a time when you stopped for a while?

Have you ever been able to "interrupt" the ED? Such as get yourself to eat when you were actively restricting? Stop a binge? Not purge following a binge? If so, what was that like for you?

What thoughts do you have about yourself when you are actively restricting/binging/purging?

Does anyone know about the ED? If so, how did he or she find out? What was that like for you?

What do you think or believe people or family members think about you or about your ED?

How is the restricting/binging/purging/exercising helping you? How do you see it as harmful to you? What does it make you believe about yourself?

PHASE 2: PREPARATION

The second phase of EMDR therapy is what is called the preparation phase. During the preparation phase, the EMDR therapist prepares the client for processing targets the therapist and the client agree upon. A major component of preparing a client to do EMDR therapy involves stabilization and affect tolerance skills, as well as resources to support the client's ability to process earlier life events that may have contributed to the development of the ED. A list of client strengths can form the basis for creating such resources via resource development and installation (RDI; Korn & Leeds, 2002). RDI is an imagery-based skill that enhances stabilization and prepares the ED client for the eventual processing of difficult traumatic material (see end of this chapter for an RDI script; also see Chapter 8).

Given the complexity of EDs and trauma work, it is often the case that a client may require substantial preparation prior to trauma processing, particularly with regard to AN and BED. Affect regulation skills are inevitably needed to lay the groundwork prior to a client doing EMDR therapy. Skills, such as those found in dialectical behavioral therapy (DBT; Linehan, 2014) and other coping skills, can be very helpful in supporting the client in doing trauma work. Breathing techniques (box breathing and the three-part yoga breath) and a technique often referred to as "The Four Elements Exercise for Stress Management" (Shapiro, 2009) are likewise helpful. The therapist should keep in mind that these skills may need to be taught, or "front-loaded," in the history-gathering phase if the client has significant difficulties regulating.

A word about dissociation and EDs. Clients with EDs, not unlike other clients, often use dissociation as a coping mechanism in dealing with traumatic life events. The EDs themselves are dissociative by nature. Trauma processing requires that a client be able to think about the traumatic memory or disturbing event while staying in the present. The reader may want to refer to Chapters 15, 16, or 17 to support the work he or she is doing with EMDR therapy.

In the case example of "Belinda," I suggested we use EMDR to access the initial anxiety attack, the target, she had described and see if we could clear out what appeared to be the precipitating event. Belinda agreed. I prepared Belinda for EMDR therapy by teaching her the Safe Place technique (Shapiro, 2001), which enabled her to achieve self-soothing and internal state change when needed. This technique is sometimes called the Calm Place exercise when a client cannot relate to the word or concept of "safe." The exercise is commonly used by EMDR therapists in the preparation phase (Phase 2) to help the client get comfortable with the eye movements, the close proximity of the EMDR therapist, as well as strong affect that arises during reprocessing. This assures the client that he or she can comfortably change from a state of disturbance to a state of no, or very low, disturbance relatively quickly.

PHASES 3 TO 7: PROCESSING TRAUMATIC EVENTS

Once the client has been prepared, the therapist is ready to begin trauma processing with EMDR therapy, a procedure that encompasses Phases 3 to 7 of the EMDR eight-phase model. Phase 3 of EMDR therapy is known as the assessment phase in which an actual target memory for EMDR processing is evaluated and accessed.

In this phase, the client is asked to think about the event or memory that has been selected. Aspects of the memory are stimulated, specifically the image of the worst moment, the accompanying negative self-belief, feelings, and body sensations. The client is also asked what he or she would rather believe about himself or herself once the traumatic memory or event has been fully processed. The degree of disturbance is measured by a Subjective Unit of Disturbance Scale (SUDS) of 0 to 10. The desired positive belief is rated on a Validity of Cognition (VoC) Scale of 1 to 7.

Once the target memory has been assessed and accessed, Phase 4 begins: the desensitization phase. During the desensitization phase, the client, with the aid of the clinician, processes the target event to a more adaptive resolution. The client holds the memory or image in mind along with the accompanying negative self-belief, feelings, and body sensations while the therapist administers bilateral stimulation in the form of eye movements, bilateral tapping, or sounds. The therapist leads the client in a series of bilateral stimulations, periodically stopping to ask the client what he or she is aware of at that moment. On the basis of the client's responses and the clinical judgment of the therapist, the clinician guides the client toward resolution. The target memory is considered desensitized when a SUDS rating of zero is achieved and all channels of associated material have been desensitized. The client is further able to incorporate the experience into a larger life context. At this point, the validity of the positive cognition (PC) increases substantially. The PC may even change to a healthier or more adaptive statement than chosen earlier during the assessment, because of the impact of the trauma processing.

After the target has been fully processed from a high SUDS rating to a SUDS of zero, the target is considered desensitized. Occasionally, this rating may remain at what is known as an ecological SUDS of 1 or 2, meaning that the remaining disturbance is appropriate for the client's life situation. A desensitized target is then held in the client's awareness while at the same time recalling the PC. This is Phase 5, installation of the PC, the purpose of which is to test the validity of the positive belief in the presence of the target memory. This is often an amazing moment for the client who, for the first time, may hold the original disturbing event in mind, while simultaneously believing a positive statement, such as "it was not my fault." Juxtaposing the negative memory and the positive belief is one of the ways in which EMDR therapy makes sure that no traumatic stone has been left unturned.

The therapist then has the client do what is called a body scan (Phase 6) while holding in mind both the target memory and the positive self-cognition. This ensures complete processing of body-related disturbances. Closure (Phase 7) ends the session (be it complete or not) and a follow-up (Phase 8) takes place in subsequent sessions to evaluate the treatment effects, ensure complete processing, and decide upon treatment direction.

Returning to our case example with "Belinda," during Belinda's EMDR session, I asked her to think about the worst part of the day on which she remembered having had the anxiety attack. She stated the worst part was when she discovered the file was corrupt. Asking her to hold that image in mind, I then proceeded to ask her, "When you hold that incident in your mind, what does that make you believe about yourself now?" In response to that question, Belinda stated, "I'm irresponsible." I then asked what she would rather believe about herself; after a long moment, she stated, "It wasn't my fault the file was corrupt, I did the work." I continued on with the EMDR protocol and began eye movements.

Through processing, Belinda's memories of earlier times in her life where she felt irresponsible came up. In EMDR, we refer to these as channels of association, and it is this free associative aspect of EMDR that can be so effective. Belinda processed several early childhood memories in which she, the oldest daughter, was often responsible for her four younger siblings. She continued to process several events involving responsibility or her perceived responsibility. Ultimately, the initial disturbing event came to a complete resolution with a zero level of disturbance.

Belinda continued with EMDR therapy to target several other experiences in which she described feeling out of control or highly responsible, and during those sessions she began to report that her binging episodes had become less and less frequent. Belinda continued to check in with therapy, attending at greater and greater intervals for 6 months following her last EMDR session. She continued to report that she noticed when she wanted to binge, and that sometimes she would actually "overeat." However, she no longer felt the guilt and shame she once associated with binging and did not consider an occasional episode of overeating a binge.

In creating a comprehensive treatment plan for the ED client, the clinician needs to keep in mind that the overall goal is to target all of the originating event(s), the worst event(s), and the most recent event(s) associated with the underlying foundations for the ED. A full and complete cleanout of all associated targets will provide the best clearing of NCs considered to be at the root of the maladaptive thoughts, perceptions, and behaviors that lay the foundation for an ED.

PHASE 8: REEVALUATION

In the follow-up session and to ensure the past memory has been thoroughly addressed, the EMDR clinician will go back to the original target and "reevaluate" to ensure the target remains neutral or if something else, undetected earlier but related, has come up. This can be the result of the "onion" effect where earlier undetected layers that support the ED become apparent as the result of EMDR processing. The clinician will ask at the next session: "When you think about the original memory that we worked on last time, on a scale of zero to 10, how disturbing is it to you now?" The therapist also inquires about the status of the VoC: "And when you hold the memory and the positive belief (PC) in your awareness," how true does the PC feel on a scale of 1 to 7? If the target remains neutral or a zero, and if the VoC remains at a 7, the therapist will address the second part of what is known as EMDR therapy's three-pronged protocol. EMDR therapy is a comprehensive psychotherapy that not only addresses the past events and experiences that laid down the bases for the ED (the first of the three prongs) but also further addresses current events triggering the ED in the present-day life (the second of the three prongs). This is accomplished by asking if there are similar or related experiences that are currently triggering, and then proceeding to desensitize the current triggers before moving on to the third prong.

The EMDR therapist also addresses future potential challenges or triggering events with future template work to complete a comprehensive treatment plan. The future template is the third prong in the EMDR three-pronged protocol. In the future template work, the client is asked to imagine similar triggering events that might happen in the future while accessing resources (positive thoughts, feelings, and outcomes resulting from previous processing). The client is asked to run a "video" of himself or herself responding in new, healthy ways to future incidents and experiences that would have resulted earlier in ED thoughts and behaviors. Another avenue in the future prong would be to apply the standard EMDR protocol to what the client fears would be the worst possible outcome in a future challenge.

Research

The only research projects that I am aware of in using EMDR with EDs involve EMDR in the treatment of bulimia (Forester, 2009) and in the treatment of negative body image (Bloomgarden & Calogero, 2008). Although EMDR therapy is extremely well researched in the area of trauma and posttraumatic stress disorder (PTSD), it is not well researched in the area of ED treatment.

In Forester (2009), I describe my dissertation research using EMDR with a group of six volunteers diagnosed with bulimia. These volunteers, all diagnosed with BN, were administered the Trauma Symptom Inventory (TSI) and the ED Inventory 3 (EDI-3). One half of the group was administered the TSI and EDI-3 followed by 8 weeks of EMDR therapy that included a 1-hour history-gathering session, a 1-hour Safe Place/state change exercise, and six 90-minute EMDR sessions, focused on the volunteer's list of 10 worst experiences. The volunteers completed a second round of the TSI and EDI-3 followed by an 8-week period of no treatment and a final, third administration of the TSI and EDI-3. The second half of the group were administered the TSI and EDI-3 followed by 8 weeks on a wait-list. At the end of the 8 weeks, they were given a second administration of the TSI and EDI-3, a 1-hour history-gathering session, a 1-hour Safe Place state change exercise, and six 90-minute EMDR sessions, also focused on their list of 10 worst experiences. After only six 90-minute sessions using the standard EMDR protocol, three of the six women no longer qualified for the diagnosis of bulimia and two others were no longer binging and purging at the 8-week follow-up. Although the sample size was admittedly small, the effect of just six sessions of EMDR therapy was notable.

Bloomgarden and Calogero (2008) used EMDR in the treatment of negative body image along with standard residential eating disorder treatment (SRT) in a residential treatment facility. This study compared 86 women admitted to residential treatment for anorexia (27), bulimia (23), and Eating Disorder Not Otherwise Specified (EDNOS) (36) who were randomly assigned to two treatment conditions. Forty-three participants received SRT and 43 received SRT plus EMDR. The individuals were given the Body Image Memory Questionnaire (BIM), the Body Investment Scale (BIS), the Appearance Schemas Inventory (ASI), the Body Dissatisfaction subscale of the EDI-2 (EDI-BD), the Sociocultural Attitudes Toward Appearance Questionnaire—Revised (SATAQ-R), and other clinical outcome measures such as the Eating Attitudes Test-26 (EAT-26), the Beck Depression Inventory (BDI), and the Dissociative Experiences Scale (DES). Although several limitations of the study were noted, the evidence suggests that EMDR reduces negative body image memories.

Case Example of Bulimia: Barbara

I love to tell this story, and often do in my EMDR trainings. I had a client early in my therapy career, actually not long after I had received my initial EMDR training in 1994. My client was a 22-year-old female who had returned home to live with her parents after having a failed experience at college. She was unable to consistently make it to class and keep her grades up because of active bulimia. On returning home, and feeling like a failure, she began sleeping more, isolating, and was "giving in" to the binge–purge process between five and ten times a day. She came to therapy at her parents' urging, as they felt she had "given up" on growing up.

I spent several sessions establishing a good rapport, gathering history, teaching coping skills, and having her demonstrate her newly gained coping skills between sessions. I then recommended EMDR, and she agreed. I had scheduled a 90-minute session to do EMDR given this was her first EMDR session, and I wanted to allow plenty of time for processing. Barbara had shared several difficult incidents with her parents and described having been sexually abused by a relative prior to the age of 5. The abuser had been prosecuted. Barbara worked very hard during her EMDR session, focusing on her earliest memory of the abuse. What I was most struck with was how she behaved when she came back the following week.

After asking her how she felt after the EMDR session and what she noticed, my client stated that she felt fine and seemed to be *under*whelmed with the process. Sensing she was not particularly impressed, I decided to let it go and asked how her week went. The client shared that she had decided to go out to the local community college to see if she could talk with an advisor regarding taking a class or two to ease back into college. Once there, she was able to register for classes that were starting in a few days. She stated that while she was at the college, she ran into a friend from high school. While both of them were talking about feeling frustrated with living at home with their parents, they decided both of them would be interested in a roommate situation. Deciding she was going to need a job to pay rent with a roommate, she had put in several applications and was scheduled for an interview a few hours after our session.

When I asked the client about her bulimic episodes, she stated she had simply been too busy to binge and purge much this week and was not sure if she had even had an episode since our last appointment. I was literally shocked at how much movement had occurred in just 1 week and at how she seemed to just feel it was time to change. When I asked her if she thought the EMDR had helped, she shrugged her shoulders and said she was not sure, but she had decided it was just time for her to do things differently.

Barbara continued therapy for a while and made healthy strides toward independence. I saw her off and on again for several years. At times her bulimic thoughts would resurface, especially around major life transitions, such as when she was preparing to get married and following the birth of her first child, a common experience for individuals with EDs. Although she continued to have times in her life when she would turn to food to medicate her emotions, she never returned to bulimia.

Case Example of AN: Anna

"Anna," age 38, came into therapy seeking help with her marriage. She had been married for 8 years and had a 6-year-old daughter. She presented with obsessive tendencies, appeared highly anxious, and was obviously underweight. She appeared unable to sit still as she jiggled and flexed her legs and abdomen throughout the session. She seemed to be in constant motion even while sitting. During the history gathering, she disclosed she had been diagnosed with anorexia as a young teenager around the age of 12. She had been in three different treatment centers between the ages of 13 and 25 for stays of between 3 and 6 months at a time. The client reported she recently had begun losing weight again when she and her husband were experiencing marital stress.

It is not unusual for an ED client to reach an age and minimal weight where he or she cannot be "forced" into treatment, but clearly is not free of the ED. He or she is just healthy enough not to require intervention and yet not free of disordered eating, exercising behaviors, and ED ways of thinking. It is unknown how many individuals meet these criteria; however, it is not uncommon for an adult anorexic to maintain restrictive patterns of behavior without requiring hospitalization. Everyone around this individual may notice patterns of restriction. However, the individual does not become "serious enough" to require hospitalization and has matured to the age whereby, without medical necessity, he or she can refuse treatment.

In Anna's case, she stated she came into treatment because she and her husband were having marital issues. However, once in treatment, she disclosed her husband had threatened that should they separate, he would use her ED history, current low weight, and obsessive patterns of restrictive behaviors against her in a custody battle.

During the history-gathering phase of her treatment (Phase 1 of EMDR therapy), I learned that Anna was adopted at birth and had one adopted younger sibling. She described her parents as upper middle class and as "highly successful" and "driven" in their careers. She described a somewhat rigid upbringing with high expectations for success. Anna was clear she was not sure her parents "expected" as much perfection as she perceived. Anna stated that she was a high achiever in school; she feared disappointing her parents and participated in several extracurricular activities.

After sufficient history gathering and developing what is known as a trauma timeline, we began with stabilization techniques (Phase 2). Anna appeared to have high levels of anxiety and her attempts to self-regulate included engaging in ritualistic cleaning routines, exercise patterns, and restrictive eating. At the time our therapy began, she was eating the same meals for breakfast and dinner and never allowed herself to eat lunch, as that was perceived as a "waste of time." Her meals were minimal in caloric intake and consisted primarily of fruits and vegetables.

One of the experiences that Anna reported on her trauma timeline was an instance, when she was aged 5 or 6 years, in which she remembered being yelled at and punished for her younger sibling getting hurt while they were playing together. Anna tearfully described feeling completely responsible for her younger sibling getting hurt when a wagon she was pulling him in tipped over, causing him to fall out.

In EMDR therapy once an appropriate target is determined, the therapist assists the client in identifying the underlying belief that resulted at the time of the incident by asking a question such as "When you hold that original memory or incident in your mind, what does that make you believe about yourself now?" In response to that question, Anna stated, "There is something wrong with me; I am a bad person." When asked what she would rather believe about herself if this memory were processed to a healthy resolution, she stated, "I was just playing; I didn't mean to hurt him."

After processing the memory from a high level of disturbance, a 9 (on a scale of 0–10 with 10 being the highest disturbance she could think of) to a complete resolution (a 0), Anna looked surprised and amazed as she stated, "I was just a little kid!" She was, perhaps for the first time, experiencing self-forgiveness.

This was just one of many EMDR sessions conducted with Anna over the course of a little more than a year. Anna's marriage improved for a time, but ultimately terminated for reasons not related to her behaviors. The couple separated amicably with a balanced custody arrangement.

Anna returned to therapy after 8 years to deal with a career change that brought up old feelings of "not being good enough to keep," which we had processed years earlier. Although the new life adjustment triggered old feelings, I learned that, at the time of her return, she still remained an active individual who enjoyed her social relationships. She no longer limited her intake, could miss exercise routines, and could eat "normal foods" and meals without feelings of guilt or anxiety. She maintained an appropriate weight and could sit calmly and comfortably throughout sessions.

■ SCRIPTS

EMDR With ED: Eight Phases and Three Prongs (Past, Present, Future)—Forester, D.

Phase 1: History Taking—Gather history appropriate to your client including information about the development of the ED or disordered eating behavior. Ask for a trauma timeline and/or the 10 worst (triggers) and best (RDIs) things that the client has experienced. Always listen for NCs and underlying adverse life events. This leads to case formulation, goals, and treatment plan.

Phase 2: Preparation—Explain EMDR, test bilateral preferences, and be sure that the client can experience self-directed state change (safe/calm place) and can contain affect when needed.

Phase 3: Assessment–Target Selection
Image
Negative Cognition (NC)
Positive Cognition (PC)
Validity of Positive Cognition (VoC): 1 (false) to 7 (true)
Emotion: SUDS, 0 (least) to 10 (most)
Body Location of Disturbance

Phase 4: Desensitization (Bilateral Stimulation)

Phase 5: Installation of the Positive Cognition (PC)—Once the target has reached a SUDS of 0, check the PC's VoC. Once the PC's VoC is as high as it can possibly go, have the client hold the original target with the PC and do bilateral stimulations to "install."

Phase 6: Body Scan—Hold the original target with the PC and go from the top of the head to the bottom of the feet, scanning the body for any discomfort or "disagreement." If anything "sticks," target it with bilateral stimulation.

Phase 7: Closure—Remind of continued processing; keep a log of dreams/nightmares. Phase 8: reevaluation—At next session and periodically to end of treatment.

Phase 8: Reevaluation—During each session after EMDR (Phases 3–7), ask the following: "When you think about the original image or target, on a scale of zero to 10, how disturbing is it to you now?" If the target is neutral or a zero, begin the second of the three-pronged protocol. Ask if there are "any similar experiences or triggers in their current life?" Then desensitize the current triggers before moving on to the third prong, the future template.

Past–Present–Future

Apply the "three-pronged protocol"—clean out the past situations and circumstances that laid the foundation for the pathology. Next, review the current life situations that are triggering the ED thoughts, ideas, and behaviors. Finally, look to the future, using the future template to imagine future situations with adaptive, healthy reactions.

Resource Development Installation Protocol (Korn & Leeds, 2002; see references and Chapter 8).

BOX BREATHING/FOUR-SQUARE BREATHING/TACTICAL BREATHING/NAVY SEAL BREATHING

Regulating your breathing is a simple way to take your brain out of a state of anxiety or stress and into relaxation in just a few minutes. I often stand up with my clients and encourage them to practice along with me.

Step 1: Stand or sit up straight and encourage the client to follow along taking full deep breaths that go beyond the shallow breathing often associated with anxiety or fear states.
Step 2: Inhale to the count of 4 filling your lungs.
Step 3: Hold your breath to a count of 4.
Step 4: Exhale to a count of 4 emptying the lungs.
Step 5: Hold your lungs empty for a count of 4.
Step 6: Repeat the process three to four times as necessary to experience the full benefit.

THE THREE-PART YOGA BREATH/DIRGA PRANAYAMA/THREE-PART BREATH

This exercise can be done sitting, standing, or lying down when the clients are home. I typically teach this breath to clients along with box breathing and invite them to compare how they feel after each exercise.

Step 1: Get in a comfortable seated or standing position. It can be helpful, if the client is comfortable, to close the eyes for this exercise.
Step 2: Begin the inhale by first pulling the air all the way down into the belly, filling it like a water balloon.
Step 3: Still pulling in air, fill up the chest.
Step 4: Still on the inbreath, pull in even more air to fill all the way up to the collarbone.
Step 5: Hold for just a second.
Step 6: Begin the exhale by first letting go of the air at the top of the chest, then the rib cage portion of the chest, and finally the belly, pulling the navel back toward the spine.
Step 7: Repeat three to four times to practice. In most yoga classes, when this breath is taught, it is repeated eight to 10 times for the full benefit.

■ REFERENCES

Basic Yoga. Dirga pranayama. (n.d.). Retrieved from http://www.yogabasics.com/practice/dirga-pranayama

Bloomgarden, A., & Calogero, R. M. (2008). A randomized experimental test of the efficacy of EMDR treatment on negative body image in eating disorder inpatients. *Eating Disorders, 16,* 418–427. doi:10.1080/10640260802370598

Divine, M. (2016, May 4). The breathing technique a Navy SEAL uses to stay calm and focused. Retrieved from http://time.com/4316151/breathing-technique-navy-seal-calm-focused

Forester, D. (2009). EMDR as a treatment for bulimia nervosa in a clinical private practice setting. In R. Shapiro (Ed.), *EMDR solutions II: For depression, eating disorders, performance and more* (pp. 151–164). New York, NY: W. W. Norton.

Korn, D. L., & Leeds, A. M. (2002). Preliminary evidence of efficacy for EMDR resource development and installation in the stabilization phase of treatment of complex posttraumatic stress disorder. *Journal of Clinical Psychology, 58*(12), 1465–1487. doi:10.1002/jclp.10099

Linehan, M. M. (2014). *DBT® Skills training handouts and worksheets* (2nd ed.). New York, NY: Guilford Press.

Navy Medicine. (n.d.). Combat tactical breathing. Retrieved from http://www.med.navy.mil/sites/nmcphc/Documents/health-promotion-wellness/psychological-emotional-wellbeing/Combat-Tactical-Breathing.pdf

Ray, L. (2017, August 14). Box breathing. Retrieved from https://www.livestrong.com/article/74944-box-breathing-technique

Shapiro, E. (2009). Four elements exercise for stress management. In M. Luber (Ed.), *Eye movement desensitization and reprocessing (EMDR) scripted protocols: Basics and special situations* (pp. 73–79). New York, NY: Springer Publishing.

Shapiro, F. (2001). *Eye movement desensitization and reprocessing (EMDR): Basic principles, protocols, and procedures* (2nd ed.). New York, NY: Guilford Press.

Sweet Escape Yoga. (n.d.). Simple stress relief w/square breathing. Retrieved from http://www.sweetescapeyoga.com/simple-stress-relief-wsquare-breathing

Yoga Outlet. (n.d.). How to practice three-part breath in yoga. Retrieved from https://www.yogaoutlet.com/guides/how-to-practice-three-part-breath-in-yoga

CHAPTER 14

Trauma-Focused Cognitive Behavioral Therapy and Eating Disorders

Irene Rovira

■ INTRODUCTION

"First do no *more* harm" is the ethical code by which trauma therapists practice. Fulfilling this duty requires careful thought and adhering to evidence-based therapy. Although we know no treatment is guaranteed to work for everyone, we do know that cognitive behavioral therapy (CBT) has proven to be the most well-supported approach for eating disorders (EDs) in the empirical research (Agras et al., 1992; Fairburn, 1981; Fairburn, 1985; Fairburn & Cooper, 1989; Fairburn, Marcus, & Wilson, 1993; Leitenberg et al., 1994; Mitchell et al., 1990).

It is considered the first-line "treatment of choice" for individuals diagnosed with bulimia nervosa (BN; Fairburn, Agras, & Wilson, 1992; Garner, Vitousek, & Pike, 1997) and recommended for the treatment of anorexia nervosa, atypical EDs, and binge eating disorders (BEDs; Fairburn, Cooper, & Shafran, 2003; Garner et al., 1997; Marcus, 1997). Furthermore, multiple studies have demonstrated the efficacy of using CBT for post-traumatic stress disorder (PTSD) and trauma symptoms (Barlow, 2002; Cloitre, Cohen, & Koenen, 2006; Foa, Hembree, & Rothbaum, 2007; Foa, Rothbaum, & Furr, 2003; Rauch & Foa, 2006; Richard & Lauterbach, 2007). Many authors suggest using CBT with abuse survivors (Briere, 1992; Frank et al., 1988), as well as eating-disordered clients (Garner et al., 1997; Wilson, Fairburn, & Agras, 1997), because the educational and collaborative nature of CBT can empower the client as an "equal partner" and decrease passivity (Fallon & Wonderlich, 1997).

■ CAUSES OF EATING DISORDERS

An ED is a multicausal disorder with various factors contributing to its development and maintenance, such as genetics, environmental triggers, and personality contributions. Using Christopher Fairburn's model for understanding EDs, low self-esteem is at the core of an ED and serves as the key to unlocking the genetic, environmental, interpersonal, social/cultural, and personality factors of an ED.

Several factors can contribute to low self-esteem including a history of childhood trauma. Children who experience trauma may implement coping mechanisms in an attempt to return to "normal," but these methods may be unhealthy and unsustainable (Cicchetti & Cohen, 1995; Konanur, Muller, Cinamon, Thornback, & Zorzella, 2015). For example, patients with trauma may engage in self-blame for their experiences of abuse (Fallon & Wonderlich, 1997) and continue to believe they were to blame for childhood physical and sexual abuse even into adulthood. Some believe they must have something inherently wrong with them to have had the misfortune of experiencing trauma. The mind attempts to make sense out of senseless acts and, especially, vulnerable and egocentric young minds strive to find an explanation for trauma; this may result in looking to themselves to blame. This unfortunate and misguided attempt to understand traumatic experiences interferes with a person's ability to believe himself or herself to be worthy of respect and happiness despite life's events. The lack of control he or she had throughout the traumatic events may interfere with the person's ability to see himself or herself as efficacious in coping with life's problems. Given that self-esteem is often defined as one's ability to see oneself as worthy of respect and happiness, as well as being efficacious in dealing with painful experience, it becomes clear that trauma can interfere with the development of healthy self-esteem.

Other factors may also contribute to poor self-esteem, for example, genetic traits, familial factors such as overly critical parenting styles, our culture's obsession with appearance and status, teasing/bullying, and personality vulnerabilities, such as having a negative or perfectionistic mindset, low frustration tolerance, obsessiveness, and/or overly rigid tendencies.

■ LEVELS OF NEGATIVE COGNITIONS

Coupled with trauma histories, these factors can form strong negative core beliefs about oneself as "unworthy" or "powerless" (low self-esteem). Core beliefs or "schemas" are filters or "road maps" by which we understand ourselves, others, and the world. For instance, a child who has been mistreated by an adult may form a neural template that signals to the child to be fearful of all adults (Perry, 2009). Traumatic experiences can negatively impact the development of core beliefs about ourselves (i.e., "I am bad"), others (i.e., "People are untrustworthy"), or the world at large (i.e., "The world is unsafe"). Although these responses may serve a protective role in an abusive environment, they are ineffective if rigidly applied across all settings (McCrory et al., 2011). Negative core beliefs can simultaneously render and be reinforced by negative and maladaptive rules/assumptions, such as "If I lose/gain enough weight, people will find me sexually unattractive, and I'll be safer." Finally, these negative assumptions can both lead to and be maintained by negative automatic thoughts such as "I must lose weight at all costs." These three different levels of negative cognitions inevitably influence the person's emotional (e.g., depression) and behavioral (e.g., ED symptom) responses.

Negative automatic thoughts are the most directly influential level of cognition on behaviors and feelings. It is the level of thinking that is the most accessible to an individual and can usually be the most easily monitored by the patient when prompted. Rules and assumptions are the second level of cognition that come from core beliefs and lead to automatic thoughts. Core beliefs are the third level of cognitions that can be identified with increased self-awareness regarding the global views one has of oneself and the world. Please refer to the work of Aaron and Judith Beck for a more detailed explanation (Beck, 1995).

An important note about all levels of thinking, including well-established, ingrained negative core beliefs, is that they all are learned. Therefore, they can be relearned with sufficient time and practice. Some patients worry they are doomed to have negative thinking, but it simply is not the case. It can be overwhelming for some, as they imagine the task of overhauling years, may be even decades, worth of faulty thinking. The good news is that there is a plan of action set forth by CBT to help an individual organize and tackle the endeavor of changing one's mindset. More of this is given in the section "CBT Stage 2: Cognitive Modification."

■ THE CBT APPROACH

CBT for EDs is approximately 20 sessions for treating BN or BED (Wilson et al., 1997), whereas treatment for anorexia nervosa (AN) can require a much longer treatment, typically lasting 1 to 2 years (Garner et al., 1997). Addressing trauma work will add to the number of sessions. CBT for EDs and for trauma can be done concurrently or sequentially. Deciding on the format can be done on the basis of clinical presentation and in collaboration with the client.

The main tenet in CBT is that thoughts, feelings, and behaviors are all interrelated. Most people understand that thoughts can influence our emotions. For instance, thinking "I'm a loser" will likely result in sad/depressed feelings. Most people can also understand how feelings influence our behavior. For example, feeling depressed can lead to behavior such as avoiding work and staying in bed all day. What may not be as obvious is the way our behavior influences our thinking. For instance, "Jane" staying in bed all day and avoiding work may likely result in negative thinking, such as "I'm terrible for having stayed in bed all day; I *am* a loser and a screw up." These thoughts can lead to feelings of guilt and even more sadness or depressed feelings resulting in a debilitating negative cycle.

Thoughts, feelings, and behaviors influence one another, so changing one will influence a change in the others. It is almost impossible to change your feelings directly simply by willing ourselves to do so. Instead, when our emotions change, it is likely because either our thinking or behavior has changed in some way first. Enter CBT. Within this treatment approach, the first step targets changing behavior rather than changing thinking, because changing behavior will lead to quicker results, which is crucial when considering life-threatening illnesses and behaviors such as ED. In the example given previously, if Jane had behaved differently (i.e., gone to work despite her feelings), she may have had experiences at work that could have led to more realistic or positive thinking (e.g., "I felt terrible this morning, but at least I got through today," or "It was nice of Mary to invite me out to lunch"). At the very least, she would not have had more reason to think and feel negatively about herself at the end of the day for avoiding work.

Cognitive change is a crucial second step to allow any behavioral changes made to have meaningful and long-lasting success. Jane can continue to force herself to go to work every day with the use of various behavioral strategies, but without addressing her faulty assumption that she is a "loser," she may find that her dysthymia maintains itself for several years. This strain could risk her success in maintaining good work attendance, and Jane may eventually find herself avoiding work once again. Not addressing maladaptive cognitions can also lead to symptom substitution. Although Jane may find herself maintaining good work attendance, she might develop a drinking problem after work as a way to escape her self-loathing.

Symptom substitution is a term used to describe the substituting of one symptom for another. People with EDs, for example, may block all ED symptoms, but then develop other self-injurious behaviors or substance abuse problems instead. In such instances, these clients have yet to properly address the cognitive dysfunction that maintains their illness. A successful treatment approach will entail addressing and changing maladaptive cognitions in addition to addressing and changing maladaptive behaviors.

CBT Stage 1: Behavior Modification

The first stage of trauma-informed CBT for EDs involves the critical first step of nutritional and symptom stabilization. It is imperative for both the therapist and the client to fully understand that no meaningful psychological assessment can occur without this critical first stage. Yet, it is not uncommon for patients to minimize the need to accomplish the goal of nutritional stabilization. They often wish to get "better" or "healthy" while maintaining ED symptoms as a way of avoiding "getting fat." Helping the client understand that recovery and ED are mutually exclusive and aiding them in setting realistic goals to stabilize their nutrition is imperative.

Patients' stated goals may not appear to be related to reducing ED symptoms at first glance. These goals may resemble those one would expect from any other outpatient client, such as reducing depression or anxiety, improving social relationships, or addressing PTSD symptoms, such as nightmares or flashbacks. Nevertheless, the need to stabilize ED symptoms as primary remains the same. Highlighting the positive impact ED stabilization would have on these stated goals will likely be useful to the task of setting treatment goals and increasing engagement. Being versed in the strategies used in motivational interviewing (Miller & Rollnick, 2013) can be a wonderful complement to CBT work. Engaging in specific techniques and interview questions that increase the patient's motivation for change can help grease the wheels of behavioral goals.

Emphasis on explaining the prerequisite of stabilization to the client and increasing his or her motivation for symptom stabilization is key. ED symptoms, including starvation, can mimic or exacerbate symptoms of depression and anxiety. When an individual stabilizes ED symptoms, some symptoms of depression, anxiety, and irritability may be neutralized. The remaining symptoms can then be addressed more directly in the later stages of CBT. Furthermore, "Do no more harm" means that a clinician must help clients identify and practice adaptive coping skills to help them deal with the difficult work that lies ahead. Jumping into trauma-laden material involving storytelling and narrative rewriting, without existing positive coping skills in the client's behavioral repertoire, is likely to backfire. Premature trauma processing may well lead the client into relying once again on his or her existing maladaptive coping mechanisms (i.e., ED symptoms, self-injury, substance abuse, etc.) and/or increased PTSD symptoms.

In addition to coping skills, providing the client with education about CBT; the relationship between EDs, trauma, and mood regulation; and the importance of establishing adaptive coping skills cannot be emphasized enough. Many clients may have a misunderstanding about the breadth and depth of the work involved. They may think "trauma work" starts when they tell their narrative of the trauma events they experienced. However, a CBT therapist knows trauma work starts with the behavior modification stage. The client must understand this as well, or else the therapist risks damaging the therapeutic alliance ("you're not letting me do trauma work"). There is also the danger of the clinician drifting away from the CBT protocol out of fear of losing the client or other "therapist interfering behaviors" (Waller, 2009), which ultimately amounts to providing a watered-down version of CBT or abandoning it all together. This scenario not only increases the likelihood that treatment will fail (Waller, 2009) but also may result in the erosion of therapeutic alliance if the patient does not experience improvement.

By way of summary, the first step of symptom stabilization involves education, engagement, increasing motivation, skills development, and behavioral modification strategies. The use of a metaphor can be helpful in emphasizing the importance of this stage to the client. Let us say the client was building a home. The first order of business would be to set the foundation. It is a crucial step, albeit not a glamorous part of the larger project. It is much more interesting to pick out new gadgets, hardwood flooring, or paint for the new home. However, would the client buy a home that had a sinking foundation despite all the latest updates in the kitchen? Even if Stage 1 can be somewhat monotonous at times, rushing through this stage is counterproductive.

With respect to teaching clients about CBT, one must teach clients about the relationship between thoughts, feelings, and behaviors. Most people easily understand that thoughts impact feelings (e.g., thinking "I am a fat pig" will result in sad or anxious feelings). People also seem to easily understand that feelings impact behavior, for example, feeling anxious about your body can lead to extreme dieting or skipping meals. Clinicians need to further emphasize the impact that behaviors have on our thinking. When a person engages in restrictive eating habits or isolates, turning down dinner invitations with friends, it will reinforce and/or help develop negative thinking, such as "I *am* too fat to eat or be seen eating," which can lead to feeling even more anxiety and generating the vicious cycle in which many clients find themselves trapped. Because individuals cannot change their feelings (e.g., body image anxiety) simply by willing it to be so, they must change one, or both, of the other factors (thinking and behavior) within the framework to ultimately modify and manage difficult emotions. Changing one's behavior is an easier (not easy) step in comparison to changing one's thinking patterns; therefore, behavior modification becomes the focus in the initial stage of CBT.

Given the health risks of EDs (see Chapter 6), changing behavior quickly is a crucial need. In addition, engaging in ED symptoms ultimately reinforces low self-esteem. Changing behavior to help the patient manage symptoms is within his or her physical capacity (e.g., one could eat dinner with one's friends), and success in this area can help build confidence for other changes. Behavioral change goes a long way in preventing an increase in the preexisting low self-esteem and supports the greater likelihood of treatment success. CBT is a highly collaborative treatment approach where the therapist and the client must work hand in hand. Despite a laughable lack of athleticism in my life, I find that a well-placed sports analogy can work well to explain, and motivate a client toward, the "heavy lifting" required in the therapy work ahead. The therapist plays the part of the "coach," whereas the client is the "player." Just like a coach, the therapist gives instruction, provides feedback, devises different "plays" to practice, and offers support and encouragement. The client or "player" is the one actually running on the field! The client, very much like an athlete, must practice for countless hours if he or she hopes to develop the necessary skills to play the sport well. Likewise, for a client who is hoping to develop the necessary skills to manage the ED and work through his or her trauma, this means practicing through therapeutic "homework."

Homework is what the patient is expected to do between therapy sessions that will develop and nurture the cognitive behavioral and emotional regulation skills necessary for recovery. It can take the form of a worksheet, journaling assignment, and behavioral or interpersonal experiment as some examples. The therapist assigns a daily homework assignment at each session. It is very important for clients to engage in their treatment through homework and through self-monitoring. If the client resists doing homework, I would refer the reader to some great tips outlined in the Fairburn (2008) manual.

Coping skills training and review are embedded in the first session all the way through to the last. Clients come to therapy to feel better. Being able to offer them a coping skill at the first session can go a long way in building rapport and therapeutic alliance, because the client will view the therapist as helpful from the start. Some commonly used coping skills include, but are not limited to, the following: journaling; self-monitoring of thoughts, feelings, and emotions; competitive cognitive or motor behaviors (engaging in a cognitive or motor activity, because it cannot occur simultaneously with a symptom targeted to be reduced/eliminated); environmental engineering (arranging your surroundings to facilitate change such as moving your living room couch in such a way that it is not in direct view of the fridge for a client with BED who might believe that "the food is calling their name"); stimulus control (identifying and planning for external, internal, and social triggers that often lead to symptom behaviors); behavior chain analysis (identifying factors that led to recent symptom behaviors and planning how to manage differently next time); distraction; delaying (pushing urges off for a prescribed amount of time); positive/negative reinforcement scheduling (rewards for change efforts); behavioral contracting; relaxation (diaphragmatic breathing, progressive muscle relaxation, imagery of safe/calm space); monitoring pleasurable activities (requires identifying and participating in positive and predicted pleasurable events); grounding (mindfulness, staying "present"); containment ("putting away" difficult cognitive or emotional material usually in a ritualistic, symbolic, or physical manner until the next therapy session); and rewriting nightmares (rewriting the ending of reoccurring nightmares). There is no "set" or "order" as to which coping skills your client needs to follow. Rather, a knowledgeable CBT therapist will help guide the client in building a "toolbox" that works best for the client in various circumstances.

Another focus of trauma work in Stage 1 is to educate and help the patient understand the impact of trauma on ED and body image development and maintenance. For instance, in one case example, the patient noted that her childhood sexual abuse had directly impacted her poor body image (perpetrator had made disparaging remarks about her "fat body" while raping her), which subsequently impacted the development of restricting, bingeing, and purging to control her weight. Another adult client still lived with her perpetrator who would make sexualized comments to her and touch her, even if just in passing, when she gained weight and looked more "female." This fueled her desire to remain emaciated, and her suicidality fueled her desire to "disappear." Yet another client reported outrage toward her abuser and felt "dirty." Her purging symptoms functioned to give her a sense of violent release of "dirty," and a "clean" feeling after self-induced vomiting.

Education at this stage may also involve helping the client understand the impact of trauma on emotional regulation, and, ultimately, on maintaining ED behaviors. This occurs when clients use ED symptoms, such as bingeing and purging, to dissociate or distract from unpleasant emotions or traumatic memories. Starvation can help reduce sexual feelings or fears associated with sexual body development. ED symptoms can help patients numb or escape dysregulated emotions (a type of self-medication, albeit maladaptive and dysfunctional).

Exploring the impact of trauma on interpersonal relationships is yet another direction and goal for Stage 1 CBT. For example, one client I worked with several years ago came to realize her tendency to attach too quickly in dating relationships. This seemed to be an interpersonal reaction to past trauma, where she learned to appease her perpetrator as a form of survival. This survival tactic was recreated in dating relationships with poor boundaries, promiscuity, and codependency. It is also not uncommon for clients to have an opposite reaction in which they have a hard time attaching to anyone and "put up walls" to avoid emotional or physical intimacy and any potential for betrayal or future abuse. Identifying and targeting these interpersonal reactions through interpersonal experiments, problem solving, discussion, and education can help clients find or deepen meaningful attachments and relationships.

In vivo or imagined exposure of traumatic material is a hallmark for trauma-focused CBT (Cohen, Mannarino, & Deblinger, 2006; Ehlers & Clark, 2000). When the patient presents with an active ED, it is my experience that exposure to proper meal intake and tolerating fullness is the best first step in the series of exposure work within the CBT model. The most thoroughly studied expansion of CBT for EDs involves using exposure with response prevention for self-induced vomiting (Rosen & Leitenberg, 1985; Wilson et al., 1997). As stated earlier, nutritional stabilization is the critical first step that should not be overlooked because of the potential for medical complications. The patient is assisted in tolerating fullness after completing a meal with coaching, planning, and problem solving. A client, for example, can use relaxation training to assist him or her in progressing through a hierarchy of increasingly higher anxiety-provoking stimuli using systematic desensitization (Cash, 1991; Giles, 1988). Another example would be the use of positive coping statements, such as "Food is my medicine to heal from past hurts. It can no longer hurt me if I take control of my eating."

As the patient progresses with greater symptom management and meal tolerance, additional exposure work around traumatic material or memories can take place. This can be especially important to help the patient manage PTSD symptoms, such as flashbacks or intrusive memories, that are interfering with life. I have asked clients to generate a list of memories that can be used for the exposure segment of the CBT work. This can include the first memory, last memory, worst memory, most intrusive memory, or some other memory with special significance (events around holidays, birthdays, or anniversaries). Giving patients a choice can be helpful in their sense of control and mastery over the treatment plan as well.

The patient is typically prepared prior to exposure work by building coping skills, such as containment, grounding, or relaxation training. These help to tolerate the postsession reactions and increase the likelihood of continued ED management. An example of containment would be to have the patient at the end of the session symbolically "send" the exposure memory on a rocket ship to outer space through the use of imagery where it would remain until the next session. Another example would be to write the memory "subject line" on a piece of paper, and fold and place it into a physical containment box, not to be opened again until the next therapy session. This may help the client "put away" memories to maintain stabilization throughout the week until the next therapy session.

Before moving on from Stage 1, it is important for the therapist to "check in" with his or her client about the client's current level of motivation. Once the client has been engaging in behavioral modification and has been increasingly able to reduce and manage symptoms, some clients may find themselves struggling to maintain these successes because of the "unmasking" of certain emotions or painful memories or thoughts. It may be tempting for them to resort to old coping mechanisms to escape from or numb disturbances. It is important for this reason for the therapist to reassess the client's motivation before moving away from the intensity of behavioral modification in Stage 1. Strong urges to return to ED symptoms or unmanaged PTSD symptoms should be addressed before adding the next level of treatment, cognitive modification.

CBT Stage 2: Cognitive Modification

The second stage of CBT is primarily focused on cognitive modification. Of note, behavioral modification strategies will continue to be reinforced and problem solved as needed throughout Stage 2. However, in the second stage, the addition of cognitive restructuring is the main objective. In this stage, it is useful for the client to understand that additional difficulties, such as body image, trauma, and interpersonal difficulties, may be incorporated into and individualize their treatment plan. These problem areas may have been contributing factors to the development or maintenance of the ED, or the result of ED behaviors, or may be additional issues that impede the client's mental health and recovery.

In Stage 2 CBT, identification and modification of negative automatic thoughts, faulty assumptions, and negative core beliefs are the main agenda. Educating patients about cognitive distortions or "errors" is an important step in helping patients understand how negative or distorted thinking maintains maladaptive behaviors and emotional distress. Ultimately, the goal is for the client to identify and modify negative thinking at each level of cognition to reduce distress and facilitate the use of adaptive behavioral responses. A word of caution here may be useful to avoid overemphasizing the impact of irrational thinking on mood for patients with a history of trauma who may become demoralized in the event they come to believe that they are "irrational" to feel the way they do. Instead, help the clients see how their basic assumptions (e.g., "I am safe") were destroyed, leaving them vulnerable, scared, and ashamed (Fallon & Wonderlich, 1997).

FIRST LEVEL OF COGNITION

A therapist usually has to teach clients what automatic thoughts are and how to identify them. Automatic thoughts are spontaneous, can be one word or a longer phrase or sentence, and are almost always believed. They are learned and, therefore, changeable! For instance, some clients may report that on seeing a full meal served to them, their automatic thoughts may include, "I'm going to gain 10 pounds if I eat that!" Or, after eating a brownie, they may think, "I better get rid of it or I'll get fat." These negative automatic thoughts are exaggerations that jump to conclusions and are dichotomous in nature. The thoughts can be directly linked to negative and inappropriate feelings of guilt surrounding food, and, therefore, can lead to maladaptive behaviors, such as restricting food intake or self-induced vomiting.

SECOND LEVEL OF COGNITION

Faulty assumptions made by an individual, such as "I'll never be loved if I am fat" or "I'm good if I can control my eating (or weight/shape)," can be the "behind the scenes" drivers to negative automatic thoughts like the ones earlier. A good clue that this level of cognition may be at play is the presence of "if-then" statements, especially those that are related to body image and the need to control weight, shape, or eating. Trauma may impact these assumptions in the form of rules, such as "If I disappear, no one can hurt me again," which is an example of how the ED serves the perceived function as a protector from future trauma.

THIRD LEVEL OF COGNITION

Core beliefs or "schemas" comprise the most deep-rooted level of cognition, are most likely developed over a long period of time, and may have been significantly impacted by trauma. Beliefs such as "The world is unsafe" and "I am powerless" can develop after experiencing trauma. These beliefs are not merely passing ideas, but rather the filter through which the individual understands his or her world and himself or herself in everyday contexts. For instance, if a rape survivor believes he or she is powerless or helpless, he or she may mistakenly believe that "disappearing" (emaciation) is the way to get control over the future by reducing sex appeal. In turn, eating a nutritious and substantive dinner becomes a threat, resulting in fear and food restriction.

Trauma survivors have unrelenting and pervasive negative belief systems or core beliefs often involving themes of guilt, unworthiness, powerlessness, helplessness, hopelessness, and unlovability (Fallon & Coffman, 1991; Fallon & Wonderlich, 1997). It is believed that if these core beliefs are not addressed and challenged to give way to more adaptive belief systems, only superficial changes will be made and relapse often occurs (Fallon & Wonderlich, 1997). A suggestion made by Fallon and Wonderlich (1997) to identify a trauma survivor's core beliefs includes having the client complete the following sentence stems:

1. I deserved the abuse because …
2. He or she could not help it because …
3. I should have stopped it because …
4. He or she did it because …

Common CBT interventions such as logging thoughts and feelings related to ED can feel intrusive to the client. If, however, the therapist exhibits a willingness to go at the patient's pace, it may help the patient formulate new schemas about relationships and ultimately ease recovery from the ED (Fallon & Wonderlich, 1997).

IDENTIFYING AND MODIFYING NEGATIVE THINKING

Cognitive distortions are common to us all. We all make them from time to time. "My folks are going to kill me for denting the car" is an error of catastrophizing. Most of the time, they are fleeting and not literally meant. However, when applied in an overly rigid and frequent manner, these distortions begin to negatively impact our emotions and can trigger maladaptive behaviors. There are many cognitive distortions, but most common ones are the following: all or nothing (dichotomous) thinking, overgeneralizations, jumping to conclusions, "should" statements, catastrophizing, discounting the positive, personalization, and mislabeling. Another common cognitive error is the information processing distortion. This is where we hold a certain belief and attend to only evidence that supports our belief and ignore or discount evidence that does not support our already established belief.

Ways to challenge distortions at any level of cognition include the following: weighing the evidence for/against the belief, identifying more realistic statements of fact, talking to yourself in a compassionate way as you would a friend, asking yourself helpful questions, such as "Will this be important 10 years from now?" and identifying shades of gray. These strategies for challenging negative distortions can work at all three levels of cognition. It is recommended, however, to begin challenging negative, automatic thoughts first. These are not easy to change, but easier than the other two levels of cognitions, which get progressively harder to challenge, given their increased entrenchment in the person's mind. Once the person has increased mastery over his or her ability to change his or her negative thinking at one level, the therapist guides the client in identifying and modifying thinking at the next level. Cognitive disputation continues until the client has learned to reframe and dispute old core beliefs, and has started to develop more realistic ones.

Cognitive modification related to ED, body image, self-esteem, trauma, and interpersonal problems (to name a few clinical target areas) can be addressed in Stage 2. In one case example, a patient who had experienced sexual abuse by her biological father believed she was "dirty and unworthy" as a result of abuse by someone who had been charged to love and protect her. She believed, "If my own father could do that to me, it must be because I'm no good. Otherwise he would not have done it." Sadly the basic assumption that "All parents treat their children well" rendered her as the exception to the rule and she explained her experience through the cognitive error "He did it because I'm damaged." Rather than believing something was wrong with her father, she internalized the blame instead. We worked for several weeks on this negative thinking by providing education of child development of egocentric reasoning, review of distortions and their impact on her ED and self-esteem, and, eventually, on generating disputations for faulty assumptions and thinking. She ultimately could report with more confidence that "My father was sick, and it's unrealistic to expect a small child to take responsibility for an adult's actions."

A clinician must be particularly sensitive and responsive to a patient while conducting cognitive modification of negative thinking related to trauma (Fallon & Wonderlich, 1997). It is a delicate balance between validating the patient's emotions and simultaneously and gently disputing distorted cognitions. For instance, if a patient were to make a "should" statement distortion, such as "I should not have disclosed the abuse; my family was never the same afterwards. I tore my family apart forever," and if a clinician were to rush into disputing this distortion with facts on child abuse, weighing evidence for/against disclosing, or messages of hope for reconciliation, that clinician runs the risk of alienating the patient and potentially recreating an invalidating experience.

Instead, it may be more effective to validate the patient's sadness for the family's disruption and the patient's pain in seeing how the abuse caused pain to other family members, too. After validating the patient's emotions, one can then gently dispute the irrational thinking. Here is how such a situation might be addressed: "I hear how sad it makes you to think of the pain it caused your family to know about what your father did. It is sad, painful, and something you and your family had to mourn on many levels, I would imagine. At the same time, the shame you are experiencing over disclosing the truth is an added layer I hope to help you with a bit better. May I offer you the chance to use one of the strategies we have studied in our sessions to see if it can apply in this situation? Perhaps it may be somewhat helpful."

This middle stage of CBT trauma work assists clients in redefining the trauma, shifting self and world views to a more realistic perspective, and working with trauma narratives as a way to accomplish this task. This type of work can be very healing and can involve writing and rewriting the meaning (or automatic thoughts surrounding the traumatic experiences) of the trauma. Writing the narrative of traumatic events is a type of exposure activity that may have been introduced at the end of Stage 1 to help manage PTSD symptoms. When narrative work continues throughout sessions, the gradual reexposure and ongoing desensitization can lead to the person integrating the event into the totality of his or her life rather than having the event remain dominant (Cohen et al., 2006). This can be seen by the length of the narrative told by the client getting shorter over sessions (Westerman, Cobham, & McDermott, 2016), a process called compression, that facilitates desensitization (Foa, Molnar, & Cashman, 1995).

In Stage 2, negative thoughts and faulty belief systems that accompanied the trauma may change into more realistic thoughts and/or a more adaptive belief system as the event continues to be integrated into the person's understanding of his or her life and experiences. An example of this may be that the patient goes from seeing himself or herself as a "victim" of abuse to a "survivor" of abuse. Learning to see himself or herself as a "survivor" may help him or her find the positive in his or her life. In one case example, the client who had been abused by her biological father eventually learned to see herself as resilient and as an advocate for others (she was even studying to be a social worker). She found purpose through her adversity, and this seemed to give her some peace. For more detailed information about trauma-focused CBT, I refer the reader to Fallon and Wonderlich (1997); Foa et al. (2007); Foa, Rothbaum, Riggs, and Murdock (1991); Resick (2001); Resick and Schnicke (1992); and Williams and Poijula (2016).

CBT STAGE 3: RELAPSE PREVENTION

When an individual has mastered symptom control, modified old negative automatic thinking and assumptions, and has developed realistic and positive core beliefs, the individual can move on to Stage 3 of CBT. The focus at this stage of treatment is relapse prevention and maintenance. The work turns toward how to assist the client in maintaining current gains and decreasing the likelihood of future relapse by reviewing common pitfalls. These pitfalls include, but, of course, are not limited to, handling body image and trauma concerns that may arise in future intimate relationships or pregnancies, or during various life transitions, such as moving into a new job or college. In other words, any kind of life stressor can trigger relapse.

Knowing warning signs ahead of time can keep clients from relapsing. Therefore, developing a wellness plan for maintaining recovery is an invaluable last step in CBT.

Recidivism is a common problem for the ED population, so careful consideration to minimize the likelihood of relapse is worth the effort. We know that many will relapse. However, following an evidence-based CBT treatment plan can and does help many achieve and maintain success with recovery on their first attempt. Others may need to return to treatment several times before reaching success, whereas others continue to struggle chronically. Regardless, it is helpful to remember: "You were born with the ability to change someone's life. Don't waste it" (author unknown).

■ REFERENCES

Agras, W. S., Rossiter, E. M., Arnow, B., Schneider, J. A., Telch, C. F., Raeburn, S. D., … Koran, L. M. (1992). Pharmacologic and cognitive-behavioral treatment for bulimia nervosa: A controlled comparison. *American Journal of Psychiatry, 149*, 82–87 doi:10.1176/ajp.149.1.82

Barlow, D. H. (2002). *Anxiety and its disorders: The nature and treatment of anxiety and panic.* New York, NY: Guilford Press.

Beck, J. S. (1995). *Cognitive therapy: Basics and beyond.* New York, NY: Guilford Press.

Briere, J. (1992). *Child abuse trauma. Theory and treatment of the lasting effects.* Newbury Park, CA: Sage.

Cash, T. F. (1991). *Body image therapy: A program for self-directed change.* New York, NY: Guilford Press.

Cicchetti, D., & Cohen, D. J. (1995). Perspectives on developmental psychopathology. In D. Cicchetti & D. J. Cohen (Eds.), *Developmental psychopathology: Theory and methods* (Vol. 1, pp. 3–20). New York, NY: Wiley.

Cloitre, M., Cohen, L. R., & Koenen, K. C. (2006). *Treating survivors of childhood abuse: Psychotherapy for the interrupted life.* New York, NY: Guilford Press.

Cohen, J. A., Mannarino, A. P., & Deblinger, E. (2006). *Treating trauma and traumatic grief in children and adolescents.* New York, NY: Guilford Press.

Ehlers, A., & Clark, D. M. (2000). A cognitive model of posttraumatic stress disorder. *Behavior Research and Therapy, 38*, 319–345. doi:10.1016/S0005-7967(99)00123-0

Fairburn, C. G. (1981). A cognitive behavioural approach to the treatment of bulimia. *Psychological Medicine, 11*, 707–711. doi:10.1017/S0033291700041209

Fairburn, C. G. (1985). Cognitive-behavioral treatment for bulimia. In D. M. Garner & P. E. Garfinkel (Eds.), *Handbook of psychotherapy for anorexia nervosa and bulimia* (pp. 160–192). New York, NY: Guilford Press.

Fairburn, C. G. (2008). *Cognitive behavioral therapy and eating disorders.* New York: NY: Guilford Press.

Fairburn, C. G., Agras, W. S., & Wilson, G. T. (1992). The research on the treatment of bulimia nervosa: Practical and theoretical implications. In G. H. Anderson & S. H. Kennedy (Eds.), *The biology of feast and famine: Relevance to eating disorders* (pp. 318–340). New York, NY: Academic Press.

Fairburn, C. G., & Cooper, P. (1989). Eating disorders. In K. Hawton, P. M. Salkovskis, J. Kirk., & D. M. Clark (Eds.), *Cognitive behavior therapy for psychiatric problems* (pp. 277–314). New York, NY: Oxford University Press.

Fairburn, C. G., Cooper, Z., & Shafran, R. (2003). Cognitive behavior therapy for eating disorders: A "transdiagnostic" theory and treatment. *Behavior Research and Therapy, 41*, 509–528. doi:10.1016/S0005-7967(02)00088-8

Fairburn, C. G., Marcus, M. D., & Wilson, G. T. (1993). Cognitive-behavioral therapy for binge eating and bulimia nervosa: A comprehensive treatment manual. In C. G. Fairburn & G. T. Wilson (Eds.), *Binge eating: Nature, assessment, and treatment* (pp. 361–404). New York, NY: Guilford Press.

Fallon, P., & Coffman, S. (1991). Cognitive-behavioral treatment of survivors of victimization. *Psychotherapy in Private Practice, 9*(3), 53–65. doi:10.1300/J294v09n03_06

Fallon, P., & Wonderlich, S. A. (1997). Sexual abuse and other forms of trauma. In D. M. Garner & P. E. Garfinkel (Eds.), *Handbook of treatment for eating disorders* (2nd ed., pp. 394–414). New York, NY: Guilford Press.

Foa, E. B., Hembree, E. A., & Rothbaum, B. O. (2007). *Prolonged exposure therapy for PTSD: Emotional processing of traumatic experiences.* New York, NY: Oxford University Press.

Foa, E. B., Molnar, C., & Cashman, L. (1995). Change in rape narratives during exposure therapy for posttraumatic stress disorder. *Journal of Traumatic Stress, 8*, 675–690. doi:10.1002/jts.2490080409

Foa, E. B., Rothbaum, B. O., & Furr, J. M. (2003). Augmenting exposure therapy with other CBT procedures. *Psychiatric Annals, 33*(1), 47–53. doi:10.3928/0048-5713-20030101-08

Foa, E. B., Rothbaum, B. O., Riggs, D. S., & Murdock, T. B. (1991). Treatment of posttraumatic stress disorder in rape victims: A comparison between cognitive-behavioral procedures and counseling. *Journal of Consulting and Clinical Psychology, 59*(5), 715–723. doi:10.1037/0022-006X.59.5.715

Frank, E., Anderson, B., Stewart, B. D., Dancu, C., Hughes, C., & West, D. (1988). Efficacy of cognitive behavior therapy and systematic desensitization in the treatment of rape trauma. *Behavior Therapy, 19*, 403–420. doi:10.1016/S0005-7894(88)80012-1

Garner, D. M., Vitousek, K. M., & Pike, K. M. (1997). Cognitive behavioral therapy for anorexia nervosa. In D. M. Garner & P. E. Garfinkel (Eds.), *Handbook of treatment for eating disorders* (2nd ed., pp. 94–144). New York, NY: Guilford Press.

Giles, T. R. (1988). Distortion of body image as an effect of conditioned fear. *Journal of Behavior Therapy and Experimental Psychiatry, 19*, 143–146. doi:10.1016/0005-7916(88)90028-6

Konanur, S., Muller, R. T., Cinamon, J. S., Thornback, K., & Zorzella, K. P. (2015). Effectiveness of trauma-focused cognitive behavior therapy in a community-based program. *Child Abuse & Neglect, 50*, 159–170. doi:10.1016/j.chiabu.2015.07.013

Leitenberg, H., Rosen, J. C., Wolf, J., Vara, L. S., Detzer, M. J., & Srebnik, D. (1994). Comparison of cognitive-behaviour therapy and desipramine in the treatment of bulimia nervosa. *Behavior Research and Therapy, 32*, 37–46. doi:10.1016/0005-7967(94)90082-5

Marcus, M. (1997). Adapting treatment for patients with binge-eating disorder. In D. M. Garner & P. E. Garfinkel (Eds.), *Handbook of treatment for eating disorders* (2nd ed., pp. 95–144). New York, NY: Guilford Press.

McCrory, E. J., De Brito, S. A., Sebastian, C. L., Mechelli, A., Bird, G., Kelly, P. A., & Viding, E. (2011). Heightened neural reactivity to threat in child victims of family violence. *Current Biology, 21*, R947–R948. doi:10.1016/j.cub.2011.10.015

Miller, W. R., & Rollnick, S. (2013). *Motivational interviewing: Helping people change.* New York, NY: Guilford Press.

Mitchell, J. E., Pyle, R. L., Eckert, E. D., Hatsukami, D., Pomeroy, C., & Zimmerman, R. (1990). A comparison study of antidepressants and structured intensive group psychotherapy in the treatment of bulimia nervosa. *Archives of General Psychiatry, 47*, 149–157. doi:10.1001/archpsyc.1990.01810140049008

Perry, B. D. (2009). Examining child maltreatment through neurodevelopmental lens: Clinical applications of the neurosequential model of therapeutics. *Journal of Loss and Trauma, 14*, 240–255. doi:10.1080/15325020903004350

Rauch, S., & Foa, E. (2006). Emotional processing therapy (EPT) and exposure therapy for PTSD. *Journal of Contemporary Psychotherapy, 36*, 61–65. doi:10.1007/s10879-006-9008-y

Resick, P. A. (2001). Cognitive therapy for posttraumatic stress disorder. *Journal of Cognitive Psychotherapy, 15*(4), 321–329.

Resick, P. A., & Schnicke, M. K. (1992). Cognitive processing therapy for sexual assault victims. *Journal of Consulting and Clinical Psychology, 60*(5), 748–756. doi:10.1037/0022-006X.60.5.748

Richard, D. C. S., & Lauterbach, D. L. (2007). *Handbook of exposure therapies.* Burlington, MA: Academic Press.

Rosen, J. C., & Leitenberg, H. (1985). Exposure plus response prevention treatment of bulimia. In D. M. Garner & P. E. Garfinkel (Eds.), *Handbook of psychotherapy for anorexia nervosa and bulimia* (pp. 193–209). New York, NY: Guilford Press.

Waller, G. (2009). Evidence-based treatment and therapist drift. *Behaviour Research and Therapy, 47*, 119–127. doi:10.1016/j.brat.2008.10.018

Westerman, N. K., Cobham, V. E., & McDermott, B. (2016). Trauma-focused cognitive behavior therapy: Narratives of children and adolescents. *Qualitative Health Research, 27*(2), 226–235. doi:10.1177/1049732315627795

Williams, M. B., & Poijula, S. (2016). *PTSD workbook: Simple effective techniques for overcoming trauma stress symptoms* (3rd ed.). Oakland, CA: New Harbinger Press.

Wilson, G. T., Fairburn, C. G., & Agras, W. S. (1997). Cognitive-behavioral therapy for bulimia nervosa. In D. M. Garner & P. Garfinkel (Eds.), *Handbook of treatment for eating disorders* (2nd ed., pp. 67–93). New York, NY: Guilford Press.

CHAPTER 15

Ego State/Parts Work in the Treatment of Eating Disorders

Andrew Seubert and Robin Shapiro

■ INTRODUCTION

In the spirit of this chapter, the "I" who weaves everything together shall henceforth be designated the "self." The elements that are woven together are contributions by two author parts: Andrew Seubert and Robin Shapiro. Both parts have learned to collaborate with each other and, at times, integrate.

The Self

A caveat: Our writers do not cover extreme forms of dissociation, specifically dissociative disorders not otherwise specified (DDNOS) and dissociative identity disorder (DID). Yet, the basic skills required to work with both are the stuff of this chapter. In their seminal book, *Ego States: Theory and Therapy*, Watkins and Watkins (1997) describe a continuum of dissociation from differentiation to DID. Differentiation is the way we shift our presentation, also known as our persona, when we move from home, to job, to socializing. From a "self" point of view, it is done somewhat consciously, albeit automatically. At the other end of the dissociative continuum are the extreme forms of dissociation in which behaviors and reactions are often outside the self's conscious awareness. This chapter explores parts or ego states somewhere in the middle of the two that are invested in one or the other form of eating disorder (ED). "Ego state" and "part" are used interchangeably in this chapter.

■ WHAT ARE EGO STATES OR PARTS?

Robin begins with a short neurological explanation of ego states, their purpose, and the difference between dysfunctional and dissociated ego states.

Part Robin

"Humans, like other animals, have wiring for all kinds of states: waking, sleeping, eating, connecting, playing, showing aggression, and, when needed, inhibiting these states.... The neurons in our big brains are constantly preparing us for the future. We have organized neuronal clusters in us for all that we habitually do, feel, and think, mostly in an unconscious, automatic way. When we have a new experience, do new activities, go to a new place, or feel a strong feeling, our brains start to build connections with the thoughts, emotions, and actions that go with the new experience. If life or conscious practice puts us in the same situation over and over, we develop thousands of thicker, stronger neuronal connections. We have conscious and unconscious programs for most of what we do and much of what we think and feel" (Shapiro, 2016, pp. 27–28).

"When a trauma is big enough or happens often enough, we may develop strong, reflexive pathways of response that act separately from our most conscious, thinking, planning brain: dissociative states" (Shapiro, 2010, p. 17). All dissociative states are ego states. They can be simple: total shutdown, full-on aggression, or terror that are triggered, but do not fit the current situation. They can be complex, with ages, names, and specific "jobs" in the system. In simple traumas or personality-disordered people, all states may be in conscious awareness. In DID or disorders of extreme stress not otherwise specified clients, the states are often not known to the "self" or "front person" or to each other.

Not all ego states are dissociative. Think of yourself in your therapist role, or playing with your dog or kids, or driving.... These roles call on different "parts" of you but are generally not separated by dissociative barriers. These are nondissociative ego states. As therapists, we may use similar techniques with dissociative and nondissociative states: Bringing the most competent, present-oriented parts to the front, and putting them in charge of caring for other parts and running the current life.

■ A BRIEF OVERVIEW OF EGO STATES/PARTS WORK AND THEIR COMMON ELEMENTS

The Self

The notion of "parts" of one's self extends back through centuries and cultures. The term "ego states" was first used by Paul Federn, a disciple of Sigmund Freud. Over the course of time the use of "parts" language has come into favor because it grew out of vernacular expressions, such as "a part of me wants to go, and another part of me doesn't." It is simply more user friendly.

Andrew begins with an overview of various traditions of parts, which, although not exhaustive, can uncover the common and universal characteristics of ego state work.

Part Andrew

Work with personality parts has been with us for quite a long time. In the 11th century, a female Tibetan Buddhist teacher, Machig Labdrön, developed a strategy called "feeding your demons." Allione (2008) writes: "This demon might be addiction, self-hatred, perfectionism, anger, jealousy, or anything that is dragging you down, draining your energy" (p. 5). She continues, "Giving our demons form by personifying them brings inchoate energies or harmful habitual patterns into view, allowing them to be liberated rather than leaving them as invisible destructive forces" (p. 8). In a word, she is describing the need to recognize and make contact with these "demons" to then be able to collaborate with them.

In the previous century, Janet (1907) used the term "dissociation" to describe systems of ideas that were split off, and thus "not in association" with other ideas within the personality (Watkins & Watkins, 1997). Carl Jung described a "complex" as having "the tendency to form a little personality of itself. It has sort of a body, a certain amount of its own physiology…in short, it behaves like a partial personality (citation)." Their intent was to get to understand that which was split off to work with it.

Roberto Assagioli (1888–1974) created Psychosynthesis (Assagioli, 2000) in which he studied the client as a personality and a soul. For him, human growth resulted from a combination of ego development and peak experiences (moments of creativity, insight, and unitive experiences). He addressed what he referred to as "subpersonalities," some of which emulated higher qualities and some that resisted integration. He focused on bringing together disparate or conflicting parts of the person, using terms like "recognition," "acceptance," "co-ordination," "integration," and "synthesis."

Fritz Perls (1893–1970), the founder of the Gestalt tradition, used his empty chair technique to resolve what he termed "polarities" within his clients (Polster & Polster, 1973). Various aspects of the person were placed in different chairs, and the client was asked to enter the consciousness of each part to achieve mutual understanding, collaboration, and integration.

The approach I personally use in working with parts has been mostly influenced by the Gestalt tradition and the seminal work of John and Helen Watkins.

John and Helen Watkins referred to their work as ego state therapy (1997), building upon the work of Paul Federn. They described an ego state as an "organized system of behavior and experience whose elements are bound together by some common principle, and which is separated from other such states by a boundary that is more or less permeable" (p. 25). They saw ego states developing "to enhance the individual's ability to adapt and cope with a specific problem or situation" (p. 29). No one, I believe, had been so clear as to the nature and purpose of ego states or parts up to this point. Their approach was similar to others in emphasizing getting to know parts, their purpose, and how to work together.

In very recent times, we have seen the development of two major approaches to parts work. The first is the Internal Family System (IFS) of Schwartz (1995), which combines principles of a family systems approach with an understanding of the multiplicity of the mind (see Chapter 16). Personality parts are ascribed to functional groups: exiles (who hold the pain from trauma), managers (who prevent painful emotion from reaching consciousness), and firefighters (who clamp down on painful feelings that get by the efforts of the managers). The purpose here is to get parts to work together to "unburden" the exile parts of their stored pain and to reconnect to the self, which for Schwartz is a spiritual concept.

Likewise, we have also seen the development of structural dissociation (SD; van der Hart et al., 2006). This is not the place for an in-depth description of this or any other approach (for that, see Chapter 17), but suffice it to say that the SD approach organizes the personality into "prototypical" parts that are dissociated from each other, parts that have specific purposes. Apparently normal parts (ANPs) are the parts that face and adapt to daily life. Emotional parts (EPs) are the parts that are stuck in or carry the pain of traumatic experiences. The task of this phase-oriented therapy is to support all parts in overcoming various phobias and achieving stabilization in Phase 1. Phase 2 addresses the trauma, whereas Phase 3 focuses on integration and rehabilitation.

The point of this brief romp through various approaches to ego state/parts work is to highlight the common elements they seem to share, elements I teach with the acronym **RUG-C**.

"R" represents the *recognition* of parts or ego states, the realization of multiplicity in the human species and the necessity of making some kind of contact with parts of the individual's internal system that usually lie outside of consciousness, yet influence reactions and behaviors. **"U"** emphasizes the task of *understanding* the purpose or raison d'être of each part: Why do you do what you do? What brought you into existence? What are you trying to accomplish? **"G"** reminds us to express *gratitude* for what that part has done to help the person navigate emotional waters and endure painful life events. It also signifies the need to negotiate *goals* because the original goals of an ego state are formed in childhood, and thus are outdated and counterproductive. Finally, **"C"** brings us to the stage of *collaboration*: How can we achieve these goals together (parts, self, and therapist)? What is needed for stability in the present (skills and resources) and what is needed to metabolize the burden of trauma?

These elements of ego state work are distilled from the traditions described, as well as from my work with courageous clients. Robin and I stand gratefully on these many shoulders. The overall purpose of ego state work is to interact with the *experienced* part, rather than thinking and/or talking about it. Eating-disordered parts are not the totality of the person, although it may seem that way quite often. They have operated automatically and reflexively, but with an ego state approach, they become known to the client (self) and each other, making the unconscious conscious. The client also becomes known to the part(s). Conscious dialogue can then take place, bringing out of the shadows dysfunctional and disruptive parts that are still stuck in past, painful experience, inhibiting healthy functioning in the present. This is about the relationship and the process of becoming known.

■ DISSOCIATION AND EATING DISORDERS: PHASE I—EVALUATION

The Self

As you can see in Chapter 3, EDs are dissociated experiences, which is why they can be so difficult to treat if the therapist focuses primarily on thoughts and behaviors.

It is so common for the clinician, attempting to use reason and common sense with a client's starving or bingeing behaviors, to ask: "What now?" The problem is that the therapist is interacting with the prefrontal part of the client's brain, whereas the "parts" of the brain attached to the ED are hiding out in deeper, nonverbal parts of the brain (see Figure 15.1). They are dissociated; hence, the need for ego state approaches with EDs to create contact between the adult consciousness and the ED parts and between therapist and parts. Here is Andrew's story of how he first became aware of that and the need to evaluate for the presence and degree of dissociation in clients with EDs.

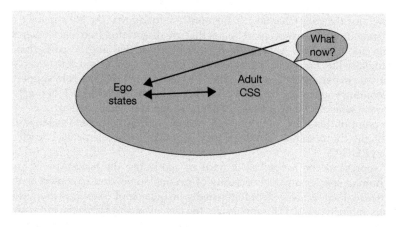

FIGURE 15.1 Conversation between therapist, adult consciousness (CSS) and ego states.

Part Andrew

Elsewhere (Shapiro, 2009) I have written, "If I am not able to tolerate who I think I've become due to trauma, then I must create a new identity, or at least displace the shameful and painful aspects of experience elsewhere, in an identity that is perceived as a 'not-I.' The shame and pain must be rendered a-part, split off, so that the person can function in daily life. Immediate painful emotion is avoided; but suffering is created" (pp. 193–194).

JB was an intelligent, attractive woman in her 40s, a mother of two boys, married to a man who could not understand her refusal to eat. She had been through several hospitalizations for anorexia nervosa (AN), yet returned to the same behaviors upon each release.

At the end of a given session, she delivered one of those "one-foot-out-the-door" bombshells.

"You need to know something about me," she said. "If I feel happy, that will make me fat!"

It did not take a great deal of brain power to realize that her statement was not the thinking of an intelligent adult. It came from somewhere or something else that sounded much younger. In a subsequent session, while exploring the first time she was teased by her siblings for being fat at the age of 7, she blurted: "I don't like that seven-year old. She's the reason I feel all this pain!" The split and lack of understanding between client and ego state was evident.

The evaluation phase is often an ongoing, not-so-neat part of the therapy. It includes the crucial aspect of relationship building between client and therapist, gathering of various histories, medical/nutritional attention, and, importantly, the assessment of levels of dissociation, which are inevitably present in EDs (see Chapter 3). Our focus in this chapter is on assessing for dissociation. Here are some of the signs I have noticed when a dissociative part is afoot in various forms of EDs:

- Stuck, intractable—typical in the addictive aspects of EDs.
- Responding without conscious choice—compulsive, addictive.
- Developmentally delayed—age inappropriateness. Poor space/time orientation.
- Shame base: Hiding from it and protecting against it.
- Separatistic quality—acting outside of higher good of the whole, for example, stuffing or starving.
- Trauma-informed aspect: disproportionate reacting in present because of past unhealed wound/deficit.
- Internal civil war—"I know one thing, but feel another."
- Emotional signals: stuck emotions, looping, avoidance, numbing, "over" reacting.
- Cognitive signals: thinking patterns indicative of a younger state of development, for example, illogical, black/white, generalized.
- Somatic signals: body disturbances (unexplained pain, tension, numbness…). Disconnected from body signals of hunger or satiety.
- Behavioral signals: repeated, persistent, compulsive, avoidant, aggressive, passive/aggressive, self-harming.

My partner, Robin, points out the following:

- Spaces out easily.
- Loses coherence when speaking about childhood events (Siegel, 1999) or cannot remember much of childhood years.
- Uses different voices, inflections, or age-specific language.
- Is easily triggered into feelings of abandonment, defensiveness, or clinginess.

- Has otherwise unexplained headaches, nausea, or pelvic pain.
- Shows inappropriate affect when discussing distressing events.
- Speaks in the third person about the self.

In addition, among others, there are the following instruments for screening and diagnosing dissociation:

1. Dissociative Experience Scale (DES)—Bernstein and Putnam (1986)
2. Dissociative Disorders Interview Schedule—Ross (1987)
3. Somatoform Questionnaire—Nijenhuis (1996)
4. Multidimensional Inventory of Dissociation (MID)—Dell (2004)

This is not the place to explore the advantages of each, but to know of their existence, and to recognize the indicators (listed previously) of the presence of ego states.

■ PHASE 2—PREPARATION

Part Andrew

Much of the preparatory work with EDs involves getting to know the internal, dissociated system of parts. Although there are approaches to ego state work that organize the internal system into categories or functional groups, my own preference is to simply *follow what is given*. When the client shows indications of dissociation, as in the case of JB, it is then that I invite that part or parts into a visualized conference room or meeting place (or to the "Dissociative Table" of Fraser, 2003), by asking, "I'd like to speak to the part(s) that believes that being happy will make her fat." This is the first of the RUG-C strategies—recognizing the part behind the problematic symptom or behavior. My first contact with JB's parts that held this thought sounded something like this (questions from the therapist were addressed *through* the adult client to the parts):

JB: *I'd like to speak with the part or parts that believes that being happy will make her fat.* Parts: *We're here. There are two of us.*

JB: *And who might you be* (parts aren't given names unless a name is offered)? Parts: *Blob and the Claw.*

Andrew via JB: *I'd like to get to know you, so could you tell me what you would like me to understand most about each of you?*

JB (JB listens to what the parts have to say, and then reports that to the therapist): *The one called Claw started out protecting. Uh…it won't let me feel happiness, because it can be taken away. If I don't feel it, it can't be taken away…. And the Blob tries to keep bad things from happening to me, by getting me to control everything around me…the little things I can control, because everything else is out of control.*

Andrew (asking the client to inquire of the parts): *Are they tired of doing all this?*

JB (reporting back): *Uh, I think so. Yes, because they want help.*

And so began the journey of approximately 5 years. Much of preparation is making contact with and understanding the purpose of ego states. From that point onward, finding common goals and collaborating to achieve them was more within reach. Without these RUG-C strategies, parts remain dissociatively split off and unreachable. Clinically, we experience this as an impasse, "resistance," and double binds. However, remember that there is a purposeful survival need behind every block and that you cannot heal what you do not know.

Much of the protective, avoidant need revolves around the inability to tolerate anxiety, shame, and other intense emotions (see Chapter 10). When preparing the client and client parts for daily life and for processing past events, the affective education must be delivered to the parts in language appropriate to the age of that part. A 7-year-old part of JB was teased at that age by an older and younger sibling about being fat. "7" had to learn to tolerate sadness, anger, and shame attacks before we could proceed with any processing of that painful event. However, "7," at the time of the teasing, had no one, except for her cat, who would listen to her, which brings in the need during preparation for the creation of resources.

Part Robin

"The point of ego state therapy is to find internal resources, bring them to the front of consciousness, enhance them, have them help heal the distressed parts, and bring choice and conscious control to the whole of each client's system" (Shapiro, 2016, p. 41). Ego state interventions bring appropriate chosen (not reflexive) capacities to current functioning. Here are a few of my favorites (Shapiro, 2016, p. 42): Ego state work can

- Create awareness of normal or pathological state-switching, and bring them under conscious control.
- Bring a mature adult state to the front to deal with people, situations, and emotions.
- Heal trauma by creating a true "dual attention" between parts stuck in a traumatic event, and the here-and-now adult in the relatively safe world, and then pull the traumatized part into the safe present, in an integrative way.
- Bring former resources to current situations. *Can you get in touch with the playful kid inside of you? How would she approach this situation?* Or else: *Think of a time when you were in control of your life. What did that feel like? Can you bring that piece of you up to this time?*
- With more dissociated clients, bring the adult ANPs into conscious stewardship of all states (van der Hart, Nijenhuis, & Steele, 2006).
- Remove negative introjects, also known as parentectomies and abuserectomies.
- Culturectomies, removing internalized cultural strictures (think expectations about race, appearance, class, gender roles, etc.; Shapiro, 2016, pp. 29, 30).
- Bring a more resourced "future self" to bring hope to and help deal with current situations.

The Self

In terms of preparation, we have reviewed the need to know the dissociative system of an ED client, develop an understanding of why a part does what it does, and create new goals and collaboration. In addition, we have seen the need for affective skills and the development of resources. Another major concern that needs to be addressed from the first meeting onward is the client's attachment status and needs because attachment injury appears to be quite prevalent among ED clients (see Chapter 3). Although attachment enhancement is taking place between a client and therapist, ego states that contain early injuries need to be contacted and supported in achieving attachment repair (AR), ideally before entering the processing phase of treatment, for without much of a sense of self (developed during the first years of life) trauma processing might easily stall. Andrew and Robin use similar approaches to ego state AR, integrating work from Watkins and Watkins (1997), Steele (2005), Schmidt (2009), Pace (2005), the Gestalt tradition (Polster & Polster, 1973), O'Shea (2009), and Paulsen (2017).

Part Andrew

There are various terminologies to describe the process of going back in time, as it were, to deliver to a "young part" of the self what was missing in terms of early nurturing and caregiving. I simply call it reparenting. The problem is that the absence of early attachment leads to self-deficits, and, without much of a sense of self, trauma processing can come to a grinding halt.

At times the AR is the treatment, particularly involving implicit memory. There is the possibility of working systematically and chronologically with development stages in the case of pervasive attachment injury (reparenting the birth baby, the 1-year-old, 2-year-old, etc.) or AR that is specific to the ego state that is involved in a particular memory (reparenting the 4-year-old part before processing the 4-year-old's memory). There is also the consideration of resources. Does the adult client want to feel able to reparent by him/herself? Does the client need one or several resources? Internal resources (helper parts, spiritual, nurturing and protective parts, future self) and/or external supports (grandmother, friends, Mother Teresa, inspirational people)?

Here is an example of setting this up:

Andrew: *That 7-year old part of you will need some support to clear up that memory of the time your siblings teased you for being fat. Would you be up for reparenting her and giving her what she needs to be stronger?*

JB: *Yes…but I don't know if I can do it alone.*

Andrew: *Who or what could do this with you?*

JB: *My grandmother. She was the only one who really cared about me. And now she's gone* (tears)….

Andrew: *Can she be with you in spirit and go back in time to help you support "7"?*

JB: *Yes, yes. It's just sad, but she can be with me. She always was.*

Andrew: *Then let's do it.*

I made sure that JB was grounded in her adult, parent, and professional consciousness. I asked her to imagine her grandmother being with her and then proceeded with the reparenting steps that can be remembered by using the letter "R" as a mnemonic device:

- *Recognize* the part that has been neglected historically and by the client as well.
- *Regress* to the child part by having the adult go back in time and introduce him/herself and any resources to the child.
- *Rescue* the child part if stuck in the memory ("Freeze the memory and invite the child out…").
- *Repair* the child's attachment wounds by asking how she or he is doing and what she or he might need.
- *Return* with the child (if the child part is willing) to present time and to a safe place.
- *Renew* contact with the child part on a daily basis ("Talk to the child!"; Steele, 2007).

The Self

Here is a wonderful example from Robin showing how this looks while working with a client entrenched in emotional, binge eating.

Part Robin

Grace was 27, single, professional, bright, personable, and a lifelong binge eater. When she walked into her apartment, she would grab any and every carb in the house, and eat until all was gone. She would eat a quart of ice cream, followed by a can of frosting, followed by many pieces of bread. When the food was gone, she would feel remorse, call herself names, and dive into shame and depression.

Grace was an only child with two professional, working parents. Her parents were not abusive, but neither were they attentive. They often did not get home until after 7 p.m., leaving young Grace alone in the house after school for several hours and not serving dinner until after 8 p.m. Grace, feeling hungry, lonely, unloved, and unlovable, would binge every day after school. When adult Grace came home from work, she reenacted the same scenario.

Here's how we fixed it:

I. Finding the adult

Robin: *Grace, I need two pieces of you up front. Go inside and find that brilliant designer part of you, the one that knows design and how to be assertive with people at work.*

Grace: *Got her! I'm thinking of dealing well with a difficult client yesterday.*

Robin: *Great! Feel your grown-up smarts and your ability to set limits.*

Grace: *Totally.*

Robin: *Now can you find that nurturing part of you? Remember when you took care of that sick friend?*

Grace: *I'm feeling the loving, caring, worrying part of me, right now.*

Robin: *Can you bring your professional and your caregiver together, for a particular job?*

Grace: *Got them lined up.*

Robin: *What do they feel like?*

Grace: *Strong, smart, loving, and ready.*

II. Finding the child part

Robin: *Can you go inside now, and find that little girl that used to come home from school to that empty, lonely house?*

Grace: *I don't really want to. But sure.*

Robin: *What's she like?*

Grace: *Little. Scared to be in that big house. Ready to eat.*

III. Rescuing the child

Robin: *Nurturing, Professional Woman, I'd like you to float back in time to the first day that that little girl came home and was alone, with no snack made, and no idea what to do with herself....*

Now I want you to walk up to that little one, introduce yourself, and tell her that you're going to get her out of there, feed her good stuff, and make sure that she never,

ever has to be in a house without a caring adult, again. Would she like that? (Client nods.) *Great! Let's do this!*

So, pick up that little girl, and start sweeping up the years, picking up every age that was home alone, feeling awful, and eating anything she could find....When you have them all, bring them up to right here and right now, with us. Are they okay to become one little Grace? (Nods.) *Let Little Grace see you as you are now: Tall, successful, assertive, and with the ability to take care of kids, buy and make tons of good food, and have it on hand for good snacking and great meals. You can even make food for other people!*

IV. Putting adults in charge

Look that Little Grace in the eye. Tell her that you're her grownup and that you are in charge of almost everything. You, Ms. Nurturing-Professional woman, are in charge of the grown-up life, and of making sure there's always good food in the house, and making sure that there's always good snacks, and making sure that Little Grace never, ever feels alone, ever again. Anytime she feels lonely, she can feel Big Grace holding her. In fact, Big Grace, you tell Little Grace that she can never be alone, because she lives inside Big Grace. Do you feel the grownup body with the little girl piece inside? (Nods.) *Great!*

The Self

And here is a synopsized example from Andrew's client, JB.

Part Andrew

JB, after almost a year of AR, was ready to process the memory of "7" being teased about being fat by her siblings. In contacting "7" via a conference room meeting, it was clear that "7" was still a bit shaky. I asked JB if she could go back in time, take "7" out of that memory, and nurture, support, and encourage her.

> JB: *I don't know if I can do that.... I'm kind of shaky myself* (here we see enmeshment, weak boundaries between adult and younger part).
>
> Andrew: *You've chosen your grandmother as a major support in your life. Would it help to bring her in spirit with you to help "7" while helping you stay in the adult mode?*
>
> JB: *Uh, okay. I think that would work.*
>
> Andrew: *Then I'd ask you to bring up a sense of your grandmother being with you.... Now let both of you go back in time through the years...the forties, thirties, twenties, teens, until you're with "7." Let me know when you've done that and you're with "7."*
>
> JB: *Okay. We're with her.*
>
> Andrew: *Tell her what she needs to hear...especially that she's a beautiful child, that she's so okay and so lovable just as she is, no matter what her brother and sister say....*
>
> JB: *(strong emotional reaction, tears...) My grandma is hugging her! She always gave me the best hugs. It felt so good* (more tears as the boundary between JB and "7" blur) ....
>
> Andrew: *Let yourself be "7" for a few moments. Feel it all, how good and how sad all at once, but stay in touch with my voice* (minutes pass...). *JB, it's time now to be the adult for "7." Can you hear my voice?*
>
> JB: Nods.

Andrew: *Okay. Remember all you do and are as an adult. Your two sons, your husband, the work you do coaching kids at school, your personal training business.... Got that?*

JB: *Yes, yes....*

Andrew: *So please take a few belly breaths, and ask "7" if she would like to return to present time with you and your grandma.*

JB: *Yes, she does. I think she's really relieved.*

Andrew: *Great. So, if you and your grandma would take "7" by the hand and move forward up through the years. Eight, nine, ten...the teens, twenties, thirties, all the way up to present time, and bring "7" to that safe and peaceful place of yours and let her know that you'll check in with her daily. And let me know when all that is in place.*

The reparenting was successful, and JB proceeded to metabolize the memory to where it no longer disturbed her at all. "7" was finally free.

■ PHASE 3—TRAUMA PROCESSING

The Self

How one metabolizes or neutralizes a traumatic event depends on the therapeutic model used. Regardless of exactly how one accomplishes that, the basic concept of a trauma-informed approach is that if a memory is stored in a state-specific form (the way it originally happened, with feelings, sensations, etc.), it influences the way we feel, think, and react in the present when we are reminded (also known as triggered) of the original event. In other words, if Uncle Harry abused me when I was 6 years old, and Uncle Harry had a beard, then the sight of a bearded man in the present will activate the unprocessed memory of Uncle Harry. I then react in the present with the thoughts, feelings, and body sensations of a 6-year-old. To live fully in the present, I need to deactivate the past memory, which has been buried, but buried alive.

EDs often develop as a way of gaining control of or avoiding feelings and need to be addressed in their dissociated form (ego states) and in the context(s) in which they arose (memories). Robin and Andrew use several strategies to achieve the "how" of trauma processing with ED clients. I'll let them speak for themselves, which they usually do! It's hard to get a word in here....

Part Robin

USING EGO STATE THERAPY AND MINDFULNESS WITH POSTTRAUMATIC STRESS DISORDER (PTSD)

Gary, a morbidly obese man in his 40s, was becoming diabetic. He came to therapy to change his nocturnal bingeing. When he was small, his abusive father would violently sexually and physically assault him, late at night, when the rest of the family was asleep. At that time, Gary would eat raw sugar and anything else he could find in an attempt to anesthetize himself. In his current, safe house, that young part would "kick in" each night when Gary's wife and children went to bed, and Gary would binge in a similar way.

Robin: *Gary, how old is that kid part of you who binges at night?*

Gary: *Four to about 12.*

Robin: *And how old are you, now?*

Gary: *Forty-five.*

Robin: *Great! Can you get that 45-year old professor, the one who is the great father, up to the front of you?*

Gary: *He's here.*

Robin: *Think about a time when you were protective of your children. Can you feel that love and protectiveness in you? (He nods.) Great! Let's do a rescue! Let's go back to that 4-year old in the kitchen with the sugar. Can you feel him inside? (Nods.) Introduce yourself, so he doesn't think you're a creep and ask him if he'd like to escape that kitchen and abuse.*

Gary: *He **really** wants to!*

Robin: *Great! Can you take his hand, and you and he start coming up the years sweeping up every age of you that got abused, all the way to until you got out of the house. ... Bring that kid/those kids all the way up to now, to this safe room with me. Now show him around here, and then to where you live now and where you work. Is your dad in sight in any of these places? Show them how many years it's been since you've seen that bastard.... Show them the safety of your current life....And let them see your grown-up body and that no one is going to take you on!*

Tell that kid/those kids that you don't need sugar and food to make yourself not feel, because you are big enough to have feelings now. And show them again, that your current life is very safe.

Because the abuse had been so pervasive and impacted so many ages, we came up with this:

Robin: *So, here's the plan: Every night, when it's bedtime, you're going to sit on your comfortable, safe, chair in your comfortable, safe, den, in your comfortable and safe house. You're going to notice the safety, and notice if any of the kid states arise. If you feel fear or those kid states arise, your adult, present-oriented, self will give them a tour of your present life and let them know that all parts of you are safe and there's no need to stuff food; no need to protect yourself from big feelings, like you used to do.*

For a few months, Gary sent me a brief, nightly email about his mindfulness exercise. When he sat and oriented to the present time, he did not binge. Once every few weeks, when otherwise triggered, he would not sit and he would binge. Now, 6 months later, he no longer binges. He is losing weight, and his blood sugar is under control.

Part Andrew

Vivian was a delightful and lively 17-year-old high school student who struggled with anorexia and body image. It all began when she was sexually abused by a peer at the age of 12. We had not yet had the opportunity to process the 12-year-old memory, when she came to session relating a more recent event.

During a class trip on a bus ride the week before, sitting next to a boy she had always considered a good friend, she was shocked as he began to fondle her, ignoring her protests as she tried to push him away. She reported this to her principal, but discovered that some of her classmates were blaming her for making a big deal of it.

Earlier, Vivian had been struggling with her body image, but was finding that what she saw in the mirror was becoming more positive, particularly because she had been staying with her eating plan, taking her brain and body out of a starvation mode.

When she arrived for her session and told me of the fondling incident, I asked her to close her eyes and imagine what her body image looked like in the mirror. The image had worsened. She imagined cuts over her now enlarged body, dressed shabbily, with bugs swarming around her head.

Her body image, as she imagined it, had become diagnostic, revealing a painful increase in her shame state (see more in Chapter 25). To alleviate this sudden shame attack, I decided to attempt clearing out the most recent event, though convinced that the fondling event 5 years earlier was feeding her reaction to the bus trip. For this, I used the Eye Movement Desensitization and Reprocessing (EMDR) protocol (see Chapter 13).

At the end of the EMDR processing of the bus experience, I checked to see if there was any disturbance left. "Nope!" I then inquired as to whether a positive belief about herself felt true when she thought about the incident. "Totally!" Finally, I invited her to do a body scan while focusing on the memory and the positive belief simultaneously to see if the scan was clear. "Clear!" I then asked how the overall experience was for her.

> Vivian: *Weird! I've never had something like the bus thing happen, and then feel totally okay! Weird!*
>
> Andrew: *Would you be willing to see if the image of the girl in the mirror has changed?*
>
> Vivian: *Sure.* (After a few minutes of bringing up the image of herself in a mirror...) *It's different. The bugs are gone and the body is not so big. There are still some of the cuts, but she doesn't look so much like a street person!*
>
> Andrew: *Sounds like you just did something very, very important.*

"The Self"

After the processing of painful life events, the client must still deal with present triggers and future challenges. Here is how Robin followed up with her client, Grace.

Part Robin

Making a Plan:

> Robin: *What kind of food are you going to get into your house for you and Little Grace?*
>
> Grace: *I need to get easy, fast stuff, for snacks, that's not too carb-heavy: pre-cut carrots, great cheese, and a big chunk of great ham for cutting and snacking. Then some easy meals stuff, until I can really cook. Maybe some of the healthier frozen dinners. And this weekend, I could cook up a storm, for left-overs for the week—maybe a good soup or stew with veggies and meat.*
>
> Robin: *How does Little Grace feel about the menu?*
>
> Grace: *She's scared, because it's different, and it won't fix the lonely feeling. She's upset!*
>
> Robin: *Turn her around to you again, and let her see she's not going to need that sugar stuff to make the feeling go away, because you're going to be there, connecting with and feeding her.*
>
> Grace: *Oh, you're right! She's settling in again.*

Practicing the plan:

> Robin: *So, you're going shopping, you're taking the good food home, and you're parking the car at your apartment. Imagine sitting in the car and engaging that kid. Can you imagine finding Little Grace and telling her, "We're going into our apartment together*

and I'm going to feed you the good stuff we bought. Any time you feel lonely, you need to notice I'm there. If I, Big Grace, feel lonely, I can name that feeling, feel it, like Robin taught us, and later, call up a friend, or find them on Facebook. I have a car and can go visit people if I want. I'm grown up!

Now imagine walking into the apartment after your talk. How will it be?

Grace: *Better. I'll have a plan. And I won't be leading with the kid part of me!*

In the next session, Grace reported that she had a kitchen full of good food, and was able to connect with her "kid part" before she went into the house to eat a good snack and make dinner. As a competent adult, she started making plans to go out to dinner or have people over, so that she would not be home alone. She still binged occasionally, on days that she was especially distressed, but usually not on walking in the door or on the sugary foods of her childhood.

The Self: And Here Are a Few Thoughts From Andrew.

Part Andrew

Particularly with JB's 7-year-old part, ongoing support was needed after she desensitized her memory of being teased. Basically, the addiction to restricted eating had to be addressed not only behaviorally (eating plan), but also at the emotional roots of the behavior. In a word, she was encouraged to bring full awareness to her thoughts, feelings, and body sensations that took place at the first thought of, or urge to, restrict. Dealing with body image at its dissociated ego state source (e.g., the shame response of Vivian) is another example of dealing with the causal level of an ongoing trigger.

Mindful awareness is in and of itself an act of courage. It is the first step in inviting the client to face the emotions, feel them, and free them, thereby reducing the need for the ED. This is particularly true of the anxiety that ED clients often experience before eating and the shame experienced after eating. The only way to reduce these automatic reactions is to go toe to toe with them (see Chapter 10).

After past events have been processed, situations and relationships in the present and future still possess an emotional charge of their own via second-order conditioning. Robin and I (this is where we integrate!) have found that whether we are processing memories, neutralizing present triggers, or facing future feared situations, addressing these issues at the dissociated heart of a disorder can make all the difference, and a difference that will endure.

The Self

And so our chapter ends: togetherness and collaboration. And this is precisely what we seek with our clients. EDs are very difficult to treat in that they demand attention on so many levels: psychological, emotional, physical, behavioral. We believe that it is the reality of dissociation that makes this work all the more difficult, a reality that demands an invitation to *all* parts of our client to come together and collaborate in the service of healing.

■ REFERENCES

Allione, T. (2008). *Feeding your demons*. New York, NY: Little, Brown.

Assagioli, R. (2000). *Psychosynthesis: A collection of basic writings*. Amherst, MA: Synthesis.

Bernstein, E. M., & Putnam, F. W. (1986). Development, reliability, and validity of a dissociation scale. *Journal of Nervous and Mental Disease, 174*, 727–735. doi:10.1097/00005053-198612000-00004

Dell, P. F. (2004). Multidimensional Inventory of Dissociation v.6.0. Retrieved from http://www.mid-assessment.com/wp-content/uploads/2017/09/English-MID-Reformatted.pdf

Fraser, G. A. (2003). Fraser's "Dissociative table technique" revisited, revised: A strategy for working with ego states in dissociative disorders and ego-state therapy. *Journal of Trauma & Dissociation, 4*(4), 5–28. doi:10.1300/J229v04n04_02

Janet, P. (1907). *The major symptoms of hysteria.* New York, NY: Macmillan.

Nijenhuis, E. R. S. (1996). Somatoform Dissociation Questionairre (SDQ-5 and SDQ-20). Retrieved from http://www.enijenhuis.nl/sdq

O'Shea, K. (2009). The EMDR Early Trauma Protocol. In R. Shapiro (Ed.), *EMDR Solutions II* (pp. 313–334). New York, NY: W. W. Norton.

Pace, P. (2005). *Lifespan integration: Connecting ego states through time* (3rd ed.). Bellevue, NY: Author.

Paulsen, S. (2017). *When there are no words.* Bainbridge Island, WA: Bainbridge Institute.

Polster, E., & Polster, M. (1973). *Gestalt therapy integrated: Contours of theory and practice.* New York, NY: Brunner/Mazel.

Ross, C. (1987). Dissociative Disorders Interview Schedule. Retrieved from http://www.rossinst.com/ddis

Schmidt, S. J. (2009). *The developmental needs meeting strategy: An ego state psychotherapy for healing childhood wounds.* San Antonio, TX: DNMS Institute.

Schwartz, R. C. (1995). *Internal family systems therapy.* New York, NY: Guilford Press.

Shapiro, R. (Ed.). (2009). *EMDR Solutions II.* New York, NY: W. W. Norton.

Shapiro, R. (2010). *The trauma treatment handbook.* New York, NY: W. W. Norton.

Shapiro, R. (2016). *Easy ego state interventions: Strategies for working with parts.* New York, NY: W. W. Norton.

Siegel, D. J. (1999). *The developing mind: Toward a neurobiology of interpersonal experience.* New York, NY: Guilford Press.

Steele, A. (2007). *Developing a secure self: An attachment-based approach to adult psychotherapy.* Gabriola, BC, Canada: Author.

van der Hart, O., Nijenhuis, E., & Steele, K. (2006). *The haunted self: Structural dissociation and the treatment of chronic traumatization.* New York, NY: W. W. Norton.

Watkins, H. H., & Watkins, J. G. (1997). *Ego states: Theory and therapy.* New York, NY: W. W. Norton.

CHAPTER 16

IFS (Internal Family Systems) and Eating Disorders: The Healing Power of Self-Energy

Jeanne Catanzaro, Elizabeth Doyne, and Katie Thompson

■ INTRODUCTION

When people are traumatized, they do what they can to avoid the painful feelings, sensations, and memories related to the trauma. Trauma is unrelenting and pervasive; it bleeds into the present moments of daily life, often stealing joy, muting a person's ability to fully connect and accomplish tasks of daily living. Trauma memories can be destructive and overwhelming, causing the individual to seek any way to get a moment's peace from his or her past.

There are many ways people can distract themselves from this kind of psychic and/or somatic pain. One way is to focus on and become preoccupied with food and weight and attempt to control the body. Although behaviors involved in this pursuit can afford some immediate relief and distance from the source of pain, they often come at a cost, especially when they become extreme enough to qualify as an eating disorder (ED). These emotional survival strategies can cause significant physical harm or even lead to death, so they often elicit strong reactions from loved ones and mental health professionals who try to get these behaviors to stop. Such efforts to stabilize or eliminate ED behaviors often result in power struggles that make the ED worse. When someone experiences another trying to control her or his behavior, a deleterious effect is set into motion that amplifies the client's fears and mistrust of relationships. These interpersonal rifts between a "helpful" other who is desperately trying to control the unbalanced eating behavior and the attachment to said behavior mirrors tensions inside ED clients, who typically vacillate between being highly reluctant to change the ED and desperately wanting to be free of it. ED clients stuck in this unresolvable conflict lose faith in themselves and their capacity to take care of themselves, often becoming depressed or anxious in addition to being stuck in maladaptive eating or exercise behaviors.

Internal Family Systems (IFS) treats trauma and EDs by helping clients establish relationships with the ED parts of themselves so they learn how the seemingly self-destructive behaviors of these parts are actually attempts to help them avoid the overwhelming feelings and beliefs related to earlier trauma and attachment injuries (Schwartz, 1995, 2001). IFS offers alternative ways of resolving the underlying issues, so the ED behaviors are no longer needed to negotiate internal and external relationships.

■ CHAPTER OVERVIEW

Starting with an overview of the IFS model, we discuss how IFS conceptualizes EDs and approaches trauma treatment. IFS differs from other approaches to trauma treatment in several ways that we elaborate, especially eschewing the idea that stabilization and explicit skills training are necessary prerequisites for processing traumatic memories. Instead, IFS asserts that clients can learn to interact with the different parts of themselves without getting overwhelmed or needing the therapist to actively manage the process. We use case vignettes to illustrate how IFS achieves the goals of phase-oriented trauma treatment to heal EDs in a nonlinear, relational way.

■ A BRIEF OVERVIEW OF THE INTERNAL FAMILY SYSTEMS MODEL

The IFS model contends that our minds comprise many different parts, or subpersonalities, that interact internally, much like people do externally. Our multiple parts are a healthy, natural phenomenon, rather than the result of a pathological process. Equipped with the capacity for a full range of thoughts and feelings, parts are present at birth and contain important attributes. Under optimal conditions, parts emerge at developmentally appropriate times as the personality naturally unfolds. In addition to parts, we all have an inner essence, which IFS refers to as Self, that is loving and capable of healing. Self can never be damaged. However, when we are young and vulnerable, parts of us are forced into extreme roles to safeguard the Self, which is an immutable healing essence that does not have access to the hardware (e.g., mature brain, muscles) when we are young to take care of the system without the help of caregivers. Protective parts keep other parts who carry pain that is too big to be processed exiled from the Self. IFS refers to the parts who hold these intolerable feelings as exiles. Protectors, who mistakenly believe the Self to be very young, fear that becoming conscious of this pain will overwhelm or incapacitate the Self and the system. Healing involves helping protectors restore their trust in the Self, to see that it is not young and vulnerable and can take care of the system.

IFS designates two types of protective parts who differ in terms of whether they work proactively or reactively to prevent pain housed in exiles from reaching consciousness. Proactive protectors are called managers, whereas firefighters reactively suppress the exiles' pain once it breaks through. Managers are thus named because they "manage" our day-to-day lives, working tirelessly to avoid anything that might make us look or feel bad. They are the parts who get us to work hard and please others. Common managerial strategies include intellectualizing, perfectionism, caretaking, and obsessing about appearance.

When managers' tactics are insufficient to ward off dangerous feelings, firefighters act swiftly to reexile the pain that has broken through. Common firefighter strategies include addictions of all kinds (e.g., to substances as well as activities such as surfing the net, exercising, and watching TV), dissociating, cutting, and suicidal thoughts and behaviors. Like real firefighters, the mission is to put out the fire of the painful affect without concern for what damage is done in the process. For example, a client whose managers work hard to avoid connecting with feelings of inadequacy may have a firefighter jump in to defend her to give her a sense of power when she has been criticized by a boss. The firefighter is not concerned about the future impact of raging at a superior. Its singular focus is to distract the client from the vulnerability the negative evaluation triggered. Following the outburst at work, another manager will typically try to undo the damage by criticizing the client for misbehaving. The critic's goal is to get the client back in good graces by suppressing the rage and motivating better behavior.

Although managers and firefighters share the goal of keeping exiled feelings at bay, they go about meeting their objective in very different, often opposing ways. Manager–firefighter polarizations often result in an escalation of symptoms as each side becomes more extreme to balance out the action of the other. So, the outburst of rage results in stauncher commitments to be accommodating and pleasing. When all that good behavior does not garner approval and affirmation, firefighters become more activated and extreme. Polarizations can also occur between different managers and different firefighters who disagree about the best way to take care of the client.

In general, the greater the underlying vulnerability, the more extreme the protectors tend to be. Although common symptoms among trauma survivors (e.g., suicidality, dissociation, rage, panic attacks, hypervigilance, EDs, and other addictions) can be frightening to clients and those who care for them, IFS regards them not as pathological, but as the initially adaptive responses to overwhelming circumstances. Parts take on extreme roles to keep the child safe and with an illusion of some modicum of control when there is very little. Parts who have learned by experience not to trust need to be reconnected to the inherent healing wisdom of their own Self. This is the goal of IFS therapy.

◼ IFS AND EATING DISORDERS

When we are young and depend on caregivers, if they are neglectful, abusive, or terrorizing, we need to adopt strategies that allow us to remain in relationship while shielding us from further harm. These may include avoiding, denying, minimizing, or dissociating from the pain endured. At some point, these coping mechanisms are insufficient, and trauma survivors find themselves grasping for numbing mechanisms that will allow them to forget the assaults of the traumatic events. Although there are various ways to do this, a strategy common to trauma survivors is to fixate on the body and its modification. Given that survivors' bodies have often been violated, finding a way to control or modify the body to minimize future intrusion makes good sense. Even when there has not been direct physical harm, the body holds the feelings, sensations, and memories related to the traumas and attachment injuries. Disconnecting from the body is therefore helpful to avoid these painful stimuli.

From an IFS perspective, EDs result from the polarization between parts who control and restrict needs and wants and other parts who rebel against such deprivation. As Catanzaro (2016, p. 51) writes elsewhere, "While an individual's specific ED diagnosis depends on which parts dominate at a given time, the overall symptom picture, even if it isn't obvious from the client's physical appearance or self-report, always involves this dialectic between restraint and rebellion against restraint." As with all protective behaviors, what distinguishes whether it is driven by a manager or a firefighter is whether it is used preemptively or reactively to avoid psychic pain. Although we tend to think of certain behaviors as managerial (e.g., restricting, extreme exercise) and others as distracting or pertaining to firefighters (e.g., bingeing, purging), each of these symptoms can be used either way. To illustrate, a part who purges after a fight would be considered a firefighter, whereas a part who purges daily to avoid conflict would be considered a manager.

The comfort clients derive from their ED symptoms can be difficult for others to fathom. The internal tug of war is preoccupying and allows clients to keep their distance from others as well as from other parts of their own. The ED behaviors also help with dysregulation common to trauma survivors. Restriction can make them feel numb and disconnected, thus helping offset states of hyperarousal. Overeating, bingeing, and purging can similarly have an analgesic effect. Other clients find that eating, bingeing, and purging help them counter hypoarousal.

Although they provide short-term relief, the behaviors of ED protectors result in more pain as the debate between the warring factions gets more extreme. For example, for some, the initial high that can accompany restriction gives way to anxiety as parts fear being overtaken by the parts they are polarized with, such as the ones who want to break through the starvation and eat. Lapses in control (actual, perceived, or anticipated) trigger harsher, more critical managers desperate to keep or get the client back on track. This in turn creates more rebellion and shame. As the ED symptoms escalate, they elicit strong reactions from the protectors of external systems (e.g., family members, therapists, teachers, physicians), whose well-intentioned efforts to control the ED symptoms can exacerbate them. Here is an example.

Jessica was a college sophomore when she entered treatment for her ED after a series of incidents indicated to college administrators that her ED had become too severe for her to remain on campus. After fainting for the second time in the student gym, Jessica was asked to come in for a meeting with her advisor, the residential assistant from her dorm, and the dean of students. In the meeting, Jessica denied she had a problem and attributed her issues to stress and a medication change. Although she was aware she had an ED, she had no intention of leaving school to go to residential treatment, as she had been in and out of treatment four times since she was 12 years old. When the dean reminded her that she had written her application essay on the strength of her recovery from the ED, Jessica admitted she had been struggling, but greatly minimized the extent of her difficulties. The college put her on probation and required her to find a local treatment team to stay enrolled in school. She also had to consent to have her progress monitored by the campus counseling center. Jessica felt trapped by the stipulations, but agreed because she was desperate to stay in school.

Less than a week later, Jessica was called in for another meeting, this time because her purging had stopped up the plumbing in her suite. This was devastating for the parts of Jessica who had worked so hard, and felt they had been able, to hide her ED from her roommates. She realized how the shame she felt about being put on probation drove her to redouble her efforts to put "her efforts to get it together." Her purging, which felt like self-inflicted punishment for messing up, was the worst it had been in years. Thus, despite feeling shame, she was somewhat relieved when the school placed her on a medical leave. She was admitted to a treatment center that used the IFS approach and, for the first time, started to realize what motivated her extreme ED behaviors.

■ IFS AND EATING DISORDER TREATMENT

ED treatment is difficult for many reasons, not the least of which is the extent of denial and minimization common to ED clients. By the time they come to treatment, often at the behest of others, the ED symptoms are well developed and have impacted both the body and the psyche. Even when the client chooses to get help, his or her ED protectors want no part of it. Often this is because of prior treatment that worked to override the protectors.

This was true for Jessica, whose prior hospitalizations involved repeated attempts to get her to eat all foods, regardless of her fears. Without exploring why she feared and "hated" so many everyday foods (e.g., peanut butter, mayonnaise), as well as palatable foods kids typically love (e.g., frosting), the treatment team devised exposure hierarchies that required her to eat these feared foods. What the staff did not know was that Jessica had been sexually abused by an uncle from the time she was 6 until she was 11 and that he often used food as a reward for engaging in the abuse or as an inducement to make it more "completable" for her. Her restricting and purging protectors had stepped in soon after the sexual abuse started to keep her from ingesting foods that triggered flash-backs, because they were linked to the abuse. When she refused to eat, she was seen as noncompliant and given a meal supplement. Not only did this erode Jessica's trust in treatment and the refeeding process but it also reinforced the need for the ED protectors. She began relying more heavily on her purging protector to cope with treatment that aimed to eliminate her restrictor, as she did years later when she was monitored by the University administrators. In both cases, well-meaning interventions resulted in protectors becoming more extreme, because they bypassed important protectors.

IFS recognizes the futility of trying to manage or eliminate protectors, understanding that they are valuable inner personalities who remain stuck in extreme protective roles they were forced to take on because of earlier trauma. Like loyal soldiers, they continue to use their protective strategies, however imperfect, because they do not know of any alternatives. Although there are times when extreme protectors need to be stabilized so they do not result in irreversible harm to the client, in IFS this is done explicitly and without overriding parts in the process. Put positively, the therapist validates the experience of the protectors whose activity is being curtailed by referrals to a higher level of care. Here is an example: A therapist refers a client to inpatient treatment when her extreme restricting and purging result in extreme weight loss and cardiac complications.

> Therapist: *I know this is difficult for parts of you. Can you ask the restricting and purging parts what this is like for them?*
>
> Client: *They're really frustrated. They say it's totally unnecessary, and they say they'll find a way to do what they need to do anyway.*
>
> Therapist: *Can you let them know we get why they'd feel frustrated, that we understand they believe they're doing what they need to do to take care of you? Also, let them know we need to stop them so they don't kill you, and so we can show them that we can heal the parts they protect.*

In the following section, we discuss how IFS approaches trauma treatment, contrasting it further with traditional approaches.

■ IFS VERSUS TRADITIONAL TRAUMA TREATMENT

IFS differs from traditional models of trauma treatment in several significant ways that derive from the IFS model of the mind, particularly in terms of how we assess clients and approach working with traumatic material. We discuss these in the following text.

Assessment: Parts Versus Pathology

In the IFS paradigm, it is natural to have multiple parts with distinct personalities, needs, and feelings. This multiplicity is not the result of a pathological process or event. Although traumas and attachment injuries force parts to take on burdens (extreme beliefs and feelings), these are extrinsic to parts. Once healed, they transform back to their naturally valuable states. Because IFS regards symptoms as the "motivated behavior of protective parts" (Anderson & Sweezy, 2016), assessment involves asking about the client's presenting problem and listening for other parts who are present or related, rather than affixing a diagnostic label. This is important because diagnoses typically capture the activity of the most dominant protector, rather than elucidating the state of the whole system. As the assessment continues, we begin to get a sense of the internal terrain, that is, which parts serve as protectors and which have been exiled. We also listen for how curious and open the client is to his or her inner experience, for this gives us a sense of how much access he or she has to her Self. Starting with the protectors, we learn about how they have served the client, and earn their trust to approach the exiles.

Rather than obtaining a detailed history at the outset, we trust that the client will reveal relevant details organically as we follow the road map provided by his or her parts. An exception to this is our assessment of the client's safety, which is a top priority of the initial interview. We evaluate the factors affecting the client's safety, both external and internal. If the safety of the client's external environment is questionable, steps need to be taken to stabilize the situation. At the same time, we establish relationships with the protectors and help them consider how they might make a shift once it becomes safe to do so.

In terms of internal safety, we do ask clients about dangerous firefighters (e.g., self-harming, raging, substance abusing, eating disordered, or suicidal parts). These parts can jeopardize the client's well-being, so we work to establish relationships with these important and extreme parts to get them onboard, so we can proceed safely and productively with our work. When the physical impact of certain firefighters (e.g., EDs) makes it impossible for outpatient work to proceed safely or productively, interventions such as day or residential treatment are sometimes necessary. In these cases, we respectfully communicate to protectors our intent to keep the client alive, so we can heal what they protect.

Preparation: Self-Energy Versus Grounding

Another way IFS differs from other trauma models is its belief that trauma survivors are not damaged or defective, requiring insights or interpretations. Rather, because of traumatic experiences, they become disconnected from the inner healing capacity we call Self. When Self is present, parts can be witnessed for what they suffered and retrieved from where they are stuck in the past. New relationships can then be established between the parts and the client's Self. This then affects external relationships, as clients can trust their capacity to be with their own needs and act to have them met directly, rather than via the ED behaviors.

IFS views survivors as already having what they need to heal, so it finds unnecessary the grounding techniques and affect regulation skills advocated by other trauma models before processing traumatic memories. Instead, IFS believes "grounding occurs in relationship of the parts with the Self" (R. Schwartz, personal communication, May 7, 2017). Helping the client remember that these intense emotions and beliefs come from a part can be calming in and of itself. The awareness that it is not all of the person, but just an aspect that can be worked with, is very relieving and aids in what is called the *unblending* process. When a client becomes overwhelmed or dysregulated, the therapist finds the part who is overtaking the client and asks it to separate, so the client's Self can be present. If the part agrees, it typically settles quickly, as it senses the genuine interest in and concern for its experience. When the part will not separate, and the client cannot access Self, the therapist's Self serves as the source of Self-energy for the client's system. This is a process known as *direct access*, so named because the therapist's Self relates directly to the client's blended part.

To illustrate, a client with a history of severe sexual abuse "blanked out" whenever she began to talk about her early childhood. The therapist expressed interest in getting to know why the part came in to block the client's awareness of any thought or feeling. "I know you're trying to help Lisa by coming in this way. What are you afraid would happen if you didn't do this to her?" When the dissociative part did not shift, the therapist continued, offering hope to the protectors by saying, "I know you don't trust this right now, but if you allow Lisa and me to go to the parts you protect, we can heal them so you don't have to keep doing this for her. You'd be freed up to do something else for her. What would you rather do for her if you didn't need to blank her out?" The therapist's Self-energy, conveyed via her calm, confident, and clear attitude about healing the exiles, gradually allowed the dissociative protector to relax and unblend. Its trust in the client's Self increased, as it saw that Lisa and the therapist could go to the exiles without Lisa being overwhelmed by the exiles' affect. Although it continued to step in from time to time, it was much more open to speaking for its concerns and stepping back so the work could continue. Because parts of trauma survivors have lost trust in the survivor's Self, direct access may last for months in those with severe trauma.

In IFS, the success of the therapy is highly dependent on the degree to which the therapist can unblend or differentiate and mindfully separate from her own parts so her Self energy is available to the client. The therapist continually checks to see if she is Self-led (unblended) and works with parts if they do step in and block her access to her Self. When the therapist can model a lack of fear and acceptance of extreme parts, the client's protectors relax and make room for the client's Self. As the client establishes and repairs inner relationships, his or her own Self gradually becomes the primary caretaker and healer of his or her system, and the therapist's Self shifts into a supporting role.

Clients discover they can work with their parts between sessions and help them heal, a realization that is a very empowering antidote to trauma's assault on self-confidence. Protectors are greatly relieved to discover that exiles can be negotiated with to not overwhelm the system. This is new for them, as is the emphasis IFS places on always getting their permission before going to an exile, which conveys both respect for their concerns and appreciation for how they have served the client. Respecting the protectors' roles and their concerns regulates some of the extreme affect, as they are not activated to defend against external efforts to control them. Exiles are similarly relieved to not be subject to external efforts to contain or control their affect, actions that send the message that they are unwanted. This is especially important for a population that, by definition, has suffered boundary violations and often a lack of attunement.

■ IFS APPROACH TO TRAUMA TREATMENT

Like all trauma treatment models, the goal of IFS is to help clients reprocess traumatic experiences so they can live fully in the present, rather than being perpetually stuck in or recreating the past. Some examples of how IFS achieves this by building relationships between the client's Self and her traumatized parts are as follows.

Helping Parts Unblend

After she was admitted to residential treatment, Jessica started her first session merged, or "blended," with a harsh critic: "I hate myself so much, I can't believe that here I am missing school and getting even farther behind. What a loser I am!"

> Therapist: *I do understand your discouragement, and I'm getting it's hard for parts of you to understand why other parts of you keep doing what they're doing when it seems to really be holding you back and causing so much pain.*

Jessica: *Of course, it's hard for me to understand! Here I am in a hospital again, no better off. Is this going to be my life?*

Therapist: *Our job is to help you get to know why parts of you continue to engage in the ED behaviors. I know that when we listen with a true openness you'll get a chance to learn their deeper intention. But I get there's a part who's feeing very critical. I'm wondering if it would be willing to separate from you a bit so we can get to know it better.*

Jessica: *Do you mean to tell me there could be reasons that I do this other than I am so messed up?*

Therapist: *I absolutely do mean that.*

Jessica: *The critical part relaxes when you say that. It's worried I will never have a normal life.*

Therapist: *Let it know that if it gives us some room we can heal the parts the eating disorder protects.*

Jessica: *It's skeptical but it would really like that.*

A Protector's Positive Intentions

Although Jessica had learned from previous treatments that her ED was connected to the sexual abuse perpetrated by her uncle, that awareness did little to change her behavior. In fact, it caused even more hopelessness, because she did not know what else she could do with this insight.

Jessica: *I remember some shrink told me that the reason I like to stay so thin is so I wouldn't look so sexy. Whatever. I don't think that's it, I just think I feel a lot better when I'm thin.*

Therapist: *Can you ask the part who wants you to be so thin what it fears would happen if it wasn't able to keep you so thin?*

Jessica: *Well, I don't know that there's much of a reason other than I don't want to be fat.*

Therapist: *I know you have a lot of thoughts about why this part works to keep you so thin. I'm wondering if you could ask the part who's thinking about it to relax, so we can be with and get to know this one who restricts.*

Jessica: *Okay.*

Therapist: *Great. So, without thinking the answers, can you focus on the part of you who needs you to stay thin and notice where you find it in, on, or around, your body?*

Jessica: *Okay, I don't feel it, I hear it in my head.*

Therapist: *What is it saying?*

Jessica: *It says it's trying to keep me in control, because I feel so much better when I'm in control.*

Therapist: *Okay, that makes sense. What is it afraid will happen, though, in moments when you're not in control?*

Jessica: (long pause) *Ohhh. This is weird. I just got a flash of that feeling I would get when I knew my uncle was going to be around.*

Therapist: *Would it be okay to stay with that feeling and see what else comes up?*

In this session, Jessica got her thinking part and her restricting part to separate, or unblend, so she could relate directly with the restricting part. As she got curious about the restrictor, she learned how it worked to suppress the exiles who carried the dread and helplessness related to the abuse. By the end of the session, Jessica felt more open to hearing from these parts who still held memories of the abuse, wondering if she might learn more than she already knew.

The Importance of Getting Permission

The following morning, Jessica reported having a nightmare in which she had sensations of terror with which she had not connected earlier. She proceeded to purge several times that morning, to her surprise and consternation.

Jessica: *It was the worst nightmare. Even recounting it now, I can barely stand it. I feel a panic. And I can't believe I made myself throw up. I was doing so well.*

Therapist: *I know it feels awful, but this is an opportunity to get to know the part who's giving you the nightmare, as well as the one who gets you to purge. Can you ask the part who's panicked and the ones who are upset about the purging to give us some room so we can see if we can help them?*

Jessica: (quiet for a moment, and then agitated) *I just feel the panic. It's right here (points to her throat). It makes me want to throw up.*

Therapist: *Does the panicked part want to throw up or is that another part responding to the panic?*

Jessica: *The panic is separate. The throwing up part wants to get rid of the panic.*

Therapist: *Can you ask the one who wants to throw up if it would give us some room to be with the one who's panicked? Let it know that if it agrees, we can help the panic. And we can ask the panic to not flood you. Also, if the purging part needs to come back in, it can.*

Jessica: (takes a deep breath) *The part who wants to throw up is okay with that, but the panicked part is right there. And I'm starting to feel dizzy.*

At this moment, Jessica was blended with several protectors, with more heavy hitters showing up who perceived the exploration of the nightmare as a threat. Jessica had little access to her Self, so the therapist's Self needed to serve as the source of Self-energy for the therapist–client system. When Jessica's protectors would not separate, the therapist switched to direct access and spoke directly to Jessica's protectors.

Jessica: *I can't help it, I'm so panicked. I think I have to leave, go for a run.*

Therapist: *Okay, I get that it feels like you want to jump out of your skin, and, if you need to move, that's okay. But if you're open to it, tell me what you're afraid will happen if you don't get moving and get out of here?*

Jessica: *I'm afraid I'm going to die.*

Therapist: *I understand it feels like you're going to die, these feelings are so intense. The nightmare alerts us to parts of you who are stuck in the past in some terrible places. If we can witness what happened to them, we can give them the help they need now that they couldn't get then. Then they won't be alone, and it will feel very different.*

Jessica: *But the feelings are so intense.*

Therapist: *This is where you may need to borrow my faith, that if the exiles feel we're genuinely interested in knowing about their pain, they'll agree to not flood you. They haven't had a chance to be known and understood, so that's why they're pushing so hard, but they'll agree not to overwhelm you if they know we're interested in hearing their story.*

Now that Jessica's go-to protectors (restricting, bingeing, and purging) were less accessible to her in residential treatment, and after she experienced more curiosity about the impact of her trauma, exiles desperate to be known revealed themselves in her nightmare. Their emergence via the intense sensations triggered firefighters, who tried to distract with purging, panic, and dizziness. As they registered the therapist's calm, clear, and confident attitude regarding the exiles' ability to commit to not flood the system, Jessica's protectors started to relax. Still, because of the repeated betrayals she'd experienced at the hands of close family members, as well as her uncle, it took some time for them to trust both the therapist and Jessica's own Self before they would allow a direct connection with the exiles.

Witnessing, Retrieving, and Unburdening Exiles

When Jessica's protectors trusted that she could work with the exiles who showed up in her nightmare without their taking over, they allowed her to go to actual memories of her sexual abuse.

Therapist: *So, Jessica, check inside and see if there are any parts who object to us going to the part we noticed in the last session.*

Jessica: *They're a little guarded, but it's okay. I was on a bus, I think it was a school bus, and suddenly I realized there was a man in the seat behind me who was coming toward me with a bad look on his face. I didn't realize who it was at first. He reached over and started to grab my chest. I wanted to scream, but I couldn't. It was like I was anesthetized. I kept trying to scream and move, but I couldn't do anything. It was the worst feeling.*

Therapist: *So not being able to move or scream was the worst feeling, right?*

Jessica: *Uh huh.*

Therapist: *So, Jessica, how do you feel toward the part of you who was paralyzed by terror?*

Jessica: *It makes me really anxious.*

Therapist: *Understandably, for sure. But as you sit here right now, how do you feel toward this part of you who could not move on that bus?*

Jessica: *I feel sad for her, because I can feel how awful that was for her.*

Therapist: *Can she feel your presence?*

Jessica: *I can feel hers, but I don't know if she can feel mine.*

Therapist: *Will you ask her?*

Jessica: *Wow, she turned to look at me.*

Therapist: *Great, now that she knows she has your attention and care, see if she wants to tell you more about what that was like.*

Jessica: *She's terrified. There's nothing she can do to stop him from touching her.*

Therapist: *Stay with her, so she's not alone. How close can you get to her?*

Jessica: (sighs) *She's relieved that she's not alone—I can even breathe a little better.*

Therapist: *Is there more she wants you to know?*

Jessica: *She wants me to know how alone she was, that when she couldn't scream or get away from him, there was no one to help her.*

Therapist: *Let her know you can help her with that now. Ask her to show you what she needed on the bus.*

Jessica: *She needed someone she knew to have her back, so she could scream at him to get away.*

Therapist: *Okay, can you do that for her?* (Jessica nodded.) *Stay with her until she feels she's been able to do or say what she needs to.*

Jessica (after a long silence): *She's really strong for a little kid. She's brave. She doesn't care that he's so big, she told him to get the fuck away from her. Now she just wants to get out of there.*

Therapist: *Tell her she can do that. Where would she like to go?*

Jessica: *She wants to be with my dog at the beach we love.*

Therapist: *Okay, can you take her there?*

Jessica: *Yes, we're there.*

Therapist: *Ask her if there are any feelings or beliefs she got from being on the bus that she'd like to get rid of.*

Jessica: *She wants to let go of the belief that she's alone in the world. She wants me to hold her in the water so it can wash away the gross smell and feel of his hands on her.*

Therapist: *Can you do that with her?*

Jessica: *She giggled. She likes the water, and she likes me holding her. She feels cleaner.*

Therapist: *Before we stop, ask the parts who were hesitant about having us work with her how they are with this.*

Jessica: *They're good with it. They're saying this is just the tip of the iceberg, but it's a good start.*

Working with the terror and paralysis of the exile who was molested on the bus reassured Jessica's protectors that, bit by bit, her exiles' pain could be healed. It was a small success that portended future relief. As treatment continued, she was able to be with the experience of the little girl and many other young parts who endured years of sexual abuse and neglect.

Full recovery from the ED entailed healing these traumatized parts by witnessing both what had been done to them externally and how they became disconnected internally. As a result, the ED protectors could be liberated from their habitual and self-limiting roles.

The Unburdening Process: A Key to Healing Traumatized Systems

In the IFS model, healing occurs when parts who have been forced out of their naturally valuable states: (a) reconnect with the client's Self; (b) feel understood by the Self for what they endured; and (c) trust the Self's ability to take care of the internal system. Parts are willing to unload the extreme beliefs, roles, and feelings (burdens) they have acquired from the trauma once it is clear they are no longer necessary. Unburdening involves a series of interactions between the client's Self and the part. With the help of the client's Self, the part identifies the burden it would like to release and locates where it carries it in its body or mind. The client then asks the part how it would like to unload the burden, offering the possibility of various elements (e.g., light, water, wind, earth, fire) or anything else the part can think of. Once the burden has been fully released, the client asks the part what qualities it would like to invite into its body to take the place of what has been unloaded. Clients do not experience these as imaginary inner conversations, but as real interactions with live inner personalities.

The process of helping parts out of where they are stuck in the past and earning their trust so they can unburden can take time. This is especially true for traumatized parts whose extreme burdens reflect the severity of the wounds they protect. To illustrate, although everyone in our culture absorbs some extreme beliefs about appearance, especially women, people with EDs often have many parts who use these unrealistic ideals as a primary way to ward off significant pain and shame. Unburdening the protectors' extreme beliefs about appearance requires patience and persistence for both therapist and client as the various exiles are healed. A resurgence of body image concerns in a client who has made a lot of progress simply points to the existence of more work that needs to be done.

■ CONCLUSION

Although all good trauma therapies help the client safely process traumatic memories and reestablish trust in one's own ability to engage in relationships and feel fully functional and alive, IFS privileges the internal trusting relationship one has with one's own Self and the capacity to be with pain and not be overwhelmed by it. Clients are therefore less dependent (or counterdependent) on others, including the therapist, and less reliant on extreme ED behaviors to manage traumatic pain. Confidence in one's own capacity is reestablished, as well as Self-Compassion and compassion for others who have also suffered.

■ REFERENCES

Anderson, F. G., & Sweezy, M. (2016). What IFS offers to the treatment of trauma. In M. Sweezy & E. L. Ziskind (Eds.), *Innovations and elaborations in internal family systems therapy* (pp. 49–69). New York, NY: Routledge.

Catanzaro, J. (2016). IFS and eating disorders: Healing the parts who hide in plain sight. In M. Sweezy & E. L. Ziskind (Eds.), *Innovations and elaborations in internal family systems therapy* (pp. 49–69). New York, NY: Routledge.

Schwartz, R. C. (1995). *Internal family systems therapy.* New York, NY: Guilford Press.

Schwartz, R. C. (2001). *Introduction to the Internal Family Systems Model.* Oak Park, IL: Trailheads Publications.

CHAPTER 17

Structural Dissociation in the Treatment of Trauma and Eating Disorders

Kathleen M. Martin

■ INTRODUCTION

A part of me can't go to bed without a full stomach. I know I am not hungry, but the fear of waking up hungry is too much to bear. I can't stop myself. L. B.

It is well established that many eating disorders (EDs) have their roots in adverse life conditions (Backholm, Isomaa, & Birgegård, 2013; Brewerton, 2007; Moulton, Newman, Power, Swanson, & Day, 2015; Smyth, Heron, Wonderlich, Crosby, & Thompson, 2008). The ED becomes a strategy to manage the unhealed feelings and mental contents associated with these difficult conditions and experiences. Adverse life conditions are also the roots for dissociative processes (American Psychiatric Association, 2013; Boon, Steele, & van der Hart, 2011; Dorahy, Middleton, Seager, Williams, & Chambers, 2016; Fisher, 2017; Fosha, 2000; Gonzalez & Mosquera, 2012; Meichenbaum, 2012; Mosquera & Gonzalez, 2014; Ogden, Minton, & Pain, 2006; Schore, 2002; Siegel, 2003; Teicher, 2002; van der Hart, Nijenhuis, & Steele, 2006; van der Kolk, 2014), which explains why people with EDs have a high probability of having a dissociative process fueling the ED. It then stands to reason that clinicians who work with EDs must have a solid foundation in dissociation theory and the treatment of dissociation.

■ WHAT IS DISSOCIATION?

Dissociation is the inability to stay present when intolerable feelings and mental contents are activated (Steele, Boon, & van der Hart, 2017; van der Kolk, 2014). It is a way of making the overwhelming less overwhelming. A dissociative process is an unconscious attempt to sequester the intolerable away into the recesses of the mind, never to be contacted again. Much mental energy is needed to keep that material protected and isolated. Symptoms and maladaptive behaviors such as EDs develop to help deflect away from that material. These maladaptive behaviors can be viewed as substitute actions for dealing with what is too much. But our minds are dynamic and each time the intolerable contents are activated by conscious or unconscious associations, the need increases to use substitute actions to push the intolerable back into its isolated place. Therefore, dissociation grows with each unwanted intrusion. This causes an increase in the use of substitute actions for self-regulation, including EDs.

■ DEREALIZATION AND DEPERSONIFICATION

When an event overwhelms the person's window of tolerance and integrative capacity, the personality cannot naturally process it and heal it. Dissociation is unconsciously used to make the intolerable less intolerable, less real. Janet called this derealization (van der Hart & Horst, 1989; Steele et al., 2017). Derealization can range from downgrading the intensity to "it wasn't that bad" to complete amnesia. A process of fragmenting the intolerable pieces of the event and storing them in different neural networks, called emotional parts (EPs) in the structural dissociation model, is used to facilitate this derealization (van der Hart et al., 2006). This process of fragmentation is described in more detail later in this chapter.

A related process is called depersonification. This is depersonalizing the overwhelming, taking on the belief that "it did not happen to me." This occurs when the personality needs even more fragmentation to defend against the intolerable. Dissociative cognitive errors of separateness are used to solidify this depersonification. This means that there are fragments of the personality, EPs that cannot claim that the full history of the intolerable experiences is also their history. This depersonification benefits the entire person. When the intolerable mental contents are either activated into consciousness or threatening activation, the person can unconsciously switch focus to the fragment of the personality that carries the dissociative cognitive error of "it didn't happen to me." This makes it less real, less personal for the entire person.

An example of this is demonstrated in the case of a 19-year-old female with bulimia and a highly critical mother. The mother's chronic harsh criticisms overwhelmed her. A dissociative process started to defend against the fear, anger, and disappointment in response to the mother's behavior. A self-critical part of the personality was unconsciously developed, internalizing some of the mother's criticism. She developed a self-belief of "I'm not good enough," and this became the self-definition through which she viewed herself in relationship to her world.

The mother's criticism continued to overwhelm her. Consequently, she unconsciously increased her dissociative process by developing a dissociative cognitive error that the internal critic is separate from self, a different entity. The internal experience grew into experiencing the critic as external. Another dissociative cognitive error was then unconsciously developed, namely that Critic was not criticized by the mother, and its role was to "shape up" the daughter so the mother did not have reason to criticize her. Another unconscious dissociative cognitive error was developed in the belief that Critic did not have this mother as her mother. This depersonification contributed to the derealization of the mother's overwhelming harsh criticism for the entire person. It must be noted that this example of derealization and depersonification can happen even with people who do not have a *Diagnostic and Statistical Manual of Mental Disorders* (5th ed.; DSM-5; APA, 2013) diagnosable dissociative disorder, although the symptoms may not be as severe (Sar, Alioğlu, & Akyuz, 2017).

■ STRUCTURAL DISSOCIATION THEORY OF THE PERSONALITY

There are many theories of dissociation. This chapter uses structural dissociation theory of the personality that began with Pierre Janet in the 1880s (Fisher, 2017; Ogden et al., 2006; van der Hart & Friedman, 1989; van der Hart & Horst, 1989; van der Hart, Brown, & van der Kolk, 1989; van der Kolk & van der Hart, 1989) and was brought into modern time by Nijenhuis, Steele, and van der Hart (van der Hart et al., 2006). Structural dissociation theory distinguishes two action systems that govern human behavior. These action systems are psychobiological states and have very specific roles. The first action system is Daily Life. This includes all the activities involved with the survival of the species: reproduction, caretaking, energy management, work, play, and exploration (learning). Reading this chapter, for example, uses the exploration (learning) system within the Daily Life Action System.

The second action system is Defense. This deals with the survival of the individual. This action system is responsible for responding to threat, actual or perceived. Its responses include the following: fight, flight, freeze, submit, attachment cry, vigilance, and recuperation from the threat. Taking a mental health day after a stressful time is an example of the Defensive Action System recuperating from the threat. The client who has bulimia and calls her therapist's emergency contact information while having urges to self-harm is in the attachment cry. The anorexic female who is concerned that someone might think she is fat or ugly and therefore does not eat is in a submit response.

▧ MENTAL HEALTH

Before trauma overwhelms the system, these two action systems communicate and cooperate with each other effectively. They stay present with each other and, together, handle life events. Daily Living handles the daily life tasks, and Defense keeps watch for danger. When there is a threat, Defense says "I'll handle this," whereas Daily Living continues to think and help figure out appropriate responses. When the threat is over, the system processes any leftover feelings and information about the event together and moves on. Both action systems view life from the perspective of the present.

Imagine this scenario. You are driving to your office with Daily Living Action System thinking about your 9:00 a.m. client. Your Defensive Action System is involved in watching out for danger. Someone runs a stop sign in front of you. Defense immediately honks the horn and slams on the brakes. Daily Living shifts its orientation to assisting Defense with rational thinking about how to maneuver away from the car in your path. With a fast response on your part, the danger is avoided and the threat is over. You continue driving to your office. The spike of anger and fear in response to the threat is metabolized by both systems together. The affect and information is processed and discharged. Defense basically says to Daily Living, "That was a close call. We avoided a crash. Thanks for helping out. You can take over now, and I'll keep watch for any other jerks on the road." By the time you arrive at your office, you have settled. If there is more affect and information to process, you might call your spouse to tell the story or complain about unaware drivers with colleagues at the water cooler. Once all the affect and information is processed, your entire system continues with your day, no longer needing to think about the morning's event. It is just a piece of historical information. Any adaptive learning from the event, for example, how to maneuver the car under those conditions, is filed away for future use.

▧ TRAUMA OVERWHELMS THIS COOPERATION

Trauma is anything that is more than what the person can tolerate and integrate. When trauma occurs, it overwhelms mental health and its internal communication and cooperation (Lanius, Paulsen, & Corrigan, 2014; van der Hart et al., 2006). It is too much for the two action systems to stay present with each other. A structural divide occurs. This is the start of dissociation. The two action systems no longer communicate and cooperate as well. Both systems must contribute to managing the overwhelming affect and information, but they do so in different ways. Daily Life must numb itself to some degree to avoid the affect and traumatic information in the interest of returning to daily life tasks. Defense has the responsibility of storing and encoding this traumatic material. It does so by fragmenting the experience and relegating it to various memory networks, sometimes called parts of the personality.

The cost of this specialization of the two action systems is that Daily Life must numb and turn away from the full experience, including the Defensive Action System. Defense becomes locked in the past, and, when activated, relives it and experiences the vehement emotions and cannot fully claim the present. Defense now sees everything through the lens of the past unhealed material stored in its memory networks. Both action systems contribute and participate in the dissociation. Dissociation occurs across both action systems. As long as there is dissociation, the entire system is dissociated; and neither action system can contribute to the processing of the unhealed events while they are doing their respective avoiding and reliving.

■ APPARENTLY NORMAL PART OF THE PERSONALITY

When a structural divide happens between the two action systems, parts of the personality are created. The part of the personality that comes from the Daily Living Action System tries to appear normal to the external world, as if nothing is wrong, thus the name *apparently normal part* (ANP) of the personality. This part goes about normal daily tasks, while simultaneously developing avoidance toward the unhealed material necessary to stay focused on daily life. Even though the ANP might be high functioning, it is disconnected from one's full internal experience. This is a common presentation with ED clients. For example, the adolescent who has anorexia excels in most endeavors, is liked by most people, and appears quite normal but avoids most feelings. Or the bulimic young woman who is always giving people advice on healthy eating habits when in public, but does not know why she cannot take her own advice when she is home alone and binging.

■ EMOTIONAL PART OF THE PERSONALITY

Although the ANP must avoid cues or reminders of the unhealed material to attend to daily life, the Defensive System must manage all the unhealed hurts and psychological pain. The Defensive System fragments this pain in the interest of making it more tolerable for the full personality. Parts of the personality called EPs are created to hold these fragments of the overwhelming experiences with all the associated affect, cognitions, sensations, self-meanings, and behaviors used to manage this pain. The cost of this specialization is that EPs become locked in this past pain, often called trauma time (van der Kolk, 2014), and cannot fully claim experientially that the past is over. An EP views everything through the experience of the unhealed material locked in its memory network. EPs might not have access to the information stored in a different memory network that the events are over. Therefore, the present is seen through the lens of the past. As more psychological pain happens, more EPs can be developed to manage that pain; EPs can be developed to assist the ANP's avoidance of the mental contents even more. These are called protector parts. To some extent, every EP (and ANP) is a protector part as they help the entire system stay away from the overwhelming mental contents (derealization).

EPs are like software packages. They can run only the contents and strategies that have been unconsciously assigned to them and held in their memory bank. They are mediated by the limbic system, so the EPs do not have access to the adaptive information that is in the cortex. Therefore, they keep using the same strategies, substitute actions, and thought processes, and experience the same affect over and over. This is why an ED with a dissociative process cannot resolve itself on its own. If there is a dissociative process involved, the dissociation has to be treated.

■ THREE LEVELS OF DISSOCIATION

Structural dissociation theory defines three levels of dissociation. The first level is called *primary dissociation*. This occurs when something happens that is overwhelming, but only one EP and one ANP are needed to manage that event. The two parts of the personality can mostly stay present with each other, except when the overwhelming event is activated. Once activated, the communication and cooperation between these two action systems diminishes, and they do their respective functions: The ANP avoids and the EP relives the overwhelming event. This presentation resolves itself quickly once the dissociation is treated followed by processing the event to completion.

The next level of dissociation is *secondary dissociation*. At this level, there is one ANP and any number of EPs to manage the psychological pain. The diagnoses included in this level are EDs, addictions, other specified dissociative disorder (OSDD), complex posttraumatic stress disorder (PTSD), and borderline personality disorder (BPD). Many Axis II personality disorders can have a concurrent secondary dissociative process. Because of the intensity of the dissociative process at this level, a significant amount of time is usually necessary to treat the dissociation before reprocessing of the (previously) overwhelming memories can be successful. Trying to reprocess this material before the dissociation is sufficiently treated only increases the avoidance of the ANP because of the reliving of the events by the EPs who are still caught in trauma time.

The third level of dissociation, tertiary dissociation, is the highest level of dissociation. The diagnosis that belongs in this category is dissociative identity disorder (DID), characterized by loss of time by the ANPs. This is where the integrative capacity is so limited because of the chronic overwhelming stressors that two or more ANPs are needed to handle daily life tasks. Each ANP typically has its own specific role in the system and its own cluster of EPs. The ANPs may or may not have co-consciousness of each other and of the EPs; thus, their loss of time and loss of executive control of the system. Many EPs are needed to manage the unhealed psychological pain, and they may or may not be co-conscious of each other. Whereas the majority of clients with EDs with a dissociative process fall into the category of secondary dissociation, there are some ED clients who have tertiary dissociation.

■ DISSOCIATIVE PHOBIAS

The terms "avoidance," "resistance," and "dissociative phobias" refer to the mental energy used to distance from the unwanted psychological pain and anything that might trigger it. Structural dissociation theory literature uses the term "dissociative phobia" to refer to this avoidance. This reminds us that there is a dissociative process fueling the avoidance. Some of the common dissociative phobias are the following: (a) phobia to parts of the personality; (b) phobia to the traumatic material and the internal experience; (c) phobia to attachment and attachment loss; (d) phobia to experiencing self in one's body; and (e) phobia to adaptive change (Steele et al., 2017).

Dissociative phobias do not resolve through exposure in secondary and tertiary dissociation. If exposure to intolerable material occurs, dissociation is either unconsciously used again and/or increased in its intensity to defend against the intolerable psychological pain. A process of classical conditioning increases ANP avoidance and EPs' use of substitute behaviors with each intolerable exposure. If the ANP cannot stay present when the mental contents are activated, no healing can take place in response to the exposure. The system must redissociate (Steele et al., 2017; van der Hart et al., 2006).

How does the window of tolerance (Ogden et al., 2006) to the intolerable increase without exposure? The answer lies in the skills to treat dissociation. The ANP's tolerance for the positive affect of calm is the first agenda item in the treatment plan. Without the ability to tolerate calm, the ANP can only avoid through shutdown, the use of addictions, or remain in the negative unhealed material (e.g., I am fat). The ANP needs to learn the difference between calm and shutdown because shutdown is often mistakenly viewed as calm by people with trauma histories. Once the ANP gains skill to deactivate EP arousal and bring the system to calm, the ANP is more of a leader in the system and can provide self-stabilization more often.

With the ANP strengthened by successfully using these calming skills, the ANP is more ready to drop into the internal experience as a leader and observer rather than an avoider. The ANP is then more likely to tolerate a process of accessing, identifying, and learning about each EP's role within the system. This helps to develop ANP compassion toward the EPs that then increases internal communication and cooperation. Time orienting the EPs living in trauma time and treating dissociative phobias and dissociative cognitive errors slowly prepares the system for readiness to begin to tell the stories to get them processed and healed. Until readiness for exposure is established, premature exposure has the risk of unnecessarily lengthening the course of treatment because of the growth of dissociative phobia. Remember, exposure to the intolerable in secondary and tertiary dissociation only increases the dissociative phobias and the need to avoid.

■ PHASE-ORIENTED APPROACH TO THE TREATMENT OF DISSOCIATION

Treating dissociation is a phase-oriented approach (Brand & Loewenstein, 2014; Brown, Scheflin, & Hammond, 1998; Courtois, 1999; Steele, van der Hart, & Nijenhuis, 2005). The international guidelines to treat dissociation as established by the International Society for the Study of Trauma and Dissociation (ISSTD) define three phases (ISSTD, 2011). The first phase is stabilization and preparation for trauma reprocessing. This is where the dissociation is treated. The second phase is reprocessing the painful memories. The third phase is full consolidation and integration where the client learns how to handle life without the dissociation, processes through the leftover psychological pain that is finally accessible, deals with fears of intimacy, fully establishes healthy relationships, and completely returns to mental health.

■ CASE STUDY

Susan, 42 years old, came into treatment for anorexia nervosa after numerous unsuccessful treatments since she was 22 years old. Her treatment history included two inpatient psychiatric hospital stays, each lasting at least 6 months. She was desperate to find relief from her unremitting symptoms, but was also discouraged and fearful that this treatment would fail like all the others. She recently disclosed the severity of her struggle with food and eating to her husband and agreed to try treatment one more time.

Her history included childhood physical and emotional neglect in a family with monetary wealth. Her father frequently prohibited food in the house to help him manage his own ED. He traveled a lot and would not leave money for groceries. Mother was narcissistic and alcoholic, and left the home for days at a time, leaving the children to raise themselves. Susan was the oldest in her sibling group of three female children. There was periodic physical abuse from the father when he was home from business trips. The physical abuse typically happened when the children complained of hunger.

Susan remembered numerous times when both parents were gone with no food in the house. She took responsibility for her sisters' well-being as much as any little girl could. She remembers stealing from the local grocery and going hungry. She was terrified to ask her parents for food because of the history of how they responded to such requests. Neither parent seemed to notice that their children needed nutrition. Susan excelled in school and successfully worked to appear happy and normal to her peers and teachers. This was because of her strong ANP.

She rated high (49) on the Dissociative Experiences Scale (DES) and clearly had secondary dissociation with an OSDD diagnosis. Fraser's Dissociative Table Technique (Fraser, 1991, 2003; Martin, 2012; Paulsen, 2009) found nine EPs ranging from a felt experience of infancy to young adult. There was a part experienced as age 6 who was locked in the memories of extreme hunger, but terrified to do anything about it because of the father's history of violence. There was also a part experienced as a toddler locked in the attachment cry for the mother. Two other significant parts related to the ED were a part experienced as a 13-year-old and another at 22 years of age. The 13-year-old part held the strategies of the binge and purge, while hating the 6-year-old and toddler parts, and used the binge and purge to distract from the activation of these two EPs experienced as young (substitute actions). The part experienced as a 22-year-old used the anorexic strategy to defend against the shame and all the previously mentioned EPs (another substitute action).

When Susan started treatment, her father was dead and her mother was living in the same town as she. Her mother demanded that her daughter visit her at least twice per week with the grandchildren. The grandchildren were latency age and pubescent, and the grandmother had become highly critical of their bodies. Grandma would tell Susan how she was being a bad parent in front of the grandchildren, including criticism of how food was managed and allowed around the children. Susan invariably responded to her mother with compliance and shutdown, snapped at her children on the way home, and then secretly binged and purged. The children told Susan that they did not like how she became mean and withdrawn after visiting Grandma. She felt badly about this, another reason for reentering treatment. She prided herself on her parenting and did not want the ED passed down to her children.

After intake, the first treatment focus was to increase positive affect tolerance that was too low for good mental health and adaptive self-regulation. The client was taught the difference between calm and shutdown and why it is so important to be able to tolerate the positive affect of calm. Many calming skills were introduced and developed. This increased the window of positive affect tolerance and strengthened the ANP who now had more control over the internal experience. She could now more often bring the full system to calm rather than shutdown. Once positive affect tolerance was increased, more distraction and stabilization skills were either taught or reinforced to help the ANP gain greater skill in deactivating EP arousal from their maladaptive strategies. The ANP became more of a leader for the entire system and less avoidant of the internal experience.

Once positive affect tolerance and calming skills were in place, the focus became treating the dissociation. The client found relief through Fraser's Dissociative Table Technique (Fraser, 1991, 2003; Martin, 2012; Paulsen, 2009) in discerning the EPs and gained hope that her struggles could be resolved. Treatment worked to develop ANP insight into the functions of each EP, resulting in compassion toward them rather than avoidance and shutdown. This further strengthened the ANP's ability to deactivate EP arousal.

Time orienting the EPs was an important concurrent component to treatment at this point. The parts experienced as 13 and 22 years old were protector parts who functioned to help the entire system make the father's violence and mother's neglect and criticism less overwhelming (derealization). They hated the parts experienced as a toddler and 6-year-old, maintaining a dissociative cognitive error that the parental abuse, neglect, and attachment breaches did not happen to them, rather only to the "younger ones" (depersonification). This dissociative cognitive error was corrected at the pace the client could tolerate. With these two protector parts attended to and not defending so much against their history, the intensity of needing the ED behaviors significantly reduced. This finally allowed access to those parts experienced as younger who were frozen in the time of the abuse and neglect.

Treatment of these parts experienced as younger included a great deal of time orientation and repair of the following dissociative cognitive errors: (a) They really are children and have young bodies; (b) they are separate entities from each other and the rest of the system; (c) they still live in the childhood home; (d) what happened in teenage and adult years did not happen to them; (e) if they were to grow up, then the abuse of the older years would happen to them; and (f) they need to stay young so they would have a chance to have a good childhood with perfect parents.

The entire treatment thus far focused on treating the dissociation **without** exposure to the traumatic memories. When EPs wanted to tell a story of a past overwhelming event, the therapist quickly changed the focus of attention back to treating the dissociative process. The dissociative process still needed to be further reduced before readiness for reprocessing could be considered adequate. Previous treatment by other clinicians had always quickly gone into the trauma stories and accompanying affect with the best of intentions. However, without treating the dissociation first, exposure to the stories only increased the client's use of dissociation and the ED strategies to distract from the exposure. This is the most common clinical mistake made in the treatment of people with dissociation.

Treating the parts experienced as younger, establishing correct time orientation, and repairing dissociative cognitive errors moved the client into readiness for the second phase of treatment: reprocessing unhealed memories. This is when the memories are finally able to be told with the full system present with each part realizing and personifying the history and associated affect. This allows the full discharge of the affect and the full processing of the (previously) intolerable events. Because the dissociation was treated sufficiently, this phase went well. The type of psychotherapy used to reprocess the unhealed memories and mental contents was Eye Movement Desensitization and Reprocessing (EMDR) therapy (Shapiro, 2001). Always keeping in mind the theory of structural dissociation of the personality, the client's window of tolerance, and what memories/affect/mental contents still cannot be realized, exposure to the memories began with cautious titration to not overload the client's system and send her back into redissociating. We agreed to start with a latency age memory of the father's violence in response to voicing hunger. By this time in treatment, all parts of the personality could accept that this memory and the associated affect happened to her as one person.

As is common in reprocessing, other memories associated into the work. A clinical decision was then required: Examine and process the newly associated memory or return to the incident of the father's violence, while containing the associated memory until a later time. This clinical decision is informed by the client's needs and the window of tolerance in each specific moment. As in every case of treating dissociation, there were typical times when the system overloaded, correct time orientation was lost, and an EP activated into its substitute behaviors and thinking. When this happened, a return to Phase 1 (stabilizing and treating the leftover dissociation) was required.

Often times, a correct time orientation intervention was all that was needed to reestablish stability and return to reprocessing the incident. Other times when reprocessing was stopped by EP activation into substitute behaviors and thinking, more time in Phase 1 was needed to treat the dissociation. Early in the reprocessing of the father's violence, for example, the EP experienced as the toddler was activated into its substitute action of the attachment cry for the mother to defend against the realities of the father's violence. This would agitate the EP experienced as 13 years old who then began its substitute actions. All attempts to reprocess were halted and a return to Phase 1 occurred. Work was done in Phase 1 with the 13-year-old EP regarding the reality that the events happened to all parts, including the EP as toddler. The EP as 13 needed to realize that the EP as toddler was a necessary component for the entire system to fully realize the impact of the father's behavior. Once this was established, the EP as 13 had more compassion toward the EP as toddler and was enlisted in providing time orientation strategies to the toddler part.

Work was then successfully accomplished with the EP as toddler to establish correct time orientation, and realize that father's violence happened to this one person including the EP as toddler and that adulthood means that the childhood dangers are over. Once both parts (and the full system) could stay present with each other and with the associated information and affect of the targeted incident, a return to reprocessing occurred. With this alternation between Phase 2 (reprocessing) and Phase 1 (stabilizing and treating the dissociative process), the client remained stable and progressed as expected. As more memories were reprocessed, the ED behaviors decreased in frequency even more and eventually stopped. Susan's boundaries around her mother changed, and she no longer felt trapped in her mother's web of criticism and narcissism.

Gradually, Phase 3, consolidation and integration, became the primary focus of treatment. Nevertheless, this phase still required reprocessing of memories that later came out of occlusion, along with deeper levels of anger and disappointment, material that can be accessed only later in treatment. An example stands out. A poignant memory that had been worked on earlier in treatment was one of the mother looking directly at Susan while raising up a glass of wine as if in agreement with the father's behavior, when the father hit and yelled at Susan for asking for a serving of food. The earlier work on this memory mostly focused on the father's behavior. The deep sense of the mother's betrayal was now available for reprocessing, and the full person could now claim the anger and disappointment. Reprocessing of this event proceeded with intense sobbing and anger over the mother's narcissism and betrayal. The deepest discharge of anger and disappointment ever experienced by Susan was tolerated by the entire system.

Phase 3 also included dealing with learning how to lead life without dissociation and the ED. Although she earlier responded to life's difficulties with fragmentation and substitute behaviors such as the ED, Phase 3 found her grieving her inability to numb out her feelings with substitute actions. More skill development to handle life without the substitute actions was necessary. This revealed itself in her reports of social and work-related situations. She was scared that others might view her as too assertive if she voiced her opinions and let her abilities fully shine. This required role-playing her desired present-day social and work-related behaviors in the treatment office, implementing these practiced behaviors in real-life conditions, and returning to the treatment room to process any leftover feelings from past memories that associated into her attempts for change.

With the dissociation fully treated, Susan experienced herself as one full person with all the parts "blended." This was her term for the lack of internal fragmentation. She described this not as an elimination of the parts, but rather a melding of the parts into a cohesive adult whole, responding to life on the basis of the present, rather than on strategies that were developed in the past. The structural divide was successfully treated. Two years and 9 months after the start of treatment, she concluded therapy, empowered and content.

■ APPLICATION OF STRUCTURAL DISSOCIATION THEORY TO THE TREATMENT OF EATING DISORDERS

The case study of Susan demonstrates the importance of clinicians needing strong skills in diagnosing and treating dissociation when working with an ED client population. Not every person with an ED will meet criteria for a diagnosable dissociative disorder, but many will have a dissociative process. A major reason why ED symptoms do not remit is that the dissociation is not recognized and treated. The theory of structural dissociation provides a framework for case conceptualization and informs the treatment plan and the entire treatment process.

Structural dissociation theory can be integrated into any type of psychotherapy: systems, cognitive, behavioral, psychodynamic, relational, transpersonal, Jungian, ego state, hypnosis, EMDR, and sensorimotor. Clinicians working with clients with dissociation need ongoing case supervision with a supervisor trained in working with dissociation. There are many ways to become trained in dissociation skills. The ISSTD offers many online and regional conferences and trainings and is a good place to start. There is much literature available on the topic. Clinicians no longer need to reinvent the wheel. We now have a vast body of written knowledge to:

1. Assess and diagnose the level of dissociation.
2. Conceptualize the client's presentation and unremitting symptoms through the lens of dissociation.
3. Develop a treatment plan consistent with the international guidelines of a phase-oriented approach to treating dissociation.
4. Use dissociation treatment skills to identify and treat parts of the personality.
5. Use advanced skills in time orientation.
6. Refrain from using exposure strategies to the intolerable material until the dissociation is decreased, the window of tolerance is expanded, and the client can tolerate exposure and reprocess what used to be intolerable.

7. Understand and treat dissociative cognitive errors.
8. Assess when client readiness for reprocessing the unhealed material is established.
9. Titrate the reprocessing of the stored psychological pain to not overwhelm the integrative capacity of the individual.
10. Help the client learn how to lead life without the use of dissociation.
11. Return the client to full mental health.

■ CONCLUSION

The case of Susan describes a typical treatment for someone with both an ED and a dissociative process. The treating clinician had training in dissociation and quickly assessed and diagnosed the dissociative process that prevented the resolution of her symptoms in previous treatments. Susan periodically commented to her therapist that she wished she had found a therapist with dissociation skills sooner in life. She terminated treatment with the following statement:

This counseling was hard, but not nearly as hard as all the others. I quickly found hope in this treatment and understood why I couldn't stop the eating disordered behaviors over all these years. Before, I just felt I was too weak, not disciplined enough, and got more and more hopeless. I remember when you first did that dissociative table. I thought you were nuts. But I also remember being blown away by realizing I had deep parts of myself with conflicting agendas. You didn't think I was crazy. I remember the day I sobbed in your office when I finally realized how much I divided up my experience to get through life. It was hard, but also a turning point for me. I developed self-compassion and the ability to stay present with every aspect of me. Sometimes I wish I could still use dissociation when something bad happens. But now I have better skills to handle life, I stay connected to myself and my full experience, and I am contented. And, I know I won't pass down the eating disorder to my children. Thank you.

■ REFERENCES

American Psychiatric Association. (2013). *Diagnostic and statistical manual of mental disorders* (5th ed.). Arlington, VA: American Psychiatric Publishing.

Backholm, K., Isomaa, R., & Birgegård, A. (2013). The prevalence and impact of trauma history in eating disorder patient. *European Journal of Psychotraumatology, 4*, doi:10.3402/ejpt.v4i0.22482

Boon, S., Steele, K., & van der Hart, O. (2011). *Coping with trauma-related dissociation: Skills training for patients and therapists.* New York, NY: W. W. Norton.

Brand, B., & Loewenstein, R. J. (2014). Does phasic trauma treatment make patients with dissociative identity disorder treatment more dissociative? *Journal of Trauma & Dissociation, 15*(1), 5265. doi:10.1080/15299732.2013.828150

Brewerton, T. D. (2007). Eating disorders, trauma, and comorbidity: Focus on PTSD. *Eating Disorders, 15*, 285–304. doi:10.1080/10640260701454311

Brown, D., Scheflin, A. W., & Hammond, D. C. (1998). *Memory, trauma treatment and the law.* New York, NY: W. W. Norton.

Courtois, C. A. (1999). *Recollections of sexual abuse: Treatment principles and guidelines.* New York, NY: W. W. Norton.

Dorahy, M. J., Middleton, W., Seager, L., Williams, M., & Chambers, R. (2016). Child abuse and neglect in complex dissociative disorder, abuse-related chronic PTSD, and mixed psychiatric samples. *Journal of Trauma & Dissociation, 17*(2), 223–236. doi:10.1080/15299732.2015.1077916

Fisher, J. (2017). *Healing the fragmented selves of trauma survivors*. New York, NY: Routledge.

Fosha, D. (2000). *The transforming power of affect: A model for accelerated change*. New York, NY: Basic Books.

Fraser, G. A. (1991). The Dissociative Table Technique: A strategy for working with ego states in dissociative disorders and ego-state therapy. *Dissociation, 4*(1), 205–213.

Fraser, G. A. (2003). Fraser's "Dissociative Table Technique" revisited, revised: A strategy for working with ego states in dissociative disorders and ego-state therapy. *Journal of Trauma & Dissociation, 4*, 5–28. doi:10.1300/J229v04n04_02

Gonzalez, A., & Mosquera, D. (2012). *EMDR and dissociation: The progressive approach*. Charleston, SC: CreateSpace.

International Society for the Study of Trauma and Dissociation. (2011). Guidelines for treating dissociative identity disorder in adults, third revision. *Journal of Trauma & Dissociation, 12*(2), 115–187. doi:10.1080/15299732.2011.537247

Lanius, U. F., Paulsen, S. L., & Corrigan, F. M. (2014). Dissociation: Cortical deafferentation and the loss of self. In U. F. Lanius, S. L. Paulsen., & F. M. Corrigan (Eds), *Neurobiology and treatment of traumatic dissociation* (pp. 5–28). New York, NY: Springer Publishing.

Martin, K. M. (2012). How to use Fraser's Dissociative Table Technique to access and work with emotional parts of the personality. *Journal of EMDR Practice and Research, 6*(4), 179–186.

Meichenbaum, D. (2012). *Roadmap to resilience: A guide for military, trauma victims and their families*. Clearwater, FL: Institute Press.

Mosquera, D., & Gonzalez, A. (2014). *Borderline personality disorder and EMDR therapy*. Charleston, SC: CreateSpace.

Moulton, S. J., Newman, E., Power, K., Swanson, V., & Day, K. (2015). Childhood trauma and eating psychopathology: A mediating role for dissociation and emotion dysregulation? *Childhood Abuse & Neglect, 39*, 167–174. doi:10.1016/j.chiabu.2014.07.003

Ogden, P., Minton, K., & Pain, C. (2006). *Trauma and the body: A sensorimotor approach to psychotherapy*. New York, NY: W. W. Norton.

Paulsen, S. (2009). *Looking through the eyes of trauma and dissociation: An illustrated guide for EMDR therapists and clients*. Bainbridge Island, WA: Bainbridge Institute for Integrative Psychology.

Sar, V., Alioğlu, F., & Akyuz, G. (2017). Depersonalization and derealization in self-report and clinical interview: The spectrum of borderline personality disorder, dissociative disorders, and healthy controls. *Journal of Trauma and Dissociation, 18*(4), 490–506. doi:10.1080/15299732.2016.1240737

Schore, A. N. (2002). Dysregulation of the right brain: A fundamental mechanism of traumatic attachment and the psychopathogenesis of posttraumatic stress disorder. *Australian and New Zealand Journal of Psychiatry, 36*, 9–30. doi:10.1046/j.1440-1614.2002.00996.x

Shapiro, F. (2001). *Eye movement desensitization and reprocessing: Basic principles, protocols and procedures* (2nd ed.). New York, NY: Guilford Press.

Siegel, D. J. (2003). An interpersonal neurobiology of psychotherapy: The developing mind and the resolution of trauma. In D. J. Siegel & M. F. Solomon (Eds.), *Healing trauma: Attachment, mind, body, and brain* (pp. 1–56). New York, NY: W. W. Norton.

Smyth, J. M., Heron, K. E., Wonderlich, S. A., Crosby, R. D., & Thompson, K. M. (2008). The influence of reported trauma and adverse events on eating disturbance in young adults. *International Journal of Eating Disorders, 41*, 195–202. doi:10.1002/eat.20490

Steele, K., Boon, S., & van der Hart, O. (2017). *Treating trauma-related dissociation: A practical integrated approach*. New York, NY: W. W. Norton.

Steele, K., van der Hart, O., & Nijenhuis, E. R. (2005). Phase-oriented treatment of structural dissociation in complex traumatization: Overcoming trauma-related phobias. *Journal of Trauma & Dissociation, 6*(3), 11–53. doi:10.1300/J229v06n03_02

Teicher, M. H. (2002). Scars that won't heal: The neurobiology of child abuse. *Scientific American, 286*(3), 68–75.

van der Hart, O., Brown, P., & van der Kolk, B. A. (1989). Pierre Janet's treatment of post-traumatic stress. *Journal of Traumatic Stress, 2*, 379–395. doi:10.1002/jts.2490020404

van der Hart, O., & Friedman, B. (1989). A reader's guide to Pierre Janet on dissociation: A neglected intellectual heritage. *Dissociation, 2*(1), 3–16.

van der Hart, O., & Horst, R. (1989). The dissociation theory of Pierre Janet. *Journal of Traumatic Stress, 2*, 397–412. doi:10.1007/BF00974598

van der Hart, O., Nijenhuis, E., & Steele, K. (2006). *The haunted self: Structural dissociation and the treatment of chronic traumatization.* New York, NY: W. W. Norton.
van der Kolk, B. A. (2014). *The body keeps the score: Brain, mind, and body in the healing of trauma.* New York, NY: Viking.
van der Kolk, B. A., & van der Hart, O. (1989). Pierre Janet and the breakdown of adaptation in psychological trauma. *American Journal of Psychiatry, 146*(12), 1530–1540. doi:10.1176/ ajp.146.12.1530

CHAPTER 18

Second Helpings: AEDP (Accelerated Experiential Dynamic Psychotherapy) in the Treatment of Trauma and Eating Disorders

Natasha C.N. Prenn and Jessica K. Slatus

■ INTRODUCTION

Accelerated experiential dynamic psychotherapy (AEDP) is an attachment-oriented, emotion-focused model of psychotherapy and trauma treatment. AEDP is grounded in the belief that we are all innately resourceful and driven toward health and wholeness. When given the care and attention of an attuned, responsive caregiver, we will naturally flourish. According to Diana Fosha, developer of the model, "The roots of … resilience are to be found in the sense of being understood by and … existing in the heart and mind of a loving, attuned, and self-possessed other" (2003, p. 228). In contrast, the roots of psychopathology—or the problems that bring our clients to treatment—lie in the painful experience of "unbearable aloneness" with overwhelming feelings or events (Fosha, 2000b). Eating disorders (EDs) and dissociation are symptoms of this plight of aloneness: They are self-protective strategies to quell anxiety and manage the distress associated with unsafe or unwelcome emotions, and they are self-reliant in design. As AEDP therapists, we assert ourselves as safe and secure attachment figures for our ED clients, undoing their aloneness and offering a warm and reliable relationship to hold and explore feelings previously experienced on their own.

The ethos and metapsychology of AEDP are organized around change—and change for the better. Current research on attachment and neuroplasticity suggests that new experiences of emotion and connection wire and rewire the brain (Siegel, 2003). In this chapter, we detail the course of AEDP treatment for clients with active EDs. We use vignettes and a transcript from a live therapy session to highlight salient concepts and illustrate AEDP interventions in action. From our initial clinical assessment to the moment-to-moment processing of affect and, ultimately, trauma healing and integration, we seek to offer our clients a *new, embodied emotional experience* within the context of a *new, authentic relational experience*. We invite our clients to connect with us and to reestablish contact with their feelings and bodies, embarking together on small rounds of focused experiential work that we follow with shared and explicit reflection and processing. Developing the capacity to "feel and deal while relating" is the hallmark of mental health in AEDP and the foundation for sustained ED recovery (Fosha, 2000b).

■ CLINICAL ASSESSMENT IN AEDP

AEDP is fundamentally an experiential model. In an initial session with a client, we are more interested in what is happening *here-and-now* than what has happened to him or her *there-and-then*. We do not conduct a formal psychosocial assessment of the client; rather, we learn a great deal about our client's lived history by working explicitly and experientially with affect and attachment. We use the schema of an upside-down triangle—*the triangle of experience*—to help us track the client and the process. With core emotion and experience at the bottom angle, and anxiety and defense on the top two angles, the therapist is able to mentally chart where the client is, moment-to-moment, in session. For clients with EDs, we pay close attention to which feelings are comfortable for the client and which seem to cause anxiety or overwhelm; how the client responds to affirmation; to what degree he or she can take in care and affection from the therapist (Slatus, 2018); how he or she interacts with young, sick, or more vulnerable parts of himself or herself; and how he or she relates to his or her physical body (i.e., self-soothing, body checking, ignoring, dissociating, etc.; see Figures 18.1–18.3 for triangles adapted to anorexia, bulimia, and binge eating).

AEDP uses two versions of the triangle of experience to conceptualize where we are in the process and what piece of work we are doing. The first represents what AEDP calls the client's *self-at-best*, or the resilient self. Here he or she is emotionally resourced,

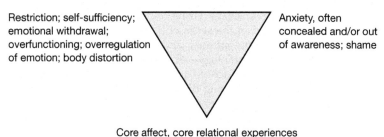

Restriction; self-sufficiency; emotional withdrawal; overfunctioning; overregulation of emotion; body distortion

Anxiety, often concealed and/or out of awareness; shame

Core affect, core relational experiences (intrapsychic and interpersonal nourishment)

FIGURE 18.1   Triangle of anorexia.

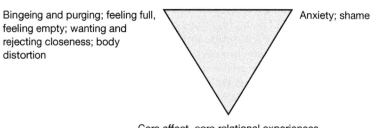

Bingeing and purging; feeling full, feeling empty; wanting and rejecting closeness; body distortion

Anxiety; shame

Core affect, core relational experiences (intrapsychic and interpersonal nourishment)

FIGURE 18.2   Triangle of bulimia.

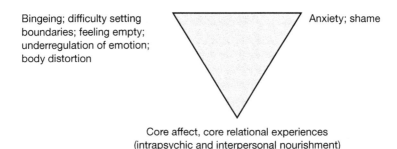

Bingeing; difficulty setting boundaries; feeling empty; underregulation of emotion; body distortion

Anxiety; shame

Core affect, core relational experiences
(intrapsychic and interpersonal nourishment)

FIGURE 18.3 Triangle of binge eating.

anxiety is at a minimum, and defenses are fluid. He or she has an accurate perception of himself or herself and his or her body. The second represents what AEDP calls the client's *self-at-worst*, or compromised self. This is an underresourced version of himself or herself, where anxiety is high, defenses are engaged, and his or her body image and sense of self are distorted.

Figure 18.4 depicts a self-at-best triangle that we have created specifically for EDs, in which the client has access to his or her internal physical and emotional cues, has minimal anxiety and shame about his or her emotional experience and his or her body, is authentically engaged with the therapist as a safe attachment figure, and symptoms are transient, if in existence at all.

Figure 18.5 depicts a self-at-worst triangle for EDs: An uptick of emotion, historically experienced alone, triggers anxiety and shame in the present moment, over-self-reliance,

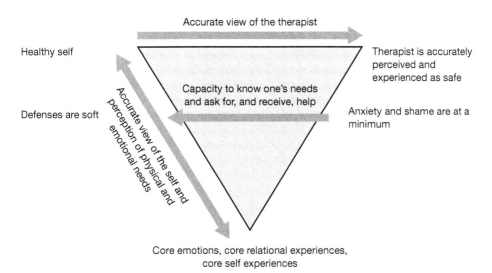

Accurate view of the therapist

Healthy self

Therapist is accurately perceived and experienced as safe

Accurate view of the self and perception of physical and emotional needs

Capacity to know one's needs and ask for, and receive, help

Defenses are soft

Anxiety and shame are at a minimum

Core emotions, core relational experiences,
core self experiences

FIGURE 18.4 Self-at-best triangle for eating disorders.

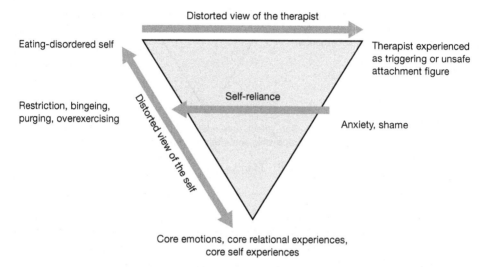

FIGURE 18.5 Self-at-worst triangle for eating disorders.

and a tendency to experience the therapist as a triggering or unsafe attachment figure, all of which sets the stage for body dysmorphia and symptom use.

It is important to keep in mind that these triangles are not intended to be hard and fast categories; rather, they are experiential descriptions of a client's manner of relating to himself or herself and to the therapist, at any given moment.

Preparing for Trauma Processing in AEDP

The arc of treatment in AEDP corresponds with a conceptual map that includes *four-state* and *three-state transformations* (see Fosha, 2009a, for further elaboration on the states and state transformations in AEDP). We seek to move clients from anxiety and defense-dominated functioning (State 1) to core affect and relational experiences (State 2). As our work together progresses, we help them to integrate these experiences through a process of mutual exploration and reflection called *metaprocessing* (State 3) that culminates in the emergence of a consolidated sense of self and a cohesive personal narrative in *core state* (State 4; Fosha, 2006b; Russell & Fosha, 2008).

From the beginning of treatment, AEDP interventions are focused on building safety and regulating anxiety so that core affect can surface. Once there is enough safety in the relationship to hold emergent affect in the present moment, the therapist's focus shifts to deepening and expanding these experiences. The therapist then metaprocesses, help-ing the client to reap the benefits of accessing his or her emotions without the burden of anxiety, shame, or defenses that were historically present. The invitation to reflect on this new experience with the therapist in the present moment helps him or her to transi-tion into core state, where he or she has an accurate perception of himself or herself and his or her own needs, and of the therapist. Much like ED recovery itself, progression through the states is not a linear process. Each treatment is uniquely cocreated by the client–therapist dyad, with the pacing and the interventions tailored specifically to the dynamic of the pair.

When we feel accompanied by another person, our capacity for growth and exploration is expanded (Bowlby, 1988; Obegi & Berant, 2009; Schore, 2001; Siegel, 1999). From the beginning of treatment, the AEDP therapist seeks to become a reliable attachment figure for the ED client and looks for opportunities to foster the relationship between the client's self-at-best and his or her ED self. We work to build safety in the therapy relationship as quickly as possible, and take great care to be attuned, responsive, and real. We are actively affirming, noticing all that our clients are doing well; we ask for their permission and check in often about how they, as individuals, and we, as a dyad, are doing. We follow their lead whenever possible and gently guide them whenever necessary (Circle of Security, 1998). We pay close attention to what we see happening emotionally, somatically, and relationally, and we make this explicit between us. To be clear, this is *not a neutral therapeutic stance*. The AEDP therapist is bravely and authentically engaged in the process. Depending on the client and the particular juncture of the work, the therapist may offer up his or her heart, brain, sense of humor, humility, tears, and/or lived experience.

AEDP is a transparent therapy process and it is collaborative: We make an intervention, track our client's reaction, and allow that to inform our next move. We invite our clients to be active partners in the work; we are explicit about the process as it is unfolding, and consolidate therapeutic gains by platforming, or reflecting on the work together. We use a combination of *moment-to-moment tracking* and *metaprocessing* to keep the process in the present moment and to guide the sequence of our interventions. Moment-to-moment tracking involves slowing down and detecting shifts in our clients' affect, body language, and manner of relating, and making these explicit (Fosha, 2000b). Metaprocessing keeps the therapy process relational and experience-near, and makes explicit all that we are doing. Asking a client "what it is like" emotionally and somatically orients him or her toward her internal experience and communicates that the therapist is interested in what is happening for him or her. Moreover, it allows the client and the therapist to have an experience together and gives them a road map for how they will proceed in their work.

AEDP is a change-oriented model. Whereas many therapies focus on what is going *wrong* in the client's life (i.e., the reasons he or she came to treatment to begin with, which seems like a logical place to start!), we explicitly focus on what is going *right*. We look for evidence of our clients' health and resilience, and *privilege the positive* whenever possible. In particular, we focus on helping our clients build their *receptive affective capacities*, or to receive—and hold onto—positive experiences of emotion and attachment (Fosha, 2006a). By positive, we do not mean to imply joyful or happy, although this may be part of it. We are talking about embodied experiences of affect and connection that "feel right and true" (Fosha, 2009b, p. 255). Our goal is to bypass the protective armor of the ED and move the client into a place of direct connection with his or her emotions and body.

Privileging the positive is an AEDP refrain that resonates frequently in work with clients with EDs: Their defenses are often organized around difficulty receiving and holding on to positive experiences (Slatus, 2018) so that just noticing a momentary sign of pride or joy can launch us directly into the therapeutic work. The following vignette is an example of how AEDP explicitly privileges health and resilience over pathology.

ROBERTA

It is their first session. Roberta, a staunchly self-reliant woman with anorexia, sits across from the therapist, arms crossed, expressing anger and disappointment with herself for continuing to struggle with food. "I can't believe I am still dealing with this. It's such a stupid problem to have," she says, looking past the therapist. The anger feels noxious, and the therapist senses that if she follows her down that path, it will lead them to a place of hopelessness and despair (see *pathogenic affects* in Fosha, 2000b). Consider what happens when the therapist chooses not to deepen Roberta's anger and disappointment and, instead, offers a new experience. "I wonder if you can appreciate how much the eating disorder has protected you, Roberta," she replies. "Would it be okay if we just made some space for how this part of you was really there for you?" The corners of Roberta's mouth turn up ever so slightly. The therapist is tracking her and can see that something is happening. She describes what she sees: "a smile. . . ." Roberta looks up for a moment and makes eye contact with the therapist before she looks away again. The therapist metaprocesses: "Your reaction?" "I've never thought about it that way before," Roberta answers. "I just spend so much time blaming myself for all that I've put my family through." "Yes," the therapist continues, "and if you do let yourself make some room—you were really just trying to take care of yourself." Roberta's face softens as she smiles again. Roberta's smile is what Fosha (2000b) calls a *green signal*, a glimmer of the healing self, the part that wants to be seen, even if momentarily.

Let us review what just happened: The therapist invites Roberta to have some compassion for herself around the ED. Roberta's smile helps the therapist to know that they are on the right track. The therapist, transparent, makes it explicit. Then, the client looks at the therapist: another green signal! The therapist seizes the opportunity to deepen and amplify the emotion behind the smile, so she metaprocesses. Had she not been vigilantly tracking the client and on the lookout for signs of Roberta's healthy self, the therapist might have tried to explore Roberta's defensive "feeling" of culpability. In privileging this glimmer of the positive, she was able to access a less self-critical part of the client. The therapist and the client are now in a much stronger position to begin the work of trauma healing.

Riding the Wave Together: Trauma Processing in AEDP

Trauma processing in AEDP involves the client and the therapist bravely accessing and riding the wave of affect and experience together. In session, how do we help our clients to "feel and deal," so that they do not resort to overregulating or underregulating their emotions, as they overregulate or underregulate their food? Using the strength and security of the attachment relationship in the present moment, the therapist invites the client to revisit past hurts from the vantage point of his or her most resourced self. Together the client and the therapist access and process emotional experiences "to completion" (Fosha, 2000b): to the point where the feelings and the pain of the trauma and its consequences are deeply felt without the burden of anxiety, shame, constriction, or flooding; to a place where the client feels okay. Through a combination of moment-to-moment tracking, relational interventions, and metaprocessing, the therapist seeks to undo the client's aloneness, helps to titrate his or her emotions, and then helps to metabolize them so that the client can use the information his or her emotions are providing—what emotion theory calls the *adaptive action tendency* inherent in all our different feelings (Frijda, 1986; Greenberg, Rice, & Elliott, 1993; Safran & Segal, 1990). The client has a new experience of feeling accompanied with his or her internal experience and emerges more emotionally and relationally versatile.

EMILY

In Emily's family of origin, feeling sad was not tolerated. Whenever she cried or was visibly sad, her father would tell her to "just grow up." She began to cope with her feelings by bingeing. In session, whenever sadness threatens to come to the fore, Emily looks away and begins to criticize herself. A moment in session: "Mmm, something shifted," the therapist says. Emily looks at the therapist briefly and looks away. "You look away …." Emily begins to tear up. The therapist continues, "I wonder if you could allow yourself to look at me." She looks at the therapist; more tears come. "This is so important," the therapist continues. "I'm so glad you're allowing yourself to." Emily nods, continuing to make eye contact. Feeling sad while staying engaged with the therapist is vulnerable, new territory for Emily. Her therapist wants this new experience to stick, so she takes care to make sure that they are safely within a "window of tolerance" (Siegel, 1999), where anxiety is controlled enough for growth and learning to take place. The therapist uses affirmation to help regulate Emily's anxiety. "You're doing great, Emily." Emily smiles. The client and the therapist are on track. There is now enough safety in this moment to invite her to access and explore previously overwhelming emotional states and memories.

The therapist harnesses this positive, new experience of attachment through metaprocessing. "What's it like to allow yourself to look?" "Scary," Emily says, shyly. The therapist continues to use the relationship to regulate the client's anxiety. "Just check in. Can you feel me here with you?" "Yeah," Emily replies. "How do you know? What is the sense of that in your body?" asks the therapist. "Just warm here *(puts hand on chest),*" Emily replies. "So let's just notice that *(therapist puts her hand on her own chest).*" Emily begins to cry. "Thank you. I've never had someone with me while I cried before."

As in mother–infant dyads, we seek to maximize the time we spend together in places that feel authentic and "right" and to minimize the time and energy that our clients spend in anxious, defensive, or traumatizing "alone" states. The therapist's caring, attuned presence, made explicit within the dyad, often unleashes the client's grief about not having had this kind of relationship earlier, a process known in AEDP as *mourning-the-self* (Fosha, 2000b). Emily and her therapist, now coordinated, are in a better position to explore this grief.

For clients with more complex trauma histories, targeting core affect and experiences may lead to roadblocks. After all, the more complex the trauma is, the more complex the client's security system has to be. The roadblocks, defenses, and anxiety at the top of the triangle of experience then become the focus of the work. A lot of therapy work is in State 1, as we endeavor to establish and reestablish safety with our clients who have been so hurt in the past. Here we maintain an attachment-oriented, experiential focus and closely track what is emerging in session. We are careful not to retraumatize our clients by reliving or reexperiencing past pain; rather, we want them to have a new and different experience with us.

We want our clients to feel accompanied, be it by the therapist or a stronger, wiser, and kinder part of themselves (Circle of Security, 1998). We titrate our closeness or distance according to what feels safe for the client, and we make a lot of room for different "parts" of the client that may come to the fore in the process. We use the term "parts" to refer to aspects of the client's self that hold distinct feelings, experiences, and responsibilities within his or her identity (Schwartz, 1995; see Chapter 16—Internal Family Systems). For example, in ED work, there is often a part of the client who wishes to get better and a part who does not; a part who understands the severity of his or her symptoms, and yet a part who feels compelled to restrict, overeat, or purge. When treating clients with complex posttraumatic stress disorder, we often use intrarelational AEDP (AEDP-IR; Lamagna & Gleiser, 2007) to call on healthier parts of the client's self to help regulate or provide for the more traumatized parts of the client.

In the following vignette, the therapist is working with a bulimic client who has been abused and neglected by multiple caregivers in the past. Historically, the client has taken great pains to get away from this traumatic past, using drinking, drugs, sex, and food to dissociate from painful memories and flashbacks. All too often she has had to fend for herself, both physically and emotionally, and her ED is but one concrete manifestation of her unwilled self-reliance. In this session, she makes contact with a memory of herself as a very lonely child cooking soup on the stove. In this particular case, the therapist engages the client in a *portrayal*, a guided imagery exercise that provides the client with the opportunity to redo a traumatic event with a different ending. We want the client to reconstruct, rather than relive, the past.

SARAH

The therapist begins by trying to bring the memory alive with great detail. She asks the client, "What do you see when you envision this little girl part of you, Sarah?" "Her hair is in braids, she's wearing a white t-shirt and old shorts. It's winter. She's crying a bit," Sarah says. "Mmm … tell me more." Sarah replies, "She's lonely … and sad."

The therapist tries to use the relationship to fortify the client. "As you go back there, feel me there with you." Sarah shakes her head and looks away. "I don't know. I feel you here, but I don't know how to take you into the scene." She looks distressed. "This is important work, Sarah. You're doing great," the therapist affirms to regulate anxiety. Sarah's shoulders relax a bit. "This is hard work," the therapist continues. "I wonder if you can feel your adult self with you as you picture that sad little girl …." Sarah, tearful, closes her eyes as she imagines. She nods. "You are there with her. What would you say or do?" "I'd give her a hug and wrap her in a big blanket, because she's so cold." The therapist reinforces the connection between Sarah's very capable adult self and her lonely child part. "Can you picture that?" "Yes, yes," Sarah says. She looks up and meets the therapist's eyes. "And how does she feel?" the therapist asks. "Oh, she feels so good. Someone finally found her. She doesn't have to be cold anymore." "Mmm, I'm so glad. She's been found." This is an important moment of reunification between Sarah's present-day self and this young, traumatized part of her. The therapist wants to deepen and expand it. "Tell me more," she says. "She feels warm, she's not alone. It's going to be okay."

The therapist continues to reinforce the work by repeating the client's words and metaprocessing the experience at every step. "It's going to be okay…. And let's just check in with your adult self. What's it like to be able to do this for your little girl?" "I'm so happy, I want to take her hand and take her away from there," Sarah says as the color comes back into her face. She looks energized. "And if you let yourself imagine …." Sarah is quiet as she imagines taking her little girl's hand and leading her away from this abusive environment.

When Sarah looks up, she has tears in her eyes. "Mmm, what's happening now?" the therapist asks. "She doesn't have to live like that anymore. She's safe now." "And these tears …?" "I'm just so happy," Sarah says. These are not tears of sadness; they are tears of relief, as her younger part is being freed of this burden (see *postaffective breakthrough affects* in Fosha, 2000b; Russell & Fosha, 2008). "Yes, tell me … what does it feel like?"

"Just like wrapped in a blanket … she can be free … to be a child. She's not worrying so much."

"Oh, I'm so glad, I'm so glad," the therapist smiles. The therapist is deeply moved by this. She tells this to Sarah, who looks up. They sit together silently for a few moments, making strong eye contact. The therapist metaprocesses: "What's it like to do this piece today?" Sarah's response is robust: "I feel strong, I feel like she's with me and she's going to be okay … and I'm going to be okay."

The previously mentioned vignette is an example of how we foster intrapsychic integration in AEDP. Sarah has revisited a painful memory and with the therapist's presence, support, and moment-to-moment attunement, she has come to a place of reunion. In the metaprocessing, Sarah is able to fully experience her child self without losing her adult footing. Both Sarah and her therapist continue to reference the image of this reunification throughout treatment, and Sarah is able to return to it outside of session when she is feeling alone and is tempted to binge or purge.

Metaprocessing and Trauma Integration in AEDP

Metaprocessing is an essential element of any AEDP treatment process. It undoes our clients' aloneness with dysregulating new experiences and helps them to metabolize them instead. It is akin to postmeal processing groups at ED treatment centers, where clients are asked to check in with their bodies and their emotions after eating (Slatus, 2018). "What was it like to try ice cream today?" "How was it to finish all of your grilled cheese and not purge?" "How was it to leave some of the peanut butter on your plate when you were full?" These groups encourage clients to be mindful of their physical experience and to disengage from distorted thoughts or symptomatic behaviors. They help them to move from fear and anxiety-based functioning (i.e., if I eat that, I will get fat/am bad) to sitting with their actual somatic and emotional experience (i.e., I feel full/queasy/proud/anxious). The more our clients can do so, the more they can tolerate it and continue to take more risks. Like good enough parents (Winnicott, 1971), we help them to stretch until they can do it alone.

Metaprocessing helps our clients to organize and cement new experiences. In many therapies, the client's arrival at new insight or experience marks the completion of a piece of work. In AEDP, "What is usually the endpoint of the therapeutic work is the starting point" for another round of work aimed at consolidating, integrating, and reinforcing the therapeutic gains (Fosha, 2000a, p. 72). When we lead in metaprocessing, we offer the opportunity to put words and thoughts, or left-brain language, on right-brain experiences. Through this process, an integrated, compassionate narrative of the self, known in AEDP as core state (State 4), emerges (Fosha, 2000b). In core state, the client's self-at-best is online, and he or she has the capacity to tune into his or her physical and emotional needs, to regard his or her body with compassion, and to accurately perceive others.

The following transcript illustrates a wave of emotion processing in AEDP, from anxiety and defense to core affect, metaprocessing, and finally core state. Dawn, a young woman who struggles with alternating between bingeing and restricting, is talking about a relationship with a previous therapist whom she had seen as a child and by whom she had felt helped and understood.

We introduce the transcript by highlighting the gains that Dawn makes in this session. By the end of the transcript, she allows herself to be vulnerable while staying connected with the therapist in the present. She has an awareness of herself as no longer being lonely, but, rather, as being connected in multiple present, responsive relationships. She takes risks and has an increased ability to tolerate her fear, and she asks for what she needs (i.e., a hug from the therapist). We have highlighted AEDP concepts and interventions in bold.

DAWN

(Client tearing up)

TH: Let's just take a moment for these feelings that are coming up as you think of her. What is her name? [**Moment-to-moment tracking; wanting to make room for these feelings**]

CL: Vanessa.

TH: What happens when you remember her and how she was there for you and how you talked to her? [**Orienting the client to her internal experience in the here-and-now**]

CL: Well, then one day I didn't see her anymore and I had to see all these horrible therapists that might have been good but I didn't like them.

TH: What happened?

CL: And then a year later, my mom told me that she died.

TH: *(empathically with pained, surprised voice)* Oh my gosh! Oh my gosh! That's terrible. [**Self-disclosure of therapist affect and impact of client's experience on therapist**]

CL: She had a stroke so she couldn't see me anymore, but my mom didn't tell me *(Client crying)*.

TH: Oh, I'm so sorry.

CL: And one day we were just shopping and I was like, "Whatever happened to Vanessa?" and she was like, "She died" *(looks pained)*.

TH: That's so hard. [**Explicit expression of empathy**]

CL: Yeah.

TH: How are you feeling as you're talking about it now? [**The therapist checks in and metaprocesses** *in the present*]

CL: *(a bit detached)* Not liking how my parents handled that.

TH: Yes, there's that piece. But I felt like a moment of heartache. [**Therapist reorienting the client to her affect by self-disclosing her own affect and reaction to what the client has shared**]

CL: Yeah *(crying)*.

TH: Like she was there for you ….

CL: I wish I could have gone to her funeral or ….

TH: *(empathically)* You didn't even know.

CL: I wish I could have made her a get well soon card or something like that.

TH: *(softly)* Yeah…. Yeah.

(Client crying)

TH: You were so connected to her. [**The therapist is explicit, organizing, and affirming**]

CL: She would say, like, "Do you know who also didn't have friends when they were younger? Me!" And I was like, that's such good news because I want to be just like you. You're awesome!

TH: I love that, that she could share that and you could really take that in and feel connected and close to her *(Client blows nose, exhales)*. I feel both. I feel both so moved by your relationship with her and really sad for you that you didn't know what was happening and didn't get a chance to say goodbye. 'Cause goodbyes are so important. [**Therapist self-discloses again and models making room for feeling moved and connected and sad**]

CL: I would love to go visit her grave now. I just want to know where to find her …. [**Adaptive action tendency associated with being able to feel her emotion and connection to another**]

TH: What's happening right now? [**Keeping it experiential**]

CL: I'm just feeling like I feel like I'm chipping away at why it's hard to let the good people in.

TH: Mm hmm, this fear of losing people suddenly. [**Organizing the client's experience**]

CL: I never thought about it like that (*Makes eye contact with the therapist*).

TH: So what is your reaction to that now as we're sitting here talking about it? [**Therapist keeps the focus on the here-and-now; uses "we" language to emphasize the attachment relationship**]

CL: Well, I don't want to not let people in because of her, because she would want me to let people in.

TH: Mm-hmm. [**Paraverbal intervention; the client is on the right track and the therapist wants to explicitly accompany her without interrupting the process**]

CL: I'm feeling also very spiritual, like I want her to know that I'm still getting help.

TH: Mm-hmm. What do you want her to know? Like if she were here and she could hear you right now ….

CL: I would want to say, "Thank you so much." [**Gratitude—State 3 phenomenon on the heels of emotion processing**]

TH: Mm-hmm, mm-hmm ….

CL: And I want to tell her that I'm not going to not let people in because of what happened to her.

TH: How does that feel to say?

CL: (*Nodding*) I think she'd be very happy.

TH: Mm-hmm. I bet she would.

(*Pause. Client making strong eye contact*)

CL: I feel really connected to you, Jessica. [**State 2 experience of connection to the therapist; client experiencing the therapist as a True Other**]

As the therapist makes room for the client's connection to the former therapist, as well as to the grief associated with this loss, a sense of connection to the current therapist arises. It is new for Dawn to be able to say this, and the therapist seeks to privilege this new experience.

TH: Mm, tell me … I feel really connected to you, too. [**Self-disclosure**]

CL: I'm really happy I have you.

TH: Mm, me too.

TH: What's it like to be really connected to me? [**Metaprocessing**]

CL: I'm trying not to let it be scary. [**A little bit of anxiety**]

TH: Maybe let's make room for that, too—scary and something else ….

CL: It's also like really comforting.

The client digresses; the therapist brings her back to the here-and-now.

TH: Mm, what's going on inside? [**Checking in with her internal experience**]

CL: I just, like, from the last time we had this conversation, I see my own progress and I'm really able to take in what you said. I'm trying to take in what you say.

TH: And how does it feel?

CL: It's like letting other people comfort me, yeah ….

TH: Mm-hmm, and what's that like to let me be here with you and comfort you?

CL: Not so lonely.

TH: And what's that like not to feel so lonely, how does that feel? [**Another round of work aimed at exploration of change for the better**]

CL: Really good.

TH: Physically, do you have a sense of the good feeling? [**In AEDP, we pay as much attention to good feelings as other therapies pay to bad feelings**]

CL: Physically, I feel myself; I'm not as closed up as I usually am.

Toward the end of the session, the therapist engages the client in metaprocessing:

TH: How has this been today?

CL: I'm glad we had that conversation about Vanessa.

TH: Yeah, me too. It felt really important.

CL: Yeah, I didn't realize how important it was until we spoke about it.

TH: Mm hmm, mm hmm…. What's going on right now?

CL: I would love to, like, make her proud in some way *(pause)*. I would love to make you proud also *(big smile, looks away anxiously)*.

TH: Mmm, how does it feel to say that?

CL: Scary, but just going for it!

TH: Mm, I am proud of you. [**Therapist self-disclosure**]

CL: Yeah, thank you.

TH: What's your reaction? [**Metaprocessing**]

CL: I'm happy to hear.

TH: So just check in. You said that, you'd love to make me proud, that was scary. What's it like to hear my reaction?

CL: It's good *(making steady eye contact, smiles)*.

TH: What's happening right now?

CL: I just feel really good, I feel like giddy. [**State 3, tremulous affects indicating new experience, on the precipice of core state**]

TH: So, let yourself absorb this.

CL: I feel like, how did I go from feeling so horribly lost and lonely to all of a sudden all of these things are popping up in my life that are so beautiful and real, and I'm just really happy I got help *(big smile)*. [**In core state, clients are often poetic and speak the truth**]

The session ends with Dawn asking the therapist for a hug. The therapist meets the client's request with a "Yes, yes!" and a hug, which unleashes another round of gratitude, and a spontaneous "thank you" from the client. Here again AEDP departs from many therapies and borrows from mother–infant research. When our clients reach for us, as AEDP therapists, we reach back.

Although recovery from an ED is never linear, in the previously given transcript, Dawn makes great shifts in how she interacts with herself and with the therapist. Let us review what happened in this session. The therapist gently tracks Dawn's facial expressions and body language. She notices a shift in Dawn's affect as she begins to talk about her previous therapist. The current therapist (Slatus) invites Dawn to drop into her feelings of loss, as well as feelings of connection with the former therapist. The processing of these emotions, both historically unacknowledged by her family, brings Dawn into contact with a feeling of closeness toward the new therapist. Feeling emboldened by the relationship, Dawn takes the risk to say this out loud. In AEDP, receptivity to the client's expression of closeness and gratitude is an important element in continuing to build security in the relationship and helping the client to "feel felt" (Siegel & Hartzell, 2003, p. 60) and received (Hanakawa, 2011). The therapist meets the client with a self-disclosure of also feeling close to her—a "me, too," which further undoes any potential aloneness or shame. "Self-disclosure [in AEDP] is neither good nor bad; *it is the quickest way to have an experience between two people*" (Prenn, 2009, p. 89).

The therapist follows with metaprocessing. The process unfolds further experientially: Dawn and her therapist are working on deepening this sense of connection and allowing it to fortify her. This, in essence, is what we ask our ED clients to do with food: Take it in, keep it in, and let it nourish you (Slatus, 2018). Dawn is subsequently able to use the therapist as a source of support and trust. Her ED behaviors significantly decrease and she is able to bring more compassion to herself in the moments when she does struggle.

Current research on neuroplasticity supports AEDP's theory and clinical practice, it helps us to understand how new experiences of emotion and attuned connection actually change the structure of the brain (Cozolino, 2010; Siegel, 2007). Accompanied by a present, brave, and strong therapist, the client can build earned secure attachment (Siegel, 1999), process trauma, and recover from her ED. With a tight focus on tracking moment-to-moment shifts in affect and relatedness, and then metaprocessing the experience *together*, the AEDP therapist is alongside the client at every step as she moves from disembodiment and dissociation to authentic connection with herself and with the therapist as a True Other (see Fosha, 2000b, for her conceptualization of the *True Other*, a counterpart to Winnicott's *True Self*). By having repeated opportunities to visit and metaprocess core state, the client grows and rewires neuronal pathways, and connects with the strong and resilient human that she always was underneath the trauma and the ED.

■ REFERENCES

Bowlby, J. (1988). *A secure base: Parent-child attachment and healthy human development*. New York, NY: Basic Books.

Circle of Security. (1998). Retrieved from http://www.Circleofsecurityinternational.com. Website: https://www.circleofsecurityinternational.com/userfiles/Downloadable%20Handouts/COS_chart-childsneeds.pdf

Cozolino, L. (2010). *The neuroscience of psychotherapy: Healing the social brain* (2nd ed.). New York, NY: W. W. Norton.

Fosha, D. (2000a). Meta-therapeutic processes and the affects of transformation: Affirmation and the healing affects. Journal of Psychotherapy Integration, 10, 71–97. doi:10.1023/A:1009422511959

Fosha, D. (2000b). *The transforming power of affect: A model for accelerated change*. New York, NY: Basic Books.

Fosha, D. (2003). Dyadic regulation and experiential work with emotion and relatedness in trauma and disordered attachment. In M. F. Solomon & D. J. Siegel (Eds.), *Healing trauma: Attachment, mind, body, and brain*. New York, NY: W. W. Norton.

Fosha, D. (2006a). AEDP: Transformance in action. *Connections & Reflections: The GAINS Quarterly,* Winter, pp. 3–7.

Fosha, D. (2006b). Quantum transformation in trauma and treatment: Traversing the crisis of healing change. *Journal of Clinical Psychology, 62*(5), 569–583. doi:10.1002/jclp.20249

Fosha, D. (2009a). Emotion and recognition at work: Energy, vitality, pleasure, truth, desire and the emergent phenomenology of transformational experience. In D. Fosha, D. J. Siegel., & M. F. Solomon (Eds.), *The healing power of emotion: Affective neuroscience, development and clinical practice* (pp. 172–203). New York, NY: W. W. Norton.

Fosha, D. (2009b). Positive affects and the transformation of suffering into flourishing. In W. C. Bushell, E. L. Olivo, & N. D. Theise (Eds.), *Longevity, regeneration and optimal health: Integrating Eastern and Western perspectives* (pp. 252–261). New York, NY: Annals of the New York Academy of Sciences.

Frijda, N. H. (1986). *The emotions.* Cambridge, MA: Cambridge University Press.

Greenberg, L. S., Rice, L. N., & Elliott, R. (1993). *Facilitating emotional change: The moment-by-moment process.* New York, NY: Guilford Press.

Hanakawa, Y. (2011). Receiving loving gratitude: How a therapist's mindful embrace of a patient's gratitude facilitates transformance. *Transformance, 3*(1). Retrieved from https://static1.squarespace.com/static/54716372e4b04acde6d0fe83/t/54c704c2e4b074a85afafc70/1422329026978/Receiving+Loving+Gratitude+FINAL.pdf

Lamagna, J., & Gleiser, K. A. (2007). Building a secure internal attachment: An intra-relational approach to ego strengthening and emotional processing with chronically traumatized clients. *Journal or Trauma and Dissociation, 8*(1), 25–52. doi:10.1300/J229v08n01_03

Obegi, J. H., & Berant, E. (Eds.). (2009). *Attachment theory and research in clinical work with adults.* New York, NY: Guilford Press.

Prenn, N. (2009). I second that emotion! On self-disclosure and its metaprocessing. In A. Bloomgarden & R. B. Mennuti (Eds.), *Psychotherapist revealed: Therapists speak about self-disclosure in psychotherapy.* New York, NY: Routledge.

Russell, E., & Fosha, D. (2008). Transformational affects and core state in AEDP: The emergence and consolidation of joy, hope, gratitude, and confidence in the (solid goodness of) the self. *Journal of Psychotherapy Integration, 18*(2), 167–190. doi:10.1037/1053-0479.18.2.167

Safran, J. D., & Segal, Z. V. (1990). *Interpersonal process in cognitive therapy.* New York, NY: Basic Books.

Schore, A. N. (2001). Effects of a secure attachment relationship on right brain development, affect regulation, and infant mental health. *Infant Mental Health Journal, 22*(1-2), 7–66. doi:10.1002/1097-0355(200101/04)22:1<7::AID-IMHJ2>;3.0.CO;2-N

Schwartz, R. C. (1995). *Internal family systems therapy.* New York, NY: Guilford Press.

Siegel, D. J. (1999). *The developing mind.* New York, NY: Guilford Press.

Siegel, D. J. (2003). An interpersonal neurobiology of psychotherapy: The developing mind and the resolution of trauma. In D. J. Siegel & M. F. Solomon (Eds.), *Healing trauma: Attachment, mind, body and brain* (pp. 1–56). New York, NY: W. W. Norton.

Siegel, D. J. (2007). *The mindful brain: Reflection and attunement in the cultivation of well-being.* New York, NY: W. W Norton.

Siegel, D. J., & Hartzell, M. (2003). *Parenting from the inside out.* New York, NY: Penguin.

Slatus, J. (2018). Bite by bite: Working with eating disorders using accelerated experiential dynamic psychotherapy. *Transformance, 8*(1). Retrieved from https://aedpinstitute.org/transformance/bite-by-bite-working-with-eating-disorders-using-accelerated-experiential-dynamic-psychotherapy

Winnicott, D. W. (1971). *Playing and reality.* London, UK: Routledge.

CHAPTER 19

Eating Disorders and Hypnosis

G. Trevor Hadfield

■ INTRODUCTION

The use of hypnosis in the management of eating disorders (EDs) poses several questions:

- Is it cope or cure? Do we presume too easily that there is no cure for EDs, that they are for life? I aim to describe how hypnosis is integrated into the diagnosis and treatment of a person with an ED.
- Are we going backwards or forwards? Apologies are due for the historical nature of part of this narrative, but in many ways, it is "back to the future!" Pierre Janet (1889/1973) gave a blueprint for management that we are only just beginning to realize.
- Is it hypnosis or hypnotherapy? The reintroduction of hypnotic techniques and hypnotic awareness moves us forward from the concept of "hypnotherapy," which for many people conjures up a view of stage hypnosis, and with it the fear of being out of control. Clinical hypnosis is the opposite. The aim is to enable the person to experience the freedom to take back control of his or her life.

■ WHAT IS HYPNOSIS?

Current research and neuroimaging show some of the mechanisms behind hypnosis. This is not the focus here. Instead, we seek to provide a pragmatic account of current practice, which is not a magic bullet but a different perspective on our existing models of treatment. "Hypnosis" relates to when a person's behavior shows he or she is in a trance-like frame of mind, dissociated from his or her usual conscious awareness. This is different from the semimagical concept of hypnosis or hypnotherapy that causes confusion. The person may present with the request for "hypnotherapy" when he or she has "failed" with his or her current therapy. For example, persons with bulimia may feel humiliated because they have failed "all over again." In contrast, anorexic persons may not realize how unwell they are, and show emotion only if we threaten their absolute sense of control. They are dissociated from the roots of their illness, and it is their loved ones who anguish over their failing health and lack of awareness of their precarious position.

This dissociated behavior can be easily recognized when the person is actively distressed or fearful, but it may take longer to recognize when trauma has produced unconscious denial, as in anorexia nervosa (AN). In both cases, because they appear to be unable to make a change, the request is for someone else to "do some magic" on them, demonstrating the conspiracy of confusion fuelled by stage hypnotism. As a clinician, I do not take over control. Instead, the patients learn the meditative skills of self-hypnosis, which restores their sense of control and self-esteem. As a result, any improvement is a personal triumph, not a magic "done to them."

■ WHY HYPNOSIS? MY OWN STORY AND THOSE OF OTHERS

The reports of many of our patients show how we fail in reaching the real source of their distress, and sometimes seem to make the problem worse. This has been eloquently expressed by a young doctor, a survivor of childhood AN. "When you live with anorexia, you fight your own thoughts and fears, your own self, every second of every minute of the day. I knew I could reach the targets this consultant was setting for me. I also knew that it wouldn't make any difference to what was going on in my head, but it would get me out of hospital" (McNaught, 2017).

She felt trapped in her illness, and, as an intelligent teenager, she had to invent numerous subterfuges to get around the system. She had first felt trapped by the illness, and then trapped by the treatment. Her account reflects the frustration of many of our patients with the way they are managed by us. They need an approach that reaches the functional purpose, or unconscious motivation of the behavior, so that they can move on and leave it behind. Have we reached the need for Kuhn's "revolutionary phase" in clinical method, a phase in which the accepted scientific paradigm is overtaken by a different one—one that is attentive to the roots of the behavioral disorder?

Thirty years ago, and with a reputation as a caring family physician, I was press-ganged by my wife into joining a basic counseling course. No doubt, she had noticed a lack of self-knowledge, even of self-delusion, about the motivation of my caring! During the course, I noticed that when dealing with our own material, we seemed to go into a world of our own, oblivious to the surrounding group, and profoundly upset. It was as though we were in a trance state, produced by reliving our own traumas.

I remarked to the tutor that we seemed to be hypnotized. He was horrified. "We don't believe in hypnosis. It is of the devil!" I was confused. If counseling technique is of the devil, what the devil are we doing? I had noticed earlier that when a patient comes scared because of a breast lump or a symptom that may mean cancer, she seems to be in a similar focused state of alarm. Is this hypnosis?

It was clear that as a physician I had been missing an important clinical sign—that of "trance state," whatever that may infer. In everyday life, some of us are familiar with becoming so deeply absorbed in a book or a film that we lose track of our surroundings, living in the world of the characters so that we find it difficult to shake ourselves back into reality. In this alternative state, we are obviously fully conscious, but with an altered, powerful focus of attention.

Earlier, I had missed the relevance of this same narrowed focus of conscious attention. It becomes more pronounced when a person is distressed or afraid. In this state, the person becomes highly suggestible, may misread negatives such as "you have *not* got cancer," and will misunderstand the reassurances given. The person is already "hypnotized"—by himself or herself. Clinical signs that suggest this altered state of mind include breathing changes, flushed cheeks with widening pupils, watering eyes with fluttering eyelids, and a child-like suggestibility to the literal meaning of words, rather than their adult inferences (i.e., "trance logic"). Therefore, an objective understanding of hypnosis starts with recognizing these different frames of mind or focuses of attention in everyday life: from the innocent times when our attention is absorbed in a book or a film, unaware of our surroundings, to the opposite extreme when in a posttraumatic state.

Recognizing this spontaneous hypnosis or trance state as a clinical sign involves a different level of listening skills, a modified approach to history-taking and to all the advice we give. It also produces a new level of rapport. For example, I discovered that patients labeled as "frequent attenders" often had an underlying fear that they could not express, except in terms of physical symptoms familiar to their doctor (Katon, 1995). By recognizing when they were in an altered state of mind, the deeper unconscious problem was exposed, eliminating their need to keep coming back. I did not need to hypnotize them, but I recognized their own spontaneous "hypnotized state." This proved especially important in conditions such as EDs, compulsive hoarding, or personality disorders where the underlying root of the symptoms or behavior followed a history of early trauma.

The first application of hypnosis in EDs has, therefore, nothing to do with "hypnotizing" a person, nor with regarding hypnosis as a model of therapy, nor as a bolt-on adjunct for relaxation. When we as clinicians and therapists become experienced in hypnotic sensitivity, recognizing when a person is demonstrating an altered or dissociated state of mind, rapport deepens, and humor combines with humanity so that the patient is motivated to understand his or her own behavior and move on.

Hypnosis and Eating Disorder Management: A Historical and Theoretical Perspective

Hypnosis challenges the polarization between the different aims of behavioral and analytical therapy. It has been promoted as a basis for assimilating the different active ingredients of both models (Alladin, 2008; Chapman, 2014), but it is in the history of hypnosis that we find a bridge between them. Janet's doctoral thesis of 1889 brought together elements of analytical and behavioral therapies via his concept of dissociation: different states of consciousness, with attention being switched between them, or fixed, as a result of trauma (Van der Hart & Horst, 1989). Traumatic memories were seen to be split off from the main personality, *idée fixe*, retrievable only by returning to the same state of mind that produced them, now known as state-dependent learning.

Although Freud initially agreed with Janet, he subsequently replaced the concept of dissociation with his concept of the unconscious as comprising defense mechanisms, repressed emotion, accessible only through analysis. He finally abandoned hypnosis after a grateful patient threw her arms around his neck. This sealed the fate of hypnosis for 100 years (Freud, 1925/1959).

This difference between Janet's concept of dissociation and Freud's concept of repression is relevant for EDs and needs to be clarified (van der Hart, Nijenhuis, Steele, & Brown, 2004). "Premature acceptance of Freud's idiosyncratic position vis-à-vis dissociation and consciousness probably delayed the appreciation of the alternative Janetian view." This is one area in which the theoretical incompatibility between cognitive and analytical models may have hindered the progress of very ill individuals (Dell & O'Neill, 2009; van der Hart & Horst, 1989).

The work of Pierre Janet came before Freud's rejection of hypnosis in favor of psychoanalysis and Skinner's development of behavioral therapy (Skinner, 1953). His system of treatment before the conceptual divide combined the use of hypnosis for relaxation and supportive behavioral management of life situations, followed by detailed treatment of the dissociated fragments of the personality through hypnosis (van der Hart, Brown, & van der Kolk, 1989). His phase-oriented approach meant that hypnosis for simple relaxation comprised the first phase. The person had to readjust his or her approach to daily life before there was any approach to the traumatic roots of the problem (van der Hart et al., 2004).

The disparity of views is not just a dispute over semantics and models. A return to a combination of cognitive and analytic methods may be helpful for us as therapists, as well as for our patients, stopping us from being so dogmatic about our preferred therapy! So, is it "back to the future, doctor?"

Janet coined the term "dissociation" to describe the difference between normal memories that become incorporated into the personality and traumatic memories that persist as "idee fixe" behind chronic conditions. Current imaging findings describe how traumatic sensory signals are blocked at the thalamus and do not reach the right prefrontal cortex, and are therefore not recorded as narrative memories.

This occurs with acute trauma resulting in PTSD, with the outlet for the dissociated fragments only via the dorsal vagus to the gut. Trauma that occurs early in life happens before the development of the prefrontal cortex and corpus callosum and lies behind chronic conditions including eating disorders, chronic abdominal pain, and irritable bowel syndrome (Janet, 1907/2007; van der Kolk, 2014, pp. 182, 194; Schore, 2009, pp. 108, 117)

In fairness, we should not presume that the cause has been a dysfunctional family or childhood abuse. ED may occur in a person from a loving, functional family (EDs attract Grade A students!). The trauma may result from the person's own exceptional intelligence and sensitivity; that is, nature as well as nurture.

We find it important to recognize these fundamental differences in planning the phased management of conditions such as ED. Early experiences that were processed cognitively form part of our healthy personality and may be retrieved through Freudian or cognitive psychotherapy. By contrast, dissociated material that never reached the cortex as a narrative memory is by definition outside these approaches, and this is where Janet discovered hypnosis to be useful.

■ AN INTEGRATED APPROACH

How do these models of neurophysiology relate to our current therapy? Cognitive behavioral therapy (CBT) is central to the current management of EDs. On the common assumption that there is no cure for AN, it challenges the content of a person's conscious thoughts (a logical "left frontal lobe" activity) to develop alternative coping strategies that modify behavior. Its logical appeal challenges the cognitive distortions, maladaptive beliefs and behaviors, body image, and perfectionism so the person can cope with life. For some, this is all that is needed. For others with a more established illness, this conscious logical approach appears to be insufficient. The logical approach and focus on behavior change appears to set them up for failure. When basic empathy has not achieved a solid therapeutic alliance, the person feels compelled to lie to his or her therapist, and continues to feel and live as a prisoner of his or her AN.

Zoe, a young professional patient, used to be anorexic. At 15, she was admitted to the hospital as an emergency and transferred to a specialist clinic for behavioral modification. She describes her treatment plan as comprising being "weighed, plotted and threatened." If she did not gain a pound in weight each week, she would be compulsorily detained, and not be able to have contact with her family, her school, and friends. The clinic instructed the school to withdraw her from all games and social activities to limit her weight loss. She stated that no one questioned her or listened to her. No one had questioned why she had become anorexic, or what life events had precipitated the behavior. The therapeutic alliance had not been established. She did not tell the truth to her therapist, defaulted the program and resolved to carry on without medical help, and now states enigmatically that she misses being identified as an anorexic yet will always be an anorexic. Her report is disturbingly familiar. She learned to cope, not to be cured. She lives with the problem; it has not gone away. In her case, the CBT program had not been helpful.

The approach is explained by Ross (2009) on the cognitive maxim that, regardless of past traumas or present mental health disorders, the ED always serves the function of being an avoidance strategy, and this coping strategy is the disorder to be addressed. For this patient, the roots of the traumatic damage, abuse, insecurity, or failed attachment seemed to lie deeper than were reached cognitively. When seen from a trauma perspective, an ED may represent a situation in which, controversially, affect may precede cognition, so treatment on the basis of cognition is focusing on the secondary rather than on the primary defect.

In psychoanalytic therapy, repressed emotional material is brought into conscious awareness on the basis that the catharsis of self-awareness is curative, rather than being mere symptom removal. Catharsis alone may reach the roots of the pain, but without the alternative cognitive approach addressing the avoidance behavior of their coping strategy and applying alternative behavior modification.

From this perspective, both models of treatment used on their own demonstrate the benefits and the shortcomings of the approaches and the difference between coping with the illness and addressing the roots of the maladaptive behavior. The integrated approach described by Janet's phased model demonstrates the inclusion of hypnosis but still in a way that separates out the components that we now see as complementary.

The understanding of cerebral function suggests a way for therapy to come full circle, combining cognitive models focusing on left frontal lobe functions and dynamic models focusing on the right frontal lobe, limbic activity, and memory formation, with the use of hypnotic sensitivity at each stage (Mizen, 2005).

■ ASSESSMENT AND CASE FORMULATION

Hypnotic awareness contributes a different emphasis in initial management. It is said that as physicians we do not get the right answers, because we do not ask the right questions! Counselors and psychotherapists criticize our medical model as being directive and focused on an organic explanation for the symptoms. Yet the questioning techniques of some therapies appear to copy this model, such as the directive nature of Socratic questioning that aims to reveal the avoidance strategies and the cognitive adjustments to be made. The metamodel of neurolinguistic programming (NLP) also follows a similar Socratic sequence, but incorporates hypnotic sensitivity to reveal the deep meaning of the communication (Bandler & Grinder, 1975). Nevertheless, although each of these aims to avoid being directive and confrontational, we may experience resistance because of the protective nature of the repressed or dissociated memories behind many EDs.

When "trance sensitivity" is incorporated into the case formulation, the efficacy of cognitive treatment can be improved through being increasingly aware of the unconscious positive intention behind the dysfunctional thinking. The young person has the experience of being listened to at a different level before being given homework to do. This uses the difference between the "superficial" and the "deep" elements of communication as described by Korzybski, and then Chomsky, and developed in NLP (Chomsky, 1956; Korzybski, 1941/1994). In this context, NLP listening techniques represent a hypnotic approach to cognition (Hall & Bodenhamer, 2001).

Our alternative approach, *Empathometrics*, incorporates hypnotic sensitivity with reflective listening (Hadfield & Walton, 2002). This involves a compassionate style of reflexive questioning as developed in systemic therapy, and an altered application of

Socratic questioning (compare Gilbert, 2010). A succession of questions designed with inbuilt presuppositions allows the patient the experience of becoming fascinated with exploring his or her own reactions to unexpected questions in the context of his or her life situation and personality. This includes an assessment of hypnotic receptivity, personality style, and psychopathology (Spiegel & Spiegel, 2004). This type of listening also explores the extent of the visceral, autonomic background to the disordered approach to eating (pain, bloating, diarrhea/constipation), rather than only the emotional causes of the problem (Coen et al., 2011).

The probing becomes a process of gentle fun and exploration without coercion as the person becomes absorbed in reassessing his or her symptoms in the light of his or her own personality. This has the Rogerian benefit of the patient feeling accepted by a therapist who is genuine and appreciative of him or her as a person. The resulting rapport also fulfills the aim of the CBT principle of collaboration and active participation (Beck, 2011). The individual questions are less important than the sequence that produces a progressive focus of attention and an inner absorption of spontaneous hypnosis.

For instance, Lisa, a student, presented at the mercy of her own inability to stop bingeing. A long history of cognitive therapy had identified the avoidance behavior, but she had not been able to move on. When presented with the hypnotic reflexive questioning, her eyes, body posture, and her replies showed that she had entered a hypnotic state. It was with this altered focus of attention that she was able for the first time to bypass the resistance and recognize her behavior in the context of the clash between her driving personality and the inability to accept affection from her parents. She was able to readjust her relationship with her parents, and accept love from her boyfriend. This was her first conscious awareness of the link with her ED.

The compassionate approach to this initial stage of management reflects the initial therapy phase of Janet, in which he incorporates hypnosis to give rest, general support, and help in modifying daily life. The compassionate development of empathy also avoids the focus on behavior change, which can set up the person for failure when he or she has not managed to achieve what has been asked of him or her.

The resulting case formulation incorporates material that had not emerged during cognitive questioning and not consciously realized by the patients earlier, but revealed in the hypnotic state. It is presented back to them in the form of a narrative on the basis of a psychodynamic model. They may be able to see ways in which their presenting situation relates to their personality style, their mental defense mechanisms, and the "unconscious motivation"/"functional purpose" of their avoidance strategies, symptoms, and behavior. Their responses are presented in a series of psychodynamic diagrams. These enable them to relate their problems to a different understanding of their own underlying personality without referring to the alternative concept of dissociation. This emerges in the next phase.

The resulting level of rapport is followed by the experience of meditative relaxation under their own control. The skills of self-hypnosis are taught before progressing to the phase of trauma investigation and modification. This is in line with the findings of Janet (van der Hart, Brown, & van der Kolk, 1989), and of compassionate cognitive therapy (Gilbert, 2010). Traditional scripts for introducing relaxation skills are still useful: Elman (1964), Old (2016), Spiegel and Spiegel (2004), and Erickson (Battino & South, 1999).

The detailed process of case formulation using the Empathometric model is only alluded to here, and beyond the confines of this chapter. We find that it is better learned in live clinical skills group situations, such as the ones we teach (Clinical Hypnosis and Related Techniques). This approach to listening and reflective questioning often feels counterintuitive to those of us who, as clinicians, are trained in the medical model.

■ TRAUMA PROCESSING

Confronting the avoidance behavior behind traumatic memories may involve confusion between positive and negative experiences. This is relevant to EDs because a child who has been physically or sexually abused by a parent may have a powerful conflict of emotions toward the parent and confusion over how to receive and express love (Gilbert, 2010, p. 123). This underlines the importance of developing a profound empathy during the first phase of treatment, aided by a heightened hypnotic awareness. Hypnotic awareness deepens the rapport and the safe base for confronting the repressed emotions.

In this way, both CBT and analytic models become more effective with a hypnotic sensitivity by developing a place of safety for the person to confront the demons behind his or her ED. It takes courage to feel. Therapy requires an emotionally supportive relationship with the therapist. When a patient presents with persistent problems, it may be that the initial therapeutic empathy has not been achieved, resulting in either the traumatic root of the problem not being recognized or catharsis being resisted.

Janet's incorporation of trance goes where CBT and analytic work have not yet gone. In his ignorance of the coming antipathy between psychological models, he used hypnosis in a way that is only being rediscovered over 100 years later. He used a mixture of cognitive and imaginative ways of altering the perception of the events. Using hypnosis, he stressed that, because traumatic memories constitute dissociated parts of the personality, it is necessary to trace the memories back to the first traumatic event.

He then used a range of different techniques to desensitize earlier events by progressively reexperiencing them, revealing that, for those with deep trauma, this may not be effective if the core memory is not reached. The patient experiences the memory as though it were happening now and reexperiences the pain. We can identify with these techniques today, but our current hypnotic techniques improve on this by avoiding bringing the emotional pain into conscious awareness. For example, the common use of "reframing" involves altering the way in which the trauma was held in the memory, putting a different frame around the picture, seeing it through a different colored pair of spectacles, altering the voices, changing the speed, and fantasizing controls over each of the sensory components of the memory.

For those for whom profound dissociation is part of their etiology, processes for uncovering and modifying the traumatic memories such as reframing are still found to be insufficient. More advanced techniques are necessary to reintegrate the dissociated part of the personality before the patient can be free from the disorder.

Current Approaches Recognizing Dissociation and Incorporating Hypnotic Techniques

The connection Janet saw between childhood sexual abuse and the dissociated behavior of EDs has become more apparent for the past 20 years, and described in different ways. Complex posttraumatic stress disorder (PTSD) as a result of early childhood abuse links with AN (Reyes-Rodríguez et al., 2011). Dissociative features are found in 75% of bulimics; many of the patients with EDs are highly hypnotizable, and it is important to identify those with a dissociative etiology for whom "ego state" therapy is now found to be effective. This combines a hypnotic approach with principles of systemic family therapy (Torem, 1987 quoted in Phillips & Frederick, 1995, p. 180).

The challenge is to address the unconscious motivation or functional purpose of the dissociated state or avoidance strategy. The comment of a psychologist on our course was: "Why would you deal with an eating disorder at a conscious associated level, when it is glaringly obvious that if you put the dissociated person into an associated state, you are going to do more harm than good?" If a young person has held traumatic memories in a dissociated state, or in Freudian terms, as a defense mechanism, this dissociation is serving a positive intention with positive motivation despite the apparently negative nature of the behavior. Uncovering the material removes the protection and may reinforce the problem. If every behavior has a positive intention, behavior modification that fails to recognize that intention will similarly be resisted and the conflict reinforced. Hence, therapy may comprise "cope" rather than "cure."

When the original trauma has not resulted in profound illness, the person may be able to reevaluate the occurrence from an adult perspective and understand it in a different way. In hypnotic practice, as in a Janetian approach, the memories are "reframed" and the perception is altered. But those who are more seriously ill, or suffering with AN in particular, present a different situation. The traumatic memories are not recognized as they are outside conscious awareness, or, alternatively, the cognitive memory of the traumas has been dissociated from their emotional content.

There is a need for being able to process dissociated memories while keeping them in a dissociated state, avoiding consciously having to relive the emotions in conscious awareness. A solution developed from another historical insight regarding the perception of time and memory (W. James, 1892/1985). This was inspired by the concepts of Korzybski (1921) and NLP (T. James & Woodsmall, 1988), and the work was further refined into the form that we use today (Bodenhamer & Hall, 1997; Hall & Bodenhamer, 2005).

This dissociative strategy is on the basis of the concept that memories are stored in a linear fashion. This has given rise to one of the most powerful hypnotic therapeutic tools in the treatment of traumatic memories. Careful questioning elicits the way in which the individual perceives the linear sequence of his or her memories—his or her own personal timeline. This may be imagined as a road, from the date of birth, through a crossroads of today, and on to the rest of his or her life. The suggestion is made to imaginatively create the multisensory experience of standing at the crossroads. From here, the person floats upwards until he or she is looking down on himself or herself below. He or she has created a *dissociated* position, with the line of all his or her memories separated from him or her on the road below. This position of dissociation from the happenings of his or her life is then used so he or she can float back over his or her life from afar, observing the good and bad times, but choosing to remain separated from them.

The initial benefit is in being able to identify the best moments, and float down to become *associated* with them, reliving and intensifying the positive emotions. These are then "anchored" with a device such as making the feeling into a parcel. The person then carries the parcel back and presents it to his or her present self, pressing it into his or her hand. The act of anchoring the experience as a kinesthetic squeeze of the hand means that, done repeatedly, the slightest squeeze on the hand can release a flood of these positive emotions.

Once the principle of harvesting the best times has been established, and the best positive memories have been anchored, then a separate technique is taught analogous to Janet's principle of liquefying traumatic memories. His method was done in an associated state, with the disadvantage of reviving the painful reactions. With the timeline approach, it is done in a dissociated state. "The traumas are down there; I am up here." The person can perceive that there is a difference between the "me" down there of the memories and traumas, and the "real me" who is observing from up here. His or her adult self is floating over the traumatic times, observing him or her from afar with an adult perspective, and allowing his or her unconscious to keep and file away the important positive lessons within the memories. Then the memories themselves seem to melt, and no longer have the emotional power to suddenly erupt as "in your face" experiences that lead to phobias, panic attacks, and compulsive or protective behaviors including those behind AN.

The detail of this method requires the development of careful professional skill. We find that it can be one of the most powerful hypnotic techniques for severe posttraumatic conditions and can reach the deeply hidden roots of childhood abuse and EDs. Because the traumatic memories are processed in the dissociated state, there is no need for the person to relive the material at the root of his or her denial. In this way, emotional catharsis is no longer needed. By continuing the process from birth to the present, the traumatic memories are reprocessed in such a way that the emotional content is dealt with and important positive intentions stored.

Rehabilitation and Reintegrating the Personality

Cope or cure? Anorexic/bulimic for life, or move on to living free from the label? The acid test of a treatment approach is if it translates from "magic cure" to a long-term lifestyle change. The timeline approach using hypnosis in the right hands can produce a remarkable initial experience of relief, even over other hypnotic procedures. But this is not to say that it is a universal panacea. A therapist from any clinical model who passionately believes in his or her therapy can transmit this same confidence to his or her patient or client. This is especially true for posttraumatic conditions in which there has been an arrest of personality development.

Almost by definition in EDs, transference illustrates that such a person becomes highly suggestible, and therefore dependent on his or her therapist. "Variability between individual therapists is more important than the variability between the therapy types" (Saxon, Firth, & Barkham, 2016). This also relates to Janet's findings. "Janet's early understanding of rapport also had roots in dissociation in that the patient seemed unable, due to dissociative restriction of the conscious field, to perceive anyone other than his own therapist" (Haule, 1986).

The timeline approach can be highly efficient in neutralizing the emotional powers of the traumatic memories found to be at the root of the condition, but what next? Janet recognized the need for the dissociated parts to be reintegrated with the whole. Does this indicate the comorbidity between EDs and personality disorders? It is logical to suppose that if the traumatic parts have been dealt with, there are gaps in the development, and the personality is fragile or "borderline." As with the previous phases of treatment, Janet used both behavioral methods and hypnosis to encourage the reintegration of the developmentally delayed parts.

It is important for the client to appreciate living first in the present, before restructuring his or her future. A tenet of the timeline approach is the importance of the "right time," the "appropriate time" for each stage. The person's identity has been centered around the dysfunctional behavior and his or her identity as an anorexic/bulimic. He or she does not want to give it up—it is scary! Time is needed for him or her to grow up into his or her adult persona.

Initial rehabilitation comprises a regular fun-based strategy for relaxation and encouragement through positive ideation, "ego-strengthening" routines (Waxman, 1989). These comprise a series of positive statements spoken while the person is in trance and timed with his or her respiratory rhythm. In the past, this has been linked with the person designing "affirmations"—groups of three truths about himself or herself that include one that is aspirational. Although this may be helpful, it is more likely to be seen as a trivialization—a sop to their immaturity! It belongs more to pop-psychology and has been superseded by a forward extension of the timeline technique.

Meditation in line with the person's own background can be a source of strength and can develop the self-reflecting consciousness leading to a creative reason for living. For those with no religious conviction, mindfulness can help focus on emotional immediacy. For those with a Judaeo-Christian background, appropriate biblical quotations can strengthen empowering beliefs and form useful affirmations, such as "God has not given us a spirit of fear, but a spirit of power, love and a sound mind," and "Forgetting what lies behind, and straining forward to what lies ahead, I press on towards the goal" (2 Tim. 1:7, Philippians 3:13 NKJV/BBE). The healthy use of a religious faith can be a great source of strength for a person at this stage of the healing of his or her vulnerable personality.

The focus of therapy is now turned from the past to the future—from regression to progression. The timeline metaphor becomes a coaching technique. The techniques that had been used for trauma management had involved age regression and the "harvesting" of good experiences before processing traumatic ones. Patients bring with them the positive resourceful states harvested from their past and the present empowering experiences, and use these to create long-term goals, with short-term interim stages along the way. This enables them to experiment with different alternatives, allowing them to try out different levels of ambition. The situation is a fluid, creative one. They float forward over the future timeline, and observe their changed identity, with freedom from the old traumas and stated in positive terms; hence, instead of "I am an anorexic" or "I am not an anorexic," the positive notion of "I am enjoying being free to be as I chose to be."

These techniques find their expression in different models of therapy. The added ingredient here is to deliberately recognize and use the person's own imaginative state of trance in a way that he or she finds is appropriate for him or her as an individual for his or her future development, not a magic bullet, but a useful and effective perspective on our therapies.

■ REFERENCES

Alladin, A. (2008). *Cognitive hypnotherapy*. Hoboken, NJ: Wiley.

Bandler, R., & Grinder, J. (1975). *The structure of magic: A book about language and therapy* (Vol. 1). Palo Alto, CA: Science and Behavior Books.

Battino, R., & South, T. L. (1999). *Ericksonian approaches. A comprehensive manual*. Carmarthen, Wales: Crown House.

Beck, J. S. (2011). *Cognitive behavior therapy*. New York, NY: Guilford Press.

Bodenhamer, B. G., & Hall, M. L. (1997). *Time lining: Patterns for adventuring in "time."* Carmarthen, Wales: Crown House Publishing.

Chapman, R. A. (2014). *Integrating clinical hypnosis and CBT*. New York, NY: Springer Publishing.

Chomsky, N. (1956). *Syntactic structures*. Hague, Netherlands: Mouton.

Coen, S. J., Kano, M., Farmer, A. D., Kumari, V., Giampietro, V., Brammer, M., ... Aziz, Q. (2011). Neuroticism influences brain activity during the experience of visceral pain. *Gastroenterology*, 141(3), 909–917.e1. doi:10.1053/j.gastro.2011.06.008

Dell, P., & O'Neill, J. (Eds.). (2009). *Dissociation and the dissociative disorders: DSM-V and beyond*. New York, NY: Routledge.

Elman, D. (1964). *Hypnotherapy*. Glendale, CA: Westwood Publishing.

Freud, S. (1959). Freud: An autobiographical study. In J. Strachey (Ed. & Trans.), *The standard edition of the complete psychological works of Sigmund Freud* (Vol. 20, pp. 1–70). London: Hogarth Press. (Original work published in 1925)

Gilbert, P. (2010). *Compassion focused therapy*. New York, NY: Routledge.

Hadfield, G. T., & Walton, I. (2002). *Empathometrics*. Waxman Memorial Lecture, Royal Society of Medicine, London.

Hall, L. M., & Bodenhamer, B. (2001). *The structure of personality*. Carmarthen, Wales: Crown House.

Hall, L. M., & Bodenhamer, B. G. (2005). *Figuring out people*. Clifton, CO: Neuro-Semantic Publications.

Haule, J. R. (1986). Pierre Janet and dissociation: The first transference theory and its origins in hypnosis. *American Journal of Clinical Hypnosis, 29*(2), 86–94. doi:10.1080/00029157.1986 .10402690

James, T., & Woodsmall, W. (1988). *Time line therapy and the basis of personality*. Capitola, CA: Meta Publications.

James, W. (1985). *Psychology, the briefer course*. New York, NY: Harper & Row. (Original work published 1892)

Janet, P. (1973). *L'Automatisme psychologique [Psychological automatism]*. Félix Alcan, Paris, France: Société Pierre Janet, Paris. (Original work published 1889)

Janet, P. (2007) *The major symptoms of hysteria: Fifteen lectures given in the medical school of Harvard University*. Kessinger Legacy Reprints. Whitefish, MT: Kessinger Publishing. (Original work published 1907)

Katon, W. (1995). Collaborative care: Patient satisfaction, outcomes and medical cost-offset. *Family Systems Medicine, 13*, 351–365. doi:10.1037/h0089387

Korzybski, A. (1921). *Manhood of humanity: The science and art of human engineering*. New York, NY: E. P. Dutton.

Korzybski, A. (1994). *Science and sanity: An introduction to non-Aristotelian systems and general semantics* (5th ed.). Forest Hills, NY: Institute of General Semantics. (Original work published 1941)

McGilchrist, I. (2009). *The master and his emissary: The divided brain and the making of the western world*. New Haven, CT: Yale University Press.

McNaught, E. (2017). *Life hurts: A doctor's personal journey through anorexia*. Central Milton Keynes, Buckinghamshire, UK: Malcolm Down Publishing.

Mizen, C. S. (2005). Neuroimaging and neuropsychotherapy. *Psychiatry, 4*(5), 10–13. doi:10.1383/ psyt.4.5.10.65103

Old, G. (2016). *The Elman induction*. North Charleston, SC: CreateSpace.

Phillips, M., & Frederick, C. (1995). *Healing the divided self: Clinical and Ericksonian hypnotherapy for post-traumatic and dissociative conditions*. New York, NY: W. W. Norton.

Reyes-Rodríguez, M. L., Von Holle, A., Ulman, T. F., Thornton, L. M., Klump, K. L., Brandt, H., … Bulik, C. M. (2011). Posttraumatic stress disorder in anorexia nervosa. *Psychosomatic Medicine, 73*(6), 491–497. doi:10.1097/PSY.0b013e31822232bb

Ross, C. A. (2009). Psychodynamics of eating disorder behavior in sexual abuse survivors. *American Journal of Psychotherapy, 63*, 211–226.

Saxon, D., Firth, N., & Barkham, M. (2016). The relationship between therapist effects and therapy delivery factors: Therapy modality, dosage, and non-completion. *Administration Policy Mental Health, 44*(5), 705–715. doi:10.1007/s10488-016-0750-5

Schore, A. (2009). Attachment, trauma and the developing right brain. In P. Dell & J. O'Neil (Eds.), *Dissociation and dissociative disorders: DSM-V and beyond* (pp. 107–141). New York, NY: Routledge.

Skinner, B. F. (1953). *Science and human behavior*. New York, NY: Simon & Schuster.

Spiegel, H., & Spiegel, D. (2004). *Trance and treatment: Clinical uses of hypnosis* (2nd ed.). Arlington, VA: American Psychiatric Publishing.

Torem, M. S. (1987). Ego-state therapy for eating disorders. *American Journal of Clinical Hypnosis, 30*, 94–103. doi:10.1080/00029157.1987.10404169

van der Hart, O., Brown, P., & van der Kolk, B. A. (1989). Pierre Janet's treatment of post-traumatic stress. *Journal of Traumatic Stress, 2*(4), 379–395. doi:10.1002/jts.2490020404

van der Hart, O., & Horst, R. (1989). The dissociation theory of Pierre Janet. *Journal of Traumatic Stress, 2*(4), 397–412. doi:10.1002/jts.2490020405

van der Hart, O., Nijenhuis, E., Steele, K., & Brown, D. (2004). Trauma-related dissociation: Conceptual clarity lost and found. *Australian and New Zealand Journal of Psychiatry, 38*, 906–914. doi:10.1080/j.1440-1614.2004.01480.x

van der Kolk, B. (2014). *The body keeps the score: Brain, mind, and body in the healing of trauma*. New York, NY: Viking Penguin.

Waxman, D. (1989). *Hartland's medical and dental hypnosis* (3rd ed.). London, UK: Balliere Tindall.

CHAPTER 20

Energy Psychology in the Treatment of Eating Disorders

Phil Mollon

■ INTRODUCTION

Energy psychology (Gallo, 1999) comprises a body of knowledge and a family of therapeutic modalities that are concerned with the interface between mind and body, mediated by working with the body's subtle energy system (Tiller, 1997, 2007)—the hypothesized energy system that is used in acupuncture, traditional Chinese medicine, Chi Gung, and related practices (Mollon, 2008a; Oschman, 2000). There is thought to be a link between particular energy meridians or channels, bodily organs, and emotions (Diamond, 1985; Thie, 2005). The nature of the meridians and acupressure points is a matter of ongoing speculation and investigation, with theories including the primovascular system (Stefanov et al., 2013) and the peripheral nervous system (Longhurst, 2010). Energy psychology approaches mostly involve guiding the client to hold or tap with fingertips certain points on the body—"acupoints"—while thinking about a troubling memory, experience, belief, thought, or bodily sensation. The effect of this typically is that the intensity of distress, or the perceived emotional potency of the target memory or belief, is lessened (Clond, 2016), along with associated physiological changes (Church, Yount, & Brooks, 2012). Further relevant cognitive and emotional material may then emerge, which is in turn addressed using the same energy psychological approach. In this way, psychotherapy is often found to be enhanced in its speed, depth of exploration, and efficacy (Marzillier, 2014).

■ THERAPEUTIC COMPONENTS AND MODE OF ACTION

The mode of action of energy psychology modalities is not fully understood. It appears that tapping on acupoints has a calming and emotion-regulating effect and seems to facilitate the flow of energy and information (Church & Feinstein, 2017). Whether this is best understood in terms of purported subtle energy systems or within more conventional cognitive and neurobiological terms is a matter of continuing consideration (Mollon, 2008b). Most of the energy psychology modalities to some extent may be described as exposure methods (targeting memories, emotions, and cognitions) with additional somatic components. Although the mechanism is uncertain, research indicates that such methods do work, bringing about emotional, cognitive, and physiological changes rather faster than would be expected with purely talk-based psychotherapies (Feinstein, 2012). Despite early skepticism (e.g., Gaudiano & Herbert, 2000), research has now more than validated the initial enthusiasm of the pioneers. At the time of writing, there have been well over 80 studies of energy psychology published in peer-reviewed journals, including 48 randomized controlled trials, four meta-analyses, and five systematic reviews (see the research pages at www.energypsych.org and www.eftuniverse.com). Dismantling studies have indicated that the effects of energy psychology are not solely because of placebo or nonspecific factors and that acupoint tapping is an important and active therapeutic ingredient (Church et al., 2016; Fox, 2013).

Another important component used by some (but not all) practitioners is that of "energy testing"—sometimes known as "muscle testing," although it is not the muscles per se that are tested, but small variations in muscle tone are considered to provide information about both psychological and energetic states (Diamond, 1979/1997). In this procedure, the practitioner presses lightly on the client's wrist of the outstretched arm while he or she speaks certain words (such as "I want to be a healthy weight"), or focuses on a specific experience or thought. In response to some statements, the muscle tone will be strong, with a subtle, "locking" feeling (indicating a "yes"), whereas to other statements, the muscle tone will be weak or spongy (indicating a "no"). In this way, the clients' unconscious anxieties and motivations that might be opposed to their conscious goal can rapidly be ascertained. Within certain modalities (such as advanced forms of Thought Field Therapy; Callahan, 2001), the method can be used to identify the most relevant acupoints to tap and in what sequence. Although this kind of energy testing data should not be viewed as infallible, and the procedure is an art requiring some skill, many practitioners find it can provide useful information to guide the work of the session.

In this writer's practice of Psychoanalytic Energy Psychotherapy (PEP; Mollon, 2005, 2008c, 2014a), much of a psychotherapeutic session would appear like any other conventional talking and listening consultation. The client speaks of what is on his or her mind in relation to the target problem. At a certain point in the session, we move into energy work. I sit alongside the client so that I can energy test him or her by pressing on an outstretched wrist. The emerging information may raise questions and issues for further enquiry. I then guide the client to tap on a sequence of acupoints, while he or she focuses on a particular thought or memory. At the same time, I ask the client to "speak of whatever comes to mind." This includes noticing somatic sensations of pain, tension, or discomfort. In this way, we follow the flow of both information and energy through the client's mind and body. The work is a mixture of structured enquiry and free-associative discourse.

Most of the published research on energy psychology for eating disorders (EDs) has made use of the relatively simple method known as Emotional Freedom Techniques (EFT)—a derivative of Thought Field Therapy, as originally developed by psychologist Roger Callahan in the early 1980s (Callahan, 2001), but then modified by Gary Craig (Church, 2013). EFT does not involve energy testing, but simply guides the client to tap through a standard set of acupoints for each element of distress. The focus might be on a thought, the narrative details of an experienced event, sensory details of such an event, an emotion, or a physical sensation. This is also combined with a statement of self-acceptance according to the formula: "Even though ... (filling in the details of the problematic event or experience) ... I completely accept myself." The skill of this method is not in the acupoint work, but in the application to the most relevant elements of distress, usually aiming to target the origins of the problem as well as its current symptomatology. EFT has been found in research studies to reduce cravings for food, improve self-esteem, and normalize dietary restraint (e.g., Stapleton, Bannatynne, Chatwin, et al., 2017; Stapleton, Bannatyne, Porter, Urzi, & Sheldon 2016; Stapleton, Chatwin, et al., 2016; Stapleton, Sheldon, & Porter, 2012a, 2012b; Stapleton, Sheldon, Porter, & Whitty, 2011).

■ TARGETS OF ENERGY PSYCHOLOGY IN RELATION TO EATING DISORDERS

When incorporating energy psychology modalities into the psychotherapeutic work, we can target, for both exploration and resolution, specific issues, experiences, thoughts or beliefs, and psychodynamic conflicts. For example, we might use energy testing (pressing lightly on the outstretched arm) to ascertain the person's less conscious response to statements such as: "I want to be well"; "I want to be a healthy weight"; "I want a healthy relationship with food." We can also test whether such potential goals or desires feel safe, whether the person feels he or she deserves them, or whether they would violate the person's identity (e.g., "I will still be me if I am a healthy weight"). Using energy testing, we obtain rapid and clear responses to these questions or statements, provided the person's energy system is functioning coherently.

Very commonly, we might find that the response to any of the statements tested (in relation to wanting to be free of the presenting problem) is "no," indicated by the arm being tested becoming slightly spongy (as contrasted with the firmer "locking" feeling that indicates a "yes"). We can then ask the client why that might be, for example, "Any idea why you might feel it is not safe (or you do not deserve) to be a healthy weight?" Typically, the client will respond initially with something like, "I've no idea. I *do* want to be a healthy weight!" This is often followed shortly by highly relevant information that does indeed provide the reason. These internal objections, which are also expressed as reversals in the energetic direction, were originally called "psychological reversals" by Dr. Callahan (Callahan, 1985). Callahan found that simply tapping the side of the hand (an acupoint on the small intestine meridian) would often help to resolve these reversals, but finding the motive behind them can obviously be a great help in the psychotherapeutic process.

Another method of exploration of the psychological reversals, favored by this writer in his PEP (Mollon, 2008c, 2014b), is to use the phrase "the roots and origins and causes of not feeling it is safe (or not deserve, etc.) to be a healthy weight (or other desirable target)," while guiding the client to tap a relevant sequence of meridian acupoints. At the same time, the client is invited to "speak of anything that comes to mind." In this way, we are taking the reversals, or unconscious internal objections to achieving the consciously desired goal, as the target. Usually this leads to very important and relevant experiences and psychodynamic material relating to childhood—very much like the free-associative process in classical psychoanalysis.

Once crucial formative experiences or traumas have been identified, these can be targeted by having the client hold them in mind while he or she taps the relevant sequence of meridians. Tapping on acupoints will usually remove the emotional charge of traumatic experiences quite easily, providing there are no internal objections ("psychological reversals") against doing so. If psychological reversals are active, no amount of tapping will make much difference. Fortunately, the energy psychology modalities allow these reversals or objections rapidly to be identified and resolved in the manner just described. Very often, the work with the reversals/internal objections is the most crucial factor, with change of emotions, cognitions, and behavior occurring rapidly once these have been addressed.

■ CASE ILLUSTRATION 1

For those readers who are unfamiliar with energy psychology, it will be best to ignore the technical procedures as far as possible, and instead allow the emerging clinical material to speak for itself. The therapist's interpretations or theoretical constructions are minimal.

Acupoint sequences were derived using a variant of the Callahan procedure taught in thought field therapy workshops.

First Session

Jessica, a 48-year-old, obese woman with a long-standing pattern of chaotic eating, approached me, because she wanted to explore the potential of energy psychology to help her achieve a healthy weight. She had a twin sister who had always been "small," whereas Jessica was "big." Both parents had tended to be overweight. She was aware of "comfort eating" to manage her emotions, also noting a compulsion in her eating: "Once I start, I can't stop." In addition, she noted that she would become very anxious if she felt there was not enough food and often felt compelled to cook two portions for herself.

We energy tested the statement "I want to be a healthy weight." This registered as "no." "It is safe to be a healthy weight" registered as "yes," but "I deserve to be a healthy weight" registered as "no." I asked for her thoughts as to why this might be so. She said she did not know, but spoke of feeling sad and of wanting to hide.

We then used the following targeting phrase: "the roots and origins of feeling you do not deserve to be a healthy weight," energy testing to find the precise acupoint tapping sequence underpinning the problem. I guided her to tap on the relevant points and to speak of whatever came to mind. The first acupoint was the chin point on the central vessel/meridian, often linked to feelings of shame and rejection. As she tapped there, she spoke of an old sense of not belonging in the family, and of her sister being preferred. She believed her parents had "only wanted one," and her sister had been born first. Further tapping of the evolving sequence of meridians evoked more feelings of shame, rejection, and feeling unloved within her family.

We moved on to using the phrase "the earliest trauma behind your feeling of not deserving to be a healthy weight." The first acupoint in this emerging sequence was again the chin (central vessel), and this evoked yet more shame and feelings that her sister had been preferred and thoughts that her depressed mother found it difficult to cope with twins. Tapping the middle finger (heart protector) led to her recalling her childhood feeling that she would be left to starve to death because there was not enough food and not enough love for her. She had felt she did not belong in the family and should not exist.

We then made a subtle shift of focus, from tapping acupoints primarily to obtain information, to tapping while replaying the themes with the aim of both evoking and clearing the emotional charge of the relevant issues. In this mode, I guided Jessica to tap the emerging sequence of points, while giving her words relating to her fears of starvation of both food and love, her feeling her mother wanted to be rid of her, and her view of her existence as a mistake.

Jessica appeared calmer but expressed doubt that any weight loss would be lasting. Therefore, I energy tested her to the statement, "I want to be a healthy weight and for this to be lasting," which indicated a muscle response of "no." Further brief testing of the statement, "I will still be me if I become a healthy weight," revealed this ambivalence to be on the basis of a problem of identity. Because her difficulties in relation to food and her weight had been part of her experience since childhood, it was understandable that having an ED had become part of her identity. To address this aspect of the problem, I guided her to tap the side of the hand while offering her words intended to reframe her identity as a person whose ED was in the past. She then energy tested strong to being ready to be free of her ED.

We then made use of a special energy center under the collarbones that I call the *Blue Diamond*, which can usefully be thought of as an access point to a person's deeper source of wisdom and healing (Mollon, 2016). Activating this point appears to bring about an altered state of consciousness that is responsive to intention and command, using "energized words"—phenomena that can be linked to the extensive research by Stanford materials scientist William Tiller on the measurable and persisting effects of intention during meditative states (Tiller, 2007). After instructing her in activating this point by placing two fingers under the collarbone, I guided her with imagery of spinning energy fields, expelling "waste" information and bringing in fresh energy and information, in a process called "deleting the lies" (Mollon, 2017)—a process intended to delete all forms of lies or corrupted information that had been put into her or that may have arisen within her. This was followed by another procedure called "desynchronizing the energy fields" (Mollon, 2017). This draws upon the work of physicist Claude Swanson (Swanson, 2011), using his theory of the synchronized universe as a metaphor for an intention-based process of dissolving all coherence and information held in the problematic energy fields (Sheldrake, 1988), which, in Jessica's case, were the energy fields of her ED.

As the dysfunctional energy fields are dissolved, it is important to bring in a new and benign information-holding energy field that contrasts with the previous field. In facilitating this process, my procedure is to give voice to whatever words and phrases occur to me spontaneously in the moment (within the Blue Diamond activation), as a description of the new field. For Jessica, this was "the new field of knowing your true inner appetite, and expressing this freely and truthfully, and choosing what is truly nutritious." At the end of this session, Jessica reported feeling "really relaxed" and surprised at this outcome.

Second Session (a Week Later)

In our second meeting, Jessica reported significant shifts in relation to food and eating. She had experienced much less urge to eat excessively. She mentioned having been given chocolate eggs for Easter. She had eaten a little, but then had not wanted anymore and had given the rest of the eggs away. Moreover, she had felt generally more comfortable with herself. Energy testing revealed healthy attitudes toward food, appetite, health, and well-being. On the other hand, she had noticed herself feeling more anxious, along with periods of feeling very negative. Both Jessica and I now understood that her ED had been functioning to ward off her anxiety, and it was this that we now needed to target.

We then used energy testing to find the acupoint tapping sequence for the following phrase: "all the roots and origins of my anxiety." After tapping middle finger (heart protector meridian) and little finger (heart meridian), Jessica reported thoughts of "all the faces of the people on the train looking critical" and then expressed fears that she might be "getting this wrong," referring to the therapeutic process, and that I might become critical of her.

The next acupoints were collarbone (kidney meridian), under nose (governing vessel), and collarbone again. She spoke of thoughts of the fountains in the town that she passed on the way to my consulting room, imagining being in the fountain and being swept down the hole (an image that acquired more meaning later in a memory about quicksand). She then talked of being overwhelmed with feelings of inadequacy and shame. We shifted to finding and tapping the acupoint sequence for the phrase "all the roots and origins of my feelings of shame." She spoke of comparing herself with her sister and with all the other clients who came to see me.

As she tapped on the eyebrow point (bladder meridian, often a focus for specific traumatic events), I asked if any specific events came to mind. She immediately replied that two events occurred to her. Regarding the first event, she said: "I was quite little. My brother wanted to go up a hill, but I needed a loo (toilet) since I had an upset stomach. I went to the loo behind every bush," a recollection associated with shame. The second memory was from age 6, walking somewhere as a family: "I was scared, because my brother said if I stepped on quicksand I would sink and never get out. I was terrified, so I stopped walking. My father got annoyed and pushed me into the quicksand. I was screaming!" I commented: "You thought you were going to be sucked away and would die, like your earlier thought of being sucked into the fountain hole. You thought your father was murdering you." She agreed.

As she continued tapping the evolving acupoint sequence, she spoke of how she would express anxiety in her body, through irritable bowel syndrome. She then wondered what it would be like not to have so much anxiety. We energy tested the statement that it is safe to be free of excessive anxiety and this tested weak, meaning she did not feel this was safe.

I then guided her to tap the side of the hand point (small intestine), while prompting her to repeat some of the words and themes she had used, for example, "Even though it is never safe to relax, and I must be anxious all the time, because my childhood was not safe, they were always trying to get rid of me, they wanted to drop me in the quicksand, and I would never be seen again, so I had to be on my guard the whole time, I completely accept myself." She then energy tested strong for wanting to be free of excessive anxiety and for this to be safe. This illustrates how tapping the side of the hand (small intestine meridian) point, while putting the anxieties into words, will often clear the internal objection/psychological reversal (although we do not yet know why!).

We then used the phrase "all my anxiety," and followed the emergent tapping sequence. This was side of hand, under eye, eyebrow, and outside eye (gallbladder meridian). The gallbladder meridian is often associated with rage, so I contributed the words "all your rage, and fears of your rage showing." She then spoke of an awareness of rage and how much she avoided showing rage. At that moment, she recalled a dream from a few days prior: "I was really angry, maybe with my mum. I wanted to hit her. I woke up crying." She spoke of instances of walking along a busy footpath and people bashing into her. She felt rage and wanted to push them away. She remarked, "Rage terrifies me."

We then shifted to using the phrase "the roots and origins of my rage," tapping the emergent sequence. Jessica spoke of feeling rage at "anything unfair, injustice, abuse of power," but then talked of the "futility of rage" and of how she expressed her rage at inanimate objects, such as by smashing her favorite mug. She likened her behavior to that of John Cleese beating the car for its misbehavior in a famous episode of the comedy program, *Fawlty Towers*. She then remarked that she once had a childhood dream of killing her sister and had subsequently felt guilty for months. She had woken in panic and went to check that her sister was OK.

As she continued tapping the sequence, she recalled that she did once hit someone at school who had been bullying her sister. She was protective toward her sister, feeling it was her role to be so. She clearly expressed her childhood ambivalence toward her sister: hatred and rage toward her on the one hand, loving protection on the other.

We had addressed crucial contributors to her childhood conflicts and associated anxieties and feelings of shame, so it seemed feasible to consider a further step of more fully dissolving the energy fields of anxiety, shame, rage, and fears of rage. She energy tested positive to wanting to be free of these. We used the Blue Diamond procedure of desynchronizing these energy fields, welcoming in a new energy field of "fully embracing myself." She spoke of feeling very calm, listening to the sound of birds singing outside. Energy testing revealed these energy fields to be no longer present, as Jessica tested "no" to the presence of anxiety, shame, or rage.

Third Session (a Month Later)

Jessica reported "a very significant change in my eating pattern," finding herself making healthy dietary choices, no longer experiencing cravings or compulsions in relation to food. She talked of more reality-based worries about her future, work, and finances. Her general level of anxiety was much reduced.

Fourth Session (After Another Month)

Jessica reported that her pattern of eating had remained improved, and she had lost weight. However, she had noticed some anxiety about food in the evening. As we explored this with tapping, she recalled as a child she would sometimes be sent to bed hungry if there had been an argument with her mother, and she remembered how she would lie awake hungry and crying. This had led to a stance of "I must eat now or later I starve." We continued addressing these experiences and associated fears, using tapping and Blue Diamond work, installing an alternative perspective of abundance. She reported feeling calm and positive. At this point, Jessica considered we had completed enough work for the time being and that she would contact me when she felt she needed to.

When I subsequently wrote to Jessica after a further 2 months, asking her to confirm her consent to my writing about the work with her, she agreed and added, "I'm still eating more naturally and healthily and am steadily losing weight. I feel very differently about food without having to try, and am no longer fearful of being hungry and there not being enough."

■ CASE ILLUSTRATION 2

[For ease of reading, the particular sequences of acupoints used are not detailed in this illustration, but these were all derived by variants on the Callahan energy testing procedures.]

First Session

Eva sought help for her ED, consisting of alternating anorexia and bulimia, because she had come across the energy method called EFT and had used it to help her pass her driving test. She wondered whether similar methods might help her gain a pattern of healthy eating. Over many years, she had tried a large number and variety of therapies, including cognitive behavioral therapy (CBT) provided by her local National Health Service (NHS) Eating Disorder Service, without success. Eva had been happily married for 20 years, and had eight children. She felt she had had babies to "fill the gaps." An additional significant and chronic health problem for Eva was her Ehlers–Danlos syndrome (EDS), which gives rise to pervasive systemic symptoms, including painful joints that easily dislocate.

Energy testing revealed various confusions and dysfunctional beliefs about weight. Her system indicated a belief that it was *not safe* to be a healthy weight. When asked why this might be, Eva replied that when she was *overweight*, people did not like her, and that "Nothing will work if I am overweight." Energy testing also indicated that her body was confused about what was a healthy weight and did not know how to be a healthy weight. These indications were apparent from testing statements, such as "My body knows what is a healthy weight" and "My body knows *how* to be a healthy weight," where her muscle tone response indicated "no." Thus, in energy psychotherapy, we are sometimes addressing the *absence* of required information or resources, as well as the *presence* of dysfunctional or traumatic information. To counter this absence, we used a simple principle found in a number of energy psychology approaches of "downloading" the necessary resources from higher parts of the person's being. Such a procedure forms the core of the method known as "Ask and Receive," developed by Sandi Radomski and Tom and Pamela Altaffer (http://askandreceive.org). Although somewhat perplexing in its mode of action, many practitioners attest to the effectiveness of this procedure. Following this, Eva tested strong to her body knowing how to be a healthy weight.

We then found the emerging meridian tapping sequence relating to her fears and conflicts about food and weight. After tapping a number of points, Eva spoke of an image of spaghetti Bolognese. She said her mother used to make it for her quite often and, as a child, she liked it, but found it contributed to her being overweight. Following a few more tapping points, she spoke of an image of ballet shoes. She had wanted to be a little ballerina, but she had never felt like a "little girl," because she was overweight and her mother would cut her hair short. She went on to speak of how her mother had many problems and had been selfish, not looking after Eva emotionally, but giving her food "to shut me up." Her mother would tell her there was something wrong with her, so that she felt herself to be "odd, strange, and blamed." As a result, Eva became quite disturbed as a teenager, leaving school and home at age 14, and turning to drugs.

We concluded this session with the "deleting the lies" procedure, using intention and imagery with the Blue Diamond (described earlier in the case of Jessica).

Second Session (a Week Later)

Eva reported that following the first session, she had kept picturing the spirals (used in the Blue Diamond exercise) and that her eating pattern had become much better. She had been able to eat every few hours and felt an absence of what she had earlier called her "anorexic wall." However, she still felt an internal pull toward her old patterns, which she felt were "so strong and entrenched." She also reported feeling very anxious.

We energy tested her again in relation to a goal of healthy eating and a healthy weight. This time her system indicated that she felt she did not *deserve* a pattern of healthy eating. We followed the emerging meridian sequence to the phrase "the roots and origins and causes of feeling I do not deserve to have a pattern of healthy eating." She talked of her earlier teenage relationship with an abusive and violent older man who broke her nose. Fortunately, she had managed to escape from him and soon after met Tom who became her husband. They have been happily together ever since. Tom had appeared to her very desirable, with an attractive slim and muscular body, while she was still overweight. She had decided to go on a diet and became obsessed with losing weight and going to the gym. As a result, she had felt much more confident. One day, however, she "got too hungry, started binge eating, and it all got out of control." She began bingeing and purging, a pattern that had then continued. Thus, her feeling of not deserving a pattern of healthy eating reflected her sense of being to blame for her own disordered eating. After tapping through these issues, she no longer tested strong to not deserving a pattern of healthy eating.

We concluded this session by installing a program for healthy eating, again using the Blue Diamond position.

THIRD SESSION (2 WEEKS LATER)

Eva reported that she was no longer experiencing a reluctance to eat, but her pattern had become more bulimic. She noted that when she was in an anorexic phase, she felt no emotion, but when she was in a bulimic phase, she experienced a lot of emotions, as well as panic and chaos. She had found some photos of herself as a child, which reminded her of childhood feelings of being overweight, uncomfortable in her body, ugly and unpleasant, and of being in pain from her EDS. She was called "lazy," because of her undiagnosed EDS-related physical discomfort. When she later lost weight, she had been strongly reinforced for doing so, by compliments on her appearance. Consequently, dieting and losing weight seemed like a solution to all her problems. She would feel "in control and not stupid."

Energy testing revealed that she believed it was not safe to resolve her emotional problems. After a moment's thought, Eva concluded that she probably thought that this would result in becoming overweight. Therefore, we energy tested the following statement: "I want to resolve my emotional problems *and* be a healthy weight." This tested "yes." Such reframing and negotiating to find a goal that is acceptable to the client can often be an important component of energy psychotherapy. As we followed the emerging meridian sequence for her emotional problems, Eva began to refer to feelings of panic, upset, sadness, and regret at all that she had missed out on during her childhood and later. She felt her ED and her EDS had blighted her life.

She then moved to feelings of anger, saying she had felt angry all the time until she became anorexic. She recognized that, in becoming anorexic, she had been taking her aggression and anger out on herself by starving and purging. Her focus then shifted to feelings of shame and helplessness. She spoke of feeling blamed by her mother and father, being told she was the problem, and her mother telling her she was "awkward, difficult, fat and lazy." Her physical difficulties and pain resulting from her EDS were dismissed and interpreted as laziness. She noted that it was easy to join in the blaming (identifying with the aggressor), punishing herself by starvation while enjoying the praise for becoming thin. This had seemed to her like the "perfect" (psychodynamic) solution!

FOURTH SESSION (A WEEK LATER)

Eva reported that she was feeling "a lot better" and that her eating was "massively better." She described an experience of lying in bed at night and smiling, feeling better about her body, and much less shy with Tom. She felt this change was "like magic." She remarked: "I feel completely different. All my anorexic behavior has gone, and I have put on half a stone (7 pounds). I feel I am finally getting somewhere after all these years." Nevertheless, she said she still experienced a residual pattern of some bingeing and purging.

FIFTH SESSION (2 WEEKS LATER)

Eva reported that she had gained 10 pounds. She said it was no longer difficult to eat. The anorexic pattern and fear of eating had gone completely, which felt like "a miracle." She felt she was "changing hugely" and that "loads of things are positive." In general, she felt much calmer, but was, however, still engaging in bulimic behaviors to some degree.

As we continued talking and tapping, Eva began to speak more of her anger with her mother and how she felt neglected. She recalled an image of herself as a child "with horrible short hair and a horrible jumper, feeling fat and ugly with unwashed hair, short like a boy's. It was how my mother cut my hair, like a boy's crew cut. I recall someone saying 'Is your hair wet?' because it was greasy." As Eva tapped on the outside of the eye (a gallbladder acupoint often associated with rage), she connected with more intense feelings of anger—of not feeling listened to, of spending time in her bedroom crying, being in pain from injuries to her collarbone and knee, linked to her EDS. "I was told I was just making it up. I can really feel the anger now!"

Further energy testing revealed that Eva was afraid to be free of bulimia for two reasons: (a) Bingeing and purging had become her way of managing stress; and (b) she feared being starved of love and, because of this, had turned away from others, preferring to be alone with food as a substitute for love. With this clarification, we moved into the procedure for desynchronizing the energy fields of the fear of starvation of both food and love, and of not being accepted. This was replaced with a new field of feeling profoundly loved throughout the fabric of her being. She reported feeling very peaceful and positive following this.

SIXTH SESSION (3 WEEKS LATER)

Eva reported continuing improvement, gaining more weight and no longer feeling afraid of this. She remarked: "When I first came to see you, the anorexia was the worst it had been—I was thinking 'Oh my God, I'm going to die!' The NHS Eating Disorder team had been making me worse—going over and over old stuff." However, she was aware of a continuing resistance to giving up her pattern of eating and purging in the evening. Eventually, through exploring her thoughts, and also enquiring with energy testing, we identified that she used purging as a means of regulating her emotional state. All kinds of aversive emotions could be "vomited out" in this way. She commented: "I realize now it is more about vomiting than about food. I never saw it like that before," and she spoke of the urgency of resolving this because of the terrible effect on her teeth. Despite her conscious desire, energy testing revealed that she did not wish to give up vomiting, and she became aware of her fear that without this she might be overwhelmed with emotions. We worked on these fears with further acupoint tapping and Blue Diamond exercises.

SEVENTH SESSION (3 WEEKS LATER)

Eva said she was doing well: "I'm such a different person now, compared to when I first came to see you." She spoke of feeling much less anxious, as well as more confident and at ease with her body. Nevertheless, she reported a continuing pattern of bulimia. She said: "I don't eat enough during the day, then I get really hungry and eat lots in the evening. I just eat whatever is there, then I vomit and feel clean and in control." In this session, we eventually identified a crucial further aspect driving her compulsion to vomit, linking to her EDS.

Energy testing revealed that she did not want to "eat normally." Initially, both of us were puzzled by this. She spoke of disliking the feeling of food in her body, of feeling "full up and bloated" and how she had always felt this way. Together we arrived at a new insight that the bloating feeling arose from her EDS, the collagen deficiency resulting in a lack of resilience in the tissue of her stomach and gut, so that they are too "stretchy." This understanding led to the awareness that a "normal" pattern of eating was not appropriate for her. A substantial meal would result in discomfort because of her EDS. Therefore, she needed to eat small amounts more frequently. This was a shocking yet relieving realization for Eva, because she had always felt she must aim to "eat like other people."

As a child, her mother had pressured her to eat large meals, thus impeding her capacity to learn to select the foods and amounts that she could comfortably manage. She now energy tested strong to wanting to "listen to the wisdom of my body and eat in a way that is appropriate for me." We reinforced this intention with Blue Diamond work.

By this point, Eva felt we had done a significant part of the required work for her to resolve her ED. She understood that she needed to eat small amounts more frequently, and she energy tested that she was willing to do this. In a subsequent session, she remarked that her view of herself had completely changed, she felt free of shame and self-criticism, and she was happily engaging with others in activities that interested her.

Discussion

These few introductory sessions with two clients suffering with chronic EDs illustrate how energy psychotherapy methods can form a useful component of treatment. Two specific functions of acupoint tapping are apparent: (a) The emergence of further relevant emotional, memorial, and cognitive material is facilitated, often rapidly; and (b) emotional distress is rapidly dissipated. Thus, the flow of information and energy is enhanced. In addition, the use of "energy testing," involving manual monitoring of subtle variations in muscle tone while the person verbalizes statements regarding his or her feelings, fears, and motives, can indicate with some precision the nature of unconscious resistances to resolving the disorder and its various components. This procedure enables incorrect hypotheses to be discarded rapidly and facilitates the search for the most relevant and truthful psychodynamics behind the presenting problems.

In the cases of both Jessica and Eva, energy testing revealed significant internal objections (psychological reversals) to resolving their EDs. These are best regarded not as obstacles to recovery (although they are), but as crucial indicators of important psychodynamics. They can usefully be selected as targets for psychoenergetic exploration and processing in their own right, for example, by finding the emerging acupoint sequence to the phrase "the roots and origins of feeling it is not safe/I do not deserve/I will not be me …," while inviting the client to speak of anything that comes to mind. Such psychological and energetic explorations usually lead to important and formative childhood experiences.

Jessica displayed a belief that she did not deserve to achieve a healthy weight. Exploration of this revealed profound feelings of guilt about existing, feeling she was unwanted and a burden to her mother. Later, her anxiety came to the surface, which was found to relate to a childhood perception that her parents wanted to get rid of her. Energy testing with Eva also revealed deep feelings of being unwanted and unloved, expressed as not deserving to have a healthy pattern of eating. As a child, she had been overfed, and felt fat, ugly, and awkward. Chronic rage had been induced by the parental failure to understand or take seriously her physical pain and other difficulties associated with her EDS. When she later met her partner, she wanted to be slim and attractive, and found that an anorexic stance was psychodynamically very effective in diverting her rage onto herself, achieving a sense of control, and being rewarded by admiring comments on her appearance. The intense starvation then resulted in a breakthrough of intense eating, which in turn gave rise to an unstable oscillation between bulimia and anorexia.

In Eva's case, we arrived at a further understanding of the contribution of her EDS, which caused her to feel unpleasantly bloated after eating because of the defective tissue of her stomach and gut. Energy testing facilitated the emergence of this understanding because it arose from the puzzling finding that she did not "want to eat normally." She needed to eat in a way that suited her own body. This illustrates how physical conditions can interweave in complex ways with the psychological aspects of an ED. What is taken into the body, and when, and what is refused are profound expressions of autonomy.

Conclusion

Energy psychology modalities can form useful additional components of a psycho-therapeutic approach to EDs, helping to alleviate the intensity of emotional distress and facilitate the flow of energy and information. The simple (albeit subtle) methods of energy testing can offer rapid indications of unconscious obstacles to achieving a conscious goal. Despite certain components (tapping and energy testing) potentially appearing somewhat strange to those trained exclusively in talking/listening therapies, the content of what emerges is entirely familiar—stories of trauma, emotional pain, dysfunctional schemas, and psychodynamic conflict. It is in working carefully with all the details and nuances of these that healing occurs.

■ REFERENCES

Callahan, R. J. (1981). *Psychological reversal.* Paper presented at the proceedings of the International College of Applied Kinesiology, Winter Meeting, Acapulco, Mexico.

Callahan, R. J. (1985). *Five minute phobia cure: Dr. Callahan's treatment for fears, phobias, and self-sabotage.* Wilmington, DE: Enterprise Publications.

Callahan, R. J. (2001). *Tapping the healer within: Using thought field therapy to instantly conquer your fears, anxieties, and emotional distress.* New York, NY: Contemporary Books.

Church, D. (2013). *The EFT manual.* Fulton, CA: Energy Psychology Press.

Church, D., & Feinstein, D. (2017). The manual stimulation of acupuncture points in the treatment of post-traumatic stress disorder: A review of clinical emotional freedom techniques. *Medical Acupuncture, 29*(4), 194–205. Retrieved from https://www.ncbi.nlm.nih.gov/pmc/articles/PMC5580368

Church, D., Feinstein, D., Gallo, F., & Yang, A. (2016, October). *Is acupressure an active or inert ingredient in emotional freedom techniques (EFT)? A meta-analysis of dismantling studies.* Presentation at Omega Institute, Rhinebeck, NY.

Church, D., Yount, G., & Brooks, A. J. (2012). The effect of emotional freedom techniques on stress biochemistry: A randomized controlled trial. *Journal of Nervous and Mental Disease, 200*(10), 891–896. doi:10.1097/NMD.0b013e31826b9fc1

Clond, M. (2016). Emotional freedom techniques for anxiety: A systematic review with meta-analysis. *Journal of Nervous and Mental Disease, 204*(5), 388–395. doi:10.1097/NMD.0000000000000483

Diamond, J. (1985). *Life energy.* New York, NY: Dodd, Mead.

Diamond, J. (1997). *Your body doesn't lie.* Enfield, UK: Eden Grove. (Original work published 1979)

Feinstein, D. (2012). Acupoint stimulation in treating psychological disorders: Evidence of efficacy. *Review of General Psychology, 16*(4), 364–380. doi:10.1037/a0028602

Fox, L. (2013). Is acupoint tapping an active ingredient or an inert placebo in emotional freedom techniques (EFT)? A randomized controlled dismantling study. *Energy Psychology, 5*(2), 15–26. doi:10.9769/EPJ.2013.5.2.LF

Gallo, F. P. (1999). *Energy psychology. Explorations at the interface of energy, cognition, behavior and health.* Boca Raton, FL: CRC Press.

Gaudiano, B. A., & Herbert, J. D. (2000). Can we really tap our problems away? A critical analysis of thought field therapy. *Skeptical Inquirer, 24*(4). Retrieved from https://www.csicop.org/si/show/can_we_really_tap_our_problems_away_a_critical_analysis_of_thought_field_th

Longhurst, J. C. (2010). Defining meridians: A modern basis of understanding. *Journal of Acupuncture and Meridian Studies, 3*(2), 67–74. doi:10.1016/S2005-2901(10)60014-3

Marzillier, J. (2014). The energy therapies. In *The Trauma Therapies* (pp. 219–237). Oxford, UK: Oxford University Press.

Mollon, P. (2005). *EMDR and the energy therapies: Psychoanalytic perspectives*. London, UK: Karnac Books.

Mollon, P. (2008a). Freud, Reich, and bioelectrical energy: From libido to chi. In *Psychoanalytic energy psychotherapy* (pp. 309–333). London, UK: Karnac Books.

Mollon, P. (2008b). Is the "energy" concept necessary? A cognitive model of Emotional Freedom Techniques. In *Psychoanalytic energy psychotherapy* (pp. 335–348). London, UK: Karnac Books.

Mollon, P. (2008c). *Psychoanalytic energy psychotherapy*. London, UK: Karnac Books.

Mollon, P. (2014a). Attachment and energy psychology: Explorations at the interface of bodily, mental, relational, and transpersonal aspects of human behavior and experience. In K. White (Ed.), *Talking bodies: How do we integrate working with the body in psychotherapy from an attachment and relational perspective?* London, UK: Karnac Books.

Mollon, P. (2014b). Revisiting "Analysis Terminable and Interminable": Expressions of death instinct by patients and analyst. *Psychoanalytic Inquiry, 34*(1), 28–38. doi:10.1080/07351690.2014.859891

Mollon, P. (2016, June 2–4). *Beyond meridians and chakras: Blue Diamond Healing*. Presentation at the 18th Annual Conference of the Association for Comprehensive Energy Psychology, Santa Clara, CA.

Mollon, P. (2017). *Desynchronizing the energy fields*. Presentation at the 19th Annual Conference of the Association for Comprehensive Energy Psychology, San Antonio, TX.

Oschman, J. L. (2000). *Energy medicine: The scientific basis*. New York, NY: Churchill Livingstone.

Sheldrake, R. (1988). *The presence of the past: Morphic resonance and the habits of the nature*. London, UK: Collins.

Stapleton, P., Bannatyne, A. J., Chatwin, H., Urzi, K.-C., Porter, B., & Sheldon, T. (2017). Secondary psychological outcomes in a controlled trial of emotional freedom techniques and cognitive behaviour therapy in the treatment of food cravings. *Complementary Therapies in Clinical Practice, 28*, 136–145. doi:10.1016/j.ctcp.2017.06.004

Stapleton, P., Bannatyne, A. J., Porter, B., Urzi, K. C., & Sheldon, T. (2016). Food for thought: A randomised controlled trial of emotional freedom techniques and cognitive behavioural therapy in the treatment of food cravings. *Applied Psychology Health and Well-Being, 8*(2), 232–257. doi:10.1111/aphw.12070

Stapleton, P., Chatwin, H., William, M., Hutton, A., Pain, A., Porter, B., & Sheldon, T. (2016). Emotional freedom techniques in the treatment of unhealthy eating behaviors and related psychological constructs in adolescents: A randomized controlled pilot trial. *Explore: The Journal of Science and Healing, 12*(2), 113–122. doi:10.1016/j.explore.2015.12.001

Stapleton, P., Sheldon, T., & Porter, B. (2012a). Clinical benefits of Emotional Freedom Techniques on food cravings at 12-months follow-up: A randomized controlled trial. *Energy Psychology, 4*(1), 13–24. doi:10.9769.EPJ.2012.4.1.PS

Stapleton, P., Sheldon, T., & Porter, B. (2012b). Practical application of Emotional Freedom Techniques for food cravings. *The International Journal of Healing and Caring, 12*(3). Retrieved from http://www.ijhc.org/wp-content/uploads/2016/01/Stapleton-12-3.pdf

Stapleton, P., Sheldon, T., Porter, B., & Whitty, J. (2011). A randomized clinical trial of a meridian-based intervention for food cravings with six month follow-up. *Behavior Change, 28*(1), 1–16. doi:10.1375/bech.28.1.1

Stefanov, M., Potroz, M., Kim, J., Lim, J., Cha, R., & Nam, M.-H. (2013). The primo vascular system as a new anatomical system. *Journal of Acupuncture and Meridian Studies, 6*(6), 331–338. doi:10.1016/j.jams.2013.10.001

Swanson, C. (2011). *Life force. The scientific basis. Volume II of the synchronized universe*. Tucson, AZ: Poseidia Press.

Thie, J. (2005). *Touch for health. A practical guide to natural health with acupressure touch*. Camarillo, CA: Devorss.

Tiller, W. A. (1997). *Science and human transformation: Subtle energies, intentionality, and consciousness*. Walnut Creek, CA: Pavior Publications.

Tiller, W. A. (2007). *Psychoenergetic science*. Walnut Creek, CA: Pavior Publications.

CHAPTER 21

Somatic Experiencing: The Body as the Missing Link in Eating Disorder Treatment

Paula Scatoloni

■ INTRODUCTION

Trauma shocks the brain, stuns the mind, and freezes the body … for effective therapy, it is critical to appreciate how trauma becomes riveted in the body's instinctive reactions to perceived threat; how it becomes fixated in certain emotions, particularly those of fear, terror, or rage, as well as habitual affective mood states such as depression, bipolarity, and loss of vital energy; and, finally, how it plays out in various self-destructive and repetitive behaviors. (Levine, 2015, p. xxi)

Eating disorders (EDs) may be among the most self-destructive and persistent behaviors that emerge in the aftermath of trauma. Difficult to treat and prone to relapse, once EDs take hold, they are difficult and at times impossible to resolve without expert intervention. Over the past decade, as professionals have continued to search for modalities that will produce long-term results in this complex population, trends in the standard of care for treating EDs have shifted from the traditional cognitive behavioral therapy (CBT) model to include more mindfulness-based approaches such as dialectical behavior therapy (DBT) and acceptance and commitment therapy (ACT). In the upcoming decade, the body, the very stage on which the war is waged, will likely move to the forefront of treatment approaches, thanks to advances in the fields of neuroscience and trauma. Researchers are becoming curious about the role of the body, and, in particular, the nervous system, as it relates to ED symptoms and the management of dysregulated affect states. In his groundbreaking book on trauma, *The Body Keeps the Score*, psychiatrist Bessel van der Kolk states, "Psychologists usually try to help people using insight and understanding to manage their behavior. However, neuroscience research now shows that very few psychological problems are the result of defects in understanding; most originate in pressures from deeper regions in the brain that drive our perception and attention. When the alarm bell of the emotional brain keeps signaling that you are in danger, no amount of insight will silence it" (van der Kolk, 2014, p. 64).

Body-oriented therapies offer a groundbreaking approach in the treatment of EDs. Rather than an obstacle to be overcome, the body is regarded as a *resource* in the recovery process. One body-oriented model that is finding its way into the treatment of disordered eating is Somatic Experiencing (SE). A neurobiology-based approach to working with trauma, developed by Peter Levine in 1997, SE was designed to disentangle cognitive, emotional, and nervous system processes that often accompany intense life events and ignite symptoms such as addictions, mood disturbance, and EDs. SE holds significant potential in the treatment of EDs in its capacity to restore body awareness and autonomic regulation by specifically targeting key areas of the brain that are known to influence both the ED behavior patterns and the alexithymia and body dysmorphia that often accompany these behaviors (Arnold, 2013; Bourke, Taylor, Parker, & Bagby, 1992; Greenberg, 1997; Kaye, 2008; Kaye, Bulik, Thornton, Barbarich, & Masters, 2004; Merwin, Zucker, Lacy, & Elliot, 2010; Miller, Redlich, & Steiner, 2003; Payne & Crane-Godreau, 2015; Payne, Levine, & Crane-Godreau, 2015; Tsakiris, Tajadura-Jiménez, & Costantini, 2011). By intervening directly with states of hyperarousal and hypoarousal, SE specifically promotes affect regulation by restoring homeostasis in the nervous system. In addition, SE targets interoceptive and proprioceptive awareness, thereby strengthening the insula, anterior cingulate gyrus, and overall connections between the limbic and cortical areas of the brain (Payne & Crane-Godreau, 2015; Payne et al., 2015).

This chapter highlights the psychobiological processes that SE is built upon with regard to working with trauma, with specific considerations for its application when working with the ED population. A natural starting point for understanding the intersection between trauma and EDs involves a brief overview of the effects of trauma on the nervous system.

■ TRAUMA AND THE NERVOUS SYSTEM

Over the past decade, contributions from the field of neuroscience and trauma have offered new perspectives on the nervous system. The work of Stephen Porges has significantly influenced our understanding of the nervous system and the neurobiology of safety and danger. Porges' (2001) *polyvagal theory* explains how the autonomic nervous system regulates three specific physiological states that are activated on the basis of the body's experience of safety or threat.

When faced with threat, humans generally engage their mammalian attachment system first, as they turn to another person for help, support, or comfort. However, if this "prosocial" behavior does not resolve the threat, a more primitive fight–flight system is engaged. If neither social engagement nor fight–flight resolves the threat, then the most primitive branch of the parasympathetic system, which governs our immobility response of energy conservation, takes over and essentially hijacks all our survival efforts (Levine, 2010; Porges, 2001). Our access to social engagement is partially restricted when we are stuck in states of sympathetic arousal, and profoundly suppressed when the immobilization system takes over (Levine, 2010). This branch of the parasympathetic nervous system reaches below the diaphragm, impacting the kidney, stomach, and intestines, and drastically reduces the metabolism, heart rate, and breath. SE and similar approaches offer a revolutionary treatment of trauma in that they work directly with the immobilization system, the system that is at the *core* of most trauma (Levine, 2010; van der Kolk, 2014).

Dr. Peter Levine began to develop his approach in the 1960s while completing a degree in medical biophysics. Ongoing research led him to conclude that trauma is not about an event. Rather, it is the physiological response to an overwhelming event or environment that dysregulates the normal physiological processes of the nervous system. Symptoms arise when residual energy from these events is not effectively discharged from the body, resulting in a state of constant threat. This ongoing activation in the nervous system has implications for our thoughts, behaviors, relationships, and sense of self (Levine, 2010). After an intense study of animals in the wild, Levine deduced that traumatic symptoms occur when one branch of the nervous system (sympathetic system) generates a flood of hormones and survival energy to meet a threat, but the impulse to defend is prevented or thwarted in the process, and thus remains incomplete. When this occurs, the survival energy gets blocked in the body, so the individual is unable to discharge the energy through actions such as bracing, fighting, or fleeing. The chemicals in the body then flood the system and kick off another branch of the nervous system that is responsible for shutting down the body through mechanisms of dissociation, collapse, and immobility. Levine further observed that animals in the wild have a natural way of restoring equilibrium when defensive impulses are overwhelmed or thwarted. This occurs by involuntary shaking movements with subsequent spontaneous alterations in the breath. The completion of this process informs the body that the threat has passed and the nervous system returns to a state of homeostasis. In contrast, humans tend to suppress these instincts and are thus denied these biologically based, restorative processes. The nervous system, having failed to realize the threat has passed, becomes stuck in either hyperarousal or hypoarousal. These states eventually take a toll on other bodily systems including circulatory, immune, digestive, respiratory, and endocrinal, ultimately driving the thoughts, emotions, and behaviors that are associated with anxiety, depression, posttraumatic stress disorder (PTSD), and many other mental health conditions, including EDs.

■ EATING DISORDERS AS SURVIVAL STRATEGIES

Viewing EDs through the lens of SE affords practitioners an opportunity for a new query into the ways in which the ED symptoms offer a window into the conditions of the nervous system. From an SE perspective, a dysregulated nervous system can occur because of a single traumatic event. However, it is more common for EDs to surface because of intense experiences that overload an already vulnerable nervous system. Such nervous system vulnerabilities can develop in utero, through birth trauma, or through early life experiences that impact nervous system resiliency. The SE practitioner has this in mind during the assessment of EDs and seeks to understand the behaviors themselves, as expressions of nervous system states.

An individual stuck in hyperarousal (fight–flight) often presents with anxiety or panic, hypervigilance, body tension, rage, and disorganized thoughts. The SE practitioner, trained to track the physical signs of *flight*, will note observations such as shallow breathing, rapid heart rate, tension or bracing in neck, shaking of the leg, or darting eyes. This same *flight* energy tends to show up in EDs through obsessive thoughts about food and food rituals, loss of appetite, binge eating, bowel irregularity, or excessive exercise. The SE practitioner recognizes that in flight, the persistent thoughts and compulsive behaviors are essentially driven by the physiology of fear. Similarly, the SE practitioner observes *fight* energy as tension in the jaw or gut, clenched hands, pressured speech, or biting of the lips. The same *fight* energy can be observed in the ED symptoms of purging, chewing and spitting, anger turned toward the body, and other self-harm behaviors.

Tracking states of hypoarousal, the SE practitioner will make note of the following: blunting of sensation, lack of emotions, disabled thought processes, lack of appetite, and lethargy around physical movement. This *freeze* response presents itself in EDs through inhibition in digestion, irritable bowel syndrome, desire to disappear, dissociation, blunted affect, and the use of extreme measures to feel the body, such as extreme sports, self-mutilation, or other impulsive actions. Often, individuals who struggle with disordered eating manifest all of the previously mentioned symptoms, shifting from one nervous system state to the other on any given day.

A trauma-informed approach to EDs requires practitioners to shift their attention away from the ED symptoms, to consider the mechanisms of the nervous system that are driving the symptoms. Trauma disrupts our capacity for regulation. ED behaviors serve as a creative strategy to help the individual return to a state of regulation (Porges & Furman, 2011). More accurately, the behaviors create a false perception that one is, indeed, *regulated*. This maladaptive response perpetuates the behaviors and nervous system dysregulation, thereby reducing one's capacity for resiliency in the face of stress.

Finally, trauma impacts one's subjective experience of the body. A disturbance in one's experience of the body is a defining feature in EDs that may be governed *not* by cognitive components, but by a broader domain that includes kinesthetic processes known as interoceptive, exteroceptive, vestibular, and proprioceptive inputs. These bodily inputs start with sensations within the body and move outward, toward the sensations that define the body (skin receptors and joint input). These basic sensory processes are responsible for the experience of one's body boundaries and the visceral feedback that informs our sense of safety (Zucker et al., 2013). For individuals with EDs, the disturbance inside the body is lost in translation, because the visceral experience of danger is projected on the body and the surrounding environment.

The SE practitioner's treatment goals may include (a) teaching interoceptive skills to increase comfort in the body and enhance autonomic regulation, increasing proprioceptive input to reduce body image distress; (b) expanding body awareness through engagement of the five senses; (c) providing safe, relational experiences to foster social engagement; and (d) working through traumatic material *in a nontraumatizing manner* to restore overall homeostasis in the nervous system. In addition, practitioners who are trained in working with attachment will focus their attention on the attachment deficits that are often inherent in this population (Tasca & Balfour, 2014).

SE treatment goals are accomplished not only by listening to the client's narrative but also by closely watching the body's expression of the nervous system (observed in the body's autonomic behavioral aspects) to slow the process down and explore the various elements of an experience. The acronym SIBAM (sensation, image, behavior, affect, and meaning) "… allows for the intimate tracking of the multiple layers and textures of the totality of experience and is the essence of *bottom up* sensorimotor processing—a sharp contrast to standard cognitive behavioral strategies" (Levine, 2010, p. 139). The SE practitioner works with each of these elements, determining whether they are *over*coupled, as evident in stimulus–response reactions that are common in traumatic triggers, or *under*coupled, presenting as dissociated parts with no apparent connection. Throughout this process, the practitioner supports the client in cultivating the capacity to tolerate the sensations associated with these elements by using self-awareness and self-acceptance of internal states.

Fundamental to this unhurried and mind–body-based approach to trauma processing is the nuanced attention to tracking of the felt sense of procedural movements (automatic motor patterns) and impulses that are stored in the precortical areas of the brain. Unlike traditional therapeutic approaches to trauma that engage an individual's explicit or autobiographical memory systems, Levine's model understands that traumatic memories are actually implicit (somatic) imprints that are stored in our emotions, sensations, and procedures, and that "… our instinctive reaction to perceived threat (bracing, contracting, fighting, fleeing and freezing) plays a crucial role in the formation and resolution of trauma memories" (Levine, 2015, p. 25; Payne & Crane-Godreau, 2015). Similarly, the SE practitioner will refrain from interpretation, changing behavior, intensifying emotion, or gathering details of the story. Using mindfulness and the slow observation and tracking of the bodily experience, including sensations, movements, and impulses, the SE practitioner supports the client's capacity to *experience* the sensation of, rather than just to *express*, emotions, to access the inherent impulses or movements that were prevented or thwarted, and to self-regulate in the presence of another to support the limbic structures that govern interactive regulation.

The application of SE when working with EDs is complex. Similar to other forms of ED treatment, the SE practitioner must consider the following in the assessment of disordered eating: (a) severity of ED symptoms; (b) significance of weight loss or malnutrition; (c) access to resources; (d) level of impairment; and (e) motivation to engage in treatment. All of the previously mentioned will guide the practitioner to determine the appropriate level of care, as outlined by the American Psychiatric Association Work Group on Eating Disorders (2000). This is particularly important when working with anorexia or bulimia, because severe restriction or malnutrition further escalates the threat response system, keeping the individual in a perpetual state of fight, flight, or freeze.

■ TREATING TRAUMA AND EATING DISORDERS THROUGH THE BODY

The initial phase of SE treatment involves education about the connection between emotional and physiological regulation and the impact of trauma on the nervous system. Inviting clients to view EDs as *management strategies* for extreme states of arousal immediately begins to reduce the shame and helplessness that often accompany such behaviors. The SE practitioner begins with the assessment of available resources, including the degree to which the body is serving as a resource. The establishment of resources simultaneously facilitates regulation in the nervous system and increases an individual's capacity to be present with difficult material in the body during trauma processing. Resources can be internal or external in nature and can include the reestablishment of lost resources, learning new resources, or strengthening existing resources. Ogden defines resources as "personal skills, abilities, objects, relationships, and services that facilitate self-regulation and provide a sense of competence and resilience" (Ogden, Minton, & Pain, 2006, p. 207).

Matthew and I have been working together for several weeks. A 36-year-old athlete, he has been struggling with anorexia and exercise bulimia since high school. Matthew spent 3 months in a residential treatment center and entered outpatient care about a year ago. Weight restored for 8 months, he recently dropped weight after relocating to the area. Matthew has been advised by his dietitian to limit his exercise because of his recent weight loss. Not surprisingly, this has significantly increased his level of anxiety. Matthew reports a history of bullying in middle school, where he was specifically targeted for his excess weight. His home life in childhood was also chaotic, colored by parental addiction, sibling health issues, and overall instability in the home.

While reflecting on resources, Matthew notes that his connection to sports was initially a resource filled with fond memories of camaraderie, a sense of mastery, and a positive connection to his body. I ask Matthew to choose his favorite sport and imagine himself engaged in the activity. I then ask a series of open-ended questions that support Matthew in entering the body with a sense of curiosity to deepen his experience of the resource. "As you imagine yourself standing on the field holding the hockey stick, what do you notice?" Matthew notices a sense of connection to his legs and uses words such as strong, purposeful, and energized to describe his experience. I ask him to stand, to feel his legs in the here-and-now as he sees the image of himself on the field holding the hockey stick. "Notice what you are aware of as you feel the heaviness or textures of the stick in your hands, see the colors of the field, and hear the sounds associated with the game." He replies "I feel strong." "Where does strong live in the body?" I ask. "In my legs, arms, and I think my chest," he replies. "Can you hang out with this feeling of strength for a minute?" I ask. My invitational language takes him deeper into this resource, as it broadens throughout his body. He notes that he can feel his chest expanding and becoming warm. I ask if this experience is positive, negative, or neutral. "Positive," he replies. "Matthew, if the warmth in the chest had words, what would it say?" I notice his breath deepen and his shoulders pull back as he states, "Strength and power." I ask him if it is tolerable to hang out with this experience a little more, to enhance and deepen this positive shift on a somatic level.

Reconnecting Matthew to his positive associations with the body and somatically anchoring this experience in the here-and-now provides a profound internal resource and an alternate bodily experience that is the *opposite* of the feelings of helplessness and fear that often accompany trauma (Payne et al., 2015). Anchoring internal resources in the body is an essential component of SE, regardless of the population one is treating. It is crucial for the SE practitioner treating EDs to take extra time and attention in reestablishing a positive connection to the body through resources. This process not only supports the client in experiencing the *body as a resource* in recovery but also aids in the construction of the somatic container that is fundamental to trauma processing. From an SE perspective, the body must be able to contain and metabolize the energy that accompanies strong affect states. If this aspect of the work is neglected in the preparation stage, the body will shift into overwhelm during the trauma processing, leaving the client to dissociate or shut down even further.

As I sat across from Matthew, I noticed his dream-like gaze, the blunted movements in his face, and lack of spontaneity in his voice. His brow was furrowed at times and his smile was short-lived. He sat across from me, straight, rigid, almost robotic. Matthew reported that he ate according to a food plan, seldom experienced the sensation of hunger or fullness, and that his urge to exercise was often driven by his fear of making bad food choices. Matthew's facial features were reminiscent of a returning combat veteran blunted and stiff with a quality of dissociation. Access to interoceptive cues, such as hunger, fullness, or affect, was also absent. Thus, it was clear to me that his body had been in a state of shutdown (freeze, an extended energy conservation state from which he has not yet emerged) for quite some time. This conditioning of the nervous system was deeply entrenched and kept him locked in an ongoing battle with negative body image. A blunting of sensory information traveling from the viscera and gut left Matthew cut off from his bodily cues and reliant on outside measures to determine his self-worth and the degree of safety or threat in the world. Associations of rejection from his peers (bullying) left Matthew in a constant state of hypervigilance about potential rejection from others. Lifting the freeze response and reconnecting Matthew to his thwarted motor patterns required a steady dose of somatic exercises to stimulate interoceptive feedback and increase proprioception in the joints and muscles. This component of the SE treatment was essential prior to processing the trauma memories to increase Matthew's capacity to tolerate the energy of fight–flight and to prevent him from going into overwhelm or dissociation during the trauma processing.

Levine offers simple proprioceptive exercises for awakening the body sense and bringing a person out of shutdown. A few examples are listed as follows:

1. Directed mindfulness of stimulation on the skin (through pressure, touch, warmth, or heat). This awakens the skin receptors and reestablishes body awareness and a sense of boundaries.
2. Mindfulness of the muscles. Tight constricted muscles are associated with alarm and hypervigilance from the sympathetic system, whereas flaccid muscles indicate collapse, which is dominated by the immobility response. Gentle resistance exercises allow the practitioner to support individuals in bringing life back into the muscles that would be used during fight-or-flight responses.
3. The use of a balance ball. This supports the expansion of muscle awareness, grounding, and centering. In addition, the ball can be used to elicit the protective reflexes and core strength that may be missing when trauma is present.

4. The use of movement classes such as yoga, martial arts, tai chi, or qigong. These allow for enhanced connectivity to the body and promote the formation of boundaries that are often missing when trauma has occurred (Levine, 2010, pp. 115–119).

Pendulation and Containment

At the heart of SE is the provider's capacity to bring the client into contact with the body through the felt sense to explore the physical sensations, imagery, metaphor, and motor patterns connected to the trauma. Touching into sensation allows the practitioner to engage the subcortical regions of the brain (limbic and reptilian brain) where the autonomic survival responses are housed. This process simultaneously slows down the nervous system and broadens the awareness of the bodily experience. As a regulation model, SE offers individuals with EDs a wide range of options for bringing the body into a state of regulation. These can include (a) orientation to the present moment; (b) therapeutic touch or self-touch; (c) movement; and/or (d) moving directly into the nervous system arousal through the felt sense and staying with the experience, until the nervous system starts to shift.

Once the SE practitioner has supported an individual in coming into contact with positive somatic states of arousal, the client is ready to start making contact with negative bodily states. Levine refers to this process of shifting back and forth between the negative (activation) and positive (relaxation) states as *pendulation*, the natural state of expansion and contraction that is needed to reduce reactivity during trauma processing (Levine, 2010) and supports nervous system resiliency. This process is done gradually as a client's ability to tolerate greater levels of affect and sensation increases, a process Levine calls *titration*.

Using the SIBAM model and the concept of over- and undercoupling, I consider Matthew's relationship to his exercise bulimia. Similar to CBT, I ask him to identify the trigger that stimulated the urge (impulse) to use the behavior. Next, I use somatic mindfulness to separate or bring together the elements of SIBAM as they emerge in the narrative, supporting Matthew to stay with the experience in a manageable way. After attending several SE sessions, Matthew has demonstrated a basic ability to identify the physical markers for nervous system activation in his body and successfully shift or pendulate the arousal downwards to manage the dysregulation. The following is an example of the use of pendulation in a session.

As Matthew recalls the encounter that triggered the urge to exercise, I ask him to notice what his body is experiencing in the here-and-now. He states, "I can feel energy in my legs—my jaw and gut are tightening as well." "As you notice your legs tensing and your jaw and gut tighten what else do you notice?" "My heart is racing and my breath is becoming shallow," he replies. I ask if this is tolerable. "It is kind of intense," he replies. I notice his eyes are now locked in front of him and shoulders are moving upwards. My own body starts to tense up and correspond with the state of his body. To pendulate away from the activation, I invite Matthew to look around the room, move his shoulders, and notice the sound of my voice or other sounds in the room. I direct his attention to the floor underneath his feet and the couch underneath his legs. Matthew follows my suggestions. He takes a deep breath, his shoulders soften, and his eyes slowly reengage with mine.

■ TRAUMA PROCESSING

Trauma occurs when the nervous system is overwhelmed by experiences that are too fast, too soon, or too much (Levine, 2010). Titration is a concept in chemistry where one tiny drop of a volatile substance is added to another volatile substance, allowing time for the chemical reaction to take place and integrate into the whole before introducing another drop. If the two substances are combined without titration, an explosion would occur (Levine, 2010). In SE, the practitioner works to break the traumatic story into manageable parts, drawing attention to the bodily experiences and moving in and out of the content *one drop at a time.* As the nervous system is given time and space to integrate each titrated dose, healing occurs without further destabilization. The combined use of titration and *pendulation* enables the individual to move into the nervous system activation in a manageable way, so that he or she can integrate the physiological and emotional moments associated with an event without becoming overwhelmed or dissociative.

Working in small, manageable doses, the SE practitioner guides the individual toward a corrective experience. The goal of the corrective experience is not to change the event, but to let the mind and body play out the alternative image of what *could have occurred* if the appropriate resources had been there in the original event. The renegotiation involves the use of visualization, imagery, creative imagination, and change in physiological and physical (postural) experiences, along with the slow tracking of interoceptive and proprioceptive cues to identify the urge toward completion of the biological defense (the procedural movement patterns and impulses that were originally impeded). Once the proprioceptive experience of the biological completion has occurred, the individual will experience a "discharge" as the muscular and autonomic activation that has been bound in the body releases through shaking, trembling, shifts in skin tone, deep breathing, yawning, tears, or heavy sighs (Payne et al., 2015). Individuals with EDs typically experience activation of the nervous system globally throughout the central nervous system, so the discharge is likely to occur deep in the viscera and spread throughout the body. As the discharge occurs, trauma memories lose their intense charge, integrating into the autobiographical timeline of ordinary memories (Payne et al., 2015). The nervous system then moves into a functional range, as the individual experiences increased resiliency and greater capacity to tolerate and process the remaining trauma memories (Payne et al., 2015). Like the finely honed skills of a wilderness tracker, the SE practitioner brings his or her sensitivity to therapeutic attunement, while simultaneously attending to the body's shifting autonomic responses. These responses include heart and respiratory rates, preparatory movements for fight or flight (which occur in the spinal reflexes, muscle tone, and posture), and mobilization of gross motor activity toward fight or flee.

Matthew reflects on the recent episode where he felt "compelled" to exercise after a conversation with his partner. He identified that the argument with his partner (the trigger) was overcoupled with the fear (affect) of rejection. Matthew's memory of rejection is associated with his early experience of rejection (bullying) from his peers. His fear of rejection was overcoupled with a belief that merged the experience of rejection with feelings of weakness that was instantly associated with the experience of being fat. As he shares this connection, he can see (image) an incident of bullying in his mind and feel a tightening in his jaw (sensation). Matthew's body is clearly beginning to tell the story of his unprocessed response during the original bullying event: the tense jaw (fight) and energy in legs (flight). He describes the feeling of immobility (freeze) as he enters into the implicit memory of the event. The following excerpt is a portion of the session illustrating the corrective experience and renegotiation that is primarily done through imagery and visualization, as Matthew tracks the intentional movements (procedural movement patterns) that were thwarted and from which he dissociated in the original experience of the event.

Matthew, who is 9 in the memory, reports that he can see a group of boys standing in front of him. He notices the time of day, season, colors, and scent in the air. He notices one particular boy is taller than he and stands directly across from Matthew. In tracking his body, Matthew is aware that his breath is shallow and his heart is racing. He notices that his extremities are activated inside (i.e., legs and arms feel tight) and yet, on the outside, they appear lifeless and limp. When I ask him to stay with this to explore it further, he states, "My legs and arms are getting tighter and there is some tingling. Now they are cool inside." The shift from tension and tingling to a cool icy stillness suggests that Matthew is primarily parasympathetic in these regions, an experience that Levine notes is at the core of the freeze response. It involves a high level of sympathetic activation coupled with the parasympathetic shutdown, much like a circuit breaker shutting down when too much electrical current overloads a power line.

The focus now is to separate the two competing impulses—the impulse to defend and the impulse to not move. In sitting with the experience further, Matthew identifies the sensation in his chest as fear. In deepening into this, he notices that he feels "blackness" around his torso and a familiar sense of doom associated with the blackness. I am aware that the darkness he describes may be overcoupled with other memories of helplessness that he experienced as a child—times when adult protection was needed, but absent. I decide to invite a "competent protector" into the image to support the corrective experience. I ask Matthew to think of someone (person or animal) that could have been there with him that day, something that would have supported him in feeling "protected." Matthew decides to imagine a large dog at his side. I ask Matthew to stay present with his body and notice what he is aware of with the dog at his side. Matthew shares that the darkness in the torso has lifted and he feels a sense of expansion in the chest. He takes a deeper breath. Returning to the image, I ask Matthew if he would be willing to stay with the energy in his arms and legs and see which feels more compelling. Matthew states that his arms feel more compelling, so he stays with the sensations in the arms first. He notices that his arms want to move, but are pulling back at the same time. I ask Matthew if he can move back and forth between these two separate and conflicting impulses. Matthew is more and more aware of his desire to move his arms. They begin to twitch rapidly. Matthew stays present with his body, as it works through simultaneously occurring impulses. Having identified danger, his system prepares for action with bracing in the arms. Concurrently, he experiences helplessness and fear, given his awareness of his size and the lack of protection that was available at the time. As Matthew slowly tracks his experience, I continue to track my own body, picking up somatic cues of his experience. I ground my feet and legs into the floor and couch to deepen my connection to the here-and-now.

Matthew suddenly says, "I notice that my hands and arms want to grip, like when I was holding the hockey stick." This is an important moment for Matthew, as he is reconnecting to the internal resource of strength and power that was awakened in earlier sessions. "Can you stay with these sensations?" I ask. "Can you see and feel yourself holding the stick in the present moment?" As he reconnects to the somatic experience of strength, I wait and then ask Matthew to notice what his arms might have wanted to do if they could have moved. He takes a few moments. "Break their heads!" he replies. I ask Matthew if in his mind's eye he could visualize exactly what his body wanted to do (wants to do now). "Yes," he replies. I wait and watch.

I encourage Matthew to slow down the imagery and let the impulse in his arms direct the movements in the image. His arm shifts and begins to organize into a movement. "Matthew, if the arm could move, how does it want to move?"

As Matthew moves through the SE session, he is able to complete the motor response that "did not" occur in the original event. Once this process is complete, his body begins to discharge the bound energy as evidenced by trembling, a deep spontaneous breath, and significant reduction of tension in his muscles.

The session ends with an integration of the experience, as we create space for Matthew to sit with his internal world, to be curious, to be open to any beliefs that may be available as he reconnects to the parts of himself that were shut down or cut off. I invite him to choose one word that is available to him, on the basis of what he is experiencing here-and-now. He chooses the word *power*.

The integration phase can take one to several sessions. Subsequent sessions for Matthew involve further exploration of the somatic experience of power, as well as recalling feelings of powerlessness that were likely woven throughout other elements of his life. As the felt sense of *power* is anchored in the body, Matthew notes that he experiences less turmoil related to feeling powerless and its association to being *fat*. He can now, with greater frequency, experience the two concepts (*powerless* and *fat*) as distinct from one another. Simultaneously, his connection to his aggressive drive (appropriate anger) is now available to him. This is evident during future episodes of conflict with his partner. Rather than attempting to flee through exercise, because of being flooded by past somatic memories, Matthew is becoming increasingly able to identify and articulate his emotional reaction (such as anger) while staying present with his partner. In such moments, when he is feeling vulnerable, rather than acting on past ED symptoms, he now has the physiological map to guide him to a sense of protection and safety.

■ ACKNOWLEDGMENT

The author would like to acknowledge the contributions of SE faculty member Dave Berger, LCMHC, PT, MA, in the review and editing of this manuscript.

■ REFERENCES

American Psychiatric Association Work Group on Eating Disorders. (2000). Practice guideline for the treatment of patients with eating disorders (revision). *American Journal of Psychiatry, 157*(1 Suppl.), 1–39.

Arnold, C. (2013). *Decoding anorexia. How breakthroughs in science offer hope for eating disorders.* New York, NY: Routledge.

Bourke, M. P., Taylor, G. I., Parker, J. D., & Bagby, R. M. (1992). Alexithymia in women with anorexia nervosa. A preliminary investigation. *British Journal of Psychiatry, 161*, 240–243. doi:/10.1192/bjp.161.2.240

Greenberg, S. J. (1997). *Alexithymia in an anorexic population: Prevalence and predictive variables* (Doctoral dissertation). Retrieved from Digital Commons at Pace University. (AAI9801921).

Kaye, W. H. (2008). Neurobiology of anorexia and bulimia nervosa. *Physiology & Behavior, 94*, 121–135. doi:10.1016/j.physbeh.2007.11.037

Kaye, W. H., Bulik, C. M., Thornton, L., Barbarich, N., & Masters, K. (2004). Comorbidity of anxiety disorders with anorexia and bulimia nervosa. *American Journal of Psychiatry, 161*, 2215–2221. doi:10.1176/appi.ajp.161.12.2215

Levine, P. A. (2010). *In an unspoken voice.* Berkeley, CA: North Atlantic Books.

Levine, P. A. (2015). *Trauma and memory: Brain and body in a search for the living past.* Berkeley, CA: North Atlantic Books.

Merwin, R. M., Zucker, N. L., Lacy, J. L., & Elliot, C. A. (2010). Interoceptive awareness in eating disorders: Distinguishing lack of clarity from non-acceptance of internal experience. *Cognition and Emotion, 24*, 892–902. doi:10.1080/02699930902985845

Miller, S. P., Redlich, A. D., & Steiner, H. (2003). The stress response in anorexia nervosa. *Child Psychiatry and Human Development, 33*, 295–306. doi:10.1023/A:1023036329399

Ogden, P., Minton, K., & Pain, C. (2006). *Trauma and the body: A sensorimotor approach to psychotherapy.* New York, NY: W. W. Norton.

Payne, P., & Crane-Godreau, M. A. (2015). The preparatory set: A novel approach to understanding stress, trauma, and the bodymind therapies. *Frontiers in Human Neuroscience, 9*, 178. doi:10.3389/fnhum.2015.00178

Payne, P., Levine, P. A., & Crane-Godreau, M. A. (2015). Somatic Experiencing: Using interoception and proprioception as core elements of trauma therapy. *Frontiers in Psychology, 6*, 93. doi:10.3389/fpsyg.2015.00093

Porges, S. W. (2001). The polyvagal theory: Phylogenetic substrates of a social nervous system. *International Journal of Psychophysiology, 42*(2), 123–146. doi:10.1016/S0167-8760(01)00162-3

Porges, S. W., & Furman, S. A. (2011). The early development of the autonomic nervous system provides a neural platform for social behavior: A polyvagal perspective. *Infant and Child Development, 20,* 106–118. doi:10.1002/icd.688

Tasca, G. A., & Balfour, L. (2014). Attachment and eating disorders: A review of current research. *International Journal of Eating Disorders, 47,* 710–717. doi:10.1002/eat.22302

Tsakiris, M., Tajadura-Jiménez, A., & Constantini, M. (2011). Just a heartbeat away from one's body: Interoceptive sensitivity predicts malleability of body-representations. *Proceedings of the Royal Society B, 278,* 2470–2476. Retrieved from http://rspb.royalsocietypublishing.org/content/278/1717/2470

van der Kolk, B. (2014). *The body keeps the score: Brain, mind, and body in the healing of trauma.* New York, NY: Viking Penguin.

Zucker, N. L., Merwin, R. M., Bulik, C. M., Moskovich, A., Wildes, J. E., & Groh, J. (2013). Subjective experience of sensation in anorexia nervosa. *Behaviour Research and Therapy, 51,* 256–265. doi:10.1016/j.brat.2013.01.010

CHAPTER 22

Boats and Sharks: A Sensorimotor Psychotherapy Approach to the Treatment of Eating Disorders and Trauma

Rachel Lewis-Marlow

■ INTRODUCTION

Alice is perched on the edge of my waiting room chair. Her legs, tightly crossed, wrap around each other so completely that her right foot reaches the inside of her left shin. Walking through the door to my office, she narrows her shoulders despite ample room between her body and the door frame. Her eyes scan the room, pausing briefly at the window, closet door, and seating, but her head remains facing straight forward, as though locked in position at the base of her skull. I intentionally deepen my breath and relax my feet as I walk in behind her. We sit, Alice on the edge of the couch in the same tightly wound position as in the waiting room. I position myself in my rolling office chair, facing but slight to the side of Alice. I recognize her postural pattern as indicative of a *sensitive-withdrawn* character strategy and the challenges with feeling safe taking up space that goes along with this attachment pattern. I make an internal note to include the exploration of this constitutional, somatic organization in my treatment approach. I take another breath, deepening into the exhale, rest into the back and seat of my chair, and say gently, "Welcome. I am glad you are here." As a sensorimotor psychotherapist, I have begun my assessment and interventions before a single verbal exchange about history or symptoms occurs.

Alice was referred by a colleague who had seen her off and on since her senior year in high school, when she was first diagnosed with an eating disorder (ED). Her first residential treatment took place during the summer between her freshman and sophomore years in college. Her second stay postponed the beginning of her junior year by one semester. She managed to complete college with the help of a summer intensive outpatient program that accommodated her class schedule. The structure and accountability of treatment helped her restore weight, but, once on her own, she quickly fell off her meal plan and returned to restricting behaviors and compulsive exercise. My colleague provided Alice with quality treatment but had come to a block in progress. Although now armed with excellent dialectical behavior therapy (DBT) skills, Alice had trouble using them. My colleague suspected that, although Alice reported that she had dealt with the date rape she experienced the summer between her junior and senior years in high school, her trauma history was impacting her ability to maintain recovery. Lacking training in trauma treatment, my colleague referred Alice to me.

This chapter presents a case study of a Sensorimotor Psychotherapy (SP) approach to ED treatment. Developed by Dr. Pat Ogden, SP is a body-oriented psychotherapy modality that emphasizes the somatic organization of human experience as a primary access route for facilitating change (Ogden & Fisher, 2015; Ogden, Minton, & Pain, 2006). In contrast to traditional psychotherapeutic approaches, such as cognitive behavioral therapy (CBT), DBT, and acceptance and commitment therapy (ACT), that lean heavily on the impact of thoughts on emotional experiences and somatic patterns, also known as top-down processing, SP also uses bottom-up processing, the effect that one's somatic organization has on affect and affect regulation, cognitive functioning, and specific beliefs about self and other.

Three other concepts distinguish the SP approach from working with trauma and EDs: the foundational principles, the five core organizers of human experience, and the differentiation of threat to physical safety (defense system) from the threat to relational safety (attachment system).

■ FOUNDATIONAL PRINCIPLES

At the very core of SP are four foundational principles that cultivate therapeutic presence and guide both content and quality of interventions. They are as follows:

- Organicity: The innate capacity for and drive toward growth and healing present in all living things
- Nonviolence: The attitude of compassionate curiosity and acceptance that guides the therapist's observations and questions
- Unity: The understanding of the connectedness among all elements of the universe
- Body/mind/spirit holism: The intersection and interconnectedness of mind, body, and spirit that create a human being

■ FIVE CORE ORGANIZERS

SP understands human experience through the lens of five core organizers: thoughts, emotions, and three somatic organizers. These three are as follows:

- Five-sense perception: Our far senses that organize information about our external world
- Sensations: Our near senses that organize information about our internal world
- Movement: The interrelationship between our internal and external worlds

By embodying the foundational principles, the SP therapist supports an exploration of the client's alignment and congruency of these five core organizers that create subjective truth and guide beliefs, actions, and relationships.

■ DIFFERENTIATING DEFENSE AND ATTACHMENT

Although some modalities expand their definition of trauma to include injuries to attachment, recognizing the life-sustaining importance of attachment relationships and the significant impact on neurological organization and affect regulation that attachment injury causes, SP differentiates between the neurological dysregulation that results from the disruption of the attachment system and that which results from incomplete defensive responses. The somatic and affective dysregulation that can result from either injury can look the same, but the two conditions require different treatment approaches. To be effective, the therapist must be able to assess whether the dysregulation the client is experiencing is attributed to the soma's need to connect (attachment) or to disconnect (defense).

The debilitating, long-lasting effects of traumatic events are now widely understood through the maps of the Window of Tolerance (WOT; Siegel, 1999) and polyvagal theory (Porges, 2011). Siegel describes a range or "window" of activation in which an individual is able to process emotions in a regulated state. Cognition, affect, and somatic responses are coordinated with each other in measured response to a given present moment situation. In other words, within this WOT, a person can metabolize experience using all five core organizers. However, emotional arousal can escalate beyond a person's capacity to regulate, effectively sending the individual out of the WOT and into hyperaroused or hypoaroused states where cognitive functioning and intentional, measured somatic responses are unavailable.

The neurological circuitry underlying the WOT model is described by Steven Porges's polyvagal theory. According to this model, the sympathetic and parasympathetic functions of the autonomic nervous systems (ANSs) function in balance because of the engagement of the ventral branch of the vagus nerve. This ventral vagal complex (VVC) is associated with social engagement behaviors including "looking, listening and ingestion" (Porges, 2011, p. 169). The VVC both receives from and sends messages to somatic structures such as eyes, ears, larynx, and mouth, which invite or reject social interaction and engagement. Thus, in situations in which this social engagement is perceived to be available and safe, the nervous system is held in balance, structures of social engagement invite connection, and all five core organizers of human experiences are available.

However, when engagement presents a threat of social rejection or physical harm, the VVC is organized by and organizes somatic structures of social engagement to disconnect from the threat. Facial muscles may change tone. Hearing may become altered. Tone of voice may reflect fear or urgency. The internal environment is similarly altered to support disconnection from threat or danger as the body prepares for actions of defense. Changes in heart rate and respiration occur. The digestive system ceases to function. Access to the relatively slow cognitive functions of the frontal cortex is diminished and eventually denied. Without the VVC oriented toward social engagement, somatic attachment responses, such as the developmental movements of yield, push, reach, grasp, and pull (Bainbridge Cohen, 1993), become truncated or absent. The individual exits the WOT, and the ANS organizes in either a sympathetic dominant state (hyperaroused) that supports defensive responses of fight, flight, and high-freeze actions or a parasympathetic dominant state (hypoaroused) that supports low-freeze and feigned death defensive responses. It is even possible that some anatomical structures are poised for fight, whereas others have collapsed into a low-freeze stance. When this neurological disorganization is pervasive and persistent, as with posttraumatic stress disorder (PTSD), the result is a sculpting, limiting, or prohibiting of emotional regulation and cognitive functioning as well as disrupted digestive processes. These "procedurally learned" patterns (Ogden & Fisher, 2015; Ogden et al., 2006), embedded in all five core organizers, are habitual, neurological patterns of dysregulation, associated with incomplete attachment or defensive responses needed to protect from danger and reestablish safety after traumatic events. Thus, therapeutic interventions that work with somatic organization through a bottom-up approach are essential for effective treatment of trauma, facilitating the repair and growth of attachment and recovery of normative ingestion and digestion.

SP offers several maps that help therapists navigate the path of ED recovery as it traverses the landscape of attachment injury and physical trauma. These maps guide specific approaches to working with fear foods when food itself is used as a weapon in either type of assault.

■ THE ACTION CYCLE

The first of these is the map of the action cycle (Kurtz, 2007). SP explores actions as a cycle with four stages: clarity, effectiveness, satisfaction, and relaxation. When applied to "normative eating," the action cycle could look like the following:

- Clarity: The ability to accurately sense and interpret hunger and fullness cues and the awareness of food preferences, which are associated with nutritional, social, and emotional needs
- Effectiveness: The ability to ask for, reject, select, and prepare foods on the basis of the information in the clarity stage
- Satisfaction: The ability to take in the food that has been prepared, to enjoy the sensations of taste, texture, and smell of the food, and to experience ease and contentment with neurological balancing that results from metabolizing food
- Relaxation: The ability to experience enough, to stop eating, digest, and allow the parasympathetic ANS to continue the metabolic process without sympathetic action

Normative eating involves actions that are both voluntary and involuntary within all of our core organizers of experience: cognition, affect, and soma.

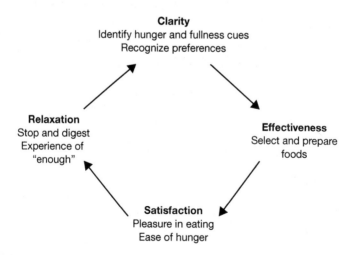

Clarity
Identify hunger and fullness cues
Recognize preferences

Effectiveness
Select and prepare
foods

Satisfaction
Pleasure in eating
Ease of hunger

Relaxation
Stop and digest
Experience of
"enough"

FIGURE 22.1   "Normative eating" through the lens of the action cycle.

■ BARRIERS TO ACTION

A person with an ED is not able to complete one or more of the action cycle stages effectively. SP identifies this as a barrier to action (Kurtz, 2007). Each of these barriers is likely to be expressed through ED behaviors. For example, a person with an insight barrier at the clarity stage will have difficulty identifying hunger and fullness cues or differentiating anxiety from hunger. Individuals with a response barrier at the effectiveness stage may know that they are hungry but restrict intake because they have difficulty asking for the foods they want, or preparing, portioning, or plating their food. Some may binge on foods that do not satiate their hunger, because they cannot reach out for what they really need or want. A nourishment barrier at the satisfaction stage may show up as aversions to actually ingesting and digesting food. We might see purging as an expression of the inability to fully take in that which is desired. People with a *completion barrier* at the relaxation stage may not be able to experience "enough." This can result in bingeing or even restriction, when there is the belief that "I can't finish, so I won't even start." When viewed through the lens of the completion barrier, excessive exercise is understood as an inability to embody relaxation and *enoughness* rather than an attempt to burn calories.

■ CHARACTER STRATEGIES

Barriers to action point to the underlying attachment disruptions and incomplete defense responses through the map of character strategies. SP describes nine different character strategies, each with its own somatic organization, attachment style, emotional capacity, beliefs about self, and preferred defense response. These strategies emerge from disruptions to the attachment relationship at different stages of somatic, affective, and cognitive development. Our effectiveness in the world around us is supported or limited by the agency we develop in our formative years. Thus, each strategy is likely

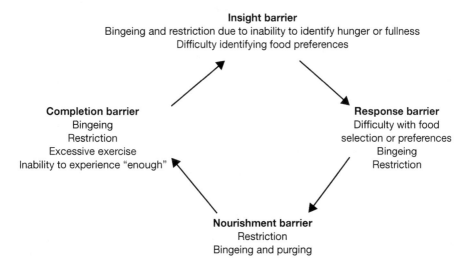

Insight barrier
Bingeing and restriction due to inability to identify hunger or fullness
Difficulty identifying food preferences

Completion barrier
Bingeing
Restriction
Excessive exercise
Inability to experience "enough"

Response barrier
Difficulty with food
selection or preferences
Bingeing
Restriction

Nourishment barrier
Restriction
Bingeing and purging

FIGURE 22.2 Eating disorder symptoms as expressions of barriers to action.

to experience a barrier and an accompanying challenge with associated developmental tasks and defensive actions. The case study presented in this chapter addresses a character strategy I encounter often in my work with EDs: the sensitive-withdrawn strategy.

Action Cycle	Barrier to Action	Eating Disorder Behavior	Character Strategy	Disorganized Somatic Organization
Clarity	Insight	Restriction because of inability to identify hunger cues, food preferences	Sensitive-withdrawn	Incomplete developmental push and associated lack of proprioception and interoception, incomplete fight response, pervasive freeze

■ ALICE

Alice's gaze briefly and quickly darts around the periphery of the room, but rarely lands on me and never on my face. Mostly she looks down toward the floor, but with a tension in her eyes that suggests she is squinting to gain more clarity about the thoughts in her head rather than about the object of her gaze. Her head remains fixed on her spine, even when her eyes move. Her breath is shallow. Her jaw is tight. Her voice is quiet and thin, resonating somewhere above her temples rather than in her throat or pleural cavity. Before we can do any substantive therapeutic work, Alice needs to arrive in the room. Alice's nervous system needs to be reorganized within her WOT. In neurological terms, this means that her VVC, or the social engagement system, must engage to support interaction with her external environment.

I begin by inviting her to take time to orient to the room. Staying out of her direct line of contact, I minimize threat and allow her to take in my presence at her own pace. I track her breath and the articulation of her head on her neck. I deepen my breath and relax my feet on the floor. I am aware of a slight scooting back on her seat as she scans the books on my shelf and brings her gaze to the fidget toys on the end table. Finally, she looks up with reluctance, as though she were gazing forward from inside a cave.

Over the course of a few weeks, Alice shares her history. I make sure to pause, allowing myself to digest each bit of her story. I repeat back the words I have heard, modulating my pacing and breath to either slow down the storytelling she has blurted out and rushed past or ever-so-slightly animate words she lets escape, like vapors from a hidden volcano. I fill in the story with musings about the emotional impact. "That could be really intense, huh?" I contact her somatic patterns by mirroring and gesturing. As she talks about aversions to food, my hand moves to my belly and makes a slight gripping motion. By slowing down the process, she can begin to register cognitively, emotionally, and somatically that I have registered her cognitively, emotionally, and somatically as well. Together we are building the experience of coming forward into the world and being met with a presence and pressure that is validating and organizing. We are beginning to repair.

Alice describes her current ED behaviors with the dispassion of a person well acquainted with psychotherapeutic jargon. Her intellect is a safe place to retreat when the constricted somatic experience of emotion is uncomfortable. She has a general restriction of food. Her daily intake is approximately one-fourth of what is required to meet her nutritional needs. She does not identify hunger cues and often feels anxious or nauseous when eating. When she does eat, her safe foods tend to be fruits, noodles, and chicken. She has specific aversions to pizza, yogurt, and ice-cream. She is often compelled to exercise after eating, and reports that the feeling of food in her belly is uncomfortable and causes her anxiety. Her preferred exercise is running, although she also enjoys swimming, particularly the crawl stroke. Although she recognized that the numbers tell her that she is "underweight," she experiences herself as "fine" when she hovers between 80% and 85% of desired body weight.

As Alice speaks, I track the somatic organization of the storyteller, as well as the specifics of the story she is telling. I listen for three things:

- The story the body is telling about how she has adapted to the circumstances of her verbal narrative
- Where and when defensive strategies are directing her decision-making ability
- How attachment strategies are shaping her beliefs about herself and her relationship with the world around her, including food

When I notice that Alice is becoming activated by her story, we slow down. We build mindful awareness of the somatic indications of her hyper- and hypoarousal and the sensations that accompany emotions and thoughts. She builds a vocabulary to describe her somatic organization. She identifies sensations such as tight, numb, breathless, and tingly. She notices when her breathing gets shallow and if it is harder to breathe in or breathe out. She recognizes impulses to move or small indicators of larger movements that want to express themselves such as a wiggle of her toes that could, if given permission, turn into a run.

I offer resources that can shift her state of neurological arousal. I invite her to orient, not just by bringing her attention to her surroundings but also by moving her head to follow her eyes and articulating the occipital–atlas juncture where her skull rests on her spine. This movement releases her frozen cranial and facial posture associated with the startle response to traumatic events, engages the VVC for social engagement, and sends signals of ease and safety to the brain. As she does this, I notice her breath deepening. A slight gurgling sound in her stomach further indicates that her VVC is bringing balance to her sympathetic and parasympathetic nervous system, making digestion a physiological possibility.

I allow myself to breathe with her and gently remark that her breathing seems to change a bit as she looks around. She nods and verbally agrees. I notice that the pitch of her voice has dropped. I ask her what else she notices changing inside, as she changes how she looks around at the room. She notes that she feels a bit more relaxed, less anxious. She agrees to experiment with orienting, collecting data when her neck locks up, and noticing how allowing it to move affects her breath and the tension in her jaw.

We set up a system for tracking how her nervous system is organized when she is in relationship with eating. With the assistance of a vocabulary list of sensation words, she completes a worksheet that charts hunger, fullness, emotions, and sensations before, during, and after eating opportunities. She notes that hunger and anxiety feel very similar. She recognizes a numbing and shutting down that occurs when she has to decide what to eat. In this hypoaroused state, putting food into her system feels counterintuitive, which in turn causes more agitation and anxiety. She recognizes that her nervous system seems to pop from hyper- to hypoarousal without spending much time inside the WOT.

We experiment and explore other somatic skills for neurological regulation. She learns to isometrically abduct and adduct her legs to help her ground. She practices breathing techniques to emphasize her exhale and reduce the hyperarousal that accompanies anxiety. She learns how to activate her inhalation to upregulate when she is hypoaroused and drifting into waters of depression. With cross-lateral movement, she is able to increase her mental clarity and ability to orient to the present moment. A self-massage protocol that stimulates her ears, jaw, and eyes helps to bring her ventral vagal nerve online and reverses her pull to dissociate. We play with the use of different sensory integration tools, such as a weighted lap pad, and she notices the regulating effect on her nervous system. "I feel safer. Calmer, but also alert."

She begins to use these skills at mealtimes and notices that she is able to tolerate more food in her system before feeling uncomfortably full. She has found that by using these resources, she can land in the WOT long enough to meet some of her needs.

Now we move on to expanding her window.

I note that part of Alice's strategy for managing the discomfort of her somatic experience is to live in her head. She gets caught up in the intellectual understanding of things, as if she can "understand" her way out of her symptoms. I offer her psychoeducation in the form of metaphors and pictures, which shifts her into her right hemisphere, waking up capacity for integrated change of neural networks. I tell her about boats and sharks.

■ BOATS AND SHARKS

Imagine you are swimming in the ocean, far enough from shore that you cannot swim to land. However, because there is a boat within reach, you feel safe. You are in your WOT. But it is not only the presence of the boat that keeps you in your Window. It is also an absence of sharks. Inside the WOT, we experience both the presence of safety and the absence of danger. Now imagine you are swimming in the shark-free water and the boat starts to move away from you. Notice what happens as you imagine that you are being left out in the middle of the ocean. What happens to your breath, heart rate, and muscles as you see the boat moving faster than you can swim to it?

As I lead Alice in this visualization, her eyes get big. She catches her breath on the inhale and leans slightly forward. Her heels come off the floor in a slight bouncing of her legs. Both of us nod, silently acknowledging the impact of the loss of safe connection on the nervous system. I explain to her that human beings are designed to become activated when connection is threatened. Our nervous systems organize at the edge of our WOT and, depending on how successful we are at reestablishing connection, we will either return to center of the window or head out of the WOT into dysregulated hyper- or hypoarousal. Humans instinctively do something to keep the boat close by. We might call out or flail around as though we are drowning to see if that will make the boat come closer. Maybe we swim toward it with an urgent speed. Imagine, too, if we catch up to the boat and see our friends in the boat, laughing at the fear and panic their "joke" caused. We might act nonchalant, disguising our fear to achieve an invitation to climb on board. Our attachment patterns and character strategies are how we attempt to keep the boat close. The conditionality and rigidity of these "rules of engagement" influence the width of our WOT.

Alice nods with recognition, and we spend some time talking about the strategies she has developed to keep herself connected to her family. Do not express anger, or fear, or grief, or even joy too strongly. In essence, do not take up space. As a young child, she came to learn that her emotions were too big for others to help her regulate, so she holds them tightly inside. We explore how scary it is when emotions start to emerge. She is afraid, not only of the feeling itself but also of the rejection she risks if she lets any emotion out. It is as though she is swimming in the ocean while trying not to make any splash.

We track the tension in her core and how her legs wrap around each other. She links this posture to her experience of fear and the belief that "I'm too much. What is inside of me is dangerous." The vehemence of this belief, intensity of anxiety, and centrality of tension in her body comprise the constellation of core organizers of the sensitive-withdrawn character strategy. Trauma experienced in the period between conception and 6 months old is another hallmark of this strategy. I ask Alice if she knows her birth story.

Alice was her mother's third pregnancy. Her mother miscarried midway through a pregnancy after the birth of her older sibling. Although Alice was not considered a high-risk pregnancy, her mother was extremely anxious the entire time. After laboring for over 20 hours, Alice began to show signs of fetal distress and was delivered by C-section. The family lore is that she was "too big" and "nearly broke her mother in two."

I suggest an experiment.

I offer her a sensory integration tool, a large piece of stretchy material sown into a tube large enough that she can cocoon herself inside. She slips it around her waist and pulls the fabric up over her shoulders, her arms tucked against her torso. She likes the feeling of being protected and notices that her arms are more relaxed. I invite her to explore what happens when she pushes her hands forward against the resistance of the fabric. She hesitates at first, but then slowly presses one hand into the protective container. I notice her eyes relax and then brighten. She is less far away. Her breathing shifts, a big inhale, followed by a smiling sigh. With a little encouragement, she explores what it is like to use both hands, to push forward, out to the side, up or down. She pulls the fabric over her head and pushes upward with the crown of her head. She plays with her options and discovers what feels satisfying.

I ask her what she notices. She tracks that her breathing is deeper and the tension in her gut has eased. She wiggles her toes and says she can feel her feet on the floor. She is less afraid. We play with feeling the difference between pushing forward inside the body sock and extending her arm forward into the air without resistance. She notes that having the containment of the material makes it feel safer for her to expand. "It is not too much or too little. It is like it is okay for me to get big, because I know it won't go too far." Her stomach gurgles. I repeat her words back. "It is okay for you to be big." She echoes these words and presses her hands upward, forward, and sideways in space, feeling the full extension of her arms. She stands, pushing her feet into the floor and elongating her spine. I ask her when, in the course of her daily routine, remembering this thought and feeling might be helpful. She muses about what it would be like to walk through the mall feeling the full length and breadth of her body. Alice agrees to integrate this new experience of self through playful experimentation over the next week.

We revisit this new idea over the next several months, as well as attending to the wound that still exists from times this had not been true. We balance resourcing and processing. She practices the new somatic resource of pushing into physical support to enhance her physical sense of self. She uses this as a scaffold to "push" into emotional support and expand her social expression of self. As she finds more safety in the resource of the therapeutic relationship, she can process her attachment wound by mindfully revisiting memories of invalidation and belittlement.

Starting with the anxiety she currently experiences when asked to make a selection from a restaurant menu, she tracks the way in which this particular flavor of anxiety shows up in her body. She notices the fluttering in her belly and tingling turning to numbness in her upper arms. This is a familiar feeling, and as she mindfully stays with the sensation, she remembers visiting her great grandmother's home. It was stuffy and formal, and the grown-ups were sitting on couches in the living room. There was a bowl of candy on the end table. She remembers seeing the candy and wanting a piece. As she reached out to take one, her mother grabbed her arm and pulled her back. Startled, Alice looked up and saw fear in her mother's eyes telling her that her desires were bad and dangerous.

Alice sees her younger self in this memory, freezing with embarrassment and shame, holding back tears to avoid further ridicule for being "too sensitive." Alice notices how, in present time, her body reflects the posture of her younger self, arms crossed at her waist, breath shallow, allowing her ribs to expand slightly and only upward.

In the context of our secure and collaborative therapeutic relationship, Alice mindfully explores the thoughts, emotions, and somatic patterns that go with this childhood memory. She experiences the felt sense of rejection of self that results from her attachment injury and recognizes the earlier unacknowledged longing to feel safe and welcome in the world. Keeping the image of her younger self in her awareness, I invite Alice to bring her gaze out to meet my eyes while I offer words that go with her missing attachment experience. Speaking to young Alice, I say, "Alice, all your feelings are welcome here." Tears well in her eyes as she takes in the words and the quality of my eye contact. She tracks changes in her core organizers. Her breath is fuller. There is warmth in her arms. She can feel the couch beneath her. I repeat the words. She holds my gaze, pushing outward with her eyes to meet me more completely, and recognizes that her younger self no longer feels afraid. I ask what young Alice is learning about herself from how my eyes meet hers. "There is nothing wrong with me. It's okay for me to be here." We move slowly through this new attachment landscape, pausing to make sure she is finding her footing on the unfamiliar terrain. She stands and walks around the office feeling the floor firmly under her feet. Her increased capacity to expand into the room and into a validating relationship helps build her capacity for clarity of self. Neurologically, her proprioception and interoception increase that result in increases in the accuracy of her body image and ability to differentiate hunger from anxiety.

But let us not forget about sharks, which represent the threat to physical safety. The actions required to move toward and get onto a boat are different from those required to fight or get away from a shark, but, as we will see, there are similarities. For example, learning to kick your legs to swim to a boat (attachment) could help you kick and then swim away from a shark (fight and flight of defense). Healthy attachment builds the capacity for effective defense. Furthermore, attachment is necessary for the nervous system to return to a balanced state after metabolizing a traumatic event and to expand the WOT.

As Alice builds the somatic and psychological scaffold of attachment, she spends more time inside her WOT and is able to increase her willingness to retry foods she has restricted, and even to try a few new selections. I ask her about her persistent avoidance of pizza. Silence ensues, the kind of silence that remains in a conversation when you leave the present moment and travel back in time. She speaks to me from this distance, not with words, but with her locked jaw, averted gaze, and the slight lift of her left shoulder.

I gently contact the somatic memory she is sharing with me. "Your muscles tighten when you think about pizza, huh?" She nods twice, eyes locked on a spot on the floor of a room she was in years ago. I recognize the frozen posture of her neck as a truncated orienting response, common in unmetabolized trauma. The locked jaw and raised shoulder are possible indicators of an incomplete fight impulse.

"Where do you notice the tension?" It is important to establish her ability to maintain a mindful awareness of how the memory is presenting itself in the moment. This is my indicator that Alice is in the WOT, and we can proceed with trauma processing rather than offering her a resource for grounding or orienting to the present time and space. Her awareness is focused on the back of her neck and jaw. She can link the tension to words "leave me alone" and reports her memory of the evening of her rape. She recalls sitting on a couch at a party with her "date." He had been drinking and she could smell the alcohol on his breath. He was eating pizza and aggressively offered some to her. She said, "No thanks," yet he pushed the pizza in her mouth. She recalls that she locked her jaw and turned her head. I track her carefully, as she relays the details of the events that preceded the assault, knowing that her defensive impulses came online and were truncated before the actual sexual assault occurred.

Her shoulder lifts and her arm pulls in. I ask her to drop the narrative and bring her awareness to the movement that is happening in her arm. She reports the impulse to pull her arm in tighter. I recognize this as a freeze response, the common defensive strategy for people who have a sensitive withdrawn character strategy. I wonder, now that she has brought the developmental push online through the use of sensory integration tools and attachment repair described earlier, can she be able to access a defensive push that is needed to enact the "fight" response? I offer her another experiment.

"Often, when a muscle contracts and brings a limb in toward the body, it is in preparation for a movement outward. I wonder, if your arm could move any way it really wanted to, what would it do?" She senses into her arm, and I notice a slight lateral movement of her elbow as she says, "It would push something away." "How about we try that?" I ask, and I help her set up an experiment that allows her to find the physical satisfaction of completing the defensive movement she was unable to complete at the time of the assault. SP calls this "reinstating an act of defense" or "restoring acts of triumph" (Ogden et al., 2006).

Using a pillow, I offer her something to push away. I work with her to find just the right amount of resistance to provide and invite her to add words to the action. Eventually, we add an orienting response so that she is looking directly at me as she pushes the pillow and yells, "Stop it! Go away!" In the wake of her effectiveness, Alice is giddy. We laugh together in response to the release and empowerment she feels. I catch her emotionally, as she sheds tears of transformative grief. We take deep breaths and land in my office. I invite Alice to look around. Her eyes are brighter and her head moves freely as she glances around the room and out the window. "Things look different. Clearer."

I invite Alice to linger with this new experience, taking time to look at familiar objects with this unfamiliar clarity. She says with slight bemusement, "The outline of things is sharper." She recognizes her own edge and is able to sense into the space between us. Alice stitches this new proprioceptive awareness to a thought about her ability to stay grounded and say "No!" As with other transformations, she anchors this new belief with a gesture and identifies situations in her current life when it would be helpful to integrate her new-found efficacy.

In the weeks that follow, Alice gradually exposes herself to pizza without feeling the familiar panic and revulsion. She accepts an invitation to a party where she knows pizza will be served. She orders a slice for herself at a restaurant. Eventually, she is able to take a bite from a piece offered to her by a friend.

As our work together progresses, we follow a similar process with more slivers of memory of the assault and of attachment injuries, each time strengthening the connection between Alice's body and mind, widening her WOT, and building her resilience. As she decreases the need for her body to hold the unspoken story of her suffering, her ED behaviors continue to wane. This dance among the core organizers is a dance of embodiment. This dance between trauma and attachment experiences is the dance of innate healing that assures survival and the capacity to thrive. From an SP perspective, this is the essential and organic dance of recovery.

■ REFERENCES

Bainbridge Cohen, B. (1993). *Sensing, feeling, and action*. Northampton, MA: Contact Editions.

Kurtz, R. (2007). *Body-centered psychotherapy: The Hakomi method: The integrated use of mindfulness, nonviolence, and the body*. Mendocino, CA: LifeRhythm.

Ogden, P., & Fisher, J. (2015). *Sensorimotor psychotherapy: Interventions for trauma and attachment*. New York, NY: W. W. Norton.

Ogden, P., Minton, K., & Pain, C. (2006). *Trauma and the body: A sensorimotor approach to psychotherapy*. New York, NY: W. W. Norton.

Porges, S. W. (2011). *The polyvagal theory: Neurophysiological foundations of emotions, attachment, communication, and self-regulation*. New York, NY: W. W. Norton.

Siegel, D. J. (1999). *The developing mind*. New York, NY: Guilford Press.

CHAPTER 23

Art Therapy: Images of Recovery

Deborah A. Good and Cynthia "Cyd" Davis-Hubler

▪ INTRODUCTION

Art therapy is a mental health profession that provides an alternative means of communication and often can be the treatment of choice for clients processing recovery from traumatic events, as well as eating disorders (EDs). Through the art making process, a visual dialogue between the client and the art images is created. The client's self-talk and internal messages can be documented in an imagistic form, releasing those images from the internal battle that occurs in clients with traumatic and/or ED histories.

People think in images first before words are attached to the thought patterns (Good, 2016; Jung, 1964) that disturb a person's psyche and interrupt normal internal processing of events and emotions. Art therapy allows the clients to pull these images from their psyche and record them in a graphic format. Psychiatrists (Jung, 1964; van der Kolk, McFarlane, & Weisaeth, 1996) and psychotherapists have long known the benefit of creatively documenting trauma to assist clients in processing their thoughts and feelings in a safe manner. Rather than addressing the trauma head on through verbal interaction with a therapist, art therapy provides a means of approaching the unapproachable in a nonverbal, nondirect manner. Often words are attached once the images are made in an art therapy session, but sometimes the images speak for themselves and release the client from the burden of carrying the unspeakable secrets hidden inside.

An art therapy session may include dialoguing with the image created (Capacchione, 2001), offering an opportunity for clients to speak safely with the shadows that haunt them. In other words, writing or journaling about the art often clarifies the artwork, which can arise from a directive given by the art therapist or from personal, spontaneous expression.

▪ WHY ART THERAPY WITH CLIENTS WHO DEAL WITH EATING DISORDERS?

In verbal therapy settings, clients often experience difficulty in finding the words to express confusion and pain. Art therapy, by contrast, is an effective means for clients to tell their personal story, safely and indirectly. When clients enter the art therapy room, the art therapist provides them with the opportunity to choose art materials that they feel will best describe their personal story. This approach allows the clients to have control over the way in which they expose their self-histories.

According to Hunter (2016), "The first art therapy session is one of the most important aspects of treatment for the individual with EDs. The initial session introduces the client to the style of the art therapist and the general feel of how art is used therapeutically" (p. 387). The client's personal story begins to unfold as he or she creates images to express his or her experiences. Imagination and creativity guide the healing process. They assist in uncovering unconscious thoughts, and, sometimes, unconscious experiences of pain. Art making offers insight and meaning that is not available through traditional verbal therapy. The making of art becomes a vehicle to communicate the story of the client's ED, cognitive distortions, body distortions, and emotions through the creative images he or she chooses to use. The art therapist becomes a witness to the client's art making process and guides him or her to find personal meaning in the completed art product.

Art therapists are extensively trained to assist the client in creative expression and in facilitation of the client's self-exploration. Processing, by writing or talking about the finished art piece, is a manner of drawing out insight from the client about his or her personal choices, while asking the right questions encourages the client's self-exploration. "Contrary to the popular caricature of the analytic art therapist arbitrarily imposing meaning on the patient or the art, the method is, in fact, highly respectful, and the goal is always to help the patient make his or her own discoveries or 'interpretations'" (Rubin, 2001, p. 18).

Using art therapy with people diagnosed with ED is a unique therapeutic approach that can expose conflicts, problems, thoughts, and behaviors that are not simply about food or a number on the scale. Creativity cultivates positive interpersonal skills, provides a means to manage behaviors, and promotes ways of reducing stress. Graphic images created in sessions help to increase the client's self-esteem and self-awareness.

Clients frequently tell an art therapist, "I can't draw (or paint)." The intense presence of an inner critic often makes them avoid the art room. Judgment from a client's internal critical voice creates fear of humiliation and preys on clients who are dealing with low self-esteem, which often accompanies an ED diagnosis. Self-criticism can be very harsh, acting out in many areas of the client's life, especially via feelings of inadequacy regarding creative expression. The art therapist's main goal is to create a safe, judgment-free zone in the art room, becoming a facilitator of art making and fostering self-growth.

ED patients have extreme fear of being negatively evaluated. The art therapist works toward eliminating those fears by giving the clients creative control over their self-expression. Together, the therapist and the client tackle the internal, critical thoughts that fuel the ED. Creative expression allows for a dialogue to be created between the ED and the client's distorted internal beliefs by using art materials as the primary means of expression. Creating distance through the art making process provides a safe means of therapeutically confronting issues relevant to the client's presenting problems.

■ A TYPICAL ART THERAPY SESSION

One of the first art directives used with ED patients is to have the clients draw or paint what their ED looks like to them. Questions and art directives that follow are to describe the following: What does the ED sound like? Is your ED a friend? Is your ED gender specific? What would your life look like without your ED? What does life with an ED look like? What would it look like to confront your ED? What does your ambivalence toward recovery look like?

Using artwork to describe the answers to these questions provides a thorough and distanced means for clients to explore the issues surrounding their ED. By giving the ED a visual description, a familiarity is developed within the art images, allowing the client a safe distance from the issues they represent. Speaking to and about the art images creates an environment for self-expression to occur in a natural and fluid manner.

When the artwork is completed, the clients may spontaneously begin to explain the images they have created. Or, a client may need to complete several pieces of artwork before he or she feels safe verbalizing about the art images. Often the client's verbalization of his or her artwork exposes the personal stories that the client has learned to believe. The client's personal stories include internal messages that fuel the ED's control. The art therapist is able to evaluate the client's current situation by the way the drawings are created, that is, whether he or she uses a heavy or sketchy line formation, the placement of images on the page, the art materials chosen to support either fluidity or control, and so on. During the art making process, the art therapist is acutely aware of the client's body language in relationship to the images being created and the final product of the art therapy session. An additional art project can be created to express what it was like for the client to create the original art piece. Assessing how comfortable the clients are during the art making process provides key information for the art therapist regarding what questions are appropriate to ask the clients, whether to introduce new art materials to expedite or slow down the therapeutic expression, and whether to help the clients expose and explore how negative internal messages and perceptions were created in the art that cause the clients to feel that they are "no good," or that there is "something wrong with them." Other common internal messages are that they are "a loser, fat, hopeless and helpless."

It is essential that the therapist help the client find motivation for changing his or her self-image. The artwork presented in the case study of Lynn demonstrates how Lynn drew her biggest fears, exposed her inner trappings, and eventually opened to change. Through a deepened therapeutic relationship with her art, Lynn strengthened her self-esteem and was ready to give up her ED. Lynn reluctantly moved through her sessions, increasing her motivation to explore the meaning behind the negative, internal messages that appeared in her art, while discovering images of strength and healing that supported her ability to face her fears.

Every client has his or her own personal timing for facing change. Persistent, creative exposure allows the client to pace himself or herself and to work at a level that is best for him or her. Because the artwork provides a distance from verbally confronting negative belief systems, the client and the therapist are able to work with the art images that are most productive in the moment. The client may continue to create repetitive, similar images until he or she reaches a saturation point. This process often leads to a resolution of the issue being dealt with, without the need to verbally confront it. As the artwork becomes more refined with image repetition, the client gains more self-confidence (Schaefer-Simmern, 1948). Also, the repetitive action of drawing similar imagery can lessen the fear of facing the hidden negative messages. Kramer (1972) supports the premise that the mere act of creating artwork can be the healing therapy that is needed in many therapeutic situations.

Lynn's artwork portrayed a deep trauma that had become an underlying cause of her ED and negative self-image. As her artwork explored her relationship with her ED, another layer of distortion—historical trauma—was added to the recovery process. It was not until nutritional restoration began that her malnourished body and brain were able to consider confronting the trauma and facing change. Lynn's artwork became a vehicle to work through her negative belief systems in a nonthreatening way, producing valuable insight that was processed in her art therapy sessions. Her recovery journey was documented with art images that demonstrated her progress through her ED.

■ LYNN'S STORY

Lynn was a 15-year-old female who was referred for ED treatment by her pediatrician because of significant weight loss. She had lost 30 pounds in just a few months. Her attitudes about food and weight fit the diagnostic criteria for anorexia nervosa (DSM-5; American Psychiatric Association, 2013). Lynn believed her ED started after she became sick with the flu. She said, "I saw an opportunity to lose weight." She began following an 800-cal or less daily diet. She reported, "I have never liked how I look." When Lynn began treatment, she was not motivated to change. She was anxious, evasive, guarded, and depressed; her answers were slow, soft spoken, hesitant, and at times mumbled. Lynn had significant depression since the sixth grade. Earlier, she had tried two different Selective serotonin reuptake inhibitor (SSRI) medications without success. One made her feel worse, and, after a short while, she went off the other believing it was not helping. Her appearance was sickly. She dressed in very loose-fitting sweat pants and a baggy tee shirt. Her thoughts were preoccupied with the belief of "I am fat," even though she went from wearing a size large to a size small. At the time of our meeting, she was very thin and difficult to hear. She seemed to be fading away in many respects.

Lynn's parents were tired of fighting with her and felt bewildered about what to do to help her. She had refused eating dinner with the family at night, and she was restricting other meals. It was recommended that Lynn start her treatment in a Partial Hospitalization Program (PHP). PHP treatment met for 6 straight days during a week, with 1 day off, and was on the basis of the Maudsley approach (Lock & Le Grange, 2013), a common component of the anorexic adolescent treatment plan. The Maudsley approach is a family-based treatment plan for adolescent patients who are diagnosed with anorexia nervosa. It is a therapeutic support plan that is used to guide the family in dealing with a family member's ED. At this level of care, Lynn's parents were responsible for serving (plating) a daily breakfast through the week, as well as an evening snack. On the weekends, they would feed her Saturday dinner and a snack, as well as all her meals and snacks on Sunday. All of this was according to a prescribed meal plan.

PHP group work was extremely difficult for Lynn, being shy and self-conscious. Lynn was quiet and rarely would speak in groups. If she did speak, it was a mumble and very difficult to hear; she literally had lost her voice. Lynn hardly participated in group during her time in higher level of care. She would speak only when asked direct questions and often times would just shrug her shoulders, avoiding eye contact. With most ED clients, the internal voice of self-loathing and fear of being judged is deafening. This seemed to be the case with Lynn. She stayed in the PHP for many months. Eventually, her care program was stepped down to an Intensive Outpatient Program (IOP), her weight was restored, and she was able to maintain a stable weight at the time of her discharge.

It was after Lynn finished the IOP program that I began individual work with her in outpatient art therapy. Lynn finally began to participate in her recovery. In our individual sessions, Lynn was better able to communicate her emotions through her artwork and was able to express her thoughts concerning her self-loathing and negative body image.

Her father brought her to the first individual art therapy session. I did not know much about the family dynamics except that her father was retired and appeared to be about 20 years older than her mother. Mom worked full time, whereas Dad stayed at home, chauffeuring his two daughters to school and to appointments. Lynn told me that her father would wait for her in the car. I conducted a verbal interview to assess the progress she had made in the past 4 months after leaving a higher level of care. She stated that she wanted to work on her self-esteem and body image. She reported that she attended school online and tended to isolate, preferring to stay at home, communicating with her two friends exclusively online, never in person. Lynn had little contact with other adolescents her age. She had become even more fearful of social situations since leaving school and entering treatment for her ED.

I noticed that Lynn used limited eye contact when talking with me. She was very reluctant to engage in conversation, much less to initiate it. Because of her negative self-image, fear of judgment, and distress in social settings, she avoided all social situations. She had a younger sister with whom she chose not to interact for fear that her depression would "rub off on her" and stated that she would include her sister only when playing with the family pets in their home. This information impressed upon me how small Lynn's world had become.

Lynn tells her story beginning with, "I came into the world with the umbilical cord wrapped around my neck, and the world was out to get me before I took my first initial breath." She drew Figure 23.1 to describe how this felt to her. Our ensuing conversation is described as follows:

Therapist: *What are the feelings that go with the belief "I came into this world and it was out to get me?"*

Lynn: *I feel fear, resentful—it's not fair—and I feel trapped.*

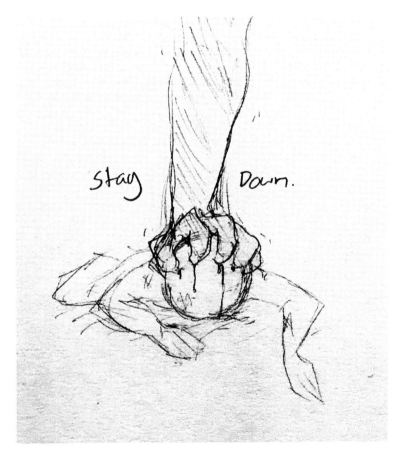

FIGURE 23.1 Trapped.

Therapist: *What is the story that you tell yourself about this?*

Lynn: *That things are bad and they are never going to get better, it is only going to get worse from here. It doesn't matter, I am suffering and don't function like a normal teen.*

Through our therapy sessions, I learned that before entering treatment for her ED, Lynn was in a regular classroom in public school. Lynn was painfully shy. She became the target of bullying and manipulation at the hands of other students. In middle school, she suffered with thoughts of suicide and chronic depression. She reached out to people online to fulfill the friendships she so desperately needed and wanted. Eventually, she met an older man online who took advantage of her. This is explained in more detail later in this chapter.

Lynn continued to attend high school online. This was partly to avoid repeating past experiences of bullying but was also the result of extreme low self-esteem and severe social anxiety. In our sessions, Lynn shared a few experiences of the bullying that occurred at school. On the day she created the "bully" drawing, she came into session very tearful, because her dad was threatening to send her back to public school. His reasoning for this decision was that her struggles with depression seemed to increase by being alone at home. She had little energy and no motivation to do her studies. Lynn was terrified of going back to public school and her depression only increased.

Lynn told detailed stories of being bullied in school from first to seventh grades. She felt that because she was shy and passive, she attracted bullies and became a target (See Figure 23.2). She shared a story of being in third grade, presenting something in front of the class and talking very softly. The teacher yelled at her to stop mumbling. The other kids laughed. Lynn returned to her chair and never again was able to speak up with volume in her voice. The bullying from her classmates accelerated. She also told a story of a

FIGURE 23.2 The bully.

FIGURE 23.3   Judgment.

fifth-grade friend who threatened to cut herself if Lynn did not do what she asked her to do. This girl wanted Lynn to talk only with her and not anyone else (see Figure 23.3).

As Lynn's art therapist, it was my responsibility to view the creative images that she constructed in sessions and respond to her personal truths as they emerged through the artwork. I slowly began to encourage Lynn to give voice to her thoughts and beliefs, creating the story that she tells herself. Her art became action centered, illustrating her life story. With pencil to paper, the themes of her emotions emerged, and her inward journey began to unfold. Her artwork exposed that on the outside, Lynn was starving herself to remain as small as possible with hopes of becoming invisible.

Lynn is an excellent artist with good, age-appropriate drawing skills (Drachnik, 1995; Lowenfeld, 1957). She normally worked with a mechanical pencil that she brought to our sessions. It gave her control over the images she made, which made it safe for her to express her feelings. She communicated well through the images she drew, creating an invitation for me to interact with her.

In a typical session, I would ask her, "Do you mind if I look at your drawing?" She never answered that question out loud; instead, she would push her drawing across the table to me. She seemed to experience great tension if I watched her draw too closely. When I looked at her artwork, she intently watched me for my reactions. In the beginning of our work, her images were painful, dark, half-nude figures with scribbles over her genitals and breasts. The drawings of her body were never complete, but showed drippings where her legs should be (Figure 23.4), as if she were melting or liquefying into nothingness. Over time, Lynn began to draw full bodies with no gender references. It became evident to me that Lynn was beginning to question her personal gender identity.

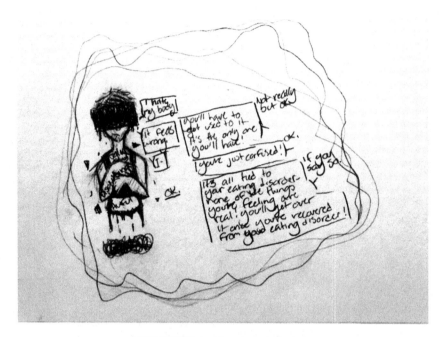

FIGURE 23.4 Gender confusion.

Lynn's artwork revealed that she hated her body. She verbalized this as well. Yet it was not clear whether her body hatred and anxiety stemmed from her ED, gender identity exploration, or past trauma. Lynn continued to deny the occurrence of any past sexual trauma. When talking about her body, she would say, "It feels wrong. I want to climb out and escape."

Tapping into the ED, Lynn noted that one reason she restricted food was so she would not develop feminine body curves. She admitted that she often bound her breasts under her clothing so they would not show. When asked why, she said this was a rejection of being female. She also admitted it was connected to her gender exploration.

Through art therapy, Lynn began to explore gender expression. Through such an exploration, a person develops a sense of personal gender preference and what it feels like to identify with it. "This awareness includes, but is not limited to, elements like clothing, language, body language, voice, name, smell, pronouns, cosmetics, and hairstyle" (Mardell, 2016, p. 73). Our conversation in therapy went as follows:

Lynn: *I want to cut my hair shorter.*

Therapist: *You have talked about being unclear about your gender identification, and I wonder if you're exploring this with a short hairstyle?*

Lynn: *Maybe. I don't know.*

Therapist: *Your clothes are gender neutral. You usually wear converse shoes, sweat pants, and a hoody—your style can be either girl or boy. I remember months ago, you were exploring with makeup, but I see you are not wearing makeup now. It seems like you're exploring who you are.*

Learning about the possibilities beyond binary gender seemed to help Lynn empower herself. She shared with me that her best friend is transgender. It was possible that this was part of what opened a door for her own self-exploration, although she never spoke to her friend about it. All of these thoughts and questions ruminated in her head long before she was able to talk about them in therapy.

One day in session, I shared an article about gender identity that appeared in a recent issue of *Time* magazine (Steinmetz, 2017). She showed the article to her mother. Her mother was confused, but open to understanding and learning more about her daughter's identity search. Her mother realized that she needed support to help her daughter and began working with her own personal therapist. Trust and safety were eventually established between mother and daughter, as Lynn's mother responded with increased empathy.

As trust and safety grew in our art therapy sessions, Lynn became receptive to working on a full-body tracing. I traced her body with a pencil. Lynn took the outline drawing and went back over it, correcting the drawing I had traced by removing all the body curves. When asked about this, she shared that she believed a more gender-neutral body felt less vulnerable. Our conversation led to issues of safety and vulnerability surrounding her body image. She still was not able at this time to talk about her personal online trauma but seemed to feel safer talking about the ED. She suddenly realized why she hated the feeling of being full after eating. When she ate a normal meal and felt full, it made her most aware of her body. Feelings of body awareness triggered negative emotions that she then directed at herself by turning her pain inward in the form of self-hatred. This self-hatred of herself as a person, and also hatred of her body, was expressed in the self-destructive restriction that left her body and brain malnourished. Lynn's artwork began to shift to a deeper denial of facing her inner fears.

In Figure 23.5, Lynn drew a small, nondescriptive, heavily outlined figure that is filled in with multiple crosshatched lines. The figure seems to be facing away from the viewer. This self-portrait figure is surrounded with random scratches of lines that depict what Lynn explains as feelings of anxiety. She labeled the eyes with words as if they could speak saying, "dislike, judgment, overstimulation, embarrassment, pressure, and disappointment." Trust had built during our sessions together and Lynn began verbally to express herself to me.

Lynn confided that she had told no one that when she was in seventh grade—3 years before entering treatment—she experienced cyber sexual abuse. Lynn, like many trauma survivors, felt guilt, shame, and pain about not recognizing or stopping the manipulation of the abuser. Through the images she created, the trauma became more evident as she expressed her personal story. In Figure 23.5, she is floating on the page without feet to stand on, or hands to help herself. There are 12 single eyes staring at her that seem to represent her shame stemming from the online abuse.

Significant art therapy research by Dr. Spring (1992) correlates repeated images of disembodied eyes in a client's drawings as an indicator of sexual abuse. Shortly after Lynn created this drawing, she was able to speak about her past traumatic online experience and the shame that she felt when she remembered what happened. Art therapy became the primary means of safety with which Lynn was able to talk about her abuse. Imagery replaced the need to verbalize her feelings. Creating artwork seemed to give her breathing room to step into sharing the experience when words were too difficult to speak.

Lynn felt overwhelming shame but was able to express that the trauma she had experienced related to the man she met online. She did not remember all the details about when she started talking online to a 20-something man named John. She had been very depressed and had no real friends at the time. John approached her online and began texting her. At first, he was very nice to her. She talked to him about her depression and

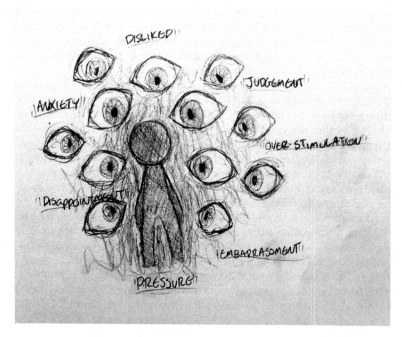

FIGURE 23.5 Shame.

suicide ideation. After establishing a trusting relationship, he used this information to manipulate her into sending him nude pictures of herself. He threatened to abandon her if she did not comply and said that he would encourage her to kill herself if she did not send the pictures. He told her that she had a nice body, but she was ugly. These comments increased Lynn's negative self-image and were used by her perpetrator as emotional manipulation. The online relationship went on for several months. Eventually, Lynn was able to end this relationship, but it left her scarred.

Today, all grown men looking in her direction, including her father, repulse her and she feels extremely uncomfortable. According to van der Kolk et al. (1996), "Traumatized patients are frequently triggered by current sensory and affective stimuli into a reliving of feelings and memories of their past trauma" (p. 198). They view a client's social isolation as a by-product of the traumatic event, causing the client to turn his or her anger at the situation inward upon himself or herself in the form of self-hatred and extreme criticism.

Through the ED, Lynn used self-starvation as a way to turn her shame and anger inward. The voice of the ED punished her with thoughts and feelings of self-hatred and criticism. At the same time, Lynn's ED became a friend in her lonely world. This situation became a double-edged sword. If Lynn were to lose control of the ED, then, potentially, she would experience increased unbearable shame and anxiety. Yet, the attempt for control that fueled the ED was driven by negative self-messages that kept Lynn in a self-loathing state of mind.

When Lynn began to work through the trauma she had experienced, she greatly minimized the effect of the trauma and blamed herself. She was reluctant even to call it trauma, feeling that, because it was not physical, it could not be trauma. She believed it was all her fault for agreeing to send the nude pictures. She told no one, because she believed the entire situation would be turned around on her and she would be judged. She experienced enormous shame that has taken many years of therapy to resolve. Lynn believed she was a horrible person because she allowed the trauma to happen. In her healing, she had to digest the idea that her abuser took advantage of her. This was a difficult concept for her to accept. She had to untwist the story she had earlier been telling herself about it.

Eventually, she was able to see that the abuser asserted his psychological control over her using the most insidious approach of "I care, and I am the only one here for you." With these words, her abuser rendered her emotionally dependent on him and she was powerless in the face of his emotional manipulations. Lynn did not have the knowledge or skills to fight back and escape his control over her. She had to accept that she did nothing wrong and was not the pathetic person she believed herself to be. Accepting that this was not her fault, or her guilt to hold, but, instead, a crime perpetrated on her by her abuser was a big step in Lynn's recovery. Lynn's ability to talk about her insecurities and shame through images in art therapy sessions helped to increase her self-confidence, reduce her anxiety, and lessen her depressive episodes. Because of these realizations, Lynn is doing well in an online school program, eats dinner with her family at the table, and is taking a self-defense class with her mother. She continues to make art in treatment and at home on her computer.

■ CONCLUSION

Art therapy treatment was used to help Lynn begin to heal. The artwork was informative and later became affirming toward her journey of change away from her core belief that "I am a pathetic person." In one session, Lynn created a simple drawing of a character that represented herself. She was asked to expose the thoughts she heard in her mind written in cartoon bubbles above the character's head. Getting her thoughts out on paper helped her to understand how her thoughts and thinking patterns affected her feelings and behaviors. When Lynn entered treatment, her negative beliefs about her self-worth were kept inside and became life-threatening. Art therapy enabled her to see how different perceptions affected how she felt about herself. She learned how to identify and change the distorted ideas and stories she told herself about the past abuse. Supporting Lynn to express herself in this way helped her to process her traumatic experience and the internal negative messages that fueled it. The creative process of art making brought forth realizations and transformation.

As is often the case with clients who have an ED and trauma recovery, delving deep into the underlying issues takes time. Lynn has begun to soften her self-talk and be gentle in the way she views herself. Making art was a safe place for Lynn to share her top secrets of being bullied and the trauma of cyber sexual abuse. Lynn became empowered expressing her pain through art and she began to heal.

Today, Lynn is setting small goals and learning to feel proud of her achievements, which are building self-esteem and self-worth. She occasionally meets with her online friends for a movie or conversation in public. She is working on expanding her meal plan and being less rigid and controlled with her food intake. Currently, she is maintaining a stable weight. Lynn has begun a daily practice of finding evidence that she is worthy of being loved.

■ REFERENCES

American Psychiatric Association. (2013). *Diagnostic and statistical manual of mental disorders* (5th ed.). Arlington, VA: American Psychiatric Publishing.

Capacchione, L. (2001). *The power of your other hand*. Pompton Plains, NJ: Career Press.

Drachnik, K. (1995). *Interpreting metaphors in children's drawings*. Burlingame, CA: Abbeygate Press.

Good, D. A. (2016). Adult art therapy: Four decades, ages 20–60 years. In D. E. Gussak & M. L. Rosal (Eds.), *The Wiley handbook of art therapy* (pp. 262–271). West Sussex, UK: Wiley Blackwell.

Hunter, M. (2016). Art therapy and eating disorders. In D. E. Gussak & M. L. Rosal (Eds.), *The Wiley handbook of art therapy* (pp. 387–396). West Sussex, UK: Wiley Blackwell.

Johnson, J., & Repta, R. (2012). Sex and gender: Beyond the binaries. In J. L. Oliffe & L. Greaves (Eds.), *Designing and conducting gender, sex & health research* (pp. 17–38). Thousand Oaks, CA: Sage.

Jung, C. G. (1964). *Man and his symbols*. Garden City, NY: Doubleday.

Kramer, E. (1972). *Art as therapy with children*. New York, NY: Schocken.

Lock, J., & Le Grange, D. (2013). *Treatment manual for anorexia nervosa: A family-based approach* (2nd ed.). New York, NY: Guilford Press.

Lowenfeld, V. (1957). *Creative and mental growth* (3rd ed.). New York, NY: Macmillan.

Mardell, A. (2016). *The ABC's of LGBT+*. Coral Gables, FL: Mango Media.

Rubin, J. A. (2001). *Approaches to art therapy: Theory and technique* (2nd ed.). New York, NY: Routledge.

Schaefer-Simmern, H. (1948). *The unfolding of artistic activity*. Cambridge, UK: Cambridge University Press.

Spring, D. (1992). *Shattered images: The phenomenological language of sexual abuse*. Chicago, IL: Magnolia Street.

Steinmetz, K. (2017, March 27). Beyond he or she: How a new generation is redefining the meaning of gender. *Time*, pp. 48–54.

van der Kolk, B. A., McFarlane, A. C., & Weisaeth, L. (1996). *Traumatic stress: The effects of overwhelming experience on mind, body, and society*. New York, NY: Guilford Press.

SECTION SIX

Phase IV—Relapse Prevention, Reevaluation, and Integration

After painful events and the resulting negative self-stories have been processed, there remain the challenges to recovery. This is particularly true of eating disorders (EDs). Chapter 24, written from a personal, as well as a professional, perspective, deals with setbacks in the form of anxiety (about having to eat) and/or shame (about having eaten), sociocultural attitudes that objectify women and glorify thinness, and lack of understanding and support from family and friends. It also looks at various triggers and the grief of letting go of the disorder. Chapter 25 reviews the history of approaches to the very challenging issue of body image disturbance (BID). In this fascinating chapter, we see where we have been regarding this disorder and the shoulders on which we stand. The chapter then guides us into contemporary developments, namely, body-focused approaches and an understanding of BID as a dissociative experience. Finally, Chapter 26 discusses the dismantling of the trauma and ED identity and the discovery of the authentic Self, primarily the spiritual Self.

CHAPTER 24

Recovery and Beyond: Dealing With Triggers and Setbacks

Marnie Davis and Joslyn P. Smith

■ INTRODUCTION

Authoring this book chapter is of importance to both of us on a personal and professional level. Although each of us has unique personal experiences that led us to work in the eating disorder (ED) field, the commonality of our stories is the following: Both of us are aware of the link between trauma and an ED and the healing power of restorying of one's struggles that leads to health and well-being. It has been important for each of us to hold tight to the fact that even in the face of trauma and EDs, the core—the true essence—of who we are remains solid and unchanged.

So, at the start, let us introduce ourselves.

Marnie is a licensed mental health counselor, certified eating disorder specialist, certified eye movement desensitization reprocessing (EMDR) therapist, and past president of her local International Association of Eating Disorder Professionals (IAEDP) chapter. She conceptualizes the stories of her clients from an adaptive information processing (AIP) lens (see Chapter 13) and assists with healing of the traumatic experiences that underlie the ED. While holding her story separate from those she hears, she uses her own healing to enhance her compassion and intuition, to guide her use of evidence-based practices in the treatment of EDs and trauma.

Joslyn is a survivor of complex trauma and is in recovery from an ED. She is intensely interested in the interchange of those two worlds—how one works to incorporate both a trauma and ED history into a productive life story, and how those who do so honestly maneuver through triggers and setbacks during recovery. Joslyn has used her personal struggle with an ED as a catalyst for professional involvement in the EDs and public policy fields. Currently, she serves as director of policy and government affairs for the Binge Eating Disorder Association (BEDA), a national organization focused on providing leadership, recognition, prevention, and treatment of binge ED and associated weight stigma.

■ WHAT RECOVERY MEANS

How do we define recovery? Each person will answer this question differently, but, as coauthors, we believe sustainable recovery is possible, even when triggers arise.

Recovery means holding tight to foundational ways of living that were learned in treatment and generalized into daily life during the healing process. Recovery from an ED and the related trauma is not free sailing. It requires standing at the helm of the boat with mindful attunement to one's present-moment experience and applying self-care behaviors that demonstrate respect for one's self, one's story, and one's body. Such practices include mindful breathing, self-compassion exercises, engaging in activities that allow connection to one's body in an enjoyable manner, leaning fully into emotional experiences even when they are painful, and maintaining an effective emotional regulation skill set to ride the waves of daily stressors and emotional experiences.

Marnie writes:

> For me, recovery means a lifelong commitment to mindful attunement to my bodily responses to stressors, while practicing self-compassion for my mistakes, failures and imperfections. I surround myself with people that love me. I practice meditation and mindfulness to center and calm myself on a regular basis. Even after fifteen years recovered and continued therapy, I recognize the importance of reprocessing negative life experiences so that the "not good enough" belief system that fueled my eating disorder doesn't rear itself into the present.

Maintaining connection is essential to recovery as one navigates through life. Loving kindness toward oneself and secure relationships on the basis of trust, compassion, and acceptance of one's vulnerability are keys to lasting recovery and moving beyond trauma. Recovery also requires learning from failures and mistakes. By embracing the resilience that is fostered from dealing with traumatic and posttraumatic events, one learns to connect with hope, even when feeling hopeless. Sometimes, members of one's support system will be invited to offer the hope that feels unattainable by the individual at that moment in the process.

Joslyn writes:

> For me, recovery is defined as being able to actively sustain behaviors that help me experience life in the most balanced, healthful way possible, and shifting my routines as needed to support recovery. Self-care and mental health is also critical to my recovery. Sometimes, for example, I need to give extra attention to that area of my life. If I need extra support, I know to set aside daily time for meditating, to see my therapist weekly, and to reach out to those people who mean the most to me. I also have to recognize needed adjustments to my nutritional routine. I recall a time when I lived in Washington, D.C. and needed to walk quite a bit every day for work. In consultation with my dietitian, I learned how much more I needed to eat daily to maintain my health and recovery when my activity level increased.

■ RECOGNIZING AND ACKNOWLEDGING SETBACKS AND TRIGGERS

Recovery can be inconsistent and unpredictable at times, demanding strength and courage to continuously redefine one's self-story and live from one's authentic self. Not everyone will define recovery in the same terms, and, as recovery becomes more ingrained, one's definition of recovery might shift. As recovery stabilizes, the components required to maintain recovery become clearer.

Marnie writes:

> At the beginning of my healing process, recovery seemed rigid, structured, painful and quite unclear. I didn't like where I was, but I couldn't see what lay ahead. I was left to trust. As I progressed, my definition of recovery progressed. Now it

allows for intuitiveness, clarity with self-care, compassion for self, and, of course, discomfort. But my relationship with discomfort has changed. I no longer fear it and avoid it, rather I live and nourish, despite it.

Likewise, although it is important to expect a shift in that definition with the progression of recovery, we also must recognize that regressions in recovery may ensue. Setbacks and relapses can go unrecognized early on by the individual caught up in the setback. Setbacks will happen, and at times will lead to full-blown relapse. Being honest with oneself is imperative to avoid unexpectedly falling back deep into ED behaviors. In addition to honest self-awareness, one of the nonnegotiables in recovery is recognizing those in one's support system who can be trusted to raise concerns if they see old patterns emerging. The persons struggling must be willing to agree that, regardless of how they feel they are doing, if one of those trusted people raises a concern, they will examine with their treatment team (reestablishing relationships, if necessary) the reality of how they are doing.

Joslyn writes:

In my experience, oftentimes setbacks occur when a piece of my trauma history is surfacing. A red flag for me that something is triggered is recognizing that I feel less aware of feelings in my body. Having lived in a somewhat dissociated state for the better part of my life, I have worked hard to rebuild a relationship with my body and with the experience of sensations and feelings *within* my body. My ability to recognize such sensations and feelings was developed by working with a therapist using Somatic Experiencing (SE; see Chapter 21). If internal sensations and feelings become less accessible to me, I am more vulnerable to setbacks and relapses. Consequently, checking in with my body regularly is a significant part of my recovery. It feels important for me to point out that when my eating disorder recovery is wavering, or trauma is acutely triggered in me, I am not personally able to utilize many of the somatic and meditative resources I find so useful. During those times, I *do* have to rely on the structure and direction of cognitively focused therapeutic tools to combat eating disordered thoughts and behaviors.

Throughout a recovery process, even after one deems oneself recovered, daily life can continue to be a difficult realm to navigate, with a plethora of stressful and negative experiences occurring that have no regard for the fragility of the individual. At this point, we would like to bring to light a few of what we believe to be common triggers that often lead to lapses or relapses in ED recovery.

Negative life events, whether they are large or small traumas, can act as powerful triggers, leading to the return of the ED. Examples of common traumatic events include the loss of a loved one or beloved pet, betrayal of trust, breakup or divorce, letdowns and failures, natural disasters, sexual trauma, and any type of physical, mental, and emotional abuse. *Stressful life events and daily life stressors* can easily disturb unprocessed traumatic material, activating memory networks and causing pain and suffering, along with adding new traumatic material to the brain and body system. Possible daily life stressors can include an argument with a friend, hearing a negative body comment, studying for an exam or managing a stressful work project, or returning home for the holidays. Even positive life transitions such as having a child, leaving or returning to college, or receiving a promotion at work can lead the individual into unfamiliar territory, thereby adding a whole new realm of stressors to the daily experience of recovery.

Marnie writes:

I chose to relocate early on in my recovery process. Not long after moving to Florida, my eager hopefulness shifted to feelings of fear, overwhelm and uncertainty.

I tried to navigate my new life in an unfamiliar place. I was lonely and nervous, trying to create a new path toward success. I felt unsafe and in that fragile moment, traumatic memories were activated. I crumbled, my recovery wavered.

Engaging in our society, for those who are *members of marginalized and minority groups,* means being inundated daily with micro- and macroaggressions. Oftentimes, these traumatic events occur in a covert manner, unacknowledged and overlooked by those of the dominant class. These daily aggressions include, but are not limited to, oppression through sociocultural barriers and social injustices, institutionalized racism and acts of inequality, self-limiting gender constructs, and dehumanizing actions and legislation. Such experiences can suffocate a person's sense of worth and ability to be authentic, while instilling self-hatred, pain, and shame, all powerful forces toward relapse.

Another all too common origin of relapse is *the lack of appropriate length of stay* in a higher level of care, including an Intensive Outpatient Program (IOP), Partial Hospitalization Program (PHP), or Inpatient/Residential Program, along with an inappropriate titration from one level of care to another. These missteps are often initiated by the insurance company denying coverage for care or limiting the number of days approved. Sociocultural barriers to treatment for those in minority populations also play a significant role in hindering appropriate care. At other times, clients may endure treatment fatigue, members of the family may lack understanding of the length of time needed for the healing process, and/or families may feel the financial burden of comprehensive care, curtailing treatment despite recommendations from the treatment team.

Surfacing of grief can complicate recovery and can be another strong activator of setbacks. If the grief is related to illness, depending on the length of the illness, many significant, developmental milestones may have been missed, leaving feelings of loss and despair. The longer the duration of the ED, the greater the chance of bypassing meaningful, developmental moments. As one reconnects with whole-hearted living, a feeling of separation from peers, many of whom will have experienced those milestones, may emerge, triggering a sense of lack of belonging, regret, pain, and loss. Grief may also surface in response to letting go of the ED, a familiar ally in the war against pain, a warm duvet cover that keeps one feeling safe and secure, a shield to barricade oneself from what feels overwhelming. Saying goodbye can be arduous.

Marnie writes:

For me, my grief related to the lost years, the lost moments, the missed milestones. Deep pain surfaced, regularly, unexpectedly and urgently. It reminded me that I had lost sight of my dream for a family, for children. My plan had been hijacked. So many years lost, and I was left feeling behind, disconnected, and lost. In these moments, I need the solidity of my recovery, the nonnegotiables of my healing process, continued therapeutic work and loving kindness from my support system. At times, it still hurts.

Body image distress typically permeates the entire recovery process, and the discomfort it creates can prompt any number of setbacks along the path of recovery. We speak in more detail on this topic later in the chapter, but we believe it important to outline a few vital areas of concern. To date, the focus of body image work has pursued an ideal goal of bodily acceptance and body love. For some individuals, this concept may not be appropriate. For individuals who present and identify outside of the gender binary, the body image ideals subscribed to by the dominant, cisgender (gender identity matches sex assigned at birth), and heteronormative group may not provide the space to experience one's body in an authentic manner. Body acceptance is impossible when a person's body and identity are not recognized or treated with respect. The bodily experience of a transgender individual can be filled with a considerable amount of torment, and the pain and distress may continue after one recovers from an ED.

In summary, the realm of possible causes of relapse is vast. Lapses will arise at any stage of the recovery process.

■ NAVIGATING INTERNAL AND EXTERNAL MESSAGES AT DIFFERENT STAGES OF RECOVERY

One's sense of self, and the relationship to one's body, begins in the early years of life, continuing over a lifetime. Memory networks in the brain link together external messages and experiences with stored memories, images, emotions, and body sensations. These memory networks affect how we feel about ourselves and our bodies, and how we experience the world around us. They emerge in messages, beliefs, and, ultimately, our "story" (Shapiro, 2001).

As stated in the previous section, minority and marginalized populations are inundated with messages and acts of oppression, discrimination, and dehumanization in ways that those of us born into white privilege may never truly understand. As heterosexual, cisgender, Caucasian females, we acknowledge that we cannot speak to this directly. However, we believe it is imperative to recognize the traumatic experiences encountered by individuals belonging to marginalized groups including lesbian, gay, bisexual, transgender, questioning, queer, intersex, asexual (LGBTQIA+) communities, various ethnic and cultural populations, and those of a lower economic status. Each oppressive act holds the power to send a message of unworthiness, nonacceptance, nothingness, and lack of safety, all of which can be activating beliefs of an ED.

Pressure for individuals belonging to a minority group to acculturate to the body standards of the dominant population can create painful internal conflicts, which can lead to activation of an ED. Limiting gender constructs that deny gender fluidity and nonbinary presentation of one's body can create powerful feelings of dissonance and shame. Individuals of minority ethnicities and other marginalized groups may experience confusion as they attempt to sort through a mixture of body messages, including body ideals of their own culture, along with ideals of the dominant group. Confusion breeds internal conflict; internal conflict leads to chaos and chaos can prompt the reemergence of trauma and ED behaviors.

Sometimes without recognizing it, because of its normalization, we are confronted daily with body shaming and weight stigma. Magazine covers, weight loss ads, healthcare providers, government-funded obesity prevention programs, and coworkers who casually chat about their new workout routine or not allowing themselves dessert, to name only a few examples, bombard us. In 2006, it was estimated that the average person in the United States was exposed to as many as 5,000 advertisements a day. With the advent of social media, that estimate is now as high as 10,000 a day. The majority of such messages aim to make us feel unhappy with some aspect of our lives, most often our bodies. No matter the shape or size of our own body, we are constantly reminded that the last thing we should feel about our body is satisfied. Moving solidly into recovery from an ED while constantly hearing these messages can feel like a herculean task. Maintaining recovery, especially when dealing with past trauma that is triggered, can feel even harder. And, as we pointed out before, setbacks will happen.

Joslyn writes:

Even during my struggle with atypical anorexia, my body has been large. One of the biggest challenges to my eating disorder recovery has been constantly hearing messages in the media and through obesity prevention programs about the size of my body being wrong and unhealthy. Those messages did nothing but shame and confuse me. Shame and confusion around what my body needs to be healthy has been a life and death problem at points in my life. Working with a treatment team to learn about the specific needs of my body in order to maintain health has been an invaluable part of my recovery journey. That education, along with building up a repertoire of knowledge sufficient to critique messages about health and beauty, helps me focus on what my body needs. As my relationship with my body becomes one built on trust and solid information specific to my own body uniqueness, it has become easier for me to make choices that are right for my own body, without falling under the spell of messages in the environment.

An increase in media literacy campaigns over the past two decades has given many of us the tools we need to think critically about images, especially those we see in advertisements and other media outlets. Yet, as important as being able to view images critically, learning to critique messages about health is of equal importance. For starters, both clinicians and those recovering from EDs must understand that health is going to mean something different for everybody. And having, or seeking, what is viewed as a conventionally healthy body is not indicative of any sort of moral superiority. Any assignment of an individual's value or worth must be uncoupled with health or ability. This is especially true for those of us with co-occurring trauma histories. Understanding one's unique body and the needs of one's body and mind, and choosing how one wishes to engage with those needs, is imperative in maintaining recovery in a world that tells us our bodies need to change or are not good enough as they are. Optimal health for each body is unique and must take one's history—including trauma, and/or EDs, and cultural and familial histories—into account.

■ TRAUMA HEALING AND HELPFUL THERAPEUTIC MODALITIES DURING SETBACKS AND RECOVERY

The healing of trauma is an ongoing process, as is recovery from an ED. In efforts to enhance stabilization, providers and clients need to stay attuned to the emergence of unprocessed traumatic material that can become activated as one interacts with daily life challenges and as one lets go of ED behaviors. Despite effective trauma processing, remnants of the traumatic material often remain, rising to the surface with new triggers. No matter how well we sweep a room, there are always dust bunnies left behind. As clinicians, we must normalize this process and encourage clients to be mindful of possible trauma activation and enhance their skillset to manage it. As clients travel along the path of healing, they must hold tight to the nonnegotiables of recovery, enhancing stabilization/grounding practices, seeking extra support when necessary, and continuing the healing work. These are the fragile moments when a client's hope may wax and wane. A provider has an imperative duty to offer a sense of hope to serve as a life-sustaining pillar, anchoring the individual to reality. Recovery is not linear, yet it is attainable.

Strategies for managing relapses vary and are chosen, on the basis of the skills and needs of both provider and client. Any of the valid and reliable treatment strategies described in this book (Section V) can be applied to the management of triggers and relapses. We have chosen to highlight a few that have proven to be most beneficial from our professional and personal experiences.

Strategy #1: Target the new traumatic material or the residual dust bunnies that may have been activated with standard EMDR protocol (Shapiro, 2001). Assist with resource development and installation (RDI) to create new adaptive resources to help manage the destabilizing experiences (Korn & Leeds, 2002). EMDR and RDI are discussed in more detail in Chapter 13.

Strategy #2: Use specific addiction protocols. Dr. Robert Miller's Feeling State Addiction Protocol (FSAP), for example, weakens the linkage between positive feelings and the compulsive behavior (ED behaviors) and uses EMDR to reprocess experiences related to that linkage. A. J. Popky's Desensitization of Triggers and Urge Reprocessing (DeTUR) protocol focuses on urge reduction through the use of positive resources and EMDR (Miller, 2017; Popky, 2009).

Strategy #3: Use SE to assist with the release of physiologically stored traumatic material, whether that be from more recent traumatic events or remnants of past traumas (Levine, 1997; see Chapter 21).

Strategy #4: Revisit Marsha Linehan's dialectical behavioral therapy (DBT) to facilitate the management of chaotic emotions and impulsivity, including distress tolerance and mindful experiencing of emotions, leading to emotional regulation. Invite the client to generalize the skills into everyday life to protect him or her from feeling overly exposed and submerged with emotions during times of stress and pain (Grilo & Mitchell, 2010; Linehan, 1993; see Chapter 8).

Strategy #5: Focus attention on mindfulness and acceptance work within the acceptance and commitment therapy (ACT) model. Practice mindful experiencing of thoughts, feelings, and bodily sensations rather than controlling, avoiding, or judging them. Assess whether a new behavior or the return of an old behavior is avoidance-driven or value-driven by using an activity, such as the ABC's of Behavior Worksheet, while engaging in mindful breath practices (Pearson, Heffner, & Follette, 2010; Sandoz, Wilson, & Dufrene, 2010; see Chapter 8).

Strategy #6: View the relapse experience through the dissociative lens of the Internal Family Systems (IFS) model, structural dissociation, or ego state approach. Provide space for ED parts to reach and share an understanding of their current role in the system, reprocessing and unburdening painful experiences and exploring more adaptive roles for the parts within the internal system. IFS, structural dissociation, and ego state approaches are discussed in detail in Chapters 16, 17, and 15, respectively.

Strategy #7: Include art therapy in the therapeutic process to encourage expression of pain and trauma without the need for words. This process allows for empowerment and the release of traumatic material from mind, heart, and body, while reconnecting with the mindful experience of being present in the body through a creative experience (see Chapter 23).

Strategy #8: Incorporate yoga and mindful meditation into the healing process to achieve moments of quietness and stillness by creating the experience of embodied movement and present-moment awareness. Breathing practices with meditation and yoga help to center one's body with awareness and soothe painful emotions, particularly fear and anxiety (Costin & Kelly, 2016).

Strategy #9: Offer psychoeducation and empowerment skills and advocate for the needs of the client when necessary. Normalize the experience of recovery, including lapses and relapses. Identify moments to empower the clients to use their voice, to stand up for themselves and their beliefs, and to set clear and specific boundaries to provide safety, security, and a space to be authentic. Ally and advocacy work is an imperative role for the therapist, especially when the client is part of a marginalized group, to foster a sense of empowerment and intrinsic self-worth.

Strategy #10: Revisit mechanical eating. Although a goal of recovery for many individuals includes fostering an intuitive eating relationship with food and body, there are times in the process when a reconnection with mechanical eating can serve as a stabilizing force. This type of eating includes shifting away from one's attunement to hunger/fullness signals and returning to a structured meal plan that can serve as a safeguard for adequate nourishment for mind and body.

Remember, maintain and encourage mindful attunement and keep an eye out for the dust bunnies. Call upon strategies/skills that have earlier fostered healing and stabilization, and hold space for something new.

Joslyn writes:

As I work through new layers of healing related to past trauma, I am especially vulnerable to setbacks in recovery from my eating disorder. The less diligently I care for myself, especially nutritionally, during times of trauma healing, the more intensely the trauma affects me. The more the trauma affects me, the less I want to feed myself and the more disconnected I am from my body. Being aware of this cycle and staying hypervigilant about my non-negotiables in recovery when my trauma history might be asking for attention is critical to moving through a period of trauma healing as healthfully as possible. One of the first things I realize when this cycle is starting is an inability to breathe deeply. I can take a deep breath, but the breath seems to stop at the level of my sternum; I am unable to breathe into my belly and abdomen. If I notice this happening, I know I need to put extra recovery supports into place.

None of us will likely come to a period in life where we face no more challenging events. Life is full of challenges. Those with a history of trauma and EDs may just have to do extra preparatory work during the less challenging times to lessen the likelihood of full relapse when the difficult times occur. As previously mentioned by Joslyn, one thing that can help with this is to identify and begin using additional supports that help maintain a connection to recovery.

Joslyn writes:

Because of my history of feeling disconnected physically, and the ramifications of that disconnection to my ability to maintain recovery, my additional supports have included things such as massage and meditation, and returning to tools learned from Somatic Experiencing. Not only do these things help me remain connected to my body, they serve as a reminder to me that my body deserves to be cared for and attended to before, during and after setbacks arise.

While I have found relying on my support system and treatment professionals most important during these times, I have also learned that life skills and relationships formed during times of strong recovery, can be invaluable resources upon which I can rely during setbacks or relapses. One example of this has been practicing heart-centered meditation. While I began this practice during a period of solid recovery, when I faced subsequent setbacks, working closely with my therapist to incorporate techniques learned from my meditation practice into therapy sessions became a key grounding component of further processing my trauma history.

■ RESTORYING THE NARRATIVE

Integrating a history of *transformed trauma* into one's present life and determining where that history will fit into the narrative of one's life can require a lengthy commitment to healing. This integration can be an urgent need when one is simultaneously recovering from an ED, because of the effect of both trauma and EDs on one's body and overall health.

Joslyn writes:

My work in the eating disorders field oftentimes includes sharing my personal experiences, I have come to recognize that neither my trauma history nor my eating disorder defines who I am. As my healing has progressed, even during times marked by setbacks or relapses, I have come to claim resilience and perseverance, rather than trauma, as the main theme of my life's narrative.

This shift in thinking is represented for me in a photograph I took on a major trauma anniversary last year. Reflecting on the significance of the date and sitting in silent meditation at a favorite secluded area next to a river, I was struck by the pattern in the large rock upon which I sat.

The rock was divided by a noticeable line, seemingly indicating a significant geological occurrence in the past. In some places, the pattern of the rock continued uninterrupted across the line. While in other places, the markings of the rock shifted at the line and took on a new direction or color. While each trauma I have experienced is a meaningful point in the timeline of my life, the essence of who I am has not changed. In some instances, trauma altered the trajectory of my life in ways that are very visible to most everyone. In other ways, it made its mark on my life, but is really only known to me and those treatment providers who have helped (and continue to help) me navigate the process of healing both my past trauma and my eating disorder.

FIGURE 24.1 Disruption. Image © J. P. Smith.

The clinician bears witness to a client's new cohesive narrative, encouraging the interweaving of resilience and intrinsic strengths into the personal story. They help shift the client's mindset from a place of helplessness and/or defectiveness to one of resourcefulness, compassion, and strength. In the end, the therapist supports and celebrates the unique image of recovery that is self-defined, value-based, inclusive of fractures and imperfections, and created by the client. Cracks and blemishes become just part of the story.

Marnie writes:

> Every experience over my lifetime, both life-halting and life-enhancing, has shaped my personal narrative, etching a pattern into my being. Each misstep and failure, each traumatic event, every painful moment, left a mark behind. But these markings do not need to define my story nor my worth. Rather, they transform me into an imperfect masterpiece; imperfection, resilience, strength, and character. My healing process has brought me to the present moment, a time to call upon my courage and to be wholly authentic, holding space for my unabridged story, personally and professionally. No matter the number of years in my recovery, growth and healing continue. Lifting me towards the light of my imperfect, authentic story.

Recovery is not pain free. Rather, it includes a blend of all emotions, integrating to create the complete human experience. This includes feelings of fear, shame, anger, and loneliness while also encompassing a feeling of empowerment as one learns to tolerate pain, suffering, and setbacks. And then there is joy, love, peace, and happiness. Recovery is accepting challenges without judgment, while inviting moments of internal peace. It is staying connected to those who love us unconditionally and respecting one's body with nourishment, movement, and compassion. It is a process, an imperfect practice, that weaves a cohesive and redemptive narrative into one's life story, filled with self-compassion and freedom from judgment of others. Recovery is possible.

FIGURE 24.2 Recovery.

Source: Correa, F. (2015). Willow Tree. Retrieved from https://www.instagram.com/tourstoyou

■ REFERENCES

Correa, F. (2015). Willow Tree. Retrieved from https://www.instagram.com/tourstoyou

Costin, C., & Kelly, J. (Eds.). (2016). *Yoga and eating disorders: Ancient healing for modern illness.* New York, NY: Routledge.

Grilo, C. M., & Mitchell, J. E. (Eds.). (2010). *The treatment of eating disorders: A clinical handbook.* New York, NY: Guilford Press.

Korn, D. L., & Leeds, A. M. (2002). Preliminary evidence of efficacy for EMDR resource development and installation in the stabilization phase of treatment of complex posttraumatic stress disorder. *Journal of Clinical Psychology, 58*(12), 1465–1487. doi:10.1002/jclp.10099

Levine, P. A. (1997). *Waking the tiger: Healing trauma.* Berkeley, CA: North Atlantic Books.

Linehan, M. M. (1993). *Skills training manual for treating borderline personality disorder.* New York, NY: Guilford Press.

Miller, R. (2017). *Feeling-state theory and protocols: Behavioral and substance addictions.* Del Mar, CA: ImTT Press.

Pearson, A. N., Heffner, M., & Follette, V. M. (2010). *Acceptance and commitment therapy for body image dissatisfaction: A practitioner's guide to using mindfulness, acceptance, and values-based behavior change strategies.* Oakland, CA: New Harbinger.

Popky, A. J. (2009). The desensitization of triggers and urge reprocessing (DeTUR) protocol. In M. Luber (Ed.), *Eye movement desensitization (EMDR) scripted protocols: Special populations* (pp. 489–551). New York, NY: Springer Publishing.

Sandoz, E. K., Wilson, K. G., & Dufrene, T. (2010). *Acceptance and commitment therapy for eating disorders: A process-focused guide to treating anorexia and bulimia.* Oakland, CA: New Harbinger.

Shapiro, F. (2001). *Eye movement desensitization and reprocessing: Basic principles, protocols, and procedures* (2nd ed.). New York, NY: Guilford Press.

CHAPTER 25

Trauma-Informed Approaches to Body Image Disturbance: A Historical Review for a Holistic Future

Madeline Altabe

▓ INTRODUCTION

I suppose everyone who studies body image for a long time comes up with a metaphor for describing it. In my mind, body image is like experiencing a 3D movie. Scripted by stories old and new but experienced in a deeply sensory way. Body image as a singular term is ill-defined. As we wrote in 1999, body image and body image disturbance (BID) are global constructs about body experience, not concretized to any component (affective, cognitive, perceptual) or particular aspect of the body (Thompson, Heinberg, Altabe, & Tantleff-Dunn, 1999). BID is an umbrella term for many things that can be problematic for individuals.

Looking at the field now, I am optimistic. At present, we have modalities that address BID, including body and sensory approaches. What used to be adjunctive or complementary methodologies are now front and center in the treatment of body image. The denial of sexual traumatization that clouded early understandings has faded to the past.

History is a great teacher and perhaps, therefore, a look at where we came from in conceptualizing BID will help us make sure we maintain all that was useful, so that our understanding can grow and our clients can do well.

I sometimes tell the story that, while writing an undergraduate thesis on body image approximately 30 years ago, I read a majority of the body image research. The literature was small and it did not take long to grasp the breadth of it. Research in body image grew exponentially after that, and the scope is broad. The tool I like to use for the study of history is one in which the same questions are posed about each approach, so they can be easily discussed in relation to one another. Patterns emerge. I ask four basic questions of each of the historical movements for this review: (a) What is healthy body image? (b) What is traumatized body image? (c) What disorders are associated with traumatized body image? (d) How is traumatized body image repaired?

Body image has been studied for at least 100 years, almost as long as psychology has been a discipline. It was named first by the Gestaltists who aimed to study many aspects of immediate perceptual experience (see Table 25.1). Freudians and analysts also took on body image issues early in trying to understand various clinical symptoms including conversion disorders and psychosis. That was the first half of the 20th century.

The feminist views of the 1970s led to analysis of the contribution of culture, systems of power that manifested in attitudes toward women's bodies. The cognitivists added their conceptualizations to create more specific techniques of rapid change of immediate

TABLE 25.1   Historical Overview of Body Image Disturbance

Model	Healthy Body Image	Traumatized Body Image Disturbance	Related Disorders	Treatment Methods
Gestaltist (early perceptual)	Representational and dynamic. Subject and object of perception. Vestibular sense	Distortions of perception	Phantom limb and other neurological disease/injury	Time
Psychoanalytic	Whole, mature expression in adult relationships Ego is libidinous (embodied self)	Traumatic experiences are fixed in the body; depersonalization; fragmentation	Conversion disorder, neurasthenia, schizophrenia	Context of healthy therapeutic relationship moves body symptoms into verbal expression of emotion
Feminist/ sociocultural	Self-defined; positive; aware of culture influences	Internalization of cultural conditions that narrowly define beauty and value for women; continuum of unwanted sexual experience	Eating disorders. Body dissatisfaction in most women	Build relationships that support core self; challenge cultural beliefs (sometimes advocacy)
Cognitive	Positive thoughts; reduced obsession; balanced evaluation	Frequent negative cognition about body image and self-worth	Eating disorders; body dysmorphia	Develop schema for positive body image thoughts; use dissonance to shift mindset
Sensory/ somatic	Relaxed; open to experience	Altered responses on the basis of trauma	Eating disorders; PTSD; dissociative disorders	Body experience that calms and creates new connections; activities such as yoga and meditation

PTSD, posttraumatic stress disorder.

experience. Finally, experiential and somatic-based views that had earlier been more adjunctive to therapy have assumed a central place in treatment, as evidenced by various chapters in this book.

Some of these views had fallen to the back of dusty library corners. Others have adapted to changing times. In the following text, we have analyzed these views and tried to come to some understanding of where we might be going in promoting change from BID to positive experience.

■ GESTALTISTS

Decades before gestalt therapy was developed, early psychologists were interested in studying psychophysiology. They had questions about the relationship between changes in sensory stimuli (light, heat, sound) and changes in subjective human experience.

Ultimately, they realized that humans had some unique ways of organizing information that smoothed sensory imperfections. Anybody who has tried to read students' or clients' handwriting uses what the Gestaltists liked to study. Whether the writer makes a perfect circle in writing the letter "o," or an incomplete circle or even some odd asymmetric oval, it is still read as the letter "o," seamless, without effort. The mind sees the broken circles as whole—a gestalt. Hence, the Gestaltists sought to recognize the incredible power of the mind to organize information, so that we can effortlessly make sense of all we take in via our senses.

It was inevitable that they would want to understand the experience of having a body because we have a long and rich sensory experience of our physical selves. Ultimately, these researchers came up with the term *körperschema*, body schema to describe the mental representation of one's own body. Their conceptualization serves a foundation of ideas we are still refining 100 years later.

Wolfgang Kohler is one of the most famous of these Gestaltists and spoke about the duality of body image experience in that the body is both subject and object and agent of perception (Kohler, 1947). In this formulation, the body is central to "I," sense of self. He further described how our representation of our own body becomes a means to understand the responses of others toward us. Thus, my mental representation of my body is built over time from my own experience and becomes the frame or lens of relating to others. A simplified example might be what we describe now as nonverbal communication, for example, noticing a person's physical and nervous habits. However, Kohler interweaves self, body perception, and social exchange in a way that we continue to disentangle today. He eventually ends this overview of psychology by calling for more inclusion of physical experience in our view of human learning, stating, "It seems to be the natural fate of Gestalt Psychology to become Gestalt Biology" (p. 359).

Paul Schilder is one of the notable figures in the history of body image, and his contributions bridge from gestalt work (Das Körperschema, 1923, as cited in Schilder, 1950) to American psychodynamic work. Schilder referenced the work of the Gestaltists that was applied to the study of patients with neurological injuries. One disorder of interest was phantom limb phenomenon, the sensation or perception of movement from limbs that have been amputated. Outside of the gestalt view of body schema, it is difficult to explain these phenomena. In essence, the mind experiences a whole leg when it is no longer present. These types of neurological disorders apply to other injuries or diseases of the brain and nervous system.

Schilder does leave us with one insight from the study of body image and the nervous system. Body image is not primarily visual. He posits that it is vestibular. He describes a patient who felt that her extremities became larger during an episode of dizziness. He describes circumstances of mescal intoxication and encephalitis that are associated with a feeling of enlargement or heaviness. Although not completely substantiated in this older text, Schilder may well have predicted our current thoughts about the relationship between BID, trauma, and the polyvagal theory (discussed later in this chapter).

Before we move toward Schilder's psychoanalytic perspectives, let us summarize what we know about BID from the Gestaltists. Body image is a mental representation that is built from experience. It may become disrupted by physical injuries. The brain learns and adapts to changes over time and can learn a new body image.

■ PSYCHOANALYTIC VIEW

The psychoanalytic view greatly helped our understanding of BID in various forms of psychopathology. However, because of the denial of the traumatizing effect of sexual abuse, it also greatly limited the potential for care.

Schilder (1950) continued in this treatise to discuss the libidinous nature of body image. He discussed how traumatic experiences come to create fixation in terms of the adult ego state. For example, Schilder describes the case of BID in a young man and the subsequent analysis. This young man had a distant relationship with his mother and a stern nanny. Father was not liked, nor present. All of this was typical of what an analyst might focus upon.

Schilder further described how this man was molested as a child, starting at age 4, by an older cousin, multiple times over a period of several years. As an adult, this man disliked himself and his body and had difficulty in relationships with both men and women. Drinking, smoking, and suicidal tendencies were part of the clinical presentation. His symptoms included an overvaluation of women's beauty. He kept seeking beautiful women and experienced repeated failure, which was the focus of his concerns. The analysis/treatment was incomplete. The patient dropped out of care.

Schilder went on to describe other patients with sexual trauma and symptoms, but focused on issues with parental figures and ego development. He introduced the term "depersonalization." "Depersonalization is the characteristic picture which occurs when the individual does not dare place his libido either in the outside world or in his own body" (Schilder, 1950, p. 140). The emotional issues create the schism of depersonalization. The resultant loss of body boundary is an experienced manifestation of problematic relations. Schilder relates it, of course, back to the vestibular system and vagal symptoms (dizziness, nausea). Although a connection is made here between psychological experience and vagal function, the causal mechanism is parental conflicts and not abuse.

Fisher and Cleveland (1958) continued some of Schilder's work on BID in psychoanalysis. They reasoned that the level of BID in psychiatric patients could be the same as those with neurological conditions. Conversion hysteria, perception of body decay, distortions of sex organs, and depersonalization were all manifestations of intrapsychic conflicts. These authors spoke of strengthening the body boundary as means of building ego strength. With regard to altered body experience, they concluded, "The phenomenon of depersonalization is perhaps the most widely described and commented upon of all the body image distortions among schizophrenic and neurotic patients" (p. 18).

These authors did not directly speak of abuse. However, they did attribute some BID to parental attitudes of disengagement in which the child becomes the object of parental anger or some other stress. At the very least, they were speaking of what we would call emotional neglect as causing a degree of depersonalization in the child. Still the retelling of sexualized body experiences as fantasy was not helpful for the model, much less the patients.

Their focus of treatment was varied. Of course, the establishment of a good therapeutic relationship and context was key. Figure drawings were one means of sharing the BID contents. Slowly the analyst would challenge the loose nature of their body boundary to strengthen the ego. Clinicians worked within the clients' symbolic systems about their bodies. Even muscle relaxation was used as a technique to help foster corrective change in body image.

A historical overview should not skip the analytical work of Bruch on eating disorders (EDs) and body image. Her model was one of diminished identity development and a resulting lack of connection to emotions or internal sensations (Bruch, 1962). According to Bruch, parental overinvolvement was the chief culprit. Interestingly, insight therapy alone was not seen as effective. Instead, the therapist needed to focus more internally on body image and emotions to create shift. Bruch's treatment focused on internal attunement and healthy expression, rather than the BID itself.

Psychodynamic approaches for BID continue today and have shifted to incorporate new research (Kruger, 2002). In this contemporary approach, a client moves from nonverbal body expression (symptoms) to mature emotional verbal expression. By means of safe therapeutic environment with empathic attunement, the client moves to "desomatize affect."

However, in the sequence of viewpoints, the analytic ones became overshadowed by behavioral ones in the United States in the 1960s and 1970s. Bruch's legacy included a warning about emerging behavioral methods that focused on confrontation and forced refeeding as the main methods of care (Bruch, 1974). In her opinion, outward change did not resolve the conflicts, nor the BID.

Psychoanalysis overall put BID front and center in our understanding of the impact of damaging interpersonal experiences. Unfortunately, they did have their own distorted thinking about sexual abuse. We may never know, if these early thinkers had recognized sexual abuse, how much further and faster we would have gone in the understanding of BID in EDs. We were introduced to the idea that depersonalization and BID may be implicated in alterations of vestibular and vagal function. Most of the treatments remained focused on verbal methods, bringing the physical experience into conscious discourse, or what Kruger (2002) called "desomatizing affect."

▪ FEMINIST AND SOCIOCULTURAL VIEWS

For many disorders, treatment models followed the historical sequence from psychoanalysis to behavioral to cognitive behavioral. The treatment of BID in EDs drew in one more viewpoint in the 1970s, that of the feminist view. Susie Orbach's famous book, *Fat Is a Feminist Issue*, took aim at BID as an individual's internalization of various cultural messages (1978). These include the fact that women's bodies are objectified and that reactions and judgments from others are overvalued in the interpersonal realm (Saguy, 2012). More specifically, women's bodies are sexually objectified in the Western context in both subtle (sexualized evaluation) and overt (sexual violence) ways (Fredrickson & Roberts, 1997). This has sometimes been referred to as the continuum of unwanted sexual experiences (Thompson et al., 1999) that are more central to BID in this model than in others.

The feminist–sociocultural model also includes changes in how a culture views women during times of economic change. Nasser, Katzmann, and Gordon (2003) argue that as other non-Western cultures become more industrialized, they similarly undergo changes in women's roles and in associated changes leading to the thin ideal and an increase in EDs.

The feminist, cultural examinations were certainly fueled by the classic study by Garner and colleagues that showed that EDs were on the rise in the 20th century in time with the rise in the thin ideal, as evidenced by changes in women's measurements in *Playboy* centerfolds and Miss America pageant contestants (Garner, Garfinkel, Schwartz, & Thompson, 1980). Although their study is more descriptive of trends than theory building, their work opened the door to empirical study of culture as it affects BID.

Cultural influences are so ubiquitous and the results so normalized that it can sometimes be difficult to conceptualize and treat the resulting BID. Central to these ideas is the emphasis placed not on one's own bodily experience, but on a schema for what others see and value (Fredrickson & Roberts, 1997). Some have argued that the focus on women's bodies is evolutionarily driven (signs that a woman is fertile). Others have argued that it is solely a means of perpetuating patriarchy.

From the feminist, sociocultural view, advocacy for cultural change is stressed (Levine & Smolak, 2002), and a healthier body image is more personally defined, less self-objectified. From this perspective, the therapeutic process focuses on exploring meanings and strengthening the self-view (Thompson et al., 1999). Finally, feminist approaches are imbued with the sense of creating connections of positive interrelationships, as Katzman and Lee write: "Recovery from anorexia nervosa calls for experimenting with new ways of relating to others and defining oneself beyond appearance" (1997, p. 392).

What was lacking in the feminist and sociocultural views was a clear connection to intrapsychic functions. Somehow the cultural environment has to come to be represented within the self to become part of self-regulation, individual experience, and psychopathology. It remains unclear what might be used to change that process. That is where we began to study cognitive schema.

■ COGNITIVE PROCESSING MODELS

Cognitive processing models to understand BID began developing in the 1980s. They were influenced in part by some of Gestaltists' older ideas about schema and the behaviorists' focus on objective measures and immediate symptom reduction. They were relatively neutral regarding the cause of the maladaptive cognition. The psychodynamic views of dysfunctional parent–child development and the feminist–sociocultural views of the social trauma of devaluation of self could be acknowledged as distal causes. However, the focus was on creating change in immediate thoughts to improve symptoms.

Cognitive views originated in what did not work well with simple behavioral methods. Size overestimation and mirror confrontation methods had their peak in the behavioral treatment of BID. Ultimately, it became clear that attitudinal measures provided just as much, if not more, information about body image (Altabe & Thompson, 1992). People could describe what they thought, how they felt, how important they considered, and how often they thought about their body image (Thompson, Penner, & Altabe, 1990). These measures were related to overall distress and other symptoms such as restrictive eating.

Butters and Cash (1987) demonstrated that improvements could be made in body image using a cognitive behavioral therapy (CBT) model. Through a combination of self-monitoring, cognitive challenge, and new experiences, a more positive, less obsessed view emerged. One could speculate that, rather than change old patterns, what was created was a new body image state that was more accessible. In a study by Altabe and Thompson (1996), the cognitive, attitudinal ideas were expanded to include an active schema model in which triggers can bring schema-relevant attitudes to the surface. These and other more process-oriented cognitive views led to refinements in treatment such as the integrative cognitive therapy (Wonderlich, Mitchell, Peterson, & Crow, 2001)

One of the more well-researched and potent process-oriented cognitive models of body image is on the basis of work in dissonance (Stice, Mazotti, Weibel, & Agras, 2000). Cognitive dissonance is a social psychological concept on the basis of the 1950s-era social psychology experiments of Leon Festinger. In short, dissonance is a feeling associated with experiencing a discrepancy between two thoughts or a thought and a behavior. That emotion motivates a tension reduction in the form of resolving the discrepancy and, therefore, prompts shifts in attitudes or beliefs.

When Stice began applying the concept to body image, he was interested in how dissonance could be used to reduce the internalization of the socially constructed, thin-ideal internalization. He noted, as had many others, that negative body image representations were ubiquitous among women in the United States, and that these attitudes represented a vulnerability to EDs early in the causal chain. In dissonance, participants indirectly create a tension between old views and new attitudes that prompts a shift. A person who internalizes the thin ideal who is prompted to explain the potential harm of such thinking to others will feel a dissonant tension that leads to a shift in body image. Stice's prevention model has been empirically validated multiple times for the prevention of BID and eating pathology (Stice, Rohde, Shaw, & Gau, 2017).

Stice's work continues in the tradition of the process-oriented cognitive models, while also integrating the sociocultural model. Participants in his prevention programming engage in counterattitudinal advocacy: They speak or write to others content that questions cultural ideals and promotes positive body image. This message directly conflicts with the participant's own internalization culture and negative thinking about his or her body image. The conflict between the behavior toward others and one's own view creates a tension, a dissonance, that is resolved by shifting the attitude to become more aligned with behavior. Body image becomes more positive in part by shifting views about the culturally based, traumatizing condition about the body.

Overall, cognitive methods remind us that body image is dynamic. Body image may be damaged by experiences and function in a rigid and repetitive way. However, new experiences change body image; new ways of thinking are always possible.

■ SOMATIC APPROACHES

As we moved into the 21st century, our research and discussions began to emphasize the role of the body itself in conceptualizing EDs and their treatment. Body image has long been part of the conceptualization of EDs, but treatment outcome studies in clinical populations showed limited effectiveness (Rosen, 1996). Cognitive therapy had some modest outcome results. However, Rosen aptly pointed out that, despite the centrality of BID to EDs, effective treatment was lagging. At the same time, the 1990s saw a paradigm shift in psychology toward neuroscience-based models. Feminist attitudes influenced the same decade, with increasing recognition of the range and impact of sexual abuse in EDs and body image (Rice, 1996). Taken together, the time was ripe for more trauma-based, body-oriented models in treating EDs and BID.

Incorporating the body takes several forms. There are those that focus on the brain and its altered state in response to trauma. In his polyvagal theory, Porges turns our attention toward the relationship between responses to threat in the autonomic nervous system and patterns of emotional and social response in psychiatric disorders (e.g., Porges, 2009). Trauma leads to chronic states of hyper- and hypoarousal, as manifested in observable posttraumatic stress disorder symptoms. The task is to keep the clients in the zone of optimal arousal, as they are asked to tolerate anxieties, shame, and painful memories. Another example, somatosensory psychotherapy, (SP) brings body-based trauma treatment into the therapy room. Therapists observe clients' nonverbal cues to trauma experiencing, and then help with reprocessing via both talk and movement in the context of the therapeutic relationship (Ogden & Minton, 2000). See Chapter 22 for an overview of sensorimotor psychotherapy.

Other approaches address the experience of body states directly. Somatic Experiencing (SE; see Chapter 21) turns our attention toward the kinesthetic, interoceptive, and proprioceptive sensations in the conceptualization of chronic stress and trauma symptoms (Payne, Levine, & Crane-Godreau, 2015). These basic systems function together as a core response network. A therapist in this framework extends his or her normal techniques of entering the clients' worldview by engaging with their body experiences, mirroring them, and encouraging movement in the therapy room (Engelhard, 2017).

Dance and movement therapy has used this approach for a longer period of time (see Chapter 9). By use of mirroring and empathic connection, what the client once experienced as isolated negative body experience becomes an interchange that leads to shared meaning (Kleinman, 2016). The therapeutic relationship is key.

Body-based practices have also been shown to have a positive effect on body image. Examples include yoga, qigong, and meditation (Payne et al., 2015). These activities promote a more optimal state of the nervous system that is actively created by the individual and can be a powerful complement to body image treatment.

Taken together, we see that BID reflects trauma, is tied to the symptom cluster from trauma, and can be a direct avenue to healing the impact of trauma and subsequent BID. Recent speculation has taken body-based treatment a step further to include the role of dissociation, both in trauma treatment in EDs (see Chapter 3) and in the treatment of BID.

■ TREATMENT OF BODY IMAGE DISTURBANCE: A NEW ROLE FOR DISSOCIATION

As discussed earlier, Schilder (1950), the psychodynamicist, helped us to see that interpersonal childhood trauma exists in adulthood as pathological body image symptoms, including dissociative body experiences. Over time, this central idea faded and other aspects of body image in EDs were explored.

In recent times, we have begun to look again to the role of dissociative experience in BID. Seijo (2016) placed BID at the center of the dissociative experience in EDs. She described how BID acts as a central defense in maintaining the rejected, dissociated personality part from the rest of the self. She describes how a focus on this rejected self in therapy can slowly improve body image.

Similarly, Seubert (2018) uses an approach that is derived from ego state therapy (see Chapter 15) and gestalt therapy. BID is seen as a shame-based ego state, projected externally, for example, into a mirror. The etiology of such a state lies in trauma and its associated shame. A path toward change is created when the client engages the dissociated self via forms of the gestalt "empty chair" strategy and eye movement desensitization and reprocessing (EMDR) therapy (see Chapter 13). As traumatic experiences are processed within the safe setting of psychotherapy, the self-view and body image become more positive.

◼ CONCLUSIONS AND DISCUSSION

I believe that we are at a true turning point in the conceptualization and treatment of BID. Each of the four historical approaches adds a valuable element. The Gestaltists gave us a snapshot of our bodily self—the way we receive the world physically. They defined a unique, fluid internal representation, built from experience and prone to problems in response to neurological injury. The psychoanalysts added the perspective that interpersonal injuries in parent–child relationships can create serious disturbance in body image and associated psychiatric illness. Although the psychoanalysts did mention some relaxation techniques and the involvement of the vestibular system, these were lost in the course of time. The feminists and socioculturalists helped us to see the social trauma that exists when cultural conditions allow for objectification and unwanted sexual experiences. Finally, the cognitivists sought to explore the internal processing that links cultural influence and learning history to psychopathology. Interventions that range from reprocessing to dissonance seek to create new learning and thought pathways that represent a more positive and functional body image.

The time is certainly ripe to reincorporate somatic and neuroscientific views into our conceptualization of BID. More specifically, we can bring a neurologically informed, somatic approach into the treatment room, one that acknowledges the impact of trauma and dissociation on body image.

Perhaps the need to include body-based methods can best be understood with regard to treatment approaches. The three treatment models we have historically experienced—psychoanalysis, cognitive behavioral, and feminist–sociocultural—are mental models, positing relations between experience and beliefs about the bodily self. The analysts sought to uncover conflicts and move the fixated body manifestations into more verbal expression and discourse. Feminist–sociocultural treatment approaches prompted therapists and their clients to become counterculturalists on the way to more healthy body image. Finally, the cognitivists brought more techniques for changing body image experience by examining and challenging cognitive components of the body image dynamic. They remind us that new connections from positive experience are always possible.

Somatic approaches build on their predecessors but bring to center stage a direct involvement with the body. Engagement in this vestibular sense seems to allow direct access to trauma experience, enabling the client to move toward a more verbal, meaning-based, and consolidated state.

Some questions remain. Although the link between trauma and body image has been identified and studied, there is great need for continued exploration of treatment approaches that include the body when addressing trauma in clients with EDs. Similarly, examining the role of dissociation in this population requires much greater attention. Potentially, we could move toward a theory that would help identify which kinds of trauma typically lead to different types of EDs, as well as to dissociated ego and body experience. It certainly would help in the assessment and treatment planning process. The approaches presented throughout this book have a great potential. We need to grow the empirical validation of these, so they do not fall to the back of the library for another 75 years.

I believe that if the early Gestaltists were here, they would be excited about the current trend. They were the first to direct our attention to the phenomenology of body image—that it is experienced with our senses in space. We would join with them to consider that if the experience is traumatic (abuse), we need to include the direct, embodied experience of the trauma to alleviate patterns of disturbance. We, therefore, look toward the somatic and neuroscientific views for a richer conceptualization, more ways to alleviate disturbance, and the return of the body into the treatment of BID. It is historically and inextricably a part of the gestalt of body image.

■ REFERENCES

Altabe, M., & Thompson, J. K. (1992). Size estimation versus figural ratings of body image disturbance: Relation to body dissatisfaction and eating dysfunction. *International Journal of Eating Disorders, 11*(4), 397–402. doi:10.1002/1098-108X(199205)11:4<397::AID-EAT2260110414>3.0.CO;2-6

Altabe, M., & Thompson, J. K. (1996). Body image: A cognitive self-schema construct? *Cognitive Therapy and Research, 20*(2), 171–193. doi:10.1007/BF02228033

Bruch, H. (1962). Perceptual and conceptual disturbances in anorexia nervosa. *Psychosomatic Medicine, 24*(2), 187–194.

Bruch, H. (1974). Perils of behavior modification in the treatment of anorexia nervosa. *Journal of the American Medical Association, 230*(10), 1419–1422. doi:10.1001/jama.230.10.1419

Butters, J. W., & Cash, T. F. (1987). Cognitive-behavioral treatment of women's body-image dissatisfaction. *Journal of Consulting and Clinical Psychology, 55*(6), 889–897. doi:10.1037/0022-006X.55.6.889

Engelhard, E. S. (2017). Body and movement in dynamic psychotherapy: Reflections on talking and movement therapies. *Body, Movement and Dance in Psychotherapy, 12*(2), 98–110. doi:10.1080/17432979.2016.1239590

Fisher, S., & Cleveland, S. E. (1958). *Body image and personality.* Princeton, NJ: D. Van Nostrand.

Fredrickson, B. L., & Roberts, T.-A. (1997). Objectification theory: Toward understanding women's lived experiences and mental health risks. *Psychology of Women Quarterly, 21*(2), 173–206. doi:10.1111/j.1471-6402.1997.tb00108.x

Garner, D. M., Garfinkel, P. E., Schwartz, D., & Thompson, M. (1980). Cultural expectations of thinness in women. *Psychological Reports, 47*(2), 483–491. doi:10.2466/pr0.1980.47.2.483

Katzman, M. A., & Lee, S. (1997). Beyond body image: The integration of feminist and transcultural theories in the understanding of self starvation. *International Journal of Eating Disorders, 22*(4), 385–394. doi:10.1002/(SICI)1098-108X(199712)22:4<385::AID-EAT3>3.0.CO;2-I

Kleinman, S. (2016). Becoming whole again: Dance/Movement therapy for individuals with eating disorders. In S. Chaiklin & H. Wengrower (Eds.), *The art and science of dance/movement therapy: Life is dance* (2nd ed., pp. 139–157). New York, NY: Routledge.

Kohler, W. (1947). *Gestalt psychology.* New York, NY: Liverwright Publishing.

Kruger, D. W. (2002). Psychodynamic approaches to changing body image. In T. F. Cash & T. Pruzinsky (Eds.), *Body image: A handbook of theory, research and practice.* New York, NY: Guilford Press.

Levine, M. P., & Smolak, L. (2002). Ecological and activism approaches to the prevention of body image problems. In T. F. Cash & T. Pruzinsky (Eds.), *Body image: A handbook of theory, research, and clinical practice* (pp. 497–505). New York, NY: Guilford Press.

Nasser, M., Katzman, M., & Gordon, R. (Eds.). (2003). *Eating disorders and cultures in transition.* New York, NY: Routledge.

Ogden, P., & Minton, K. (2000). Sensorimotor psychotherapy: One method for processing traumatic memory. *Traumatology, 6*(3), 149–173. doi:10.1177/153476560000600302

Orbach, S. (1978). *Fat is a feminist issue.* New York, NY: Berkeley Books.

Payne, P., Levine, P. A., & Crane-Godreau, M. A. (2015). Somatic experiencing: Using interoception and proprioception as core elements of trauma therapy. *Frontiers in Psychology, 6,* 93. doi:10.3389/fpsyg.2015.00093

Porges, S. W. (2009). The polyvagal theory: New insights into adaptive reactions of the autonomic nervous system. *Cleveland Clinic Journal of Medicine, 76*(Suppl. 2), S86–S90. doi:10.3949/ccjm.76.s2.17

Rice, C. (1996). Trauma and eating problems: Expanding the debate. *Eating Disorders: The Journal of Treatment & Prevention, 4*(3), 197–237. doi:10.1080/10640269608251177

Rosen, J. C. (1996). Body image assessment and treatment in controlled studies of eating disorders. *International Journal of Eating Disorders, 20*(4), 331–343. doi:10.1002/(SICI)1098-108X(199612)20:4<331::AID-EAT1>3.0.CO;2-O

Saguy, A. (2012). Why fat is a feminist issue. *Sex Roles, 66*(9-10), 600–607.

Schilder, P. (1950). *The image and appearance of the human body. Studies in the constructive energies of the psyche.* New York, NY: International Universities Press.

Seijo, N. (2016, December). The neglected self: Working with body image distortion in eating disorders. *ESTD Newsletter, 5*(4), 5–13.

Seubert, A. (2018). Becoming Known: A relational model utilizing Gestalt and ego state-assisted EMDR in treating eating disorders. *Journal of EMDR Practice and Research, 12*(2), 71–86.

Stice, E., Mazotti, L., Weibel, D., & Agras, W. S. (2000). Dissonance prevention program decreases thin-ideal internalization, body dissatisfaction, dieting, negative affect, and bulimic symptoms: A preliminary experiment. *International Journal of Eating Disorders, 27*(2), 206–217. doi:10.1002/(SICI)1098-108X(200003)27:2<206::AID-EAT9>3.0.CO;2-D

Stice, E., Rohde, P., Shaw, H., & Gau, J. M. (2017). Clinician-led, peer-led, and Internet-delivered dissonance-based eating disorder prevention programs: Acute effectiveness of these delivery modalities. *Journal of Consulting and Clinical Psychology, 85*(9), 883. doi:10.1037/ccp0000211

Thompson, J. K., Heinberg, L. J., Altabe, M., & Tantleff-Dunn, S. (1999). *Exacting beauty: Theory, assessment, and treatment of body image disturbance.* Washington, DC: American Psychological Association.

Thompson, J. K., Penner, L. A., & Altabe, M. N. (1990). Procedures, problems, and progress in the assessment of body images. In T. F. Cash & T. Pruzinsky (Eds.), *Body images: Development, deviance, and change* (pp. 21–48). New York, NY: Guilford Press.

Wonderlich, S. A., Mitchell, J. E., Peterson, C. B., & Crow, S. (2001). Integrative cognitive therapy for bulimic behavior. In R. H. Striegel-Moore & L. Smolak (Eds.), *Eating disorders: Innovative directions in research and practice* (pp. 173–195). Washington, DC: American Psychological Association.

CHAPTER 26

Finding Self Again: The Dismantling of Eating Disorder and Trauma Identity

Michael E. Berrett, Sabree A. Crowton, and P. Scott Richards

■ INTRODUCTION

Trauma and disordered eating are illnesses in which the sufferer becomes more deeply connected to the illness over time, and less connected to self, others, and important ideals, principles, values, dreams, and desires. In this chapter, we use the term "trauma" as defined by the Substance Abuse and Mental Health Services Administration (SAMHSA, 2014), "an event, series of events, or set of circumstances that is experienced by an individual as physically or emotionally harmful or life threatening and that has lasting adverse effects on the individual's functioning and mental, physical, social, emotional, or spiritual well-being." We also understand the term "disordered eating" to refer to any abnormal eating behavior that adversely impacts psychological health. Both of these conditions are associated with persistent negative thoughts and beliefs that damage identity development. In this chapter, we discuss the following: (a) research on the connections between identity and trauma and disordered eating, (b) definitions of identity and spiritual identity, (c) the importance of spiritual identity in treatment and recovery, (d) guidelines for assessing spiritual identity, and (e) interventions for helping clients heal and reclaim their spiritual identity.

■ IMPACT OF EATING DISORDERS AND TRAUMA ON IDENTITY

Research indicates that individuals with eating disorders (EDs) have fewer positive and more negative self-schemas (Stein & Corte, 2007). Self-schemas are "chronically accessible cognitions" that "are automatically activated and exert a powerful influence over the processing of relevant information" (Stein, 1996, p. 104). Among a sample of college women, those with a fat schema were more conscious of negative comments and experiences related to weight and shape than healthy controls (Stein & Corte, 2008). This study found that identity impairment was predictive of the number of fat-related schemas, which then predicted disordered eating.

Identity is a critical focus and emphasis in the treatment of and recovery from EDs. The reasons for this are many. In EDs, those suffering have had the very roots of their sense of identity shaken. As a by-product of the nature and course of development of the illness, the person afflicted becomes, over time, more and more connected to the illness, and less and less connected to critical facets of normal development and meaningful life. These include the following: identity, family, friends, values, spiritual beliefs, passion, purpose, priorities, desires, and dreams. The illness becomes preeminent, whereas awareness, attendance, and engagement in other critical arenas of self and life diminish over time. In severe and long-term illness, individuals begin to believe that their ED is not just an illness which they struggle with, but a core part of who they are.

Other studies show that trauma in the form of emotional deprivation and physical abandonment during childhood is associated with negative self-beliefs (Caslini et al., 2016; Lejonclou, Nilsson, & Holmqvist, 2014; Pignatelli, Wampers, Loriedo, Biondi, & Vanderlinden, 2017). Among female university students, mistrust and abuse beliefs fully explained the relationship between childhood abuse and drive for thinness (Jenkins, Meyer, & Blissett, 2013, p. 248). These connections are further strengthened by findings that shaming social comparisons correlated with feelings of inferiority and ED pathology in individuals with EDs (Matos, Ferreira, Duarte, & Pinto-Gouveia, 2015).

Identity is also a critical focus and emphasis in the treatment of and recovery from trauma. The impact of trauma on an individual's sense of safety, sense of belonging, self-concept, integrity, self-worth, and sense of wholeness and goodness can be devastating. One common wound of physical, emotional, and sexual abuse is a deep sense of shame, which challenges an individual's understanding of experiences. The enveloping shadow of shame changes "I experience" into "I am." This is often in the form of thoughts such as, "I am bad, horrible, broken, or damaged," rather than the more accurate, "Something scary, horrible, bad, or hurtful happened to me." This residual and unrelenting shame often damages or separates an individual from his or her identity. Disconnected from one's sense of worth, the victim of trauma may be more vulnerable to seeking external evidences of self-value such as appearance, achievement, or approval, which are already too broadly embraced as the evidence of worth in Western culture.

Trauma and disordered eating are associated with certain roadblocks that make it difficult to attain or reclaim identity. Some of these include the following: feelings of worthlessness, lack of healthy attachments, shame, perfectionism, making oneself the exception, avoidance, isolation, damaged integrity, loss of self-confidence, lack of support, inability to separate illness from oneself, lack of tools for recovery, and unprocessed trauma (Berrett, 2014, 2016). Other roadblocks involve beliefs that are false, negative, and self-defeating. There are too many of these common beliefs to list them all, but some examples are as follows: "I can't trust my body"; "I can't and shouldn't trust myself"; "Vulnerability is stupid and painful"; "I need to keep secrets to stay safe"; "I have to do this alone." With an established pattern of disconnection from others and from self, it seems clear that the collateral damage of trauma and disordered eating is a significant loss of the sense of self that needs to be assessed, understood, and treated in the search for recovery, healing, and wellness.

■ DEFINITIONS AND IMPORTANCE OF IDENTITY AND SPIRITUAL IDENTITY

We believe that children are born with a primary sense of self and identity that can be attributed to genetics, spiritual nature, or a combination of the two. It is generally accepted that a child's identity is nurtured and developed over time, and is influenced by caretaking, environmental influences, and life experiences. These include the very best that loving relationships and circumstances have to offer, as well as the very worst that relationships and circumstances can bring, including violence, shame, neglect, and other forms of trauma.

Another point of view, which the authors share, assumes that the identity of a child is also influenced by his or her spiritual nature and beliefs (Miller, 2016). This spiritual sense can be influenced by primary caretakers toward extinguishment or development. Of course, we know that these experiences are tempered and influenced by the personality and strengths of each child. Whatever the constellation of predisposing factors and life experiences, it can be said that the development of self occurs for us all—that our sense of identity is malleable and grows and develops over time.

Identity is not just a psychological construct. From our perspective, it is also a spiritual reality. Spiritual identity can be conceptualized in several ways:

1. Spiritual identity is the very core of personhood, the wholeness of an individual, and the goodness and worth of one human soul.
2. Spiritual identity represents a full and complete identity. It is the recognition, awareness, and embodiment of the whole self—the integration and acceptance of self in various sectors of life: physical, mental, emotional, relational, and spiritual.
3. Spiritual identity is not only accepting and embracing who we are but also recognizing our potential and the capacity to become who we most essentially are.
4. Mature spiritual identity provides meaning, purpose in life, a sense of value for each human life, a real and enduring love for others, and a deep desire to live by internalized principles.
5. Mature spiritual identity is demonstrated in a life of integrity and the internal peace that comes from it.
6. Spiritual identity is a sense that can be experienced by both those who seek a transpersonal spiritual reality and those who seek "higher self" or "the best in oneself."

We are not treating a fragmented part of a person—we are treating the whole person. We are not treating symptoms—we are treating individuals. We are treating them, not only for who they are right now but also for who they might become. The capacity to learn from mistakes and experiences, make new choices in the moment, and transcend adversity is a hopeful stance and a key part of a mature sense of spiritual identity. Focusing on helping clients explore and reclaim their sense of identity—including their spiritual identity—is a powerful resource during treatment.

Spirituality is important to the vast majority of human beings on the planet. Spiritual practices, experiences, beliefs, and identity ward against mental illness and self-defeating patterns (Miller, 2016). Research has shown that spirituality is associated with wellness, happiness, recovery, and healing (Koenig, 2009). There are many studies that document the importance of spirituality in treatment of and recovery from mental, emotional, and addictive illness (Hook et al., 2010; Pargament, 2007; Richards & Bergin, 2005; Sperry & Shafranske, 2005). Research has also documented the importance and value of the inclusion of spirituality in the treatment of EDs and trauma (Buser, Parkins, & Buser, 2014; Marsden, Karagianni, & Morgan, 2007; Matusek & Knudson, 2009; Richards, Berrett, Hardman, & Eggett, 2006).

We have also found that spirituality can bolster clients' motivation for recovery. We call this "helping clients find, remember, and make good use of reasons for recovery." When we help clients understand and stay connected to personal and imperative reasons for recovery, they do better in treatment and make greater gains. The importance of finding personally meaningful motivations for recovery has been well documented in the science of motivational interviewing (Macdonald, Hibbs, Corfield, & Treasure, 2012). We also know that, although any reason for recovery is a good reason, the most impelling and motivating reasons are tied to one's sense of spirituality. Thus, we consider it important to include spirituality in the treatment of EDs and trauma for clients who are, in their own individual way, spiritually inclined.

■ ASSESSMENT BEYOND ASSESSMENT

Assessment is critical to understanding clients and is beneficial to the therapeutic process for both clinician and client. We believe not just that assessment is preparation for therapeutic intervention but also that assessment is intervention itself. One simple example of this is when we ask clients to talk about a source of shame. Their sharing increases understanding for both clinician and client, and, in addition, their declaration, act of vulnerability, and trust of self and others in the moment of sharing become therapeutic and healing.

It is not the purpose of this chapter to cover the routine assessment measures for EDs and trauma. It is well understood that there are many formal psychological assessment measures. Interested readers are directed to previous work that provides specific recommendations for trauma (Carlson, 1997; Richards, Hardman, Lea, & Berrett, 2015) and ED assessment (Mitchell & Peterson, 2007).

We have found that it is helpful to assess the following aspects of a client's life to gain an understanding of his or her sense of identity at a deeper level: (a) the client's individual needs, (b) ED-generated beliefs, (c) events, circumstances, impact, beliefs, and meaning of trauma, (d) the client's spiritual framework, (e) the client's spiritual beliefs and practices, (f) the client's reasons to recover, (g) the client's model of, and criterion for, self-worth, (h) the client's sense of self-worth and identity, and (i) the client's strengths, gifts, and offerings. Following are a few examples of ways to develop a deeper understanding of the client's sense of self and spiritual identity.

Who is one of your spiritual heroes? This is a powerful assessment exercise that helps clients become clearer about their spiritual beliefs, values, principles, priorities, and identity. We accomplish this by asking them about spiritual heroes in their lives in some way similar to the following imagery exercise:

> "Choose one person you feel is a spiritual hero in your life. This spiritual hero may be an icon such as the Dalai Lama, or it may be a person in your family, circle of friends, or even an acquaintance. No matter who this person is, it is one who has had an important and positive impact in your life. In your mind's eye, picture this person. Allow yourself to get in touch with your feelings, memories, and experience of this spiritual hero."

When the client's imagery experience is over, we might ask any of the following process questions: "Who is the person you pictured?" "Why did you choose this person?" "What is it about the person that leads you to view him or her as a spiritual hero or exemplar?" "What does this teach you about your own spirituality and spiritual beliefs?" "From this, what can you learn about who you are as a person and your character as you ponder the importance of this spiritual hero in your life?" You can share with the client the idea that we may be attracted to those who are similar to ourselves in our intentions, desires, character, and principles by which we live our lives. By seeing clearly our heroes, we can more clearly see ourselves.

Other identity-related assessment questions. The following are additional questions for "deeper understanding," which work well with our clients. These questions are related to a more internal sense of identity: "How do you know of your sense of self-worth and value?" "Please tell me what you know about who you are." "What are your reasons for fighting for recovery from illness?" "What do you know about the meaning and the purpose of your life?" "Have you ever felt that you have a 'calling' in your life which you must attend to?" "What principles of character do you strive to live by each day?" "What do you have to offer the world?" "If you could change only one thing in the world, what would you change?" "If you had only 72 hours to live, where would you go, who or what would you see, and what would you do?" "What do your answers to these questions teach you about your character, your internal self, your spirituality, or your identity?" For more ideas, refer to "Assessment Beyond Assessment" (Berrett, 2015).

◼ TREATMENT INTERVENTIONS FOR IDENTITY RECLAMATION AND RECONSTRUCTION

Treatment for mental, emotional, and addictive illness will best serve the client when it considers and treats the "whole self." The whole self both includes and transcends the physical, mental, emotional, relational, and spiritual. Treatment that considers anything less may risk fragmentation or compartmentalization of the person, despite positive intentions to serve and extend care. Every human being has inestimable and incomprehensible value and worth and therefore deserves to be treated always with the utmost respect, dignity, and compassion. With this attitude in mind, we present recommendations from research and from our own clinical experience with regard to treating EDs and trauma from an identity point of view.

For EDs, some researchers recommend that treatment focus on interpersonal communication, attachment style, self-concept, identity differentiation, and emotional awareness (Demidenko, Tasca, Kennedy, & Bissada, 2010). Others advise the use of spiritual interventions (Richards & Bergin, 2005). Hardman and colleagues submit that healing for individuals with EDs comes through reconnection with themselves and others (Hardman, Berrett, & Richards, 2003). Trauma treatment endorsements include dance and movement therapies, sensorimotor therapy, eye movement desensitization and reprocessing (EMDR), yoga, and mindfulness (van der Kolk, 2015). For comorbid trauma and eating disorders, several researchers propose that clients develop more positive self-schemas (De Paoli, Fuller-Tyszkiewicz, & Krug, 2017; Stein, Corte, Chen, Nuliyalu, & Wing, 2013). Another recommendation is EMDR with a focus on ego state work and attachment repair (Seubert & Lightstone, 2009).

We propose several themes, principles, and interventions in psychotherapy for trauma and ED clients in the reclamation and reconstruction of self and spiritual identity. These methods are consistent with available research, have proven successful in clinical practice, and are just a small sampling of interventions available. These methods are addressed in the following text—some of the items are adapted from Berrett, Hardman, & Richards (2010, pp. 373–382).

1. **Addressing Core Components of Personhood: The Nine P's of Personhood**
   In the following text, we briefly discuss nine components of personhood, which clients can ponder and consider to understand and conceptualize their identity. Each of these components is considered a building block for identity and is

followed with a brief explanation. We then offer questions to ask or activities to initiate to advance the therapeutic work. Some of the items are adapted from *Life Quest: A Leader's Guide* (Allen, 2003).

Physical Self. This component of self includes body, gender identification, sexuality, sexual orientation, genetics, ability to do and move, and physical competencies. **Interventions/Activities**: (a) Consider family body types. (b) Explore DNA heritage tests. (c) Consider family illness history. (d) Discuss the capabilities of the body.

Progenitors. Progenitors are the families, clans, tribes, people, and groups that we are descended from. Reflection on and understanding of biological ancestors and adoptive caretakers (physical and spiritual) can provide clients with a better picture of who they are and where they come from. **Interventions/Activities**: (a) Read family histories and journals. (b) Consider the adversities, strengths, accomplishments, and character of progenitors. Ponder and discuss what you want to "keep" and "let go of" in the example and legacy that progenitors have given.

Personality. Explain to clients that personality is an amalgamation of attitudes, memories, habits, relationships, and skills. Discuss the idea that we all have personality traits that we like and do not like. We do not need to eliminate the traits we dislike, but rather learn to refine and use them for our benefit. **Interventions/Activities**: (a) Participate in objective and subjective personality measures and analysis. (b) Ask for feedback from trusted group or family members. (c) Reflect on personal journal entries/autobiographies. (d) Decide which traits you view as strengths and are grateful for, as well as those that are slated for a process of refinement.

Passion. Sacker (2008) said, "When people with eating disorders discover their passions, they discover their own true selves, and the eating disorder self starts to lose its control over them" (p. 87). In this quote, Sacker is talking about a passion that reflects what we love to do and are excited about. **Interventions/Activities**: (a) Ask clients: "What is it that you get up in the morning for?" "What do you look forward to and what do you love doing when you have the time?" Explain how it is important to find, honor, and engage in one's passions. (b) We can ask, "What is in your closet?" referring to those things that you love, but which have also been ignored and neglected (Schaefer & Rutledge, 2014). (c) Reveal your passions to yourself and others and design a life that includes more of these activities.

Purpose. Frankl (2006) taught, "Everything can be taken from a man, but one thing: the last of the human freedom—to choose one's attitude in any given set of circumstances, to choose one's own way" (p. 86). If the meaning and the purpose of our lives is a choice, then we can find, decide, and create purpose. Teaching this truth is the beginning of this intervention. **Interventions/Activities**: (a) Ask clients to share in dyads or small groups: "One thing I know about the meaning of my life …." "If I had 72 hours to live, what I would do with my time is …." "If I could change one thing in the world, what I would change is …." "One thing I am drawn to or I feel is a calling for me and my life is …." In these activities of reflection and disclosure, it is important to remind clients to focus on what they know and not to waste energy on what they do not know.

Principles. One of the cornerstones of identity is the set of principles that an individual has internalized as his or her own and that govern and guide everything he or she does. In other words, it is where I come from, how I live, and who I am at the internal and deepest level of soul and spirit, and that is expressed in choice, behaviors, and relationships. **Interventions/ Activities**: (a) Have clients share: "One of the most important principles I live by is ...." Then ask why that principle is important to them and from whom or where they learned it. (b) Invite clients to share a time when they violated one of their core principles of living and what they learned from that, in addition to a time when they honored one of their key principles for living and the consequences of that decision—both external and internal.

Perspectives. Our personal perspectives include our opinions, viewpoints, beliefs, and attitudes. These come to life when they are lived, expressed, and declared. **Interventions/Activities**: Provide opportunities for "declaration," in which clients honor their beliefs by "making a stand." Examples are as follows: "One spiritual belief I have is ...." "In the upcoming election, I am voting for ... because ...." "I think the world would be better if ...." As clients "declare" and "stand for something," it gives them a chance to ponder their stance and beliefs and either refine or solidify them.

Priorities. Our priorities best come from attending and being true to ourselves and our beliefs about that which is most important in life. **Interventions/ Activities**: Have a discussion with clients about their values. Explore how these values compare with where the client's thoughts, intentions, energies, and time are actually spent. The disparity between stated values and lived values can be illuminating and guide strategies for realignment and accountability as therapeutic work progresses. Literature on motivational interviewing (Macdonald et al., 2012) and the values portion of acceptance and commitment therapy (ACT; Hayes, Strosahl, & Wilson, 2016) provide other possible activities.

Potential. We propose that the identity of an individual is not only "who I am" but also "who I can become." The potential or capacity of a person is truly a part of him or her. This honors the idea that identity is both static and fluid—that the concepts of both being and of becoming have value. **Interventions/Activities**: (a) Discuss with clients the potential meaning of this quote from George Eliot, "It's never too late to become who you might have been." (b) Discuss with clients the idea that integrity is "conscious becoming" and that, when we are striving to be who we are, and who we can and must be, we are living with integrity, which increases internal peace.

2. **Finding a More Truthful Self-Image: Telling the Truth and Telling Your Story**
One major task in helping clients reclaim their lost sense of identity is to help them understand that the identity that comes from the effects of trauma and disordered eating is not accurate or true. Using strong and clear language invites clients to begin to think about this in a deliberate, rather than a passive or avoidant, manner. Telling "their truth" out loud helps clients find their voice, strengthen needed boundaries, and, in a group of those who truly care, create an opportunity for acceptance, love, and compassion, which heals their sense of shame. This process of abandoning shame and reclaiming self can be taught, as well as experienced through clinical intervention. It is important also to teach clients that their ED is not who they are, but rather an illness from which they are suffering. A more accurate sense of self can come when clients separate themselves from what

happened to them, as in the case of trauma and disordered eating. The concept of "separation from illness" is well taught, along with specific interventions, in *Life Without Ed* (Schaefer & Rutledge, 2014).

Interventions/Activities: (a) Have clients bring photographs of themselves as children. Use these in session to help them see and experience a more accurate understanding of who they are and what they were really like, and what they felt, thought, desired, and intended, at the time of abuse or trauma. (b) Have clients write an autobiography about their life, that is, to "tell their story." Invite clients to include those memories that are difficult to discuss, and ask them to share their story. (c) Invite clients to regularly write reflections in their personal journal about what they are proud of in themselves, as a way of witnessing their goodness.

3. **Improving Self-Identity by Ending the Cycle of Self-Judgment and Embracing Feelings**

One of the things that keeps clients in a place of shame and negativity is self-judgment. Self-judgment of the thoughts and feelings we have leads us to avoiding, rather than embracing, feelings. Self-judgment often includes inappropriate and misplaced judgment from traumatic experience, abandonment by others, and disordered eating. Long-term healing requires a lessening of self-judgment.

Interventions/Activities: (a) Address self-judgment by helping clients understand that feelings are not bad or morally wrong. (b) Teach clients that self-judgment about feelings is an obstacle to noticing, accepting, embracing, and learning from their feelings. (c) Often clients would not feel, own, or accept their emotions, because of the judgments they make about themselves for feeling what they are feeling. (d) Teach clients to look beyond behaviors to their intentions. Understanding intention lessens judgment. (e) Teach the practice of self-correction without judgment, which means simply learning from both feelings and mistakes. Additional ways to encourage emotional honesty and competence can be found in *The Courage to Feel* (Seubert, 2008).

4. **Reclaiming a Sense of Self by Overcoming Helplessness, Avoiding Avoidance, and Doing Hard Things**

Bednar, Wells, and Peterson (1989) wrote that no matter the cause or origin of poor self-esteem and self-worth, there is one thing that maintains that place of poverty: "avoidance." We also know from clinical experience that clients often learn in the moment and aftermath of trauma that they are powerless and helpless. It is important, therefore, that the treatment of both trauma and EDs focuses on action rather than on inaction. We acknowledge the value of evidence-based psychotherapy, and that the talking, sharing, and voicing that occurs in psychotherapy is in itself a form of action. We also propose, however, that psychotherapy is best used in conjunction with experiential therapy, which requires a higher level of acting, moving, and doing.

Interventions/Activities: (a) Encourage, ask, and support clients in speaking up, having a voice in sessions and in appropriate social relationships and forums. (b) Discuss with clients the theme of "we do hard things." In treatment, focus on those things in the life of the clients that they are avoiding and address them directly by creating step-by-step plans and actions. (c) Most importantly, keep focusing on helping clients to notice their abilities, strengths, bravery, courage, efforts, good works, steps taken, successes, and progress, so that successes and qualities can contribute to their self-esteem and identity.

5. **Recognition of Impact: Accepting Positive Truth About Oneself**

   In a study on social support among adolescents, Berrett (1985) found that it is not only the support that an adolescent receives that makes a difference in his or her sense of self-worth and well-being but also the giving of his or her support that positively impacts sense of self-worth. This finding is aligned with a well-accepted truth—that understanding that one has something to offer, and then actually being able and willing to offer the gift, makes a positive difference in one's sense of self and fulfillment in life. One gift clients can give to themselves, which impacts their sense of self and worth, is allowing the recognition of impact. This is the awareness that they have something of value to offer, that their many "gifts of self" and talents have made and make a difference in the lives of those around them.

   Interventions/Activities: (a) Create a sociogram, that is, a visual image of their social support system. (b) Write down and discuss the specific, desired kinds of support and specific steps in creating that support. (c) Ask clients to make a written list of the kinds of support that they give others. (d) Invite clients to participate in a "recognition of impact" imagery such as: "… I would invite you to go inside of yourself and find the moment and circumstance in which you influenced a person's life for the better. This may be a parent, sibling, child, student, neighbor, friend, or stranger. In your mind's eye look towards them, look into their eyes and into their heart. Hear and receive from the expression on their face, communication of their eyes, and words they share their message of gratitude for what you have done for them …."

6. **Improving Sense of Self and Worth by Giving, Receiving, and Deepening Love**

   Although love is arguably the most powerful force for good and healing in the world, the word and concept of love is complicated in the field of psychotherapy, especially among those suffering from EDs and trauma. Societal confusion about the connection and difference between love and sex; legitimate concerns about professionalism, ethics, and boundaries in the practice of psychotherapy; and the difficulties of trust and vulnerability with those suffering from EDs and trauma—all make this a complicated matter indeed. Nevertheless, love is important in healing and should not be shunned, ignored, or avoided. We believe that when clients become more willing and able to give and receive love, their loving relationships with self and others deepen, and, through these, the reclaiming of a sense of self is bolstered. The practice of love increases a sense of identity and worth, because, as we love, we treat ourselves as one with something valuable to offer, and, as we receive love, we also treat ourselves as one deserving and worthy of love. Over time, our identity becomes aligned with the concept of "I love and I am loved." This aspect of identity can gradually begin to replace the old and false sense of self damaged by trauma and disordered eating.

   Interventions/Activities: (a) Teach clients to notice love in their lives, both received and given, so that they can become their own mirror and see that love is a part of who they are. (b) Help clients examine how they refuse and even reject love in their lives and the consequences of those patterns.

7. **Nurture the Spiritual: Seek the Therapeutic Mirror of Spiritual Identity, Spiritual Individuation, Exploration, and Transcendent Relationships**

   The Spiritual Child, a groundbreaking book by Miller (2016), is on the basis of more than 200 studies of children and their spirituality. Relying on research, she makes a case that (a) children are innately and naturally spiritual, (b) primary caretakers can either extinguish or nurture and bolster spirituality depending on their response to the expressed spirituality of the child, and (c) spirituality is a buffer against many illnesses and problems that our youth are facing in our current day. This sense of spirituality or spiritual identity is innate and comes intact at birth, so it simply needs space to grow and develop, and encouragement and nurturance to thrive. In the case of a lost sense of self, such as in the aftermath of trauma and disordered eating, the task is to help the client reclaim the self, including his or her spirituality or spiritual identity.

Interventions/Activities: (a) Encourage clients to engage in their own spiritual rituals, practices, activities, and contemplations. (b) Encourage clients to become involved in their spiritual community, community at large, or humanitarian services and other efforts to create a culture of love. (c) Help clients engage in open conversations about the moral issues and spiritual struggles that arise in their everyday lives (taken and adapted from *The Spiritual Child*, Miller, 2016).

8. **Reclaiming Self Through Principled Living: The Pathway of Integrity**
In recent years, the development of ACT (Hayes et al., 2016) has reintroduced the avoided topic of "values" in mainstream psychology and psychotherapy. ACT has been found useful in helping clients clarify, declare, and stand by those things they most want in their lives, or those things that are of most importance. Through therapy, clients begin to observe the lack of congruence between what their words say and what their behaviors say. This process can increase motivation and help clients to make behavioral realignments. The positive psychology movement has also reintroduced the notion of "virtues." When positive virtues are nurtured, internalized, and lived, not only are individuals happier and healthier, but communities are also more unified (Snyder & Lopez, 2009).

It is common knowledge that when we live by the principles we consider important, we enjoy internal peace and have a more positive and clear sense of spiritual identity.

Interventions/Activities: (a) Help clients notice their courage, bravery, and integrity in striving to live in harmony with their internalized principles of living (Berrett, 2016). (b) Help clients to understand the power of commitments and promises, and to once again make commitments to themselves, to higher power, and to significant others. (c) Teach clients that although trust of others is important, the most important trust is trust in oneself. Work with clients on earning their own trust and recognizing their own trustworthiness. (d) Ask the following reflective questions to clients: "What does it mean in your life to take the high road?" "When have you taken the lower path, and what were the consequences, and what did you learn?" "When have you taken the higher path and what were the consequences and what did you learn?"

9. **Reclaiming Self Through Honoring Self: Listening to and Following the Heart**
The heart has been a symbol of love, wisdom, understanding, connection, light, spirituality, and life for thousands of years. Of course, there is the physical heart, which, along with the brain, is central to individual life. Then there is the figurative, artistic, psychological, philosophical, and spiritual heart—the heart that is central to the most important things in life: love, relationship, desires, nonlinear ways of knowing and understanding, and a pathway to change and growth. These are connected to the identity of a person—the core and essence of who he or she is.

The meaning of "listening to heart" is individual and understood within the spiritual framework of the individual. Some, for example, consider the heart to be synonymous with the unconscious mind, sensitivity, and sensibility; others understand it to be my true self, my best self, the wizard within, intuition, inspiration, God talking to me, or attunement with the universe.

Listening to the heart entails three distinct steps: (a) Listening to the heart (receiving the message), (b) honoring the heart (regarding the message as important and connected to self and spirituality), and (c) following the heart (acting according to the message received).

Interventions/Activities: (a) Invite clients to consider the idea that the heart is an important source of information, which is an expression of "who they are." (b) Imagery: Ask the clients to place their hand on their chest (over their heart) and to close their eyes if they feel comfortable doing so. Do some breathing/relaxation work. When they are ready, ask them to focus on their heart under their hand and to ponder the following questions: "What is it that you know in your heart to be true about you, your life, or your spiritual understandings?" "What do you know in your heart to be true about being loved and loving others?" "What do you know deep in your heart about the purpose of your life?" "What do you know in your heart about what you need to change in your life?" "What is a dream in your heart that you hope for and must continue to strive for?" (c) Invite clients to write in their journal about messages of the heart such as: "What did my heart teach me today?" "Impressions of the heart which I need to listen to, embrace, honor, and follow are …."

◼ CASE VIGNETTE

Stephanie was a 20-year-old single female attending a private religious university in the Western United States (Lea, Richards, Sanders, McBride, & Allen, 2015). She was an active member of the Church of Jesus Christ of Latter-Day Saints (LDS). At the time of treatment, Stephanie was failing all of her classes and unable to focus at work. Stephanie endorsed a history of restricting calories, bingeing and purging, and exercising excessively. Her previous therapy at an ED treatment center resulted in limited success. Consequently, Stephanie was referred to Dr. H, a licensed psychologist and ED treatment specialist with 30 years of experience. On the basis of a psychological evaluation, Stephanie met criteria for Eating Disorder—Not Otherwise Specified (307.5), Major Depressive Disorder (296.32), Unspecified Anxiety Disorder (300.00), and Personality Disorder—Not Otherwise Specified (301.9). Over the course of 3 months, Stephanie met with Dr. H a total of eight times for individual psychotherapy in her college counseling center, using a spiritually oriented therapy approach with an emphasis on identity development. Because of space limitations, we discuss only the interventions Dr. H used as they relate to identity.

Dr. H observed that Stephanie was "so dependent on externalized information that there was no clear distinction between 'who I am' and 'what I do'" (p. 195). In other words, Stephanie defined herself solely by her failures rather than her successes. Consistent with her religious beliefs, Dr. H proposed an alternative to this mindset. He explained to Stephanie how unlike most of the world, God sees not only our outward behaviors but also our internal desires as well. Dr. H "shared his perception with Stephanie that she had only been focusing on one aspect of her identity, namely the eating disorder" (p. 195). This allowed Stephanie to understand how her identity consisted of more than just her disordered eating. Along with this, Dr. H drew attention to the fact that Stephanie had allowed her ED to take the place of important priorities, such as her relationships with herself, God, and others. Dr. H used the

"Six Spiritual Pathways to Recovery From an Eating Disorder," described in Berrett et al. (2010), to help Stephanie reorder her priorities. The six pathways are: (a) listening to and following the heart, (b) learning a language of spirituality, (c) mindfulness and spiritual mindedness, (d) principled living, (e) giving and receiving good gifts of love, and (f) holding up a therapeutic mirror that reflects spiritual identity.

In a qualitative interview, Stephanie revealed her experience of the treatment. She prefaced this with a description of the pressures within her religious community "to be perfect" (p. 197). Stephanie attributed this pressure and her self-criticism to the development of her ED. According to Stephanie, a vital aspect of her recovery was learning "how to resist comparing herself with others and to impart self-kindness" (p. 197). She said that this enabled her to love and accept herself, in spite of imperfections. Stephanie reported that the development of a deeper sense of identity and reconnection with her passions was essential to her healing. After treatment, Stephanie "continued her process of discovery" (p. 198). She started to engage in activities she had enjoyed prior to the development of her ED. Furthermore, she was able to be more vulnerable and develop more meaningful relationships with others. Her case is a notable example of why and how identity interventions can be valuable in the treatment and recovery of EDs and associated conditions.

■ SUMMARY AND CONCLUSION

In this chapter, we have discussed what happens in the aftermath of trauma, abuse, and disordered eating. This aftermath includes connection to illness as identity and disconnection from sense of self, spiritual identity, higher power, and significant others. Furthermore, there is disconnection from spirituality, passion, purpose, meaning in life, internalized principles, dreams, and deepest desires. We have also provided a few of the many interventions that we have found valuable in reducing suffering and helping clients to reclaim their identity.

We chose to focus our attention on the processes of assessment and therapeutic intervention, and, by so doing, directly address the building and nurturing of self. We have attempted to describe the journey from ED and trauma identity to knowing, strengthening, valuing, honoring, and sharing self. It is through this that an individual is able to withdraw trust and faith in illness as a way of dealing with life, and, in incremental steps, begin to walk toward, and trust in, one's authentic self and well-being.

The reclamation of identity after trauma and disordered eating is a long and difficult pathway, but one that can and must be taken by clients. It is one that clinicians with the necessary knowledge, skills, and action can help clients accomplish. We believe that it is our calling: to decrease human suffering by helping clients know who they are and by lifting them toward becoming who they can and want to be.

■ REFERENCES

Allen, R. K. (2003) *Life quest*. Waco, Texas: Touchtone International, LLC.

Bednar, R. L., Wells, M. G., & Peterson, S. R. (1989). *Self-esteem: Paradoxes and innovations in clinical theory and practice*. Washington, DC: American Psychological Association.

Berrett, M. B. (1985). *Reciprocal social support of adolescents: An assessment model and measure* (Unpublished doctoral dissertation). Brigham Young University, Provo, Utah.

Berrett, M. B. (2004). Understanding one's worth: A cornerstone of recovery from eating disorders and other mental and emotional illness. *Center for Change Clinical Newsletter,* November. Retrieved from https://centerforchange.com/understanding-ones-worth-cornerstone -recovery-eating-disorders-mental-emotional-illness

Berrett, M. B. (2015, January 30). *Assessment beyond assessment: Understandings which enhance individualized care.* Presentation at Center for Change National Conference for Eating Disorder Professionals, Orem, Utah.

Berrett, M. B. (2016, November 6). *Finding self again: The dismantling of eating disorder and trauma identity* [PowerPoint slides]. Workshop presentation at the 26th Annual Renfrew Center Foundation Conference for Professionals, November 11–16. Philadelphia, PA.

Berrett, M. B., Hardman, R. K., & Richards, P. S. (2010). The role of spirituality in eating disorder treatment and recovery. In M. Maine, B. H. McGilley, & D. W. Bunnell (Eds.), *Treatment of eating disorders: Bridging the research-practice gap* (pp. 367–385). San Diego, CA: Elsevier Academic Press.

Buser, J. K., Parkins, R. A., & Buser, T. J. (2014). Thematic analysis of the intersection of spirituality and eating disorder symptoms. *Journal of Addictions & Offender Counseling, 35,* 97–113. doi:10.1002/j.2161-1874.2014.00029.x

Carlson, E. B. (1997). *Trauma assessments: A clinician's guide.* New York, NY: Guilford Press.

Caslini, M., Bartoli, F., Crocamo, C., Dakanalis, A., Clerici, M., & Carrà, G. (2016). Disentangling the association between child abuse and eating disorders: A systematic review and meta-analysis. *Psychosomatic Medicine, 78,* 79–90. doi:10.1097/PSY.0000000000000233

De Paoli, T., Fuller-Tyszkiewicz, M., & Krug, I. (2017). Insecure attachment and maladaptive schema in disordered eating: The mediating role of rejection sensitivity. *Clinical Psychology & Psychotherapy, 24,* 1273–1284. doi:10.1002/cpp.2092

Demidenko, N., Tasca, G. A., Kennedy, N., & Bissada, H. (2010). The mediating role of self-concept in the relationship between attachment insecurity and identity differentiation among women with an eating disorder. *Journal of Social & Clinical Psychology, 29,* 1131–1152. doi:10.1521/jscp.2010.29.10.1131

Frankl, V. E. (2006). *Man's search for meaning.* Boston, MA: Beacon Press.

Hardman, R. K., Berrett, M. E., & Richards, P. S. (2003). Spirituality and ten false beliefs and pursuits of women with eating disorders: Implications for counselors. *Counseling & Values, 48,* 67–78. doi:10.1002/j.2161-007X.2003.tb00276.x

Hayes, S. C., Strosahl, K. D., & Wilson, K. G. (2016). *Acceptance and commitment therapy: The process and practice of mindful change* (2nd ed.). New York, NY: Guilford Press.

Hook, J. N., Worthington, E. L., Davis, D. E., Jennings, D. J., Gartner, A. L., & Hook, J. P. (2010). Empirically supported religious and spiritual therapies. *Journal of Clinical Psychology, 66,* 46–72. doi:10.1002/jclp.20626

Jenkins, P. E., Meyer, C., & Blissett, J. M. (2013). Childhood abuse and eating psychopathology: The mediating role of core beliefs. *Journal of Aggression, Maltreatment, & Trauma, 22,* 248–261. doi:10.1080/10926771.2013.741665

Koenig, H. G. (2009). Research on religion, spirituality, and mental health: A review. *Canadian Journal of Psychiatry, 54,* 283–291. doi:10.1177/070674370905400502

Lea, T., Richards, P. S., Sanders, P. W., McBride, J. A., & Allen, G. E. K. (2015). Spiritual pathways to healing and recovery: An intensive single-N study of an eating disorder patient. *Spirituality in Clinical Practice, 2,* 191–201. doi:10.1037/scp0000085

Lejonclou, A., Nilsson, D., & Holmqvist, R. (2014). Variants of potentially traumatizing life events in eating disorder patients. *Psychological Trauma: Theory, Research, Practice, & Policy, 6,* 661–667. doi:10.1037/a0034926

Macdonald, P., Hibbs, R., Corfield, F., & Treasure, J. (2012). The use of motivational interviewing in eating disorders: A systematic review. *Psychiatry Research, 200,* 1–11. doi:10.1016/j.psychres.2012.05.013

Marsden, P., Karagianni, E., & Morgan, J. F. (2007). Spirituality and clinical care in eating disorders: A qualitative study. *International Journal of Eating Disorders, 40,* 7–12. doi:10.1002/eat.20333

Matos, M., Ferreira, C., Duarte, C., & Pinto-Gouveia, J. (2015). Eating disorders: When social rank perceptions are shaped by early shame experiences. *Psychology & Psychotherapy: Theory, Research & Practice, 88,* 38–53. doi:10.1111/papt.12027

Matusek, J. A., & Knudson, R. M. (2009). Rethinking recovery from eating disorders: Spiritual and political dimensions. *Qualitative Health Research, 19,* 697–707. doi:10.1177/1049732309334077

Miller, L. (2016). *The spiritual child: The new science on parenting for health and lifelong thriving*. New York, NY: Picador.

Miller, W. R., & C'de Baca, J. (2001). *Quantum change: When epiphanies and sudden insights transform ordinary lives*. New York, NY: Guilford Press.

Mitchell, J. E., & Peterson, C. B. (Eds.). (2007). *Assessment of eating disorders* (1st ed.). New York, NY: Guilford Press.

Pargament, K. I. (2007). *Spiritually integrated psychotherapy: Understanding and addressing the sacred*. New York, NY: Guilford Press.

Pignatelli, A. M., Wampers, M., Loriedo, C., Biondi, M., & Vanderlinden, J. (2017). Childhood neglect in eating disorders: A systematic review and meta-analysis. *Journal of Trauma & Dissociation, 18*, 100–115. doi:10.1080/15299732.2016.1198951

Richards, P. S., & Bergin, A. E. (2005). *A spiritual strategy for counseling and psychotherapy* (2nd ed.). Washington, DC: American Psychological Association.

Richards, P. S., Berrett, M. E., Hardman, R. K., & Eggett, D. L. (2006). Comparative efficacy of spirituality, cognitive, and emotional support groups for treating eating disorder inpatients. *Eating Disorders, 14*, 401–415. doi:10.1080/10640260600952548

Richards, P. S., Hardman, R. K., Lea, T., & Berrett, M. E. (2015). Religious and spiritual assessment in trauma survivors. In D. F. Walker, C. A. Courtois, & J. D. Allen (Eds.), *Spiritually oriented psychotherapy for trauma* (pp. 77–102). Washington, DC: American Psychological Association.

Sacker, I. M. (2008). *Regaining your self*. New York, NY: Hyperion Books.

Schaefer, J., & Rutledge, T. (2014). *Life without Ed: How one woman declared independence from her eating disorder and how you can too* (10th ed.). New York, NY: McGraw-Hill.

Seubert, A. (2008). *The courage to feel: A practical guide to the power and freedom of emotional honesty*. Conshohocken, PA: Infinity.

Seubert, A., & Lightstone, J. (2009). The case of mistaken identity: Ego states and eating disorders. In R. Shapiro (Ed.), *EMDR Solutions II: For depression, eating disorders, performance, and more* (pp. 193–218). New York, NY: W. W. Norton.

Snyder, C. R., & Lopez, S. J. (Eds.). (2009). *Oxford handbook of positive psychology*. Oxford, UK: Oxford University Press.

Sperry, L., & Shafranske, E. P. (Eds.). (2005). *Spiritually oriented psychotherapy*. Washington, DC: American Psychological Association.

Stein, K. F. (1996). The self-schema model: A theoretical approach to the self-concept in eating disorders. *Archives of Psychiatric Nursing, 10*, 96–109. doi:10.1016/S0883-9417(96)80072-0

Stein, K. F., & Corte, C. (2007). Identity impairment and the eating disorders: Content and organization of the self-concept in women with anorexia nervosa and bulimia nervosa. *European Eating Disorders Review, 15*, 58–69. doi:10.1002/erv.726

Stein, K. F., & Corte, C. (2008). The identity impairment model: A longitudinal study of self-schemas as predictors of disordered eating behaviors. *Nursing Research, 57*, 182–190. doi:10.1097/01.NNR.0000319494.21628.08

Stein, K. F., Corte, C., Chen, D.-G., Nuliyalu, U., & Wing, J. (2013). A randomized clinical trial of an identity intervention programme for women with eating disorders. *European Eating Disorders Review, 21*, 130–142. doi:10.1002/erv.2195

Substance Abuse and Mental Health Services Administration. (2014). *SAMHSA's concept of trauma and guidance for trauma-informed approach* (HHS Publication No. SMA 14-4884). Rockville, MD: Substance Abuse and Mental Health Services Administration.

van der Kolk, B. (2015). *The body keeps the score: Brain, mind, and body in the healing of trauma*. London, UK: Penguin Random House.

AFTERWORD

In the Japanese tradition of kintsugi ("golden joinery"), when a piece of pottery is cracked, the fracture is filled with gold or silver powder and lacquer. The piece is then positioned in such a way that the repair receives center-stage attention. Its beauty is highlighted by the fact that it now has a history and, having survived its own trauma, is more beautiful than ever before for having been fractured.

Source: Shutterstock

Our clients and patients may have felt fractured, even shattered. But we stay with them. We walk beside them as they journey. We help them pick up the shards of their lives, piecing them together with the gold we call love, reminding them every step of the way that they have been fractured, but never broken.

Index